guatamala

P9-BZS-417

GREENLAND SEA

0 500 1000 1500 2000 kilometres

ICELAND

10°W

Québec

G R E E N L A N D

Trois-Rivières

Montréal   Sherbrooke

Ottawa R.

Ottawa-Hull

Rideau R.

Georgian Bay

St. Lawrence Seaway

Lake Huron

Kingston

Davis Strait

Oshawa
Toronto

Lake Ontario

Iqaluit
(Frobisher Bay)

Kitchener-Waterloo

St. Catharines-Niagara

island
juaq

LABRADOR SEA

London

Lake Erie

0 100 200 300 400 500 km

ignituk

Windsor

Nain
- Voisey Bay
Labrador

N E W F O U N D L A N D

50°N

questions 9+10

Happy Valley-Goose Bay

P. 59.

#9

Q U É B E C

L A B R A D O R

St John's

Moosonee

Corner Brook

Gulf of
St. Lawrence

50°W

Chicoutimi-Jonquière

P R I N C E
E D W A R D
I S L A N D

Sydney

N E W
B R U N S W I C K

Charlottetown

Québec

Moncton
Saint
John

Halifax

udbury

Montréal

Ottawa R.

Fredericton

Bay of Fundy

N O V A   S C O T I A

Georgian Bay

St. Lawrence Seaway

40°N

Ottawa-Hull

Toronto

Lake Ontario

Hamilton

Lake Erie

A T L A N T I C
O C E A N

80°W   70°W   60°W

Rebecca "
Brewer
2002-2003

global
connections: canadian and world issues

Bruce Clark

John Wallace

Prentice
Hall

Toronto

The authors of this book have benefited from the knowledge, skills, and dedication of many people. We would like to extend our sincere appreciation to the publisher, editors, coordinators, designers, formatters, and artists at Pearson Education Canada. Many of the materials were field tested by our students and we are indebted to them for their assistance. Finally, we would especially like to thank our wives, Laurie Wallace and Rosemary Clark, for their support, editorial suggestions, advice, and patience.

Bruce Clark and John Wallace

National Library of Canada Cataloguing in Publication Data

Clark, Bruce, 1948–
        Global connections : Canadian and world issues

Includes index.
ISBN 0-13-041067-5

1. Geography. 2. Economic geography. 3. Human geography.
I. Wallace, John K., 1946– II. Title.

G128.C53 2003   910   C2002-900919-7

Statistics Canada information is used with the permission of the Minister of Industry, as Minister responsible for Statistics Canada. Information on the availability of the wide range of data from Statistics Canada can be obtained from Statistics Canada's Regional Offices, its World Wide Web site at http://www.statcan.ca, and its toll-free access number 1-800-263-1136.

Publisher: Mark Cobham
Product Managers: Anita Borovilos, Melanie Trevelyan
Managing Editor: Elynor Kagan
Developmental Editors: Jenifer A. Ludbrook, Kelly Ronan, Judy Dawson
Consulting Editor: Dennis DesRivieres
Production and Copy Editor: Francine Geraci
Coordinating Editors: Angelie Kim, Kelly Ronan
Proofreaders: Gail Copeland, Rebecca Vogan
Research Editor: Cheryl Freedman
Production Coordinator: Zane Kaneps
Permissions/Photo Researchers: Jane McWhinney, Michaele Sinko
Art Director: Zena Denchik
Interior Design and Page Layout: Jennifer Federico
Cover Design: Monica Compter
Illustrator: Deborah Crowle

Cover Photographs: Polar Bear/Corel Image Library; Electricity Generators/Eyewire; Hong Kong Harbour: www.comstock.com; Globe/PhotoDisc; David Emmite Photos/GettyImages/Stone; Farm in Desert/PhotoDisc.

2 3 4 5   FP   06 05 04 03 02

Printed and bound in Canada.

The publisher has taken every care to meet or exceed industry specifications for the manufacturing of textbooks. The spine and the endpapers of this sewn book have been reinforced with special fabric for extra binding strength. The cover is a premium, polymer-reinforced material designed to provide long life and withstand rugged use. Mylar gloss lamination has been applied for further durability.

Contents

v

Preface

You are about to discover the significant issues facing you as a citizen of Canada and of a complex and interdependent world. This textbook will broaden your horizons as you explore some of the world's major issues. It will provide you with opportunities to develop analytical skills, encourage you to think critically about your values, and assist you in making reasoned decisions about how best to resolve Canadian and world issues.

There are a number of special features in the book that will help you in your study. The book is divided into 28 chapters, grouped within 7 units. All chapters are linked by two themes: globalization and sustainability, which could become the two dominant themes of the 21st century. Each chapter begins with a list of the **Key Terms** that appear in bold throughout the chapter. These key terms are defined in the text and/or in the **Glossary**. The **concepts**, **skills**, and **applications** that you will cover are listed at the beginning of each chapter. Throughout the book there are **Internet** references that take you to a central Pearson Education Web site, where you can link to additional material about a particular topic. A wide variety of **Activities** and **Questions** will give you opportunities to examine a specific aspect of an issue, to interpret statistics, to create and interpret a graph, and to work with others to solve a problem or develop a point of view.

When examining Canadian and world issues, it is possible to become overwhelmed by the enormity of the issues and the apparent difficulty of resolving them. This book attempts to give you a realistic view of world issues but at the same time provide you with a sense of optimism. The last unit is entitled "Responsibility and Hope for the Future" because it is your idealism, your enthusiasm, and your efforts that will be needed to meet the challenges of the future.

Acknowledgements

The authors and publisher of this book would like to acknowledge the dedicated efforts of the team of reviewers for their important suggestions and helpful comments at the various stages of development of the text.

Bob Bray
Dennis DesRivieres
Don Evoy
Rob McDowell
John McNorgan

Ed Mizzi
Stuart Nicholson
Tom Oliveri
Michele Reid
Paul Van Zant

Unit 1: Getting Started

1

Key Terms

life experience
perspective
issue
opinion
subjective
fact
objective
bias

Expectations

In this chapter, you will:

- explain how points of view influence how a person perceives a place

- produce a case study where resource development disrupts an ecosystem

- describe biases that inform different viewpoints on geographic issues

- understand that there are many possible solutions to a geographic issue

- understand the need to consider social differences in analysing global issues

- distinguish between fact and opinion in information sources

Image above: *Day and Night* by M.C. Escher

Canadian and World Issues

Throughout this course, you will be asked to explore issues, to seek and examine facts, and to develop ideas through reading, discussion, and statistical analysis. It is important first to understand a few basic concepts such as motivation, perspective, issue, and bias. These ideas will help you to become aware of how aspects of yourself and the rest of society affect your study and your learning. These concepts also affect how you view yourself and the world around you.

Setting Goals for Your Study of World Issues

This activity has a dual purpose. On the one hand, it will help you to understand yourself as you begin your study of world issues. On the other hand, reading the answers to these questionnaires will help your teacher to learn more about you and your classmates. Your teacher will then be better able to meet your needs in this course. Try to answer each question honestly, since this activity will not be marked as an assignment.

Your Motivations for Taking This Course

1. Why did you choose to study world issues? In your response, consider such factors as your need for this credit, your hope for a satisfying mark, the reputation of the course or teacher, the nature of the course material, or your desire to make a difference in the world.

2. Which specific world issues do you wish to explore?

3. Which specific skills would you like to develop?

4. Is this course related to your post-secondary plans? If so, how?

Your Expectations of This Course

5. What mark, or range of marks, do you hope to obtain in this course? Would this mark be typical of your other marks? If it is significantly higher or lower, explain why this would be so.

6. What are you prepared to do to ensure that you will get this mark? Be specific.

7. What expectations do you have of the teacher? Again, be specific.

Personal Reflections

8. Describe your current knowledge of the world compared to that of your classmates.

9. As a student, what are your two greatest strengths?

10. As a student, what are your two greatest weaknesses?

11. a) In what non-academic activities are you involved? Consider such things as a part-time job, volunteer work, hobbies, religious involvement, music lessons, sports teams, etc.
    b) How many hours per week do you spend on each of these?
    c) What will you do to ensure that these activities do not adversely affect your schoolwork?

12. List, in order of importance, the school-related and personal goals that you would like to achieve this year.

What Is Your Point of View?

Look at the image at the beginning of this chapter. What do you see? Do you see a flock of dark-coloured birds flying against a light background, or a flock of light-coloured birds flying against a dark background? The way that you perceive the birds will influence the way you perceive the rest of the drawing. The drawing changes depending on your point of view.

At one time or another, most of us have played the game of identifying shapes in the clouds. Again, what you see depends on your point of view. If you are an avid hockey player, you may see a goalie's stick or a puck. If you are very interested in music, you might see a violin or a musical note. In each case, what you see depends to a great extent on your **life experiences**. Your life experience includes such factors as your age, education, religion, and ethnic background.

As you begin your study of world issues, you should realize that you possess a particular set of economic and social **perspectives** that have developed over your lifetime. They will colour how you view the ideas that are presented in this course. These perspectives are the product of many influences—your family, your schooling, the countries in which you have lived, your religious beliefs, the media, and your friends. To see how your life experiences influence your viewpoints, consider Figure 1–1. What do you see in this photo—police trying to maintain law and order in the face of violent demonstrators, or citizens trying to fight for their rights in the face of a repressive government? What you see depends on your personal perspective on the world. In the same way, throughout this course, you will find that your experiences will colour all your viewpoints. It is important to remember that other people will have very different perspectives on the world than yours, and it is critical that we understand and respect these differences. Many of the issues that will be examined in *Global Connections* exist, or are made worse, because one group of people is ignorant or intolerant of the nature of others.

Figure 1–1   *What you see in this photo depends largely on your personal perspectives.*

Your Perspectives: A Questionnaire

The questionnaire that follows will help you gain some insight into your attitudes. It doesn't matter if your score is high or low; however, it is important to understand the perspectives that you bring to your study of world issues and how they compare to those of your classmates and your teacher. Try to give honest answers to each question, rather than what you think you "should" say. You will receive a scoring sheet on which to place the numbers that represent your answers. For each question, choose one of the following:

1—I strongly agree with this statement.

2—I agree with this statement.

3—I am not sure about this statement / I do not have a strong opinion about this statement.

4—I disagree with this statement.

5—I strongly disagree with this statement.

After you have finished the questionnaire, complete the remaining steps on the scoring sheet to determine your attitudes about social and economic issues.

Questionnaire

1. People who receive welfare should have to work or take job training.

2. I am opposed to all capital punishment.

3. Canadian courts generally do not give harsh enough sentences to criminals.

4. Richer countries should increase their aid to poorer nations.

5. Possession of small amounts of marijuana should not be a criminal offence.

6. Private companies can provide public services (such as highway maintenance, school busing, and jail operation) more efficiently and cheaply than the government.

7. Canada's gun-control laws make the process more difficult for honest citizens to obtain guns for legitimate purposes.

8. Government spending cuts have been too extreme in recent years. The government should increase taxes to allow higher spending on social programs.

9. I would consider marrying a person from a different racial, ethnic, or religious group.

10. Canada should accept fewer immigrants.

11. The ability of Canada's businesses to compete internationally has been harmed by labour and environmental laws that are too strict.

12. Trade unions provide needed protection for the rights of working people.

13. In no case should gays and lesbians be allowed to adopt children.

14. Canada's economic system is less productive than that of the United States.

15. Schools pay too much attention to teaching children about the arts. They should concentrate more on preparing young people to have successful careers.

16. Affirmative action programs are essential if women and minorities are to achieve their full potential.

17. University and college fees should be reduced or eliminated so that family wealth does not determine access to higher education.

18. People should be able to purchase private medical care in Canada.

19. The government has the responsibility to eliminate homelessness in our cities.

20. Governments should be prepared to run deficits in order to pay for essential needs like better schools and improved health care.

What It All Means

The scores that you calculated on your scoring sheet will give you some indication of your attitudes on economic and social issues. Each scale goes from +20 to −20, with a score of zero representing a neutral position (Figure 1–2). On the economic scale, +20 would mean you believe that the government should not interfere with the operation of the free-market economy, while −20 means you believe that the government should play an active role in managing the country's economy. On the social scale, +20 would mean you feel that significant restrictions on personal freedoms can be justified if society benefits, while −20 would mean you feel that the government should not interfere unduly with personal freedoms.

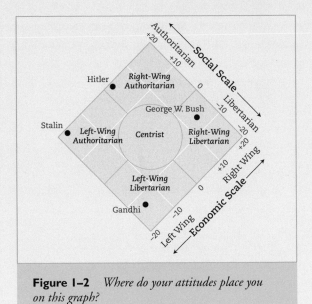

Figure 1–2 *Where do your attitudes place you on this graph?*

Social and Economic Attitudes

The terms "right wing" and "left wing" have most often been applied to social values, not economic views; further, they tend to oversimplify complex issues. One way to broaden their usage might be to describe five categories:

- *Right-wing Authoritarian*—People in this category believe that the economy works best if the government leaves it alone, but that a significant measure of social control is required to have a fair and effective society.
- *Left-wing Authoritarian*—People in this category agree with the right-wing authoritarians that social control is required, but they also believe that government control of the economy is essential.
- *Left-wing Libertarian*—People in this category feel that the government has an important role to play in the economy, but feel that

government should allow people to make their own social decisions.
- *Right-wing Libertarian*—People in this category want to minimize the role of government in all aspects of life.
- *Centrist*—People in this category believe that social and economic controls should be applied if they are in the public good, or dismantled if they do not benefit a society.

People's attitudes, along with those of entire governments, can and do change. Frequently, individuals find that their attitudes change as they get older. Perhaps the best example of a government that has changed its attitudes is China. The China of Mao Tsetung was an extreme example of left-wing authoritarianism. Since Mao's death, the country has changed dramatically. While China's government remains distinctly authoritarian, economically it has become quite right-wing.

What Is an Issue?

This course is called "Canadian and World Issues: A Geographic Analysis." When you chose to take this course, you undoubtedly expected to learn about **issues**. But what is an issue? More specifically, what are Canadian issues and what are world issues? Are they similar or different?

By completing the following activity, you should gain a better understanding about the concept of an issue, which issues are primarily Canadian in nature, which are primarily global, and which ones span both geographical perspectives.

Focus on Issues

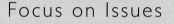

Defining an Issue

1. In a group, discuss the question "What is an issue?" Write out your group's definition.

2. Choose a representative from each group to write their definition on the board or on chart paper.

3. As a class, examine each group's definition, and then try to arrive at a consensus in answering the question "What is an issue?"

What Are the Major Issues?

4. In your group, make a list of six major issues facing humanity.

5. Choose a representative from your group to write the list on the board or on chart paper.

6. As a class, examine the major issues that are suggested. Create four or five headings under which they may be grouped (e.g., environmental issues). Explain why you selected these headings.

What Are Canadian and World Issues?

7. In a group, examine a major daily newspaper.

Look at some of the major issues in the newspaper, and list them under the headings created in the previous section.

8. On your list, indicate which issues are primarily local, which are national, and which are global. Discuss, within your group, whether any of the local or national issues also have global consequences.

9. Draw a flow chart or make a web diagram to explain how an issue may be related to other issues.

Music/Poetry As an Educational Medium

10. Working in a group of three or four people:
    a) Find a musical selection or a poem that addresses a world issue.
    b) Interpret the song/poem.
    - What is the purpose of the song/poem?
    - Analyse the lyrics of the song/poem.
    - If your choice was a song, how are the words and music used together to convey the message?
    c) How successful is the song/poem in achieving its goal? Explain.

Distinguishing Opinions from Facts

In the previous section, you were asked to give your opinion about which issues are the most important facing humanity today. Even though you may be friends with your classmates and for the most part lead similar lives, you probably noticed that the issues you selected as most pressing were not the same as theirs. Why?

Your **opinions** are the beliefs you hold and the judgements you make about the events in the world around you. They develop as you consider the facts and as you make judgements about these facts in light of your values, life experience, and the ideas of others. Your opinions are **subjective**, meaning they form as a result of your personal outlook on life. When two people have differing opinions about an issue, you can be sure they will argue about them! So, we can say that opinions are not only subjective, but also arguable. Being able to argue for, and defend, your opinion is one of life's most useful skills.

Before you can judge an issue and form your subjective opinion, you have to know the facts. **Facts** are indisputable truths, knowledge that is certain and incontestable. They can be verified by measurement, observation, or personal experience. You cannot argue about facts because they are reality. Your own personal experience cannot change the nature of the factual information you have. In other words, facts are **objective**.

Here is an example that uses population and food supply to illustrate the difference between a fact and an opinion. It is a fact, measurable and verifiable, that the world's population reached six billion in 1999. Accepting this fact, an environmentalist might conclude that there will not be enough food to feed the world's future inhabitants because most of the world's arable land (land suitable for growing crops) is already in use. An agronomist, who studies soil management, climate trends, and innovations in crop production, might conclude that there will be enough food for billions more people in the future. Although the information is the same, the two opinions are highly subjective and very different, and each opinion reflects the experience of the observer.

Can Opinions About Facts Alter Behaviour?

There is an important, subtle relationship between opinion and fact that might surprise you. Your opinion, which is based on fact, can cause a change in human behaviour. A change in human behaviour can then alter the information on which your opinion was originally based. Do you find this confusing? Examine the following example to see how opinion can influence facts.

In 1942, scientists discovered the potent effects of the insecticide DDT, and it was widely put into use. DDT kills the mosquitoes that transmit malaria and the insects that attack crops. During the 1950s, however, some insects developed immunity to the chemical, while others began to reproduce rapidly when DDT eliminated their natural predators. Scientists also discovered that DDT was adversely affecting the reproduction of fish-eating birds. The birds were feeding on fish that had accumulated DDT in their tissues. The birds bioaccumulated even greater levels of DDT in their tissues because of the amount of fish they ate. DDT was interfering with the birds' production of calcium carbonate, a mineral necessary for sturdy eggshells. The loon, osprey, cormorant, and bald eagle began laying eggs with very thin shells, and fewer eggs than normal were surviving the incubation period. As a result, many fish-eating birds faced extinction.

The experts held the opinion that DDT was extremely harmful to the environment, and that

Figure 1–3 *Dr. Masumeh Ebtekar, of Iran, signs a global treaty in Stockholm, May 2001, banning 12 highly toxic chemicals. The "dirty dozen" includes PCBs, dioxins, DDT, and other pesticides that contribute to health problems in humans and animals.*

countries should adopt more varied approaches to controlling insects. As a result, by 1970, most countries had banned the use of DDT. Opinion, based on the facts about DDT, influenced people's behaviour to the extent that DDT was no longer used in North America.

Opinion based on fact does not always alter human behaviour, however, because different interpretations of the facts are possible. Some developing countries still produce and use DDT because they believe that its low cost and high degree of effectiveness against pests outweigh the environmental damage it causes. For example, about 300 million people suffer from malaria and about one million die each year. The most cost-effective method of combating malaria is to spray DDT inside houses. The mosquitoes that spread the disease are either killed or driven away. In 2001, 120 countries signed a UN treaty agreeing to ban "persistent organic pollutants," but exempted DDT from the list as long as it was being used to control malaria (Figure 1–3). Studies indicate that when DDT spraying stops, the incidence of malaria increases. In South Africa, for example, spraying was stopped in 1996 and the number of cases of malaria increased by 150 per cent. When spraying resumed a few years later, the number of cases dropped dramatically.

How May Bias Be Detected?

In order to understand and evaluate an issue, it is important to realize that all viewpoints and perspectives are biased. **Bias** is the presentation of an issue from a single point of view. Today you and your peers are in a fortunate position: you can be highly informed about what is happening in the world. You can get information about almost any event if you have access to the Internet. But be careful. Although some of the information you collect may be true, your sources may have, consciously or unconsciously, included only those facts that support their point of view. Personal biases may have led your sources to omit any other data.

Bias can be detected by examining your source's use of language, especially the choice of verbs and adjectives. For example, one observer might describe a protest march in the following terms: "A well-organized, peaceful group of marchers arrived at the government offices." Another observer might describe the same scene: "An unruly mob descended upon the government offices." Biased words have great power to persuade the unwary towards opinions they might not otherwise hold.

You may want to think of the reliability of your sources in terms of three levels of confidence:

- You should have the highest level of confidence in academic articles, professional journals, and most scholarly books because independent editorial boards review them before they appear.
- You should have a lower level of confidence in magazines and newspapers that are not subject to peer review, although they can be held financially responsible for what they print.
- You should have the lowest level of confidence in those sources where peer review or financial accountability are absent. Many Web sites, for example, have not been scrutinized by independent reviewers, and they are not accountable to anyone for their point of view.

Your sources—whether newspapers, journal articles, Web sites, films, television documentaries, or personal accounts from friends—may reflect a bias, and you have to be aware that you may not be getting an objective point of view. The questions in Figure 1–4 can be used as guidelines when you are trying to detect bias in sources of information and in articles.

When examining a source of information, ask yourself the following questions:

- Who wrote the document, and why did he or she write it?
- Was the author or organization closely involved in the event? Could that have affected what was written?
- What credentials does the author have to indicate that she or he is a reliable source?
- What organization published the document? Does this organization have a particular point of view or agenda that would bias the information?

To assist you in detecting bias in an article, ask yourself the following questions:

- Do the arguments and evidence support only one side of an issue?
- Are generalizations and simplified solutions used to explain complex points of view?
- Are value-laden adjectives used?
- Are stereotypical comments used?
- If counter arguments are used, are they weak and poorly explained?

Figure 1–4 *These questions will help you determine the reliability of a source of information and bias in an article.*

Three Gorges: Different Perspectives

For any issue, there will be many pieces of true information, or facts, available to you. Each fact is only a small part of the total reality, and you need as many facts as possible to form a balanced, responsible opinion. The following activity gives you an opportunity to evaluate both sides of an issue.

The Chang Jiang (Yangtze), China's longest river, is the longest river in Asia and the third longest in the world. Rising in the Kunlun Mountains of Tibet, its main channel flows eastward for 6300 km through nine provinces of China before emptying 1000 billion cubic metres of water annually into the East China Sea near Shanghai. It has 3600 tributaries that drain the plateaus, mountains, and plains of 19 per cent of China's total area, or 1.8 million square kilo-metres. Described as China's lifeline, the Chang Jiang River flows through the most important industrialized part of China, and its delta has the highest population density in southern China. The upper portion of the Chang Jiang near the city of Yichang flows through three major gorges, as well as several smaller ones, for a distance of 126 km. The gorges are surrounded by mountain peaks, and in places the river narrows and flows between perpendicular rock faces. The scenery is breathtaking (Figure 1–5). This is the setting for the world's largest dam-building project. As with every human endeavour, there are those who support the project and those who object to it. Read the following two points of view, and evaluate their validity.

Figure 1–5 *The Three Gorges offer some of China's most beautiful landscapes. Some people view this area as natural beauty that inspires authors, artists, and poets. Others see the Three Gorges as a resource to be exploited for electricity to power the nation's industries.*

Some Facts About the Three Gorges Project, November 1, 1997

1. World's Largest Water Conservation Project

Taking the total amount of concrete work as one example, the Three Gorges Project totals 26.43 million cubic metres, ... twice that of the Itaipu project in Brazil.

2. World's Largest Hydropower Plant

Upon completion, the Three Gorges Project will be the world's largest hydropower plant in terms of both total installed capacity and annual average power generation volume.

3. Three Gorges to Take 17 Years

The ongoing Three Gorges Project, which will be the world's largest water conservation facility when completed, will take 17 years to build. Construction of the project consists of three stages.

4. Dam Won't Affect Navigation on Chang Jiang (Yangtze) River

The Chang Jiang River, the world's third longest, is one of China's leading transportation routes. One guarantee made by developers of the Three Gorges Project ensures smooth navigation at the construction site during the six-year second phase (1997–2003). Permanent ship locks will be in operation after the year 2003.

5. Three Gorges Reservoir Inundation

The Three Gorges Reservoir will inundate 632 square kilometres, the world's largest inundated area by a single project. The normal water level of 175 m will be achieved in the year 2003, with the reservoir covering 1045 square kilometres and stretching some 663 km, an area capable of controlling floods expected to occur twice in one decade. The Three Gorges Project will inundate 31 000 ha of farmland, and will require the relocation of 1599 industrial and mining enterprises, as well as power transmission and telecommunications facilities, harbours, small and medium-sized hydroelectric power plants, roads, and pumping stations.

6. Charm of Three Gorges to Remain

The Three Gorges, one of the world's most famous scenic sites around Qutang, Wuxian, and Xiling, features breathtaking scenery which attracts hundreds of thousands of tourists from at home and abroad each and every year. The charming scenery will be left untouched following the damming of the mid-section of the Xiling Gorge. The high-water mark once the dam is completed will stand at 82.8 m, or 4 m higher than before.

7. Preliminary Success Scored in Three Gorges Resettlement Drive

Some 90 000 local residents are expected to move out of the reservoir area of the Three Gorges Project by the end of this year, leading to a favourable start of the massive resettlement drive. To this end, China will inject approximately 100 billion yuan into the relocation of the reservoir residents by the year 2009 when the whole project is completed.

Source: Adapted from materials provided by the Embassy of the People's Republic of China in the United States of America.

Three Gorges Dam Project

History of the Project

Sun Yatsen first proposed building a dam on the Chang Jiang (Yangtze) River in 1919 for power generation purposes, but the idea was shelved owing to unfavourable political and economic conditions. Major floods resurrected the idea, and the government adopted it in 1954 for flood control. Later, Vice-Minister of Electric Power Li Rui concluded that the dam should not be built at all since it would be too costly. He added that the dam would also flood many cities and fertile farmland, subject the middle and lower reaches of the river to catastrophic flooding during construction, and would not contribute much to shipping.

Former Premier Li Peng crusaded for the dam and pushed it through the National People's Congress in April 1992, despite the opposition or abstention from one-third of the delegates. ... Resettlement soon began, and physical preparations started in 1994. But corruption scandals plagued the project. It was believed that contractors have won bids through bribery and then skimped on equipment and materials. ... much of the project's infrastructure was so shoddy that Premier Zhu Rongji ordered it ripped out in 1999 after a number of high-profile accidents. ➤

Figure 1-6 *Blacksmiths at work in the town of Fengdu were among those to be relocated. Although a trading centre for 500 years, Fengdu will be underwater when the Three Gorges Dam is filled.*

Summary of the Arguments Against the Dam

Cost: The dam will far exceed the official cost estimate [with unofficial estimates as high as US$75 billion or more], and the investment will be unrecoverable as cheaper power sources become available that lure away customers.

Resettlement: Relocated people are worse off than before [they are often crowded onto poor land with unsatisfactory living conditions and few job opportunities and are not being taught new job skills], and their human rights are being violated.

Environment: Water pollution and deforestation will increase, the coastline will be eroded, and the altered ecosystem will further endanger many species.

Local culture and natural beauty: The 600-km long reservoir will flood many historical sites [such as 1300 archaeological sites] and ruin the legendary scenery of the gorges and the local tourism industry.

Navigation: Heavy siltation will clog ports behind the dam within a few years and negate improvements to navigation.

Power generation: Technological advancements have made hydro dams obsolete, and a decentralized energy market will allow ratepayers to switch to cheaper, cleaner power supplies.

Flood control: Siltation [530 million tonnes per year] will decrease flood storage capacity of the reservoir; the dam will not prevent floods on tributaries caused by deforestation; and more effective flood control solutions are available [such as channel improvements, better zoning, flood proofing and flood warning systems].

Political Motives

Given the evidence that the dam may not achieve its stated aims and may in fact cause irreparable damage, many critics wonder why the Chinese government continues the project. Their conclusion seems to be that the primary motive is political. The dam would be the world's largest hydroelectric dam, which would confer prestige on China and confirm its technological prowess and the superiority of socialism.

Source: Adapted from Probe International.

Questions

1. Determine the reliability of the source of each point of view, using the criteria in Figure 1–4.

2. How effectively were the arguments presented in each case?

3. "Biased words have great power to persuade the unwary towards opinions they might not otherwise hold." Did you detect biased language in either of the readings? Explain.

4. Evaluate the positions of the Chinese government and Probe International on this issue.

Map Projections: A Surprising Source of Bias

Because of its spherical shape, a globe is the only accurate representation of the world. On a globe, shapes and sizes of landmasses, water bodies, or other geographical features are free from distortion. Compass directions are true, and distances between points are represented accurately according to scale. Maps, however, are more practical for recording information about the world's geographical features. They are more portable and can be stored more easily than globes. They can also present highly detailed information about small areas of the Earth's surface.

When cartographers project the features of a globe onto a flat surface, they create a "map projection." Unfortunately, all map projections misrepresent the surface of the Earth in some way. They may create errors in distance, provide inaccurate compass directions, distort the shape of regions, or enlarge or shrink areas. However, the globe's features can be projected in such a way that the resulting map will have characteristics that make it useful for a specific purpose.

For example, one of the most useful map projections for navigational purposes is the Mercator, created in 1569 (Figure 1–7). It is useful because compass directions along a straight line between any two points on the map are always accurate. But, like all maps, the Mercator has some built-in distortion, specifically in the shape and size of regions. It shows countries in equatorial regions as smaller than they actually are, and countries in polar regions as larger. Since

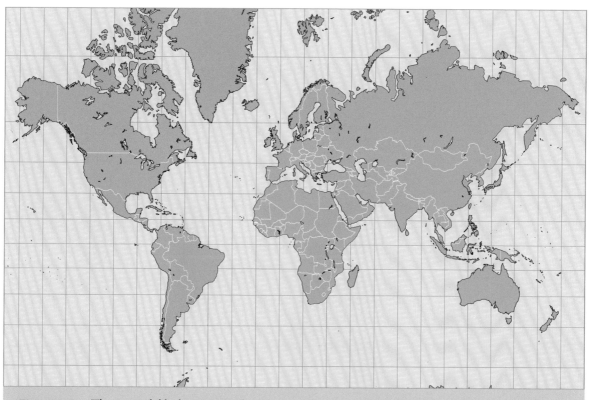

Figure 1–7   *The unavoidable distortion in the Mercator projection undoubtedly biased people's opinions about the size of certain countries and the power these countries wielded.*

the landmasses appear progressively larger with distance away from the Equator, Canada, Russia, Australia, South Africa, and Europe appear larger than they actually are. The Mercator projection was used to emphasize the extent and size of the British Empire during the 19th century. British influence and power around the world were perceived to be very great as a result. For almost 400 years, most people who used world maps based on the Mercator projection were unaware that their perception of the size of the world's countries was badly distorted.

To counteract the biases in size and shape that exist in some projections, cartographers have created other projections that depict areas of Earth in more accurate proportion. Unfortunately, some distortions cannot be avoided. The Robinson projection, used by the National Geographic Society between 1988 and 1998, minimized the distortion of the size and shape of most regions, but it compressed and badly distorted the shape of the countries in polar regions.

In 1921, Oswald Winkel developed three projections, the last one becoming known as the Winkel Tripel projection. The Prime Meridian and the Equator are straight lines, and all other parallels and meridians are curved. The Winkel Tripel projection was adopted by the Society in place of the Robinson in 1998 because it better represented the size and shape of Earth's features, especially in the polar regions (Figure 1–8).

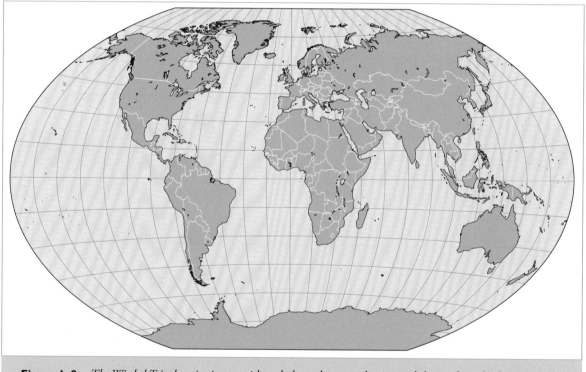

Figure 1–8 *The Winkel Tripel projection provides a balance between the size and shape of Earth's features.*

Chapter Questions

Knowledge and Understanding

1. How do your scores in the "Your Perspectives" questionnaire compare to the majority of your classmates' scores? How do they compare to those of your teacher?

2. Describe your social and economic attitudes. What influences have helped develop these attitudes?

3. Describe how maps may present a biased perspective, using specific examples.

Thinking and Inquiry

4. a) Try to explain why differences exist among the scores for the "Your Perspectives" questionnaire.

   b) What effect might these differences have on class discussions throughout the course?

5. How can you tell that your sources of information may be biased?

Communication

6. In this chapter, facts were defined as "indisputable truths, knowledge that is certain and incontestable." Yet, our understanding of facts is always changing. For example, in 1929 astronomers knew for a fact that there were eight planets in our solar system. The discovery of Pluto in 1930 changed this fact. Research another example of how additional evidence has changed a "fact," and describe the resulting impact on human activity. Present your research in the form of an essay, graphic display, or PowerPoint presentation.

7. Some countries continue to use DDT despite the toxic effects of the chemical on the environment. Find another example of people's continuing to behave in a certain manner despite knowing the negative implications of their actions. Write a short report on this topic.

8. With the aid of a Geographic Information Systems (GIS) computer program, create a world map from the perspective of a country other than Canada. You might want to choose a country in Asia, South America, Africa, or Oceania. Your teacher will give you detailed instructions that will enable you to draw a map of the world from the perspective of the country you have chosen.

Application

9. How might your "Perspectives" questionnaire scores differ from those attained on a similar test by students in other parts of the world? Try to give specific examples of how this might be so.

10. a) What are the differences between opinions and facts?

    b) Examine a recent newspaper or magazine article. Make a list of facts and opinions, explaining your reasons for your choices.

11. Explore the statement: "An individual's point of view influences how he or she sees the world and solves problems."

    a) If a developer and an environmentalist were looking at a wetland area, how would each perceive it?

    b) Pick an issue that was identified in this chapter. Show how three different individuals or groups with differing perspectives might suggest the issue be handled.

2

What Do You Know of the World?

Key Terms

social development
economic development
developed/under-
  developed/developing
  worlds
North–South model
Three-World model
Five-World model
logarithmic graphing

Expectations

In this chapter, you will:

■ identify different ways
to group countries and
evaluate the implica-
tions of doing so

■ select and compare
different statistical ways
to measure quality of life

■ understand the value
and use of the scatter
graph method in
geography

■ use statistical analysis
to interpret and analyse
information

■ use visual communi-
cation skills to present
the results of analysis

Image above: *A New
Description of America,
or the New World*, a
map from Ortelius'
*Theatrum Orbis
Terrarum*, 1590

The map shown above was created in the 16th century, a time
of great exploration and discovery. Yet, much of the world remained
unknown. Perhaps that is why early map makers often drew fanciful
creatures in the least-explored regions, sometimes adding the warning:
"Here be dragons." How much of the world remains unknown to you?

Your Mental Map of the World

Each of us has a "mental map"—a virtual atlas of the world that we carry around with us. One goal of this course is to improve and expand the contents of your virtual atlas. Take a standard piece of blank loose-leaf paper and turn it sideways. In this space, sketch a map of the world. On it, label what you regard as important features, such as continents, regions, countries, major cities, and important bodies of water. Don't be too concerned if your map seems incomplete. Try not to look at other people's maps until after you complete your own.

1. Examine your map. Which parts of the world do you know best? Which parts are most incomplete? Why?

2. Do you feel it is important to know where places are in the world? Give reasons for your answer.

3. Save your map. It might be a good idea to do a similar map at the end of this course—there should be a considerable difference!

Classifying Countries

There are more than 180 countries in the world. However, there is no clear agreement about what constitutes a country. One common way of deciding if a political entity is a country is membership in the United Nations. There were 188 UN members in 2000, but this does not include places like Taiwan and Palestine which, by many standards, are considered to be countries. Only an international affairs specialist would be able to keep track of the economic, social, and political similarities and differences of so many nations. For the rest of us, however, it is easier to learn the characteristics of countries by grouping them according to the similarities in the level of their social and economic development.

A country's level of development can be measured in a variety of ways. For example, looking at measures of educational achievement—such as literacy rates or the percentage of children who complete elementary education—can show the degree of **social development** (Figure 2–1). Measures of health care, such as a country's infant mortality rate or the number of people per doc-

Figure 2–1 *The average level of educational achievement is an indication of a country's social development.*

tor, also indicate a country's level of social development. The level of **economic development** can be shown by such measures as the per capita GDP or the ratio of cars to people.

If you have ever used terms such as "First World," "developing nation," or "North–South," then you are probably already familiar with the idea of grouping countries. Such terms, when used properly, are useful forms of shorthand to discuss and understand world issues.

How may we group countries according to their social and economic development? How many groups should we designate? These are important questions. If we have too few groups, each will have members that are very different from one another. Imagine, for example, that we use only two groups and that these are based on economic wealth. It is easy to put rich countries like Canada and Japan into the wealthier group, and poor countries like Haiti and Ethiopia into the poorer group. But where would you put a country such as Brazil? Its per capita GDP is ten times as much as that of very poor countries, but only one-fourth as much as very wealthy countries. Clearly, having only two groups makes useful grouping difficult and inaccurate. On the other hand, having a large number of groups may make comparisons unnecessarily complex. Many different approaches to grouping have been used over time, with anywhere from two to nine groups being used.

Using Two Groups

Developed/Underdeveloped Worlds

In this older model, the world was divided into economically **developed** countries (such as Canada, the United States, and Germany) and **underdeveloped** countries (such as Brazil, China,

Nigeria, and Jamaica). A major problem with this approach is that there can be confusion between economic and non-economic development. For example, some economically underdeveloped countries, such as India and China, are highly developed culturally.

Developed/Developing Worlds

Many people thought that the model described above tended to be static, or unchanging. It ignored the fact that countries typically become more developed over time. The **developed/ developing worlds** model more fairly reflects the dynamic nature of this process. Over time, countries are able to move from developing to developed status. For example, in the years after World War II, South Korea and Singapore were clearly in the developing world. Fifty years later they had joined the developed world.

North–South

If you look at the locations of developed and developing nations on a world map (Figure 2–2), you will notice a surprising pattern. Most developed nations are farther north than the developing nations. There are some obvious exceptions to this: Australia, New Zealand, and Argentina are quite far south and yet are clearly developed countries. South Africa's situation is unique. In spite of the end of the apartheid system, it continues to have an economy that is partly North (the part that continues to be white-dominated) and partly South (the rest of the economy). A geographer looking at this pattern would quickly conclude that a more accurate theory is that developed countries tend to be located in temperate regions, while developing countries tend to be located in tropical areas. Unfortunately, the simpler, if somewhat inaccurate, use of the **North–South model** remains.

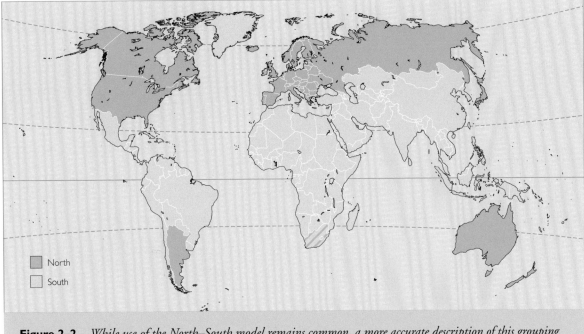

Figure 2–2 *While use of the North–South model remains common, a more accurate description of this grouping would be "temperate–tropical." (Note that South Africa is "striped" to indicate its unique situation.)*

North

South

Using Three Groups

First/Second/Third World

In the **Three-World model**, which originated in the 1950s, First World nations are the developed, capitalist countries like Canada, the United States, Japan, and the United Kingdom. Second World nations are the (formerly) communist countries like Russia, Poland, and Hungary. Non-European, communist countries like Cuba, China, and Vietnam are in an unusual situation. They have some characteristics of Second World countries (in particular their social development) and some characteristics of Third World countries (in particular their economic development). The Third World countries were included in what we called "developing" or "South" in the models previously described.

Developed/Newly Industrialized/Developing

This model, which is entirely economic in nature, adds a transitional stage for countries moving from an agriculturally based economy to an industrial or service-based economy.

Using More Than Three Groups

Several models have more than three groups; for example, some models allow for more than one transition group. One might include countries that are close to being developed or those that are just beginning the process of transition. You could also have country groups that reflect particular types of economic development. A good example of this would be a model that has a separate group for rich oil-producing countries.

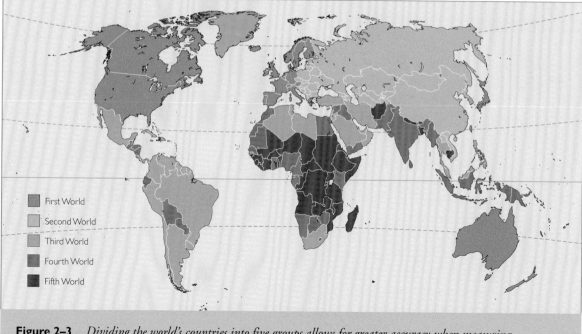

Figure 2–3 *Dividing the world's countries into five groups allows for greater accuracy when measuring similarities in economic and social development.*

Legend:
- First World
- Second World
- Third World
- Fourth World
- Fifth World

Five Worlds

In this book, we will focus on a **Five-World model**. This number was chosen as a reasonable compromise between accuracy and simplicity (Figure 2–3).

- First World countries include those with the highest level of economic and social development. Canada, Japan, and France are examples of countries in this group.
- Second World countries include those that are, or in most cases were, communist. Cuba, China, and Russia are members of this group. Often, they have levels of social development similar to those of First World nations, while their economic development is more like that of much poorer nations (Figure 2–4). Hence, they do not conveniently fit into one of the other worlds. It is logical to assume that, since most of these countries no longer have communist governments, they will eventually take

Figure 2–4 *A Russian woman sells a home-made tablecloth outside an exchange booth in Moscow. Many Russians, especially pensioners, have been forced to become street vendors, unable to subsist on their meagre pensions since the break-up of the former Soviet Union.*

on the characteristics of one of the other groups, depending on their overall level of economic and social development. When this happens, the five worlds will become four.

■ Third World countries include those such as Brazil, Mexico, and Malaysia, that are well advanced in the transition to development. As a result, their levels of social and economic development are between those of the First and Fourth Worlds. The "Third World," as the term is used with a three-world model and in the popular press, includes the Third, Fourth, and Fifth Worlds as described in our model.

■ Fourth World countries include those that are in the early stages of transition towards being developed. This group includes countries such as Indonesia, India, and Ecuador. They have somewhat higher levels of social and economic development than Fifth World countries.

■ Fifth World countries include those such as Bangladesh, Ethiopia, and Haiti, that show little evidence of starting the transition towards development (Figure 2–5).

Figure 2–5 *Faces of the Fifth World: Young women weave straw mats in a village in Mauritania.*

An Exercise in Country Grouping

1. Examine the statistics in Figure 2–6. When you look at this mass of numbers, you can see some similarities between countries; for example, countries 9 and 10 seem comparable. Trying to divide these countries into five worlds by examining the table is a formidable task, to be sure. A much better approach is to look for groups on a scatter graph, which relates two measures of development. For example, Figure 2–7 shows the relationship between per capita GDP and motor vehicle ownership. From a graph like this, it is sometimes relatively easy to identify the countries that have similar characteristics. That is not the case here, though.

2. Depending on the kind of data you have, several values can overlap when you create a graph on linear graph paper, making it difficult to interpret the pattern you want to see. This is certainly the case in parts of Figure 2–7. In a situation like this, the use of semi-log or log-log graph paper can help. If you are not familiar with the use of logarithmic scales, read the following section. If you are comfortable using them, skip to #4.

Country	A	B	C	D	E	F	G	H
1	8.9	7.7	98	16 100	6	226	4 661	438
2	21.9	80.5	43	2 000	25	8	419	22
3	16.7	69.9	56	1 570	30	1	83	3
4	9.2	28.1	82	3 600	15	8	804	86
5	3.0	4.5	99	24 400	3	530	8 106	582
6	25.9	146.5	31	510	43	6	42	4
7	11.2	9.4	95	8 500	4	110	2 474	207
8	0.2	9.4	99	6 800	5	273	3 490	263
9	1.7	3.9	99	24 900	2	560	7 319	558
10	3.7	5.0	97	24 800	3	560	15 463	655
11	16.7	95.2	45	1 800	32	7	106	29
12	16.0	40.9	84	2 900	21	22	266	98
13	24.6	34.1	90	2 900	14	22	625	69
14	26.9	100.0	36	600	45	2	20	3
15	−4.5	20.1	98	7 700	7	154	5 267	210
16	16.5	63.2	52	2 200	25	7	442	27
17	9.1	37.0	83	6 500	9	77	1 833	149
18	5.5	6.8	97	36 200	2	767	13 137	664
19	19.5	20.3	84	10 300	14	42	629	203
20	5.0	7.4	96	1 700	7	32	1 371	39

A Natural increase in population per 1000 people (2001)

B Infant mortality per 1000 births (2001)

C Literacy percentage (2001)

D Per capita GDP $US (2000)

E Percentage of GDP from agriculture (2000)

F Motor vehicles per 1000 people (1998)

G Per capita electricity use, kWh (1999)

H Number of phone lines per 1000 people (1999)

Figure 2–6 *You can use these data to determine the characteristics of each of the five worlds.*
Source: Columns A to E from CIA, *The World Factbook 2001*; Columns F to H from World Bank 1999.

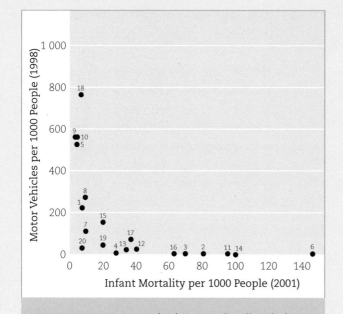

Figure 2–7 *Linear scales do not work well with these data, since too many values are clustered in a few locations.*

3. a) **Logarithmic graphing** sounds a lot more complex and intimidating than it really is. In fact, the difficult mathematical part is done for you when you use special graph paper with a logarithmic scale (Figure 2–8). Graph paper that has one logarithmic scale and one linear scale is called semi-log paper. Sometimes you might want to use a logarithmic scale on each axis. This type of graph paper is called log-log paper. b) You should consider using a logarithmic scale any time you have data that extend over three or more orders of magnitude. For example, if you have numbers in the tens, hundreds, and thousands or in the millions, tens of millions, hundreds of millions, and billions. In the first example, there are three orders of magnitude, so you would need a logarithmic scale with

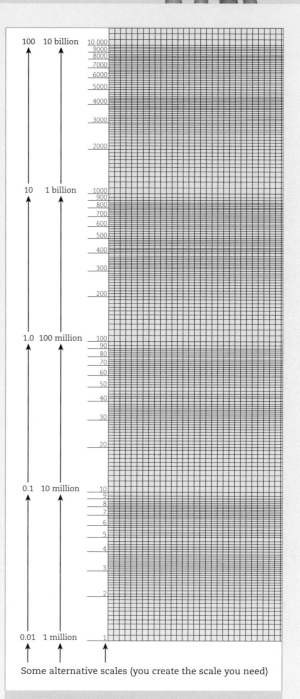

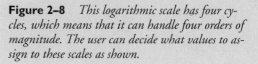

Some alternative scales (you create the scale you need)

Figure 2–8 *This logarithmic scale has four cycles, which means that it can handle four orders of magnitude. The user can decide what values to assign to these scales as shown.*

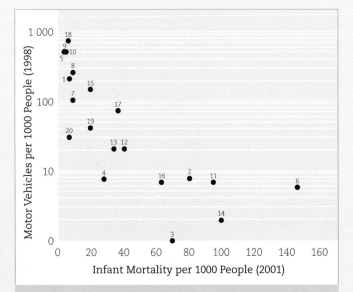

Figure 2–9 *A semi-log graph makes the data in Figure 2–7 easier to interpret.*

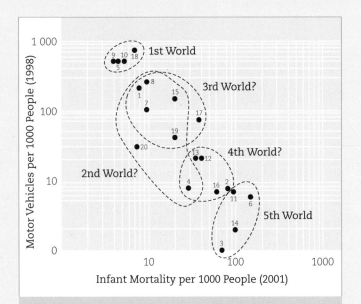

Figure 2–10 *Log-log paper makes country groupings easier to see. While First and Fifth Worlds are clear, you will have to discuss, with your group, the members of the other worlds. For example, there are five possible members of the Fourth World.*

three cycles. In the second example, there are four orders of magnitude, so you would need four-cycle logarithmic graph paper. In particular, if you have a large number of values at either end of the overall range, a logarithmic scale is useful. Generally, if you have one or two orders of magnitude, you can use regular, linear graph paper successfully.

Computer spreadsheets are also helpful in creating logarithmic graphs. The specifics vary from program to program, but in general involve modifying the format of the axis of the graph.

c) There are two restrictions on the use of logarithmic scales: you cannot show negative values, and you cannot show zero. In both cases this is because there would always be another smaller, positive cycle to the left of (or below) the one currently being shown. For example, if you have a cycle that goes from 1 to 10, the cycle below this would go from 0.1 to 1, and the one below that from 0.01 to 0.1 (and so on). You can never reach zero.

d) Figure 2–9 shows what the data in Figure 2–7 would look like if we use semi-log graph paper. On this graph, a logarithmic scale has been used for the number of motor vehicles per 1000 people. This graph spreads out the data and makes it easier to see the differences. If we now move from semi-log to log-log paper (Figure 2–10), it gets even easier to identify the country groupings, since we have now expanded the infant mortality scale.

4. Work in a group of three or four students. Each of you will draw a minimum of two scatter graphs, all showing different pairs of data. From each graph, you should identify which countries you think are in each of the five worlds. You will have to decide which type of graph paper is appropriate for the data you are analysing.

5. Some hints to help you with this analysis:

a) When you want to use a logarithmic scale, follow these steps:

- Count how many orders of magnitude there are in the data. For example, the motor vehicles per 1000 data range from 1 to 767, which is three orders of magnitude (ones, tens, and hundreds). You will need to use three logarithmic cycles to show these data.

- Label the cycles 1 to 10, 10 to 100, 100, and 1000 from the bottom or left.

- Locate the values using the logarithmically placed grid lines.

b) There are four countries for each world in this data set.

c) Remember that the Second World countries will not follow the same transitional pattern as countries in the other groups. For social data they may look like First World countries, while for economic data they may look like Third or Fourth World countries. If you graph two economic data sets, it may be difficult to identify Second World countries.

d) On any particular graph, there may be ambiguous results. For example, there may be five countries that appear to belong to a particular world. Compare your results with those of the other members of your group so that you can arrive at a consensus about the membership of each world.

e) Your teacher will tell you the number of countries of each world. How did you do?

Your Paper Map of the World

It is very likely that you now know more about the world than you did when you started this chapter. One of the things you will have to do throughout this course is keep track of the locations of many unfamiliar countries and places. A useful aid in doing this is to create a location map of the places that you encounter in the course. Start with a blank map of the world on which you can record the location of any countries, regions, cities, or other places that you learn about. To start with, locate the 20 countries from the previous exercise, along with any other places that have come up in class discussions so far. Later you can add more places as they come up in this course. Remember to give your map an appropriate title.

Chapter Questions

Knowledge and Understanding

1. Name the four members of each of the five worlds from the activity you completed.

2. Why might higher levels of development of a country be related to temperate locations?

3. Compare the map of the Five Worlds (Figure 2–3) to that of the North–South grouping of countries (Figure 2–2). What relationships do you see between the two?

Thinking and Inquiry

4. a) Look at the eight criteria across the top of the table in Figure 2–6. Write a brief description of each measure, indicating why it is a useful measure of development. You may wish to refer to the Glossary for an explanation of some of the terms.

   b) Indicate whether each measurement is primarily related to economic development or social development.

Figure 2–11 *Faces of the Third World: A worker on the assembly line at the Mercedes-Benz plant in Toluca, Mexico, works on an engine block.*

World	A	B	C	D	E	F	G	H
First	1.7–5.5							
Second								
Third								
Fourth								
Fifth								

A Natural increase in population per 1000 people (2001)
B Infant mortality per 1000 people (2001)
C Literacy percentage (2001)
D Per capita GDP $US (2000)
E Percentage GDP from agriculture (2000)
F Motor vehicles per 1000 people (1998)
G Per capita electricity use, kWh (1999)
H Number of phone lines per 1000 people (1999)

Figure 2–12

5. a) What countries still have communist governments?
   b) Over the next few years, what is likely to happen to the development level of the following communist or formerly communist countries: i) Poland and Hungary, ii) China and Vietnam, iii) Russia, iv) Cuba?

Communication

6. a) Copy and complete the table in Figure 2–12 to show the range of values that is typical within each of the five worlds for each measure of development. Use the data from Figure 2–6.
   b) Create a graphical summary of these data. You are not limited to showing the data in graphs; you can use drawings, cartoons, collages, or some other medium to do this.

Application

7. Consider the mental map that you completed at the beginning of this chapter. What factors have influenced your knowledge of the world? How might these influences affect how you approach this course and learn about world issues?

8. a) Look at your list of countries for the five worlds. Suggest two additional members of each world.
   b) How could you check to see if your choices are correct?

3

Two Themes for World Issues

Expectations

In this chapter, you will:

- identify ways in which countries and regions are becoming more interdependent

- explain how different cultures perceive resources and sustainable development

- explain how selected natural and human systems interact

- identify current world sustainability issues and environmental threats

- evaluate viewpoints of different stakeholders in a geographic issue

- predict probable futures based on current trends, including technological change

Internet use grows explosively

US forest industry opposes increased production in Canada

Dangerous new forms o malaria appear in Africa

Governments struggle to meet needs of growing number of older citizens

China to all more famil a second ch

Rising oil prices threaten prosperity of developed countries

Poor countries demand debt relie

The headlines above might make the news in any given month. Although they appear to cover a wide range of issues, they are linked by two significant themes: *globalization* and *sustainability*. Some people think these concepts will become the two dominant themes of the 21st century, affecting every aspect of life.

Globalization

Globalization is a word that has recently become commonplace. In fact, this word has two vastly different connotations. To some people, mention of globalization inspires visions of the "global village," a place where every citizen of the world is linked by the latest high-technology communications systems. To others, globalization is the reason a local factory shuts down, only to reopen thousands of kilometres away in a country with cheaper labour and weaker environmental laws.

Why should there be such different views of the same concept? First, globalization as it exists today is not fully understood, and its impacts are as yet unclear. Second, there is not just one form of globalization; there are in fact eight types that can occur separately or in a wide variety of combinations.

Financial globalization

The world's financial systems have become intimately interconnected. For example, oil prices in the Persian Gulf and the North Sea have a direct impact on the oil prices of western Canada. Another example can be found in the stock market. The world's stock markets are constantly affecting one another like a wave that ripples around the Earth each business day. Trading on the New York stock exchange influences what happens a few hours later in Tokyo and Hong Kong. In turn, their trading affects that of the European markets. The next day, the wave continues as European trading influences North American markets. An interesting characteristic of this kind of globalization is that it does not involve interconnections of nations. Rather, it reflects what happens in a network of world cities that have significant financial markets (Figure 3–1).

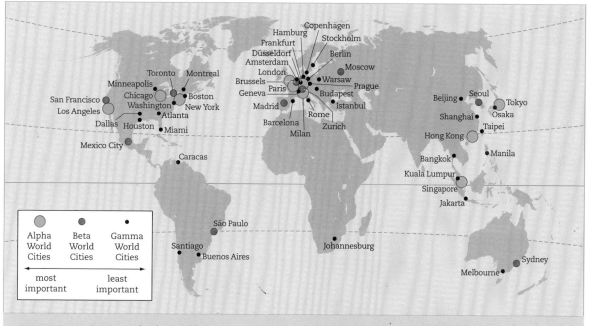

Figure 3–1   *Increasingly, the world's business is dominated by what happens in a network of world cities.*
Source: P.J. Taylor and C. Flint, *Political Geography* (4th ed.). Harlow, UK: Prentice-Hall, 2000, p. 323.

Economic globalization

In the past, a corporation tended to be identified with one particular country. For example, when the Ford Motor Company started, its ownership, production, and market were primarily located in the United States. Now, a growing number of huge companies, including Ford, are multinational or **transnational** in nature, since they have integrated operations across much of the world. Examples include Coca-Cola, Nike, and Shell, who move their production and capital, and seek markets anywhere in the world that will benefit the company. This type of globalization has been one of the most controversial. Supporters of it maintain that economic globalization is producing much greater global wealth, which will mean a higher standard of living. Opponents say that economic globalization only tends to increase the difference between the world's "haves" and its "have-nots," and produces a situation in which transnational corporations become more powerful and influential than most countries (Figure 3–2).

Technological globalization

When we talk about the global village, we are referring primarily to technological globalization. This has occurred because of the explosive growth of communications and computer technology in the past 50 years. The impact of this technological revolution affects you almost every day. For example, you are able to communicate with much of the world, by phone and the Internet, instantly and cheaply.

Political globalization

As the world's countries become more interdependent, economically and technologically, it is not surprising that there are pressures on them to adopt more uniform policies. In the 1990s and early 2000s, the economic pendulum swung towards a neo-liberal agenda. This meant that many countries cut government expenditures, reduced economic and environmental regulation, privatized government operations, and opened their economies to the world. (You can learn more about neo-liberal economics in Chapter 11.) Canada's move to join with the United States and Mexico in a free trade agreement is typical of this trend towards less national sovereignty and more powerful international cooperation.

Cultural globalization

This type of globalization refers to the gradual harmonization of the world's cultures at the expense of distinctly different local cultures. Eventually, most people in the world will watch the same television shows and movies, listen to the same music, eat the same foods, have the same values, and so on. This trend is so strong that a major British magazine, *The Economist*,

Figure 3–2 *Transnational companies, like McDonald's, are transforming the appearance of cities around the world. This McDonald's restaurant is in Prague, Czech Republic. What other effects might the presence of transnationals have on the life of local residents?*

is able to use the price of Big Macs in different countries to compare the values of currencies. Critics suggest that cultural globalization can happen only with the loss of the world's cultural diversity, and that the "world culture" that develops will be primarily an American one.

Sociological globalization

Central to this form of globalization is the increasingly common belief that we are members of a single world society that has become more significant than the distinct national societies that previously existed. This perception goes far beyond the elements of popular culture that are part of cultural globalization. It can be seen in the growing belief that certain common attitudes and standards of behaviour should exist in every country. An example can be found in the reactions of Westerners who decry the policies of so-called fundamentalist Islamic countries, such as denying equality to women and using punishments that include amputation, stoning, and whipping.

Ecological globalization

In recent decades, there has been abundant evidence that the planet must be treated as a single ecosystem rather than a collection of separate ecological systems. A good example is the problem of ozone depletion. The connection between the use of some aerosol sprays, refrigerants, and fire extinguishers and a higher incidence of skin cancer may not seem immediately apparent, but scientific studies have shown this to be the case. Ozone depletion, global warming, and dozens of other environmental problems have led many to believe that humanity's demands on the planet are exceeding Earth's ability to respond.

Geographical globalization

Even the study of geography has been globalized. In the past, geographers tended to look at the world in terms of relationships between and among countries—for example, trade, geopolitics, and war. Increasingly, they now see a borderless world that is dominated not by countries, but by worldwide ecological concerns and by the political, cultural, economic, and other relationships that exist among the network of world cities and the regions that surround them.

Concerns About Globalization

Globalization is a debatable topic in the world today because it has taken new forms, and this newness has raised several concerns. First, the full impacts (both positive and negative) of globalization have not yet been felt. For example, supporters of cultural globalization might say that, in time, all people of the world will have access to the information that the Internet provides. Opponents might say that time will bring only the loss of many unique cultures. A second concern is that the trend towards globalization emphasizes short-term gains over long-term benefits. For example, opponents say that economic globalization places corporate profits before workers' rights and environmental protection. Supporters say that governments will eventually agree to global labour and environmental laws,

Did you KNOW? Globalization is not a new phenomenon. In the late 18th century, sea otter pelts were taken by English, Russian, and American traders from the west coast of North America to China to be traded for silks, tea, porcelain, and other goods that were then sold in Europe.

Figure 3–3 *Demonstrators against the World Trade Organization march through downtown Seattle in November 1999.*

but that appropriate international legislation or controls will require more time to be developed.

What is clear is that the growth of these many "globalizations" must change the rules about how we look at the world.

> These eight dimensions [of globalization] are interconnected in many complex ways and are themselves subject to much academic debate and rancour. ... However, there is one thing that everybody does seem to agree about: some fundamental changes are at large which involve some reforming of the geographical scales through which we live our lives as workers, consumers, investors, voters, viewers, vacationers and many more of our social activities. — P.J. Taylor and C. Flint, *Political Geography* (4th ed.). Harlow, UK: Prentice-Hall, 2000, p. 3.

The divergence of opinions about globalization can be confusing. A wide divergence exists even among people who oppose it. For example, in recent years several important international gatherings—including a World Trade Organization meeting in Seattle, USA, a Free Trade Agreement of the Americas conference in Quebec City, Canada, and a Group of Eight meeting in Genoa, Italy—have attracted large demonstrations by opponents of globalization who represent a variety of backgrounds, opinions, and tactics (Figure 3–3). For example, the environmentalists, who focus on the demands that development places on the Earth, would like to see reductions in world economic growth. At the same demonstration, however, union members might protest the loss of their jobs because of economic globalization, yet still proclaim that they favour a growing economy. The issues surrounding globalization affect people in so many different ways that it is difficult to single out one aspect and determine its impact. Clearly, globalization is an important and complex idea that must be central to our study of world issues.

Sustainability

In all its forms, globalization today demonstrates how closely interconnected are the world's environmental issues, social problems, and economic growth. The depletion of Canada's cod stocks, for example, has greatly affected the east-coast fishers' economic prosperity, the subsequent welfare of their families, and inevitably, the economy of Canada. It has consequences for people in other countries who have lost an important food source as well as the economic benefits that come from the business of buying and selling fish. What can we do to make sure that our actions, in whatever sphere of globalization, do not negatively affect other people and their environment? The answer is to adopt the principle of **sustainability**. Development is considered to be sustainable when it meets the needs of people today without jeopardizing the well-being of future generations. This means we need to raise the standard of human life without harming Earth in the process.

Historical Perspective

Throughout most of human history, people hunted animals and gathered plants to survive. Hunter-gatherers had relatively little impact on the environment because there were so few of them and because they lacked the technology to cause significant environmental damage. Later, as agriculture developed and urban civilizations became more widespread, humans had greater impact on their environment. We know, for example, that there was serious soil erosion and destruction of vegetation in North Africa and Mesopotamia in the Middle East.

Some early civilizations, such as those of Aboriginals, were aware of their destruction of the environment and, consequently, practised conservation: they used manure to maintain soil fertility, created terraced fields on mountain slopes to prevent soil erosion, and instituted religious taboos to protect certain animals and sites. Nevertheless, in pre-industrial times, when most of Earth was sparsely populated, people generally viewed wilderness and resources as unlimited. As a result, there was not much concern for the state of the environment.

By the end of the 1700s, globalization was well under way as Europeans explored and colonized parts of the Americas, Australia, and Africa. During this period of exploration and colonization, the acquisition of wealth was the ultimate goal. Most Europeans were ethnocentric and did not care about the impact of their actions on indigenous peoples, many of whom were attacked or even wiped out. Few thought either about the impact on the environment. Colonization brought soil erosion and the gradual destruction of vegetation and wildlife. By the 1800s, settlers and adventurers rampaged across North America, hunting birds, predatory animals, and the great herds of deer, elk, and bison almost to extinction. The magnificent virgin forests of the east were lost to the loggers' axes, and the native grasses and vegetation of the central plains disappeared as a result of overgrazing by domestic livestock. The West Indies, Africa, and Australia suffered the same sort of environmental damage when Europeans settled in these "new" lands.

Expansionist world view

During the 18th century, Europeans developed an expansionist world view. For 200 years before, the prevailing economic policy in Europe was that of mercantilism. This theory advocates that states increase their wealth through trade and the acquisition of colonies, which then supply the mother country with raw materials and a market for its manufactured goods. Mercantilists believed that there was a fixed amount of wealth in the world and that all countries were competing for a share of it.

The 18th century in Europe was also a time of social change. The idea of mercantilism started to be replaced with the idea of freer trade. The Industrial Revolution, which began in England in the middle of the 18th century, gave rise to mechanization, factories, railways, and steamships. Rural inhabitants flocked to the coal fields to mine the fuel to support new industries, or to urban areas near the coal fields looking for jobs in factories. As people lost their direct contact with the land, their knowledge of and respect for nature diminished. They believed that they were justified in exploiting nature and its resources because the ensuing accumulation of wealth went hand-in-hand with progress.

Why were Europeans so destructive of the lands they colonized? They perceived the "new" lands as having limitless natural resources and space, and set about to use their technology to exploit the environment. They believed that science and technology could control nature for the benefit of humankind.

Ecological world view

A more nature-centred world view developed in the late 18th and early 19th centuries as a reaction against the destruction of the environment. The ecological world view of the 20th century was based on this reaction to the expansionist world view (Figure 3–4). Instead of viewing nature as something to be exploited and tamed, some people placed emphasis on the emotional and spiritual relationships that bind humans and the environment together. In the early 19th century, English poet William Wordsworth wrote about the spirituality found in the natural environment (Figure 3–5). He was critical of urban environments, stating that they were artificial and dehumanizing.

At the same time in the United States, writers and activists were raising awareness about

Expansionist World View	Ecological World View
▪ Nature is a resource to be used, not preserved.	▪ The universe is a totality with all parts interrelated and interlocked.
▪ Conservation must work together with the dominant values of the surrounding society, not against them.	▪ The biotic community and its processes must be protected.
▪ The primary value of natural areas lies in their value to modern society.	▪ Nature is intrinsically valuable—animals, trees, rock, etc., have value in themselves.
▪ Conservation should work against the wastefulness and environmentally disruptive excesses of a developing society.	▪ Human activities must work within the limitations of the planet's ecosystem.
▪ Conservation is equated with sustainable exploitation.	▪ Preservation works against the dominant societal values.
	▪ Nature provides a forum to judge the state of human society.

Figure 3–4 *A comparison of early 20th century approaches to conservation*
Source: D. Draper, *Our Environment: A Canadian Perspective*. Toronto: Nelson Thomson Learning, 1998, p. 38. Adapted from D.M. Taylor (1992), Disagreeing on the basics: Environmental debates reflect competing world views. *Alternatives, 18* (3), p. 29.

Lines Composed a Few Miles Above Tintern Abbey
by William Wordsworth

… For I have learned

To look on nature, not as in the hour

Of thoughtless youth; but hearing oftentimes

The still, sad music of humanity,

Nor harsh nor grating, though of ample power

To chasten and subdue. And I have felt

A presence that disturbs me with the joy

Of elevated thoughts; a sense sublime

Of something far more deeply interfused,

Whose dwelling is the light of setting suns,

And the round ocean, and the living air,

And the blue sky, and in the mind of man:

A motion and a spirit, that impels

All thinking things, all objects of all thought,

And rolls through all things. Therefore am I still

A lover of the meadows and the woods,

And mountains; and of all that we behold

From this green earth; of all the mighty world

Of eye and ear, both what they half-create,

And what perceive; well pleased to recognize

In nature and the language of the sense

The anchor of my purest thoughts, the nurse,

The guide, the guardian of my heart, and soul

Of all my moral being.

Figure 3–5 *For Wordsworth, nature held a value that could not be reduced to economic worth.*

the destruction of natural resources and argued for the preservation of wild places. The concept of setting aside land for national parks was first proposed in the United States in 1832; the first textbook on conservation was published in the United States in 1860, and the Sierra Club was founded in 1892. In Canada, Clifford Sifton, Minister of the Interior, promoted forest conservation in 1909. He believed, however, that conservation in Canada should take the form of managing resources for economic benefit rather than for preservation.

Environmentalism

After World War II, population growth and industrialization caused increased pressure on land and resources. The 1950s and 1960s gave rise to even more forms of pollution as the chemical and other industries expanded. Air pollution in larger cities sometimes reached toxic levels, and water supplies in some heavily populated areas became contaminated with industrial waste. Oil spills and the careless dumping of toxic wastes severely threatened the world's oceans and the survival of species that depend upon the seas. Synthetic pesticides that were extremely successful in increasing agricultural production had severe, damaging consequences for the environment.

In her 1962 book, *Silent Spring*, Rachel Carson warned about the damage caused by the indiscriminate use of pesticides such as DDT. Carson's book was at the forefront of a popular environmental protection movement, based on an ecological world view, that began to develop in the 1960s. By the end of the decade, environmental awareness of issues related to pollution, resource depletion, nuclear waste, population growth, and oil spills had increased among all segments of society. The first Earth Day took place in the United States in April 1970, when ecologists, scientists, government officials, and citizens' groups came together to discuss environmental concerns. During this first wave of **environmentalism**, many governments responded by placing certain environmental issues on their lists of priorities. The Canadian government took these issues very seriously, and in 1971 created the Department of the Environment.

In the mid-1980s, a second wave of environmentalism began, in which the issues were frequently international in perspective. Scientists argued that global warming, ozone depletion, rainforest and old-growth forest cutting, and loss of animal and plant species had negative implications for people everywhere in the world. By the 1990s, environmental awareness was widespread throughout the developed countries. Companies, both large and small, were eager to link their corporate image to environmentally friendly behaviour. Environmental awareness led to such practices as recycling, epitomized in Canada by the Blue Box program. But awareness does not ensure that people will always adopt behaviour that is good for the environment. Often, the person who agrees that recycling is important will drive a gas-guzzling sport utility vehicle or live in an oversized house with only one other occupant. Companies too, in spite of what they preach, often allow their economic goals to take precedence over environmental ones when hard times occur.

Resources and Resource Use

Resources *are* not: they *become*. They are not static but expand and contract according to human wants and human actions.— Erich W. Zimmermann, *World Resources and Industries* (rev. ed.). New York: Harper & Row, 1951, p. 15.

All the material components of the environment taken together are called the total stock. The total stock includes energy, living organisms, and non-living materials. Any part of the total stock that becomes useful to human beings is called a **resource**. The term resource is most often used in the context of natural resources, such as water and air, which are necessary for life. The term also applies to those components of the total stock that we use for specific purposes, for example, oil for fuel or fish for food.

The quotation at the beginning of this section tells us that something becomes a resource only when humans need it, and that therefore something may be considered a resource at one time in history and not at another. For example, flint was an important resource to early hunting and gathering societies because it was used to make fire. Today it has little value. When uranium was first discovered, it had little value because there was no technology to exploit the energy stored within it. Once the technology was developed, it became a valuable resource. On the Pacific coast of North America, the Douglas fir and Pacific yew grow in the same environment. The Douglas fir was used for timber, but the Pacific yew was burned as a trash tree. In the 1980s, however, a substance in the yew called taxol was found to have cancer-fighting properties. By the 1990s, the US government had established conservation guidelines to protect the yew and to encourage its replanting. The tree's new value to humans had changed it to a valuable resource. If an inexpensive means were found to create taxol synthetically, the Pacific yew would return to non-resource status.

What conditions lead a society to develop a given item in the environment? Three conditions must exist before something in the total stock becomes a resource.

- It must be physically possible to exploit the would-be resource. In other words, the technology must be in place in order to develop the item for human use.

- It must be economically feasible to develop the resource. There must also be money, skills, and equipment to develop it. Furthermore, the return on the investment must be greater than the cost of developing the resource. The Athabasca tar sands in Alberta is an example. A huge amount of oil is embedded in the tar sands. When extraction was costly, only a few processing plants were built; in recent years, newer, more cost-effective production techniques have enabled this industry to expand.

- It must be culturally acceptable to develop the resource. If development goes against prevailing values, or endangers the well-being of anyone, the resource should not be exploited. For many years, the seal hunt was an important source of income in some villages of Newfoundland and Quebec. The hunt was reduced in size, however, in the 1980s when conservation groups persuaded the European Parliament to ban the import of Canadian sealskins.

Most of the world's resources may be classified as renewable or non-renewable (Figure 3–6). **Renewable** resources are infinite; that is, they should exist for as long as humans need them because nature replenishes them. Air, vegetation, water, and fish are examples. But, if humans interfere with the natural processes that produce resources, they may destroy the resources altogether. **Non-renewable** resources are finite; once we have used up our current reserves, no new ones will replace them. Geological processes take tens or hundreds of millions of years to create resources, and humans probably won't be around when the next batch is ready! Some non-renewable resources may be recycled; for example, about half the steel currently produced comes from recycled scrap. Recycling prolongs the use of limited resources, but is feasible only if it is economically profitable.

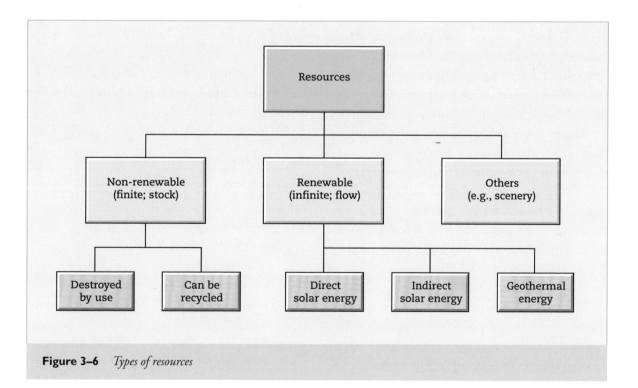

Figure 3–6 *Types of resources*

Different Views of Our World

Spaceship Earth Concept

Throughout most of history, humans have viewed themselves as living in a world of unlimited resources and space. They believed that there was always somewhere else to go: as they used up resources, they could move on to a new place and start over. As long as there were few humans with limited technology, people could view Earth as a reservoir of infinite resources.

This view is no longer reasonable. Earth viewed from space (Figure 3–7) resembles a spaceship travelling through the universe. The **Spaceship Earth concept** regards Earth as a tiny, fragile sphere with limited resources and a rapidly growing population whose life-support system is in jeopardy. According to this view, we must change the way we live because there is nowhere else we can go if our air, water, and food run out or become too polluted to use.

Figure 3–7 *Earth, as seen from space, is an astonishing sight.*

Gaia Hypothesis

Some ecologists have criticized the metaphor of Spaceship Earth as a simplistic view of our huge, complex environment. A better metaphor may be that Earth is a dynamic organism alive in its own right. Scientists know that Earth's temperature has remained relatively constant for over four billion years, while during the same period, the Sun's temperature has increased by about 25 per cent. Something has regulated Earth's greenhouse gases with the result that temperatures have remained stable enough to allow living organisms to survive. In 1972, chemist James Lovelock concluded that Earth's climate has been regulated by its living organisms. Through evolution, living organisms have regulated the amount of carbon dioxide and other substances to keep temperature and precipitation at levels suitable for their survival. Lovelock called his theory the **Gaia hypothesis**, named after the Greek goddess of Earth.

In 1988, Lovelock further developed his Gaia hypothesis by equating Earth to a single living organism. In this view, the world is a self-regulating, living entity made up of organisms, from bacteria to humans, that modify the atmosphere, oceans, climate, and crust of the Earth to ensure their survival. In other words, there is constant feedback between living and non-living matter to maintain an equilibrium of life-giving components. For example, the salt content of the oceans has remained at about 3.5 per cent for millions of years despite the fact that salt is constantly added by rivers and evaporation.

Organisms such as coral and algae regulate the salt levels so that oceanic life can survive. Similarly, oxygen is maintained at just the rights levels required by plants by the constant balancing of oxygen and carbon dioxide through photosynthesis and respiration. If oxygen levels were to fall below 21 per cent, plant life could not survive; if they rose above 25 per cent, vegetation would burn through spontaneous combustion. The current state of the environment, therefore, is optimal for the present, although not necessarily for the future. There is concern that humans are overriding the regulatory mechanisms by causing temperatures to rise and the number of animal and plant species to decrease, and by polluting the air and oceans.

Limits-to-Growth Thesis

In 1972, an international group of experts, calling themselves the "Club of Rome," wrote a report called *Limits to Growth*. The **limits-to-growth thesis** is based on computer models predicting what might happen if current growth trends continue. These experts started with the premise that there are limits to population growth because finite resources will be used up

and renewable resources can be overused or damaged. They found that if trends in population growth, economic development, resource use, and consumption were to continue, within 100 years the limits to human growth would be reached. In other words, world population would exceed Earth's **carrying capacity**—the maximum number of people that can be sustained by Earth's resources.

Cornucopian Thesis

The **cornucopian thesis** is an alternative view to the limits-to-growth thesis. It states that science and technology will continue to advance, with the result that new resources will be developed to take the place of the old resources as they are depleted. Implicit in this thesis is the idea that Earth's resources are not really finite. In essence, there need not be limits to growth as long as technological development continues. The cornucopians, many of whom are economists, feel that the only way to create jobs and produce materials is through constant economic growth. This viewpoint seems to prevail in much of the world today.

The Need for Sustainable Development

Throughout history, many societies have collapsed because of imbalances they created in the environment upon which they depended. For example, the Mayan civilization of Central America appears to have declined around the year 900 CE because of its overuse of soils and overdependence on one crop: maize.

The concept of sustainable development was introduced in 1980 in the *World Conservation*

Strategy, a publication of the International Union for the Conservation of Nature and Natural Resources, the United Nations Environment Program, and the World Wildlife Fund. It set three objectives that should be incorporated into all sustainable development programs:

- maintenance of essential ecological processes
- sustainable use of Earth's resources
- preservation of genetic diversity

Nick Middleton, a lecturer at Oxford University, has formulated three cycles to illustrate how human interaction with the environment can bring about sustainable development (Figure 3–8). This model may be used locally or globally, and across timelines. Cycle A represents the global economy of the past, when wealth was accumulated largely by the degradation of the environment. The wealth reduced the negative impacts or "stress" on society by increasing standards of living. Once standards of living improved, people were better able to increase their wealth. Efforts to increase wealth led to further inappropriate exploitation of the environment. At this point, Middleton suggests that society moves into Cycle B.

We have entered Cycle B on a global scale because of our large population and the scale of human impact on Earth. The degraded environment causes less wealth to be generated, and reduced wealth increases stress on society. For example, inappropriate development such as cutting old-growth forests may occur as society tries to overcome stress such as debt. A feedback loop is created as stress promotes further inappropriate development, such as deforestation,

to acquire wealth to relieve stress. The only way to get out of Cycle B is to enter Cycle C, in which our parasitic relationship with the environment becomes a symbiotic one. Cycle C requires a permanent, long-term strategy. If the stress on the environment is reduced through sustainable development, we will not revert to the destructive behaviour of Cycles A and B.

While there is international agreement on the goals, there is no consensus about how sustainable development can be achieved. In 1987, the United Nations publication, *Our Common Future*, gave the concept of sustainable development worldwide prominence. It defined sustainability as development that meets the needs of the present generation without compromising the ability of future generations to meet their own needs. This definition presents problems, however. Who determines what a "need" is? One person's need may seem an unnecessary luxury to another. And is "development" different from "growth"?

In spite of difficulties with the concept of sustainable development, nations will have to cooperate in making ecologically sound decisions in accordance with the carrying capacity of Earth.

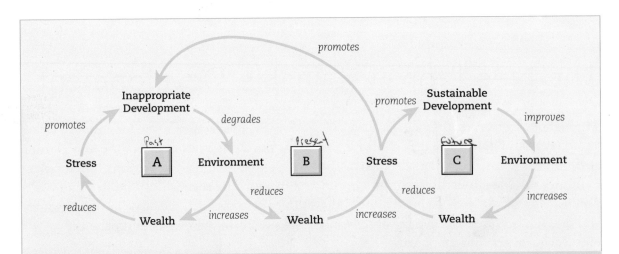

Figure 3–8 *These three cycles show the relationship between modes of development and the environment.*
Source: N. Middleton, *The Global Crisis: An Introduction to Environmental Issues* (2nd ed.). New York: Oxford University Press, 1999, p. 33.

Chapter Questions

Knowledge and Understanding

1. a) In your own words, describe the meaning of each type of globalization.
   b) For each type, give a specific way in which it might be a positive and a negative development for the world.
   c) Using examples from at least three types of globalization, identify ways in which countries or regions are becoming interdependent.

2. In your own words, compare the expansionist world view with the ecological world view. Use examples from the text.

3. a) Explain the Gaia hypothesis.
   b) What is your opinion about this hypothesis?

4. Compare the limits-to-growth and cornucopian theses.

5. What three conditions must exist within a society for it to turn something in the total stock into a resource? Use examples in your explanation.

Thinking and Inquiry

6. Think specifically about yourself for a moment. Do you view globalization, in all its forms, as an opportunity or a threat for your future? Give reasons for your views.

7. "Resources *are* not: they *become*…." Explain this statement, using specific examples.

8. Using Figure 3–8, explain how human interaction with the environment can bring about sustainable development.

9. Re-examine the newspaper headlines that appear at the beginning of this chapter. Determine whether each one relates to or demonstrates globalization, sustainability, or both. Explain your answers.

Communication

10. As a class, organize an informal debate on the statement:"Globalization offers the world our best chance to solve the problems that we face." Prepare your arguments on this topic, assuming that you are either:
    - a resident of a First World country such as Canada, Germany, or Japan
    - a resident of a Fifth World country such as Haiti or Sudan
    - a resident of a Third World country such as Mexico or Brazil

11. Write a short paragraph in which you predict how globalization will make your study of Canadian and world issues different from that undertaken by a student 20 years ago.

12. a) All human activities directly or indirectly have an impact on the natural environment. Write two scenarios, with supporting visuals, about what the global environment will be like by 2025. One should be optimistic and the other pessimistic.
    b) Which one do you think will come to pass? Explain.

Application

13. a) Look at the eight types of globalization. Identify one advantage and one disadvantage of each.
    b) How might the impact of each of these disadvantages be minimized?

14. In your own words, and using examples, explain the concept presented in Figure 3–6.

15. a) Explain the concept of sustainable development.
    b) What can you do to make your own use of resources more sustainable?

16. Search the Internet for a group that promotes sustainable development. Determine such facts as who the group is, what projects it supports, from where it receives funding, and the type of sustainable development on which it focusses. You may wish to start with the Canadian Global Change Program. For more information, go to <www.pearsoned.ca/globalconnections>.

17. Is globalization likely to make sustainability easier or more difficult to achieve? Explain your answer.

18. Earth Day is celebrated every April. Develop an activity that your class (or school) could perform that would address the spirit of Earth Day.

19. a) What harmful environmental damage was created for you by previous generations?
b) What obligations do you have, if any, in preventing environmental damage for the next generation?
c) How might you address these obligations?

Unit 2: The Human Population

4

Demography

Expectations

In this chapter, you will:

- understand the status and roles of men and women in different parts of the world

- explain world demographic trends

- explain how new technology affects employment and resource management

- analyse cause-and-effect relationships in geographic data

- draw conclusions and make judgements using a reasoned analysis

Image above: A poster advertising the one-child policy in China

Demography is the statistical study of human populations. It helps explain the causes and consequences of population change within local communities, across Canada, and worldwide. Governments and businesses rely on demographic data to predict future needs for such essentials as schools, housing, and labour, as well as consumer goods and services.

World Population Graphing

The world's population growth is summarized in Figure 4–1. Graph these data using semi-log graph paper and then answer the following questions. (A brief introduction to the use of semi-log graph paper can be found in Chapter 2.)

1. Along the line showing population growth, label the point at which each of the following events occurred. If you are not sure of some dates, you may have to do some research.
   - the beginning of the Common Era (CE)
   - the arrival of the Vikings in North America
   - the invention of the printing press
   - the beginning of the Industrial Revolution
   - the year Canada became a country
   - the landing of the first human on the moon
   - the year of your birth
   - today

2. Social scientists have estimated world populations in the period before 1 CE. These estimates suggest that the world had 125 000 people one million years ago, 3 000 000 people 35 000 years ago, and 86 000 000 people 10 000 years ago. What do these figures tell you about the rate of population growth during this time?

3. During which time periods did the world's population decrease? Suggest why this might have happened.

4. In what time period did the population boom begin? Suggest three reasons why this occurred. You may need to do some research.

5. a) Much of the world is affected by ongoing food shortages. What must be done to alleviate this shortfall while, at the same time, allowing for an ever-increasing population?
   b) What are some of the possible outcomes if we are not able to produce enough food to meet everyone's needs?

6. a) What advantages are there to using semi-log graph paper for this type of data?
   b) What approach would you use if you wanted to create a world population growth graph that would go back one million years? Why would you choose this approach?

World Population Growth Since 1 CE

Date	Population (millions)
1 CE	300
200	310
600	300
1000	400
1200	500
1400	400
1500	440
1600	540
1700	720
1800	800
1900	1 600
1920	1 800
1940	2 300
1950	2 500
1960	3 000
1970	3 600
1980	4 400
1990	5 300
1999	6 000

CE = Common Era

Figure 4–1

Trends in Population

On October 12, 1999, the world's population reached 6 billion. While the total world population of over six billion is a significant figure, the rate at which the population is growing is equally important. The graph you have just created will give you some idea of this. A summary of growth rates appears in Figure 4–2. The values

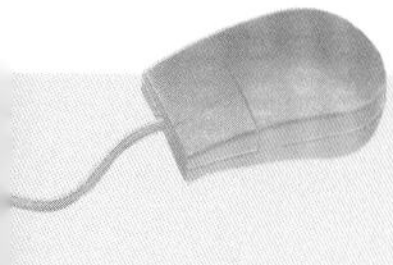

To obtain a wide variety of information, including demographic data for various countries, go to <http://www.pearsoned.ca/globalconnections>.

in this table are simple growth rates based on how much the population grew between the years shown. The calculation is as follows: The population in the "To" year minus the population in the "From" year divided by the number of years between the dates divided by the population in the "From" year expressed as a percentage.

In Unit 2, we will concentrate on two trends shown in this table: the population explosion since 1600, and the decline in population growth rate since 1980.

Average Annual Growth Rate of Population		
From...	To...	Average Annual Growth Rate (%) (ignoring compounding)
1 000 000 BCE	35 000 BCE	0.002
35 000 BCE	8000 BCE	0.007
8000 BCE	6000 BCE	0.488
6000 BCE	1 CE	0.041
1 CE	1400	0.010
1400	1660	0.232
1660	1750	0.506
1750	1800	0.467
1800	1850	0.579
1850	1900	0.621
1900	1920	0.488
1920	1940	1.209
1940	1960	1.687
1960	1980	2.397
1980	2000	1.854

BCE = Before Common Era

Figure 4–2

The Population Explosion

The first trend is the population explosion that began in the latter half of the 1600s and accelerated through much of the 1900s. One remarkable statistic illustrates what happened to the world's population during the 1900s. In 1960, the world's population reached three billion. What this meant was that it had taken more than one million years for the world's population to reach this level. Less than 40 years later, in 1999, the population had doubled to six billion. Consider what this growth meant for people, governments, and economic systems in the latter half of the 20th century. In only 40 years, the world had to provide for twice as many people. This meant, among other things, twice as much food, twice as many homes, and twice as many jobs.

The remarkable thing was that the world did a pretty good, if uneven, job of doing this. A minority of the world's citizens enjoyed an enhanced standard of living over this period of time. Most of this privileged group lives in the First World, with some in the Second and Third Worlds and a few (the wealthy elites) in the Fourth and even Fifth Worlds. A much larger group of people, concentrated in the Fifth and Fourth Worlds, lives in abject poverty, at a level that most Canadians could not even imagine.

Declining Growth Rate

At first glance, the second trend—the decline in the growth rate that has occurred since 1980—seems relatively insignificant. The reduction from 2.397 per cent to 1.854 per cent might seem small (Figure 4–2). In fact, the latter figure is, by historical standards, still very high. At the same time, it is the largest decline in world population growth rate in human history. Also, the magnitude of the decline is partially hidden by the fact that different parts of the world are currently experiencing two entirely different population situations. While many countries continue to face high growth rates and the problems that this brings, other countries are coming to terms with the fact that their populations are declining (or, at least, will soon decline). These countries are discovering that having a declining population can bring its own set of challenges.

The Canadian social system and economy are based on the assumption that our population will continue to grow. The following examples, one very general and one quite specific, show the great impact that a declining population will have on you.

As its population declines, a country will find that its percentage of older people booms (Figure 4–3). These seniors, most of whom will be retired, will place great demands on those who are working. They will need pensions, health care, and retirement homes. You, as a young Canadian, will have to pay for much of these costs. An aging population also affects the economics of home ownership. For generations, young Canadians have looked forward to buying a home and then seeing their home become more valuable over the years because of constantly growing demand. The enhanced value of this home could be used to help pay for a more costly home, or to help provide for a more comfortable retirement. But what happens to housing values when the population is declining and there is more housing available than is needed? What impact would this have on traditional family values and on families' economic progress?

Figure 4–3 *A group of Japanese seniors pose for a photographer in Yokohama, Japan. Fifteen per cent of Japanese people are under the age of 15, while 16 per cent are 65 or older. In contrast, in Ethiopia, 47 per cent are under 15, while only 3 per cent are 65 or older.*

Technological Change and Population Growth

Earth's carrying capacity is the number of people that can be supported by the world's resources at any particular time, with the technology that exists at that time. At different points in human history, revolutionary discoveries in technology have produced corresponding revolutions in the way in which people live and in the carrying capacity of Earth. In this section, you will have an opportunity to learn about the relationships among technology, lifestyles, and population.

Stage 1: Hunting and Gathering

In the earliest stages of human history, people were nomadic **hunters and gatherers** of food. These two activities played a distinct and important role in ensuring the survival of the extended family groups that lived together. The gathered food, typically collected by the women and children, provided a meagre but somewhat reliable source of nutrition. The hunted food, usually provided by the men, furnished occasional feasts that would allow people to build up reserves of fat that would help them through the hungry times between major hunting successes.

Two facts stand out about hunting-and-gathering societies. One is that people were always at the edge of starvation. If food was abundant in a certain year, survival rates would increase; but if winter was severe or game was scarce, death rates would skyrocket. A second reality is that a very large area of land was needed to support a relatively small number of people. Hence, the carrying capacity of the world was very low. The world's population was a few tens of millions at most. Before the world's population could substantially increase, a new means of support had to be developed.

Stage 2: The Agricultural Revolution

The discovery of agriculture is undoubtedly the most important invention in history. Without it, none of the cultural and technological advances that came later would have been possible. Yet, we do not even know who invented agriculture. Many inventions, for example, the telephone, photography, and the Internet, can be tied to one or more clearly identified inventors. This was not the case with agriculture, which developed independently in many places around the world at different times. We know it was practised almost 10 000 years ago throughout what is now Israel, Jordan, southern Turkey, and western Iran. Later, it developed in China, India, Africa, and the Americas (Figure 4–4).

Did you KNOW?

In hunting-and-gathering societies such as Canada's Inuit or Australia's Aborigines, it was considered acceptable to abandon unproductive members of society, for example the elderly or disabled children. By our standards this may seem heartless, but to hunters and gatherers an attempt to save the old or a disabled baby could endanger the entire extended family.

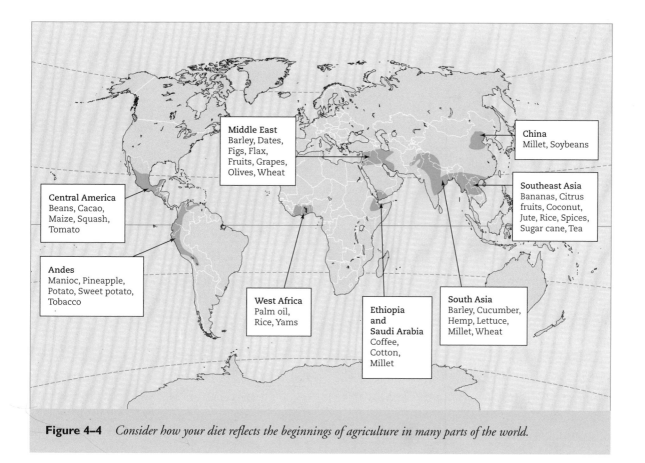

Figure 4–4 *Consider how your diet reflects the beginnings of agriculture in many parts of the world.*

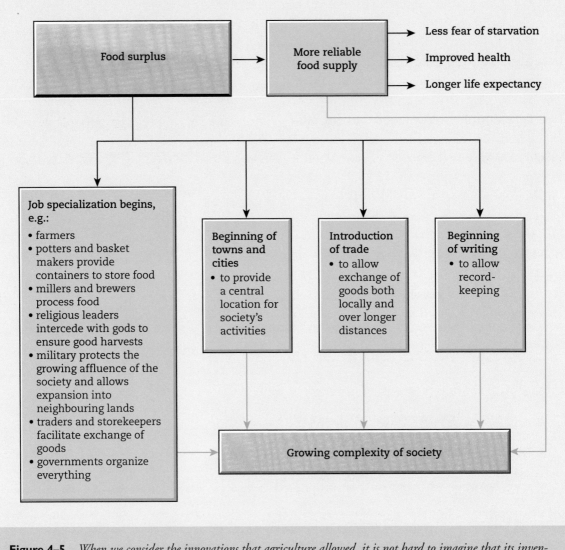

Figure 4–5 *When we consider the innovations that agriculture allowed, it is not hard to imagine that its invention was the most profound advance in human history.*

While no one knows for certain how agriculture was invented, it might have happened something like this. A woman noticed that edible plants grew in abundance in the locations where the previous season's gathered plants had been processed and where a few seeds had fallen on the ground. Next came the hard step: She would have to convince those she lived with to "throw away" some of their food (in the form of seeds) in the hope that there might be more to eat several months later. This obviously required a great leap of faith in an environment of constant hunger and the ever-present threat of starvation. The suggestion to try farming might have been made many times before it was actually attempted. Once it was done, life would never be the same. The most important result of farming was the creation of a food surplus, which had some staggering impacts (Figure 4–5).

As you might expect, the **agricultural revolution** also had a profound effect on the world's population. The fact that much more food could be produced from each square kilometre of land meant that the carrying capacity grew significantly. In the centuries that followed the development of farming in any particular location, agricultural productivity and the carrying capacity continued to increase. At times, specific inventions advanced agricultural productivity. In 1701, for example, a man named Jethro Tull created a device called a seed drill that ensured that seeds would be planted quickly and at the appropriate density (Figure 4–6). All these improvements were evolutionary rather than revolutionary, in the sense that they were merely improvements in an existing technology.

Figure 4–6 *Seed drills, such as these from the mid-19th century, planted seeds evenly and easily in the field.*

Stage 3: Industrial Revolution

By the 1700s, agriculture and the production of manufactured goods in the more technologically developed parts of the world (principally Western Europe) had become quite advanced, but further progress was being impeded by an "energy crisis" of sorts. The only source of energy was the muscle power of people and domesticated animals, such as horses and oxen. The solution to this energy crisis—the invention of non-muscular sources of power—produced what we now call the **Industrial Revolution**.

The earliest sources of power used were ones that we would now consider to be modern and desirable because they relied on clean, renewable resources. Examples included the famous windmills of Holland, which were used to pump water, and the water-powered gristmills and sawmills, which were crucial to the development of southern Ontario. Soon, even more powerful energy sources were developed. Coal came first, in the latter half of the 18th century, followed by oil a century later.

Just as with the agricultural revolution, the Industrial Revolution fundamentally changed the nature of life. Both in the factory and on the farm, one person's efforts were multiplied many times by the use of external power sources. In fact, one's physical strength became much less important than one's skills and intellect.

The agricultural economy was transformed. For example, in 1833 an American named John Deere invented a steel plough that was strong enough to break up the thick sod layer of the western plains of North America. This plough was possible only because the Industrial Revolution provided strong, inexpensive steel. Without this plough and similar devices, agricultural settlement of the western United States and Canada would have been seriously impeded.

The many impacts of the Industrial Revolution on agriculture meant that substantially fewer farm workers were needed, and yet the amount of food being produced was much greater than ever before. The extra agricultural workers who were forced off the land migrated to the cities or, in some cases, to the new colonies in the Americas or Australia. The migration to the cities became the great urban boom that continues today in many countries, while the migration to the colonies fundamentally changed the nature of the population in these parts of the world. The Industrial Revolution greatly increased the carrying capacity of Earth. As with the beginning of farming, each square kilometre of land was made to produce ever more food and support more people.

Measuring Demographics

There are two types of demographic measures: absolute and relative (Figure 4–7). *Absolute* measures are simply the number of something. For example, Country A has 400 000 births while Country B has 200 000 births. Absolute measures are of limited usefulness because they are difficult to compare in a meaningful way. *Relative* rates relate absolute measures to the country's population. For example, if Country A has a population of 40 million, then with 400 000 births, it would have 0.01 births for every person in the country. To avoid fractions, we would usually express this measure as 10 births for every thousand people. If Country B has a population of 10 million, with 200 000 births, it would have 20 births per thousand people. With relative values like these, comparison becomes much easier. Accordingly, we will focus on relative measures in the form of rates.

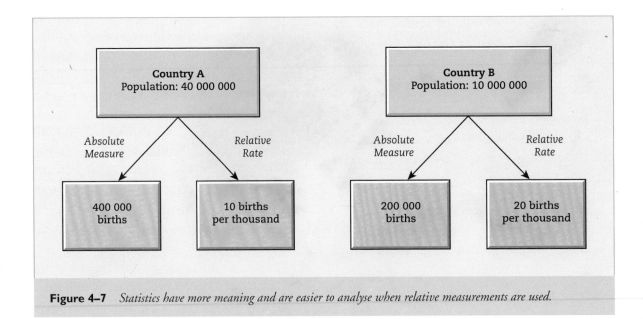

Figure 4–7 *Statistics have more meaning and are easier to analyse when relative measurements are used.*

A Primer of Demographic Terms

In this section, you will have the chance to learn some of the terminology that will help your study of world populations. You will notice that these terms are used frequently in all parts of the book. They should become part of your working vocabulary.

- **Birth rate** is the number of births in a country for every thousand people in the population. For example, if 150 000 children are born in a given year in a country with a population of 5 000 000, the birth rate is 30 per thousand (150 000 ÷ 5 000 000 × 1000 = 30). A birth rate over 30 is considered high, while less than 15 would be considered low. Canada's birth rate was 11.4 per thousand in 2000.

- **Death rate** is calculated in a fashion similar to birth rate. For example, if our sample country of 5 000 000 people had 100 000 deaths in a year, the death rate would be 20 per thousand. High and low death rates are similar to those for birth rates (over 30 and under 15 per thousand, respectively). Canada's death rate was only 7.4 per thousand in 2000.

- **Dependency load** is the percentage of a country's population who are under the age of 15 and over 65 that must be supported (housed, fed, educated, etc.) by the independent, working population. Some countries have a large number of dependent children, while others have large numbers of older people. If the dependency load is too large, it can put great stress on the country's economy. There is no single percentage that can be used to determine when a dependency load is too high. Many factors complicate this judgement. For example, a wealthy country has more resources to meet the needs of its dependent population. On the other hand, the dependent people in these countries may have higher expectations for things such as advanced medical care and comfortable housing. What is clear is that a rising dependency load puts pressure on a country. In 2000, about 19 per cent of Canadians were younger than 15 years of age, while another 13 per cent were 65 or older.

- **Emigration rate** deals with the number of people who permanently leave a country. It is calculated like the birth rate. For example, if 10 000 people leave our sample country of 5 000 000 in a given year, the emigration rate would be two per thousand. Canada's emigration rate in 2000 was 2.0 per thousand.

- **Immigration rate** deals with the number of people who permanently move to a country. It is calculated in a fashion similar to the birth rate. For example, if 15 000 people move to our sample country, it will have an immigration rate of three per thousand. Canada's immigration rate in 2000 was 6.7 per thousand.

- **Infant mortality rate** is the number of children in a country who die in the first year of life for each 1000 births. It is commonly used as a measure of economic and social development. An infant mortality rate over 80 would be considered high. A rate less than 15 would be considered low. Canada's infant mortality rate in 2000 was 5.1 per thousand.

- **Life expectancy** is the average lifespan that a newborn will have. A short lifespan would be less than 50 years, while a long lifespan would over 75 years. The life expectancy for Canada's population in 2000 was 79.4 years.

- **Natural increase rate** is the difference between the birth rate and the death rate of a country. In our sample country, with a birth rate of 30 and a death rate of 20, the natural increase would be 10 per thousand, or 1 per cent. A less developed country might have a natural increase rate over 2 per cent, while a more

For a range of population data and facts about Canada, go to <www.pearsoned.ca/globalconnections>.

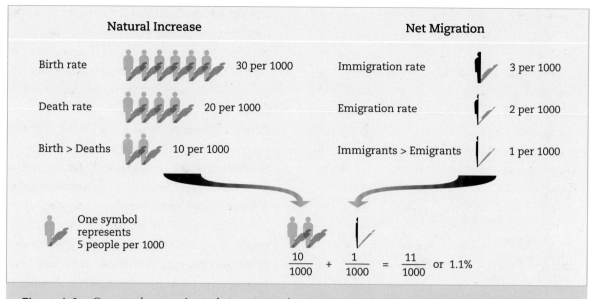

Natural Increase

Birth rate	30 per 1000
Death rate	20 per 1000
Birth > Deaths	10 per 1000

Net Migration

Immigration rate	3 per 1000
Emigration rate	2 per 1000
Immigrants > Emigrants	1 per 1000

One symbol represents 5 people per 1000

$$\frac{10}{1000} + \frac{1}{1000} = \frac{11}{1000} \text{ or } 1.1\%$$

Figure 4–8 *Our sample country's population increase has two parts: natural increase and net migration.*

developed country would have a natural increase rate less than 1 per cent (perhaps even less than zero). For Canada, a birth rate of 11.4 and a death rate of 7.4 mean a natural increase of four per thousand, or 0.4 per cent.

- **Net migration rate** is the difference between the immigration rate and the emigration rate. In our example, with an immigration rate of three per thousand and an emigration rate of two per thousand, the net migration rate is one per thousand, or 0.1 per cent. Only a few countries (Canada, the United States, and Australia are the best examples) have large positive net migration rates, while most countries have relatively small negative net migration rates. For Canada, an immigration rate of 6.7 per thousand and an emigration rate of 2.0 per thousand mean a net migration rate of 4.7 per thousand, or about 0.5 per cent.

- **Population growth rate** is the rate at which a country's population is changing. It combines the country's natural increase rate and its net migration rate (Figure 4–8). For the vast majority of countries, migration is much less important than natural increase as a deter-

minant of population growth (or decline). Population growth rates are most commonly given as percentages. A high rate of growth would be anything in excess of 2 per cent. A few countries are experiencing negative growth rates. Canada's natural increase of four per thousand and net migration rate of 4.7 per thousand give a population growth rate of about nine per thousand or 0.9 per cent.

- **Population pyramid** is a special type of graph that summarizes the age and sex structure of a population (Figure 4–9). Each bar graph in the pyramid indicates the number or percentage of people of a particular sex in a specific age group; for example, females aged 15 to 19. Sometimes you will be most interested in some detail of the pyramid; for example, the impact of a world war on the balance of men and women. More often, though, you will want to look at the overall shape of the pyramid. With practice, you will be able to tell a great deal about a country from this shape. Figure 4–10 summarizes some of the characteristics of the two countries whose pyramids are shown in Figure 4–9.

- **Total fertility rate** is the average number of children that each woman will have in her fertile years, assuming that the birth rate does not change over this period. The fertile years are assumed to be between the ages of 15 and 45. A high fertility rate would be greater than five, while a low fertility rate would be below the replacement rate of 2.1 (see below). Canada's total fertility rate was about 1.6 in 2000.

- **Replacement rate** is the total fertility rate that would produce a natural increase rate of zero. If we ignore migration, which is of little importance in most countries, this would mean that the country's population would not change. The replacement rate is 2.1. At first glance it might appear that this fertility rate should be 2.0, since each woman would bear two children who would eventually replace her and her partner. The extra 0.1 is required to make up for women who are unwilling or unable to have children or who die before having children.

- **Rule of 70** is a simple way to estimate how long it would take for a country's population to double. To do this, you divide 70 by the country's population growth rate (as a percentage). For example, a population that is growing at 2.3 per cent per year will double in about 30 years (70 ÷ 2.3). If the population growth rate of 0.9 per cent were to be maintained, Canada's population would double in about 78 years.

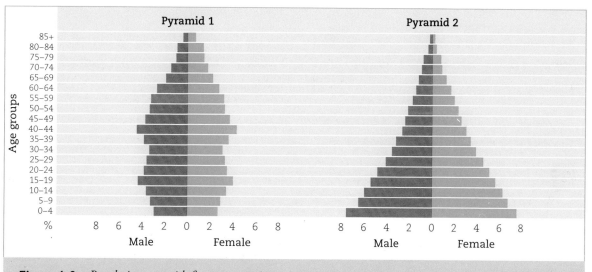

Figure 4–9   *Population pyramids for two countries*

	Pyramid 1	Pyramid 2
Country group	First World	Fifth World
Infant mortality	Low	High
Fertility rate	Low	High
Life expectancy	High	Low
Nature of dependency load	Mainly older people	Mainly young people

Figure 4–10   *A description of population pyramids 1 and 2*

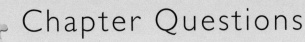

Chapter Questions

Knowledge and Understanding

1. Why was the support of a very old person or a disabled child a luxury that a hunting-and-gathering society could not afford?

2. Examine Figure 4–5. Briefly describe how any three of the innovations mentioned depend on the creation of a food surplus.

Thinking and Inquiry

3. a) Cultural development has not occurred in all parts of the world at the same rate. Give at least two examples of hunting-and-gathering societies that still exist today.
   b) Give two examples of agricultural societies that still exist today.

4. a) Most experts would say that we are now moving into a post-industrial age. What is meant by this term?
   b) What influence might living in the post-industrial age have on the world's population? Why?

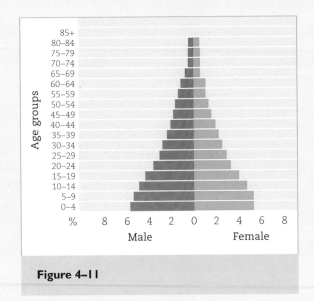

Figure 4–11

5. a) Figure 4–10 suggests some of the things that can be learned from a population pyramid. How are these characteristics determined?
   b) Examine the population pyramid shown in Figure 4–11. Give a brief overview of the population characteristics of this country.

Communication

6. Write a word equation for each of the following terms.
   Example:
   Birth Rate = Births ÷ Population × 1000
   a) death rate
   b) dependency load
   c) emigration rate
   d) immigration rate
   e) infant mortality rate
   f) natural increase rate
   g) net migration rate
   h) population growth rate

7. a) Use the special graph paper provided by your teacher to create a population pyramid for the data provided in Figure 4–12.
   b) What population characteristics are revealed about this country?

8. A country had a population of 31 850 000 at the beginning of the year. During the year, the following changes occurred in the population:
   - 1 038 000 babies were born
   - 594 000 people died
   - 86 000 people emigrated
   - 53 000 people immigrated
   - 93 000 babies died during the year
   - 9 159 000 women were aged from 15 to 45

   Calculate the following values:
   a) the population at the end of the year
   b) the birth rate
   c) the death rate
   d) the emigration rate

Age Group	Male (%)	Female (%)
0–4	3.1	3.0
5–9	3.0	2.9
10–14	3.3	3.2
15–19	4.3	4.1
20–24	3.7	3.5
25–29	3.3	3.2
30–34	3.1	3.0
35–39	3.9	3.9
40–44	4.0	4.0
45–49	3.3	3.4
50–54	2.9	3.2
55–59	2.4	3.0
60–64	2.4	3.0
65–69	2.1	2.9
70–74	1.6	2.6
75–79	0.7	1.2
80+	0.9	1.9

Figure 4–12 *Population data for Country X (for question 7)*

e) the immigration rate

f) the natural increase rate

g) the net migration rate

h) the population growth rate

i) the infant mortality rate

j) the total fertility rate

Application

9. Explain how a declining population might affect Canada's economy and lifestyles. Consider such areas as government priorities, consumer spending, the role played by economic growth in our society, and environmental demands.

10. a) Being dependent is defined as being under age 15 or over 65. Is this definition realistic in modern Canadian terms? Why or why not?

   b) If it is not realistic, why is this definition used?

5

Population Theories

Key Terms

demographic transition
pre-transition
early transition
germ theory of disease
late transition
birth control
post-transition
theory of demographic
   regulation
Malthusian
phantom carrying
   capacity

Expectations

In this chapter, you will:

■ describe world
demographic trends
and explain the factors
influencing them

■ identify individuals
who have made contri-
butions to addressing
global issues

■ evaluate factors that
compound the prob-
lems of hunger and
poverty

■ predict probable
futures based on cur-
rent trends, including
technological change

■ evaluate the effec-
tiveness of techniques
used to predict the
future

■ produce a chloro-
pleth map to show
global patterns

Image above: An
American family, circa
1940s

How many children would you like to have? While this is a personal question, your answer likely reflects the changes in social and economic conditions and attitudes that have occurred over recent generations. In this chapter, we will examine some of the theories that have attempted to describe and explain the population changes that have occurred and are occurring around the world.

Changing Family Sizes

1. Calculate the average number of children that each person in your class would like to have.

2. Calculate the average family size of your classmates.

3. Calculate the average size of the families your parents grew up in.

4. Calculate the average size of the families your grandparents grew up in. (You may not know all these family sizes, especially going back a couple of generations, but try to give answers for as many families as possible.)

5. Make a graph of average family size over the four generations. What pattern do you see in family size over these generations?

6. State at least five reasons why you are likely to have fewer children than your ancestors did.

The Theory of Demographic Transition

In the previous activity, you undoubtedly found that family sizes have decreased significantly over recent generations. This pattern is being repeated in every country in the world. In fact, in about 60 countries, the total fertility rate has fallen to below the replacement rate of 2.1 children. Canada is one of these, with a fertility rate of only 1.55 in the period from 1995 to 2000. This tendency has not occurred by accident. As you will see in this chapter, such changes are predictable and are the result of a range of economic, social, and scientific developments that continue to occur in various parts of the world. The phenomenon of population changes in a country over time is called **demographic transition**.

Stage 1: Pre-transition

The best way to understand what happens to a population over time is to compare birth rates and death rates at various points in the country's history. Consider Sweden's situation between 1740 and 1830 (Figure 5–1). As you can see from the graph, the birth rate was relatively stable while the death rate went up and down in response to specific events like wars and famines. The result of this combination was that at some times the population grew, while at other times it decreased. Over many centuries, though, the population remained relatively stable. A similar pattern can be seen 150 years later in Mexico (Figure 5–2).

Did you KNOW?

One of the biggest problems in the study of historical population development is that few countries have kept reliable records long enough to show the full sequence of changes. In Canada's case, the first accurate records date from 1851, after the country's pre-transition stage was completed. Because Sweden has kept adequate records since about 1740, it is often used to show demographic transition.

Figure 5–1 *Before 1830, Sweden's population stayed relatively stable. The birth rate was relatively constant, while the death rate fluctuated in response to particular events like good harvests, famines, and wars.*

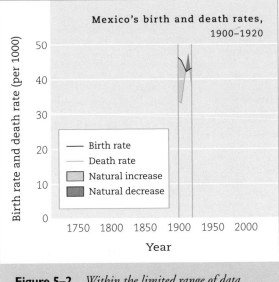

Figure 5–2 *Within the limited range of data available, Mexico's population before 1920 demonstrates a pattern of alternating increases and decreases similar to those of Sweden.*

A **pre-transition** country has a very distinctive population pyramid (Figure 5–3). The very wide base that rapidly narrows reflects both a very high birth rate and extreme infant mortality. The number of people in each age group is noticeably less than in the previous one. These characteristics indicate the precarious nature of life as people die off at every age. Old age in such a society would be 45 or 50. Life in a pre-transition society was difficult and uncertain.

For example, in Sweden in 1750 the life expectancy was barely 35 years. Food supplies were erratic, and diseases like smallpox, whooping cough, and measles could sweep through the population with devastating results. Most children died before reaching adulthood. A couple might have 10 or more children to ensure that they had at least one son who would be able to take care of them in their old age. Remarkably, such huge families provided only for a stable population.

Specific birth and death rates are not the most important element in identifying that a country is in the pre-transition stage. In fact,

not all pre-transition countries have similar rates, as the contrast between Sweden and Mexico shows. In Sweden, these rates tended to be in the low to middle 30s, while in Mexico they were in the upper 30s to upper 40s. What is really important is that both rates are high and relatively the same.

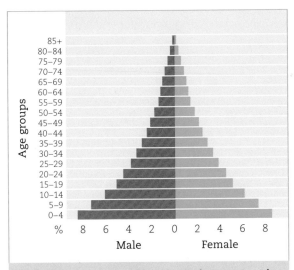

Figure 5–3 *A pre-transition population pyramid has a very distinctive shape.*

Stage 2: Early Transition

No country in the world is still at the pre-transition stage. In fact, there may not even be isolated societies that are still at this stage; every country has progressed to at least the **early transition** stage. In early transition, a dramatic drop occurs in the death rate. Some people have described this as the beginning of "death control." Consider what happened in Sweden (Figure 5–4) and Mexico (Figure 5–5). In each, the death rate dropped while the birth rate remained high. As a result, a period of sustained natural increase began. At first, the rate of natural increase was small, but before long it grew. The result was the beginning of the remarkable population explosion that caused Earth's population to rise from one billion in 1850 to more than six billion by 2000.

While the pattern in developed and developing countries is similar, there are at least two significant differences. One is that the beginning of early transition occurred much later in less developed countries such as Mexico than in developed countries such as Sweden. The other is that the death rate declined at a much faster rate in less developed countries. Each of these trends is easily understood if we consider how "death control" occurred.

At first glance, it might seem that the most important factor in the decline of the death rate would be the development of modern medicines and vaccinations. Surprisingly, this was not the case, at least in the more developed nations of Western Europe and North America where early transition occurred first. Certainly, deaths from some diseases were substantially reduced by medical breakthroughs. The invention of the small-pox vaccination in 1801 is perhaps the greatest medical advance in history. More often, though, drops in death rates were not linked to a specific medical advance.

Consider the situation of tuberculosis (TB). In 1830, the number who died each year from TB was 4000 per million people in the population. By 1850, the rate had declined by more than 50 per cent to about 1800 per million. This reduction was achieved in spite of the fact that scientists

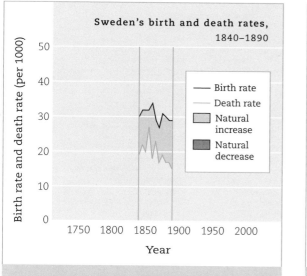

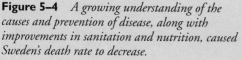
Figure 5–4 *A growing understanding of the causes and prevention of disease, along with improvements in sanitation and nutrition, caused Sweden's death rate to decrease.*

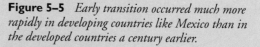
Figure 5–5 *Early transition occurred much more rapidly in developing countries like Mexico than in the developed countries a century earlier.*

him worldwide acclaim, but it did not turn out that way. Instead, he was forced to leave Vienna in disgrace because the older doctors did not understand what he had done. The struggle for recognition eventually broke him; he ended up in a mental institution, and died soon after from an infection similar to puerperal fever. However, his work inspired others, such as Joseph Lister, who fought disease by such simple means as promoting personal sanitation, providing clean drinking water, fighting against insect and animal pests, and handling human and animal sewage in an appropriate fashion.

Death rates declined relatively slowly in the developed countries because the germ theory had to be pioneered and implemented gradually. A century later, in the less developed countries, the various means of sanitation and disease control could be imported from Europe and North America. As a result, death rates fell much faster.

The population pyramid of an early transition country can be seen as a progression from that of pre-transition (Figure 5–6). There are still relatively few older people, but a growing number of children are surviving beyond infancy.

were unable to identify the bacterium responsible for the disease until 1850, and did not develop a vaccine to prevent TB until 1955. Yet by 1955, more than 97 per cent of deaths from tuberculosis had been eliminated—even before people could be protected from this disease.

What caused the death rate to fall if it was not the development of advanced medical technology? The reason was a growing understanding that most diseases came from organisms so tiny that they could not be seen. Acceptance of this **germ theory of disease** did not come easily, as the sad case of Ignaz Semmelweis shows. Semmelweis was a doctor in Vienna's maternity hospital in the 1840s. He was horrified by the fact that almost 20 per cent of the women who entered the hospital died from a disease called childbirth fever (also called puerperal fever), which they caught while they were patients. Semmelweis decided he could do something about it. He instituted a rule that required the medical students to wash their hands in a disinfecting solution before delivering a baby. To the surprise of most people, the death rate dropped to barely 1 per cent. This should have made Semmelweis a medical hero and brought

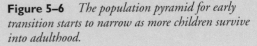
You can learn more about Ignaz Semmelweis and his work at <www.pearsoned.ca/globalconnections>.

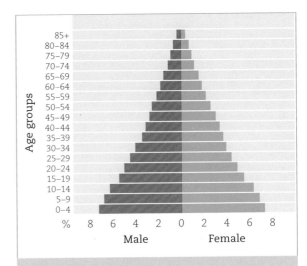

Figure 5–6 *The population pyramid for early transition starts to narrow as more children survive into adulthood.*

Figure 5–7 *Maternity hospitals like this one in Ho Chi Minh City, Vietnam, contribute to the increased survival of infants in early transition countries.*

This latter fact has two impacts. At the individual level, it means that family size is increasing. Most people in early transition countries are farmers, and more children mean more labour is available. Also, it becomes much more likely that one or more sons will survive to support their parents in their old age. At the societal level, greater family size means that the dependency load of children is dramatically increasing. A further result is that societies at this stage must concentrate on meeting ever-increasing demands for such facilities as schools and maternity hospitals (Figure 5–7). If you want to identify an early transition country, you must look for two things: one is a birth rate that remains at the high level of pre-transition; the other is a death rate that drops and remains below the birth rate.

Stage 3: Late Transition

Before too many years had passed, citizens of European countries in early transition realized that life had fundamentally changed. Women continued to have 10 or 12 children, but were finding that seven or eight were surviving instead of two or three. This caused some novel problems. For example, after a generation or two,

there was not enough land available to support all the people who wanted to farm. As a result, second, third, and subsequent sons had to find another way to support themselves. For some, this meant moving to new areas to farm. For others, it meant moving to the growing cities that were developing in response to the Industrial Revolution. Keep in mind that, for the developed countries, late transition occurred at the same time as the beginnings of mass intercontinental migrations in the 1800s and early 1900s.

If early transition was marked by "death control," then **late transition** was characterized by **birth control**. This trend is shown clearly in the graphs for Sweden (Figure 5–8) and Mexico (Figure 5–9). The same two differences between these two countries occurred as in early transition—that is, birth control happened later and faster in Mexico than in Sweden. Countries in late transition continue to experience a population explosion, although this decreases as the birth rate drops and approaches the death rate.

When we discuss birth control here, we are not talking about the technological means used to prevent births. For example, the oral contraceptive was not introduced until the early 1960s, long after birth rates had significantly decreased

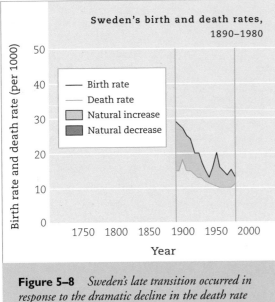

Figure 5–8 *Sweden's late transition occurred in response to the dramatic decline in the death rate that occurred earlier.*

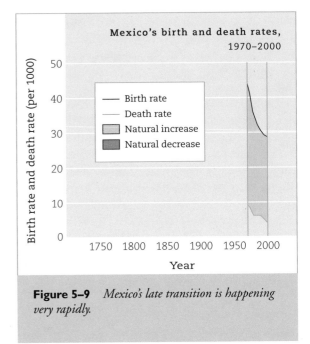

Figure 5–9 *Mexico's late transition is happening very rapidly.*

in developed countries. Rather, we are talking about the desire of couples to limit the size of their families in response to several factors. Most important of these factors was the simple fact that a higher survival rate for children meant that fewer babies were needed. Another important reason was that a growing number of people were living in cities. While having many children might be a benefit for a family living on a farm, rarely would this be the case in the city, where children tended to be a financial burden and had little opportunity to contribute significantly to their family's support.

Another reason for falling birth rates was the changing character of the family. In particular, more women were working outside the home, and families were therefore more affluent. All these trends contributed to the desire for smaller families. At times, this change in attitudes towards large families has occurred very quickly. For example, Thailand's total fertility rate dropped from six to two in only one decade.

The population pyramid for a late transition nation looks less pyramidal (Figure 5–10). Fewer children are being born and more people are

living longer, so the number of people in each age group is becoming more alike. To identify the time at which a country moves into late transition, you need only look for the point where the birth rate starts to drop from its pretransition levels. During late transition, you will notice that death rates continue to decline, but that the rate of this decline decreases until the death rate stabilizes at a low level.

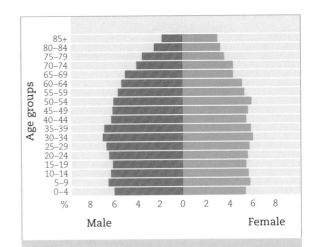

Figure 5–10 *In late transition, the population pyramid becomes more block-like.*

Stage 4: Post-transition

In the final stage of the demographic transition model, the birth rate declines to the point where it approximates the death rate at a low level. This situation is shown in Figure 5–11 for Sweden. (We cannot show it for Mexico because it has not happened yet.) Obviously, if the birth rate equals the death rate, the natural increase will be zero and the population will stabilize. Life in a **post-transition** country is typically highly urbanized and involves people having small families. There is a high dependency load, particularly of older people. The population pyramid for a post-transition country has a characteristic bullet shape (Figure 5–12).

The world has had abundant experience with the first three stages of the demographic transition model. Hence, we know that they "work." However, the post-transition stage is new: countries began to reach this stage only in the 1970s. There is a certain intellectual "neatness" in suggesting that the birth rate and the death rate will become equal, but there is no particular reason why this should happen. In fact, in most countries that have reached post-transition, the total fertility rate has dropped substantially below the replacement rate of 2.1. In extreme cases, it is below 1.2 and is continuing to decline. Lowest of all is Spain, which had a total fertility rate of only 1.15 in 2000. Some experts have suggested that these low fertility rates are a temporary phenomenon and that family size will increase in the future to something approximating the replacement level. Other experts think that average family sizes will remain small, with the fertility rate substantially below two. If this does happen, the population will decline. Some authorities even suggest that the demographic transition model should have a fifth stage to account for this decline.

Did you KNOW?

Because a population that has been growing will have more people entering their childbearing years than leaving them (remember the shape of a late-transition pyramid), it will take a number of years for the population to stabilize after the birth rate and death rate are the same.

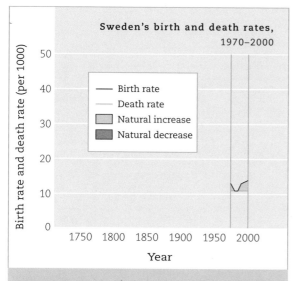

Figure 5–11 *Sweden's population has stabilized in the post-transition phase.*

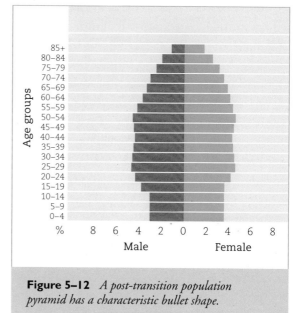

Figure 5–12 *A post-transition population pyramid has a characteristic bullet shape.*

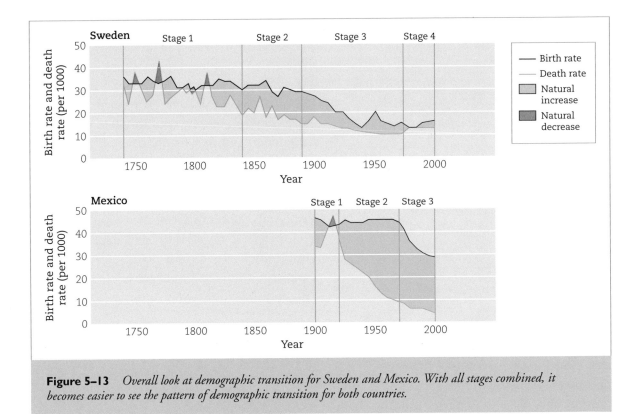

Figure 5–13 *Overall look at demographic transition for Sweden and Mexico. With all stages combined, it becomes easier to see the pattern of demographic transition for both countries.*

Summary

If we combine all stages of demographic transition for Sweden and Mexico (Figure 5–13), we get similar patterns with minor variances due to differences in each country's history. For example, you can see the impact of the Great Depression and World War II on Sweden. The population history of any country in the world would show similar patterns. If we generalize these, we get a theoretical pattern of demographic transition (Figure 5–14). You can use this model to understand how a country's economic and social development occurs. Demographic transition can also be shown by a sequence of population pyramids (Figure 5–15). These pyramids can be classified as either stable or changing. Pyramids for the pre-transition and post-transition stages of demographic transition can be regarded as stable. That is, they

represent populations that are not growing. All the other shapes show populations that are either growing or shrinking.

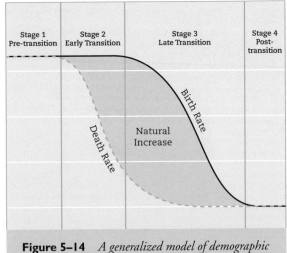

Figure 5–14 *A generalized model of demographic transition. No one is entirely sure whether there should be a fifth stage.*

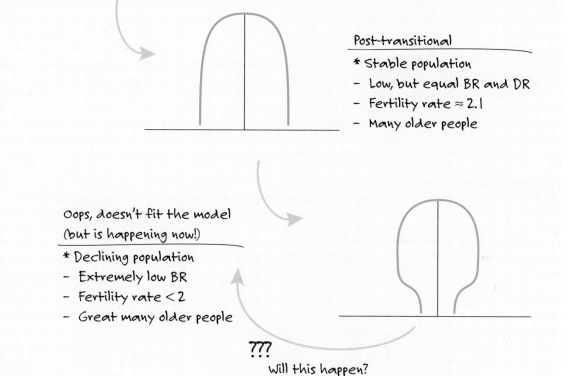

Pre-transitional

* Stable population
- High, but equal BR and DR
- Fertility rate 8+
- Extreme infant mortality
- Many young children,
  very few older people

Transitional

* Large population growth
- Declining DR, followed by
  declining BR
- Fertility rate declines
- Increasing number of
  older people

Post-transitional

* Stable population
- Low, but equal BR and DR
- Fertility rate ≈ 2.1
- Many older people

Oops, doesn't fit the model (but is happening now!)

* Declining population
- Extremely low BR
- Fertility rate < 2
- Great many older people

???
Will this happen?

Figure 5–15 *This sequence of population pyramids provides an alternative way of looking at demographic transition.*

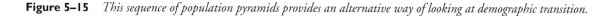

Divergent Ideas
About Population Growth

For more than two centuries, authors have written about why and how population growth occurs. Some have concentrated on the ability of the human race to adapt to the demands of population growth, while others have written about the problems that population growth might cause. Accordingly, in this chapter we have divided these approaches into those that are optimistic and those that are pessimistic.

Optimistic Views

Through most of human history, there has been general agreement that large families and a growing population were highly desirable. Such opinions were expressed both by religious and secular authorities. Similar thoughts were expressed, with different motivations, by a wide range of emperors, kings, and dictators who needed large and growing populations to support their economic and military expansionist desires.

Cornucopians

Even when there is a desire to expand the human population, a crucial question remains about whether Earth can support it. Many people have faith in the human ability to find technological innovations that will produce revolutionary increases in the carrying capacity. As we saw in Chapter 3, people who hold these beliefs are called cornucopians. As evidence, they would point to both the agricultural and industrial revolutions, each of which allowed unprecedented increases in world population. The obvious question to be asked is, "What might be the nature of this next revolution?" Cornucopians would respond that, before the agricultural and industrial revolutions, no one could have predicted that they would happen. If pressed, a cornucopian might say that the breakthrough(s) to come would have to solve the most serious threats that we face. For example, an innovation that would allow us to use solar or wind energy (Figure 5–16) very cheaply would address both a future energy shortage and the environmental damage caused by our current energy use.

Bogue

Writing in the 1960s, D.J. Bogue described what he called the **theory of demographic regulation.** By this he meant that, over an extended period of time, a society naturally limits its population. The population will grow only in response to Earth's ability to support a larger population. In view of the population explosion of the last 150 years, it might appear that this theory does not work. Supporters of demographic regulation would say that it is just a matter of time—that the Industrial Revolution dramatically raised Earth's carrying capacity, and the world's population has been adjusting to this increase. They would say that in developed countries, like Sweden, this adjustment has been completed, while in developing countries, like Mexico, the process continues. This population regulation can be seen in a number of ways. The demographic transition model seems to point to the concept of demographic regulation. We can also find support for regulation in the fact that many countries have tried to limit their population growth in recent years. The best example of this is China's one-child policy, which has done much to accelerate the rate of China's demographic transition.

Figure 5–16 *Wind turbine generators in California, USA. Cornucopians believe that revolutionary break-throughs in energy production could be used to support a much larger population.*

Pessimistic Views

While most people throughout history have been optimistic about ever-increasing population levels, there have been critics of this belief, particularly as population levels have exploded in recent decades. In various ways, all have made basically the same point: Earth is of finite size and has a limited ability to support its population. These critics feel that, ultimately, we will reach a point where the size of the world's population exceeds this ability.

Malthus

Thomas Malthus (Figure 5–17) is one of those remarkable thinkers whose ideas were so powerful and revolutionary that his name became part of the language. Any person or idea described as **Malthusian** (or neo-Malthusian) takes a pessimistic view about population growth. Malthus was an English minister who wrote about the danger of increasing population starting in 1798, far earlier than others. His thesis was simple. He surmised that population would grow in a geometric sequence (1, 2, 4, 8, 16…) while food could only increase arithmetically (1, 2, 3, 4…)—obviously not a sustainable situation. To Malthus, the only possible result would be the onset of what he called "misery," including famine, disease, and warfare, which would produce a terrible collapse of the population and great suffering for millions.

Figure 5–17 *Thomas Malthus (1766–1834)*

Catton

William Catton, writing in the 1980s, did much to modernize and expand the views of Malthus. He introduced the concept of Earth's carrying capacity, which he states can be exceeded only at the expense of environmental damage. This concept is closely related to the idea of the ecological footprint, which you may have learned about in previous courses. (Also see Chapter 28.)

Renowned Canadian author and professor of political science, Thomas Homer-Dixon, feels that humankind may be in trouble because society is changing faster than we can develop ideas to cope. You can read about his views on society, technology, population growth, and ecology at <www.pearsoned.ca/globalconnections>.

Catton would suggest that Earth's population has been exceeding its carrying capacity for many years. This excess has been possible only because we are using up the world's fixed stock of non-renewable resources. For example, our immense population and high standard of living require us to burn the oil and coal that our descendants will need as industrial raw materials in the future. Using non-renewable resources in this way produces a **phantom carrying capacity** that, while allowing a higher population, is ultimately non-sustainable. Sooner or later, our economic and ecological systems must collapse (Figure 5–18). When this collapse occurs, we will find that the true carrying capacity has been diminished because so much of our stock of non-renewable resources is gone.

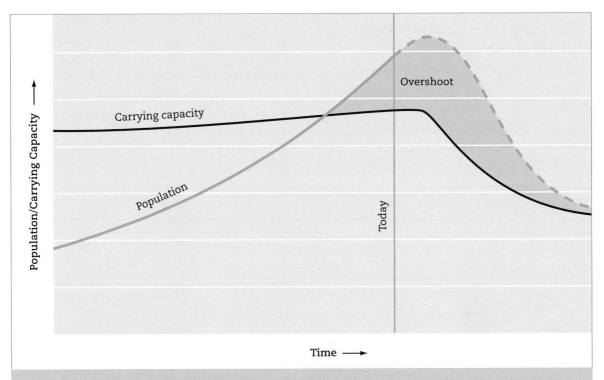

Figure 5–18 *Those who support Catton's ideas believe that we are already living in an "overshoot" condition—that is, the population exceeds Earth's true carrying capacity. This has been achieved by relying on the phantom carrying capacity provided by overuse of non-renewable resources. Ultimately, as these resources run out, Earth's population must fall. Earth's true carrying capacity will also decrease because of the massive environmental degradation that has occurred.*

Population Projections

It is crucial that we learn to predict the world's population for the years to come. If we do not know something as simple as how many people there will be, it will be impossible to plan in such vital areas as food supply, health care, education, and environmental management.

The United Nations has made three projections for the world's population, ranging from low to high (Figure 5–19). These projections vary greatly—indeed, the difference between the high and low projections for the year 2050 is more than three billion. The variance occurs because each projection is based on a different set of possible circumstances. For example, the low projection assumes that demographic transition will occur more quickly than expected in developing countries and that fertility rates in developed countries will remain lower than anticipated.

Recent population projections have been somewhat lower than those made in previous years. This trend indicates that, on a worldwide basis, demographic transition is occurring faster than anticipated. Clearly, one of the most important questions that we must answer in the next few decades is where our population is heading. As well, we must be able to determine how to support this population in a sustainable fashion.

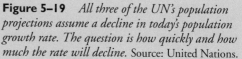
You can read a discussion of the UN population projections at
<www.pearsoned.ca/globalconnections>.

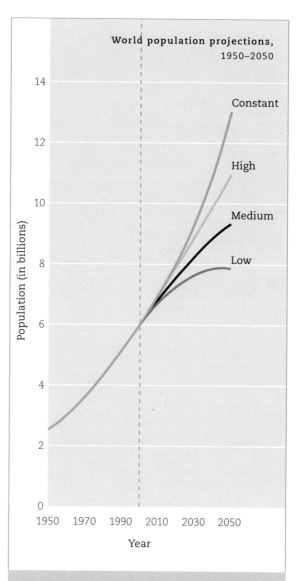

Figure 5–19 *All three of the UN's population projections assume a decline in today's population growth rate. The question is how quickly and how much the rate will decline.* Source: United Nations.

Chapter Questions

Knowledge and Understanding

1. In your notebook, complete the table in Figure 5–20 to summarize the characteristics of each stage of demographic transition.

2. Briefly summarize the two reasons why the onset of early transition and late transition occurred later and faster in developing countries.

3. Contrast the factors responsible for "death control" (the decline in death rate) during demographic transition with those responsible for birth control.

Thinking and Inquiry

4. Acceptance of the germ theory of disease has made infection control a major health goal worldwide. Provide one example of each of the following:
   - a household product named after a pioneer in the fight against germs
   - a major Canadian public health tragedy caused by inattention to infection risk
   - something you might have to do to protect yourself against infection
   - a major concern of international travellers
   - a major concern in Canadian hospitals

5. Explain why Mexico's current death rate is lower than Sweden's in spite of the fact that Sweden is more highly developed and has more advanced health care.

6. a) Do you think Earth has an ultimate carrying capacity? Explain.
   b) What natural and human factors would influence the magnitude of Earth's carrying capacity?
   c) Coal, oil, and natural gas can be used as fuels or as industrial raw materials. What is the difference between these two possible uses? How is the difference related to the idea of a phantom carrying capacity?

Indicator	Pre-transition	Early Transition	Late Transition	Post-transition
Typical birth rate				
Typical death rate				
Typical natural increase				
Major population feature				
Dominant economic activity				
Population is primarily urban or rural?				
When occurring (developed countries)				
When occurring (developing countries)				

Figure 5–20

Year	Birth Rate	Death Rate
1921	29.3	11.6
1926	24.7	11.4
1931	23.2	10.2
1936	20.3	9.9
1941	22.4	10.1
1946	27.2	9.4
1951	27.2	9.0
1956	28.0	8.2
1961	26.1	7.7
1966	19.4	7.5
1971	16.8	7.3
1976	15.7	7.1
1981	15.3	7.0
1986	14.2	7.0
1991	14.3	7.0
1996	12.2	7.1

Figure 5–21 *Birth and death rates, Canada 1921–1996.* Source: Data reproduced from Statistics Canada publications "Births and deaths, vital statistics, volume I," Catalogue 84-204, 1975 to 1985, "Vital Statistics Compendium," Catalogue 84-214, November 1999, and "Historical Statistics of Canada," Catalogue 11-516, 1983.

7. In a short essay, describe the implications of the three population projections made by the United Nations. Consider the environmental implications, economic impacts, and resource demands.

Communication

8. The elimination of smallpox is one of the great medical advances in history. There may be evidence of the fight against smallpox in your class and in your family. Conduct an informal survey to determine who has and who has not been vaccinated against smallpox. Relate this information to the age and place of birth of each person you interview. What conclusions can you draw? (Hint: The vaccination leaves a circular scar on the arm or upper leg that is about the size of a dime.)

9. Construct a map showing the demographic transition stage of each country in the world. This can be done in two different ways: by hand on a base map, or by using ArcView GIS software. Your teacher will suggest which method to use and will provide you with full instructions.

Application

10. The table in Figure 5–21 summarizes Canada's birth rate and death rate since 1921. Graph these data, and describe Canada's demographic transition by labelling the stages.

11. Describe the relationship, if any, between the theory of demographic transition and each of the four divergent views of population growth discussed on pages 70–72.

6

Demographic Issues in Developing Countries

Expectations

In this chapter, you will:

■ demonstrate the need to respect the cultural and religious traditions of others

■ understand the status and roles of men and women in different parts of the world

■ evaluate ways to promote sustainable development and assess their effectiveness

■ explain how economics and culture influence a country's population policies

■ explain how local participation in development can build sustainable communities

■ predict global population changes and assess their implications

Two potential flaws in the theory of demographic transition suggest a need to consider two different sets of world population problems. The first—the subject of this chapter—involves developing countries with very high birth rates (such as Pakistan, above) that are dealing with overpopulation. The second, involving developed countries whose birth rates have dropped well below death rates, will be discussed in Chapter 7.

The Population Explosion

Typically, countries shift into the post-transition stage as they benefit from economic and social growth. A number of social and economic factors increase the likelihood that this will happen. These include the level of education in the population, the degree of urbanization that has occurred, the advancement of health care, the role that women play in the society, the richness of the resource base, and the accessibility of advanced technology. Such factors, albeit in differing combinations, are responsible for the completion of demographic transition in places as varied as Britain, Canada, and Singapore. But what happens if a country does not achieve the level of economic and social development needed to move to post-transition?

Too Many People: The Demographic Trap

Experts fear that there may be a large number of developing nations that may not reach the stable (or declining) population levels of post-transition. These developing nations may become stuck in what has been called the **demographic trap**. When this happens, a country finds itself in a deadly, self-perpetuating cycle.

A country can become "trapped" demographically somewhere in the late transition stage, when there is a relatively low death rate and a still-high birth rate. The resulting high natural increase is the root of the problem. All the country's economic growth ends up being used to support the needs of the booming population; there is nothing left over to promote the economic and social development that is necessary for the country to proceed to post-transition. The fear is that the country's birth rate will stop declining, and the population

explosion will continue until a Malthusian collapse becomes inevitable (Figure 6–1). This devastating collapse would occur because the population has grown so much that it exceeds the carrying capacity of the area.

The problems that a country faces when it is experiencing a population boom can be demonstrated by one simple statistic: Each year, India's population grows by an amount almost equal to the entire population of Australia. This means that, annually, the Indian economy must provide food, housing, health care, education, and everything else that 18 million additional people need—before being able to improve the standard of living of the existing population. Even if this task is possible in the short term, ultimately the demands of the growing population must exceed the carrying capacity of the country. When this situation arises, a country can be described as suffering from **overpopulation**.

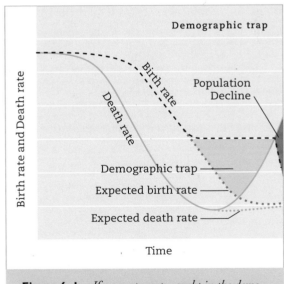

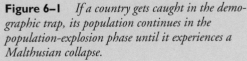

Figure 6–1 *If a country gets caught in the demographic trap, its population continues in the population-explosion phase until it experiences a Malthusian collapse.*

Food

The problems of overpopulation are pretty much what one might expect. The most basic problem, of course, is providing enough food. In recent decades, India has been able to maintain an adequate supply of food for most people. This has been possible only because India was one of the major beneficiaries of the so-called Green Revolution.

Between 1950 and 2000, India was able to double its total production of rice and wheat without increasing the amount of cropland being used. This was necessary since virtually all the arable land in India was already being farmed. By the end of the century, though, the rapid gains in agricultural productivity had slowed, since the benefits of the Green Revolution had already been realized and no new, comparable innovations were occurring. What is most worrying for the future is that, as the population continues to increase, the per capita amount of cropland diminishes. In 1960, there was about 0.21 ha of land being used to produce India's staple crops (wheat and rice) for each Indian resident. By 2000, this amount had declined to about 0.10 ha. During the Green Revolution, increased productivity made up for this decline. It has been predicted that by 2050, India will have only 0.07 ha of cropland per capita. Whether this decline can be offset by similar increases in productivity is not yet known.

Education

Having an educated population is generally accepted as vital if a country is to move through demographic transition. Unfortunately, an exploding population has a serious impact on the ability of a nation to educate its citizens. In 2000, India had 338 million children under 15 years old. Compare this to Canada, which had only six million children in that age group. India had the daunting task of trying to educate 56 times as many children with an economic base (GDP) that was only 2.5 times larger than Canada's.

While India has made enormous efforts to educate its people since independence, more than half of the country's adults are not yet literate. This relatively low level of educational advancement has hindered India's demographic transition.

Employment

Countries with booming populations also have difficulties providing jobs for the great number of people entering the work force each year. In India's case, this means about 10 million new jobs annually. Traditionally, most of these people would work in agriculture, but, as you learned earlier, the amount of farmland available per capita is being constantly reduced. This is illustrated by the fact that between 1960 and 1990, the number of farms increased from 48 million to 105 million, while the average farm size decreased from 2.7 ha to 1.6 ha. These tiny farms do not provide many new jobs.

Because the rural, agricultural economy cannot support the ever-growing population, increasing numbers of people are moving to cities. (You will learn more about migration to the cities of the developing world in Chapter 8.) The problem with this migration is that most of these people lack the education to take advantage of the opportunities that exist in India's growing urban economy. For example, India has

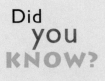

Figure 6–2 *Many high-tech US companies are taking advantage of India's low labour costs and are expanding production operations in cities like Bangalore.*

a large and growing software industry (Figure 6–2), but this is of little interest to an illiterate person who has just moved from a depressed agricultural region. At the same time, the growth of the software industry is being hindered by a shortage of workers with the necessary skills. This is a good example of a **feedback loop** (Figure 6–3).

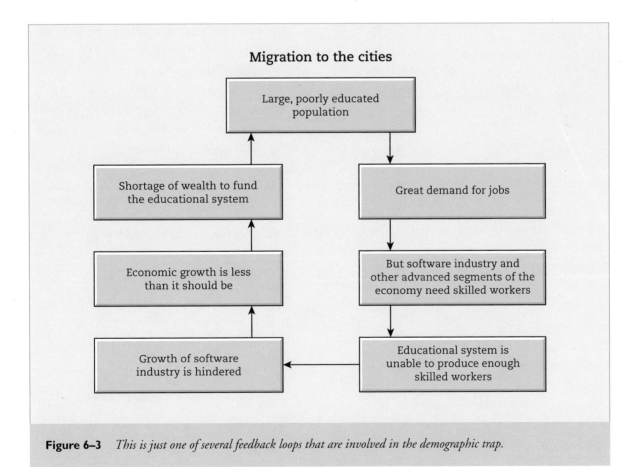

Figure 6–3 *This is just one of several feedback loops that are involved in the demographic trap.*

India's Approach to the Problem

We could have used any one of dozens of countries as an example of the most common approach to fighting overpopulation. India was chosen for a couple of reasons. One is that it will soon have the largest population in the world. The other reason is that India is typical of a great many nations, in that the efforts it has made to control population have had mediocre success at best. India recognized its population problem after it became independent in 1947, by which time it was moving into early transition (Figure 6–4). This growth has continued to the present day, with India's population exceeding one billion in 2000. The United Nations has projected that this population will reach more than 1.5 billion by 2050. The problem is obvious, the solution less so.

Want to know the current population of India, China, and the world? Go to <www.pearsoned.ca/globalconnections>.

In the 1950s, India's **population control** was focussed on providing urban clinics that encouraged sterilization and contraception. By the 1960s, attention had shifted to the rural areas, where most of the country's people lived and where family size was greater than in the cities. These efforts, which continue today, have tended to have two shortcomings.

One flaw was that they were target-driven, that is, quotas were established for each district. What mattered was how many people were sterilized or how many family-planning meetings were held— not whether sustainable birth rate reductions had been achieved. No attention was paid to factors such as the role of women in society, education levels, economic development, and health, all of which are important in reducing fertility rates.

A second problem was that a national, one-size-fits-all approach was adopted. This centralized program did provide certain administrative efficiencies, but was insensitive to the enormous cultural, religious, and economic differences that

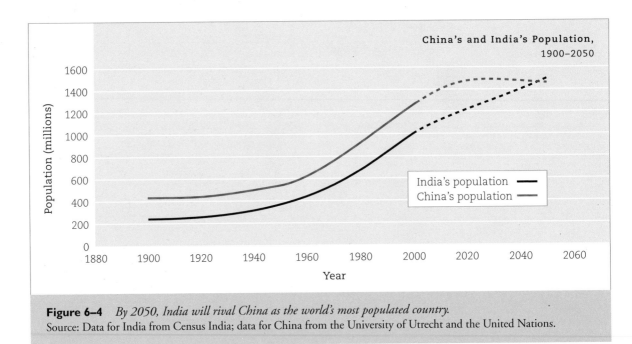

Figure 6–4 *By 2050, India will rival China as the world's most populated country.*
Source: Data for India from Census India; data for China from the University of Utrecht and the United Nations.

exist in a country as complex as India. Population control was pursued diligently—at times, too diligently. During the mid-1970s, mass sterilizations were carried out, often without the consent of the patient.

In spite of this great effort, India's fight to lower its birth rate and its rate of natural increase has been at best partially successful. Most other countries that pursued similar policies have experienced a similar lack of success in accelerating their demographic transition. Is there a better way? The remainder of this chapter will explore other approaches to population control.

China's Approach to Overpopulation

Put yourself 10 years or so into the future. You have been married for a couple of years and have decided that you would like to have your first child. How would you feel if the next step in the process were that you had to face a committee at your workplace and ask for permission to have a child? By Canadian standards, this would be an unconscionable interference with your human rights; but in China, it is just one small part of the current population control program, the **one-child policy**.

By any standard, China has an enormous population problem. In 1950, it had a population of 550 million, with a total fertility rate of more than six babies per woman. The birth rate was 37 per thousand and the death rate was 18 per thousand, which meant that the population was growing at 1.9 per cent per year. By 1998, in spite of drastic efforts to limit population growth, China had 1.25 billion citizens, in a land area that is a little smaller than Canada's. Imagine what life would be like in Canada if we had to support 40 times as many people as we do (Figure 6–5).

The Great Leap Forward

By the mid-1950s, the communist government of China, under the leadership of Mao Tsetung, decided that dramatic steps would be necessary to control population growth. In a totalitarian government with a leader who was venerated almost as a deity, virtually any policy was possible. The first attempt was the **Great Leap Forward**, which was begun in 1958. This was nothing less than an effort to revolutionize the very nature of China's economy and society. Agricultural land was organized into huge collective farms, and industrialization was acceler-

Figure 6–5 *Crowds fill a street in Shanghai, China's most populated city.*

ated. From a population perspective, this initiative was an attempt to accelerate the process of demographic transition.

The Great Leap Forward had disastrous results. The massive reforms were not well planned or organized. Most critically, food production dropped precipitously. The country's population problem was eliminated, but not in the way that anyone wanted. As Figure 6–6 shows, the death rate skyrocketed because of food shortages. As well, the birth rate collapsed since no one wanted to have children. For a brief time, China's population even declined. As soon as the reforms of the Great Leap Forward were abandoned, the birth and death rates returned to their previous levels.

The One-Child Policy

In the late 1960s, China experienced the Cultural Revolution. This was a time when radical elements in the Communist Party controlled the country, and the nation's attention was focussed on the massive disruptions that these elements brought. Little was done in these years to address the nation's population growth. It was not until the 1970s that the country gradually moved towards the one-child policy.

The one-child policy is the foundation of China's population planning program. It includes a number of initiatives, many of which would be unacceptable in Canada.

- With few exceptions, just one child is allowed per couple.
- People are expected to marry at an older age than was typical in the past. This measure reduces the likelihood of a couple's having multiple children.
- All pregnancies must be pre-authorized by the woman's work unit. Each workplace is assigned a limited number of births each year, and a woman must apply for a "birth coupon" which allows an approved pregnancy. A woman who becomes pregnant without permission may face a large fine or even be forced to abort the baby.
- Abortion is routinely used for birth control, and women are often pressured to abort a second child. In contrast to standard practices in

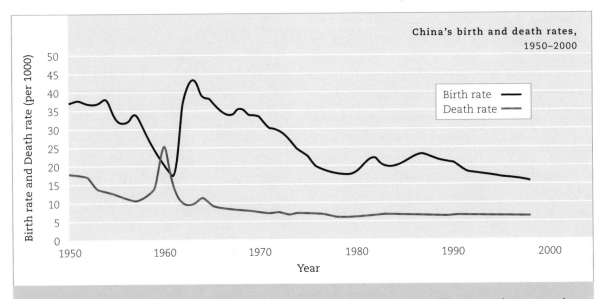

Figure 6–6 *Before the one-child policy was adopted in the early 1970s, the results of China's population control efforts had ranged from indifferent to disastrous.*

the West, abortions are common in the third trimester of pregnancy, when the babies are well developed and viable outside the womb.

- In addition to other penalties that may be imposed, female sterilization is encouraged and, in some cases, required after a second child is born.
- A woman's menstrual cycles may be publicly monitored at her workplace or in the couple's village, and their sex life is open to public discussion. Generally, family planning is considered a community responsibility, not a private matter.
- Couples who do not follow the one-child policy can be ostracized. The "granny police" help enforce the policy and chastise offenders.
- Central to the entire program is the use of rewards and penalties for those who follow or do not follow the program. For example, a couple with only one child may receive extra government payments. A woman who agrees to be sterilized after her first child may receive extended paid maternity leave. On the other hand, a couple who has a second child may lose preferred housing or a promotion at work, or may face a fine as large as $40 000. A farm couple may lose land grants or loans.

Does the Policy Work?

The goal of China's family-planning measures was to reduce population pressure and allow improvement in people's standard of living. By most objective measures, there has been considerable success in both these directions. For example, China's population control measures have been much more successful than those of India. By 2000, China's population of 1.3 billion was increasing by about 11 million per year, while India's population of 1.0 billion was increasing by 16 million per year. Demographers estimate that China's population will peak at between 1.402 billion in 2026 and 1.550 billion in 2045 and then decline. In fact, Chinese

demographers are starting to consider the problems the country will face as it moves into post-transition—labour shortages and a higher dependency load of older people. At the same time, China's economy has experienced dramatic advances that have brought a higher standard of living to the great majority of citizens.

On the surface, the one-child policy seems to have been successful, but the cost has been great. A number of serious problems are tied to China's population control policies.

- There is evidence that female babies have been aborted or killed after birth by parents who would prefer a male child. (Sons are expected to provide for their elderly parents and also continue the family name.) One authority has estimated that as many as 3.5 million female children were killed in a 10-year period. The growing use of medical technologies that allow gender determination in the womb made this problem worse, although a shortage of women is now making female babies more valued. Some chinese men have even started to advertise overseas for brides.
- Some international observers believe that many of these measures infringe on the human rights of Chinese citizens. This is a complex ethical question, since the Chinese government might reply that the one-child policy is a lesser violation of individual rights than would be the case if population growth had not been curbed in this way.
- Some doctors have also expressed concern about the use of medical procedures such as sterilization and abortion to implement public policy rather than to meet the health needs of individuals.

For more information on Chinese population projections, go to <www.pearsoned.ca/globalconnections>

Is There a Better Way?

So far, we have considered three possible models to account for a country's movement towards post-transition.

- Many countries, including those in Europe, North America, and parts of Asia and Latin America, have reached (or are reaching) post-transition without the use of specific fertility control policies.
- India's national population control program includes measures that are fairly typical in most other countries in the world. There is only one problem: quota-based plans that concentrate on the technical methods of controlling fertility just do not work very well.
- The third model, that of China, has proven to be quite effective, but it has serious implications for human rights.

Is there a better way? Can we find a means for a poor country to reach post-transition quickly and effectively without requiring a wealthy economy (which may not be possible) or coercing its population (which is not desirable)? Interestingly, there is such an effort under way—in the state of Kerala in India (Figure 6–7).

Kerala's Demographic Transition

Examine Kerala's demographic characteristics in Figure 6–8. First, compare Kerala in 1947 and in 1997. Next, consider two pieces of 1947 data. By any standard, a birth rate of 47 per thousand is very high, while an infant mortality rate of 150 per thousand births is higher than that of almost any country in the world today. From these facts, it is fair to conclude that, in 1947, Kerala was in early transition. Now look at the 1997 Kerala data and those for India and the United States. Surprisingly, Kerala's values are more like those of the United States than those of the rest of India, suggesting that Kerala is in (or, at least, is entering) the post-transition stage. This Indian state has apparently gone through demographic transition faster and more successfully than the rest of the country. You might conclude that Kerala is an aberration in India—that it must be wealthier, more industrialized, and more urbanized than the rest of the country. Your conclusion would make sense based on what we know about demographic transition elsewhere. But it would be entirely wrong!

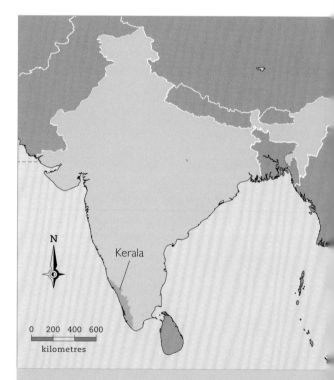

Figure 6–7 *Demographic transition in the Indian state of Kerala has followed a very different course from that of the rest of the country.*

Indicator	Kerala (1947)	Kerala (1997)	India (2000)	United States (2000)
Birth rate (per 1000 people)	47	17	25	14
Death rate (per 1000 people)	25	6	9	9
Natural increase (%)	2.2	1.1	1.6	0.6
Life expectancy (years)	N/A	72	63	77
Infant mortality rate (per 1000 births)	150	13	65	7
Total fertility rate (children)	6.0	1.7	3.1	1.6

Figure 6–8 *Demographic statistics for Kerala, India as a whole, and the United States. There are two separate comparisons you should make when you look at these data. One is the demographic transition that occurred in Kerala between 1947 and 1997. The other is between contemporary Kerala and the rest of India and the United States.*

Factors in Kerala's Transition

In fact, Kerala does not fit the model of a post-transition society. It has an agricultural economy with limited manufacturing and service sectors. It has a very high population density (747 people/km² in 1991), with more than 70 per cent of its people living in rural areas. More remarkably, Kerala is poor even by India's standards. In 1970, Kerala's per capita income was 90 per cent of that of the entire country. By the 1990s, this figure had declined to 70 per cent. Not only is Kerala poor; its economy is stagnating while that of most of India is growing steadily. Yet, demographic transition has occurred.

Several factors have contributed to Kerala's successful demographic transition.

Did you KNOW? Kerala's population density is more than twice as great as all of India and 250 times that of Canada.

Education

Educational levels in Kerala are significantly higher than in India in general. In Kerala, the literacy level for men in 1991 was 95 per cent, while for women it was 87 per cent. In contrast, India's literacy rates in 1995 were only 66 per cent (for men) and 38 per cent (for women). Essentially, all Keralese in their reproductive years are literate.

The importance placed on education in Kerala is not new. Historically, the masses were educated informally in the temples. More recently there has been the widespread growth of publicly and privately funded schools, and even an extensive public library system. This development is significant because, everywhere in the world, people with more education tend to have fewer children than those with less education.

Status of women

Elevated female literacy levels indicate the high standing of women in Kerala. This status is also shown by the fact that Kerala is the only Indian state in which there are more females than males. In Kerala in 1991, there were 96 men for every 100 women. In the entire country in 1995, the

Figure 6–9 *Keralese fishers in a dugout canoe. Many factors, including education, health care, and land reform, have helped Kerala move into a post-transition society.*

The major health concerns in Kerala today—heart disease, cancer, and diabetes—are not those of a developing country. Rather, they are the degenerative diseases common in an economically developed nation. An advanced health care system has a number of impacts on fertility levels. A healthy couple does not need to have many children in order to ensure that one child reaches adulthood. Also, an effective system of clinics and hospitals means better access to birth control.

Land reform

In most developing countries, the majority of the agricultural land is owned by a relatively small number of people, while most families are either poor tenants who own no land at all or who struggle to survive on holdings that are too small to provide a living. Kerala has gone in a different direction by instituting a series of effective land-reform policies. (You will learn about land reform in Chapter 10.) These reforms limited the maximum individual farm size to about 4.5 ha and ensured that every farmer, including the tenants who used to rent land from the richer landowners, would gain ownership to at least some land. Kerala's huge rural population means that the supply of land is tight, but at least every family has its fair share.

Government

Kerala's governments have also contributed to the state's demographic transition. In colonial times, it was ruled by a series of progressive-thinking monarchs. For example, in 1817 the Maharani of Travancore, who ruled southern Kerala, decided that the state should defray the whole cost of educating of its people. Similar decisions would not be made in more "advanced" societies—like Canada, Britain, and the United States—until many years later.

Since India's independence in 1947, the citizens of Kerala have most frequently elected

comparable ratio was 107 males to 100 females. A well-educated, empowered female population is very likely to take control of its fertility levels.

Since 1947, the mean age of marriage in Kerala for women has increased from 15–16 years to 22–23 years. Since wives in the 15-to-24 age group tend to have more children, this delay in marriage has had a substantial impact on the total fertility rate.

Health care

Kerala has a long tradition of advanced health care. The state's leaders, past and present, have provided considerable funds for preventing and curing disease. There are hospitals throughout the state; health care is readily available and relatively inexpensive. For example, there are more than three times as many hospital beds per capita in Kerala than in the rest of India. Mass immunization against disease is common, and most births occur in hospitals.

governments that have been dominated by one or another of India's two communist parties. These governments have effectively provided for land reform, education, and health care, and established "fair price stores," which ensure that limited food and fuel supplies are available to everyone equitably and at minimum price.

Travel and employment

Since the mid-1970s, Kerala has been a major source of expatriate workers for the oil-rich countries of the Persian Gulf, including Kuwait, Saudi Arabia, and the United Arab Emirates. These workers, who fill many of the menial jobs in the Gulf, bring two things back to Kerala with them. One is money, and the other is the experience of living in a modern, post-transition society, where the advantages of having a small family are evident.

Change by Diffusion

Kerala's demographic transition has occurred because of a complex interaction of all these factors. Geographers talk about two different models that can be used to describe how significant change occurs in a society. The first is the **structural change** model. This is what has happened in China, and has been attempted in India and most other developing countries. In these countries, governments have adopted measures to force, or at least strongly encourage, people to have smaller families. This has not been the case in Kerala, where **change by diffusion** has occurred. In this second model, people did not reduce their fertility in response to encouragement or intimidation. Instead, an understanding of the benefits of smaller families gradually spread through the state. Figure 6–10 shows how this happens.

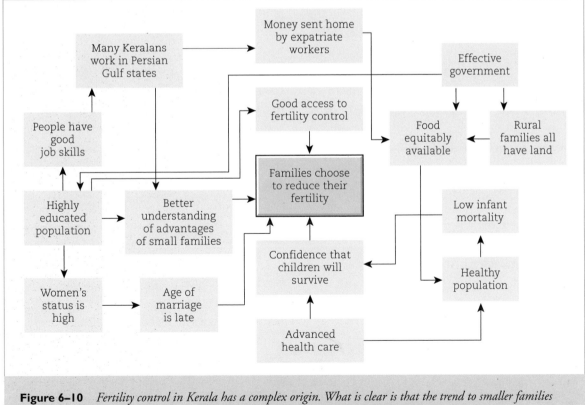

Figure 6–10 *Fertility control in Kerala has a complex origin. What is clear is that the trend to smaller families occurred as a result of a series of individual choices rather than a program of government measures.*

The Future of Population Control

What is next for the many countries of the world that are still in the midst of demographic transition and face the possibility of being caught in the demographic trap? Can they follow the model of Kerala? Should they try, given that Kerala has achieved its transition even while living with a stagnant economy?

The United Nations has attempted to address these questions at a series of conferences that began in Cairo in 1994. The Cairo conference, more properly known as the **International Conference on Population and Development (ICPD)**, had the daunting task of developing a series of policies that would be effective in helping countries complete their demographic transition while developing economically. At the same time, the measures to be adopted must be politically and morally acceptable to all nations of the world.

The title of the conference shows that the world's nations have come to realize that trying to control population by acting narrowly within the field of fertility control is doomed to failure. Rather, population growth will be controlled only by looking at the "big picture" of economic and social development. Some of the principles that were adopted by the ICPD, and are specifically related to population growth, are shown in Figure 6–11.

The purpose of these principles was to provide a framework within which each country could make its specific plans for population and development. The principles were not easily agreed upon. The cultural, economic, and religious differences that exist among the world's nations caused profound splits that threatened the possibility of any agreement. At times, alliances developed that seemed odd at first glance. For example, Principle 8 proved contentious. Countries as different as Ghana, the European Union, Brazil, and India wanted to change the wording of one sentence to "… sexual and reproductive health," while an equally disparate alliance, including the Holy See and some Catholic countries, joined with traditional Islamic countries like Libya and Sudan to oppose the change. (The Holy See is the diplomatic representative of the Catholic Church.) In other situations, there was a split between the so-called G77 and developed nations like the United States, Canada, the European Union, and Japan.

The issues that the ICPD deals with are so fundamental and complex that it will be 15 or 20 years at the earliest before we will know how successful the agreement has been. Its success is far from guaranteed, even though more than 175 countries agreed to it. The success of international agreements like the ICPD depends entirely on the willingness and ability of the participants to adopt policies that are in accord with the agreement.

In keeping with its title, the International Conference on Population and Development dealt broadly with population and development issues. You can learn more at <www.pearsoned.ca/globalconnections>.

But "willingness" and "ability" are each potentially huge hurdles. A few examples will illustrate this point. Principle 15 calls on the developed countries to take particular responsibility for sustainable development. What Canadian or US government facing re-election every few years would be "willing" to pass laws that would seriously restrict their citizens' ability to purchase large, fuel-consuming vehicles?

Similarly, a developing country that has a strong cultural and religious tradition of male dominance would not be very "willing" to pass laws to uphold Principle 4. Comparable problems exist on the "ability" side. Many of the principles—for example, 7, 8, and 11—are ideals to which any country might aspire. However, achieving these principles may be beyond the ability of many countries.

Principle 2 calls on all nations to ensure that all individuals are given the opportunity to make the most of their potential, since human beings are at the centre of concerns for sustainable development, and they are the most valuable resource of any nation.

Principle 4 calls for advanced gender equality and equity and the empowerment of women, and the elimination of all kinds of violence against women. The human rights of women and the girl-child are an inalienable, integral, and indivisible part of universal human rights.

Principle 5 says that population-related goals and policies are integral parts of cultural, economic, and social development, the principal aim of which is to improve the quality of life of all people.

Principle 6 identifies sustainable development as a means to ensure human well-being. States should reduce and eliminate unsustainable patterns of production and consumption and promote appropriate policies in order to meet the needs of current generations without compromising the ability of future generations to meet their own needs.

Principle 7 calls on all states to cooperate in the essential task of eradicating poverty as an indispensable requirement for sustainable development.

Principle 8 says that everyone has the right to the enjoyment of the highest attainable standard of physical and mental health, and that states should take all appropriate measures to ensure universal access to health-care services, including those related to reproductive health care, family planning, and sexual health.

Principle 9 states that the family is the basic unit of society, and as such, should be strengthened. In different cultural, political, and social systems, various forms of the family exist.

Principle 10 says that everyone has the right to education, which shall be directed to the full development of human resources, and human dignity and potential, with particular attention to women and the girl-child.

Principle 11 calls on states and families to give the highest priority to children. The child has the right to the highest attainable standards of health, and the right to education.

Principle 15 requires that in the context of sustainable development and social progress, sustained economic growth be broadly based, offering equal opportunities to all people. All countries should recognize their common but differentiated responsibilities, and the developed countries acknowledge the responsibility they bear in the international pursuit of sustainable development.

Figure 6–11 *Some of the principles of the International Conference on Population and Development that are most closely related to population.*

Chapter Questions

Knowledge and Understanding

1. What is the demographic trap, and why is it a threat for developing countries?

2. a) A number of factors that contribute to the completion of demographic transition were mentioned in this chapter. List these, and explain one way in which each contributes to transition.
   b) Explain why an educated population is vital in helping a country to move through demographic transition.

3. a) Why does China have a significant shortage of girls and young women in some rural areas?
   b) Suggest an entirely different reason why the count of young women is short.
   c) The Chinese government has told its people that it is the responsibility of every child (not just male children) to look after his or her parents. What is the purpose of this move? Is it likely to work? Explain.

4. a) Why is the status of women a critical factor in demographic transition?
   b) Why is it so difficult to make changes in this area?

Thinking and Inquiry

5. a) Per capita grain production in India is expected to decline between now and 2050. Briefly describe the human, economic, and political impacts that this decline might have on the nation.
   b) India's population is projected to be at least 1.5 billion in 2050. Give two reasons why this might not occur.

6. China's one-child policy has been highly contentious. In your opinion, was (is) the Chinese government justified in imposing this policy on its people? Include specific references to the policy and to China's population situation in your answer.

7. a) Do you find Kerala's experience surprising? Why or why not?
   b) The experience of Kerala has produced strong reactions from supporters and from critics. Visit the Web site <www.pearsoned.ca/globalconnections> and respond to the question, "Does the experience of Kerala point the way to demographic transition for the poorest developing countries?"
   c) Compare the efforts of Kerala and China to control population growth. Which of these approaches will have the most desirable long-term results?

8. Explain why the following alliances developed at the ICPD and ICPD+5 meetings:
   - Catholic countries and Islamic countries
   - many developed countries in opposition to many developing countries

Communication

9. Create a table (or an organizer) in which you relate the principles of the ICPD to the demographic transition experience of:
   - India (excluding Kerala)
   - China
   - Kerala

10. Write a paragraph to suggest how each of the following groups of countries would react to the directions implicit in the ICPD principles. Give reasons for your suggestions.
    - China and other G77 countries
    - developed countries

11. There are several ways in which a country can move towards the completion of demographic transition. Consider the examples of Canada, India, China, and the Indian state of Kerala. Research two countries in the world to see which approach has been followed. Give evidence to support your choice.

Application

12. a) What is a feedback loop?
b) Show how a feedback loop can hinder demographic transition, using an example different from the one given in this chapter.

13. Examine Figure 6–12. What evidence is given here about the relative success of China's and India's attempts to control fertility? Give specific references to the pyramids in your answer.

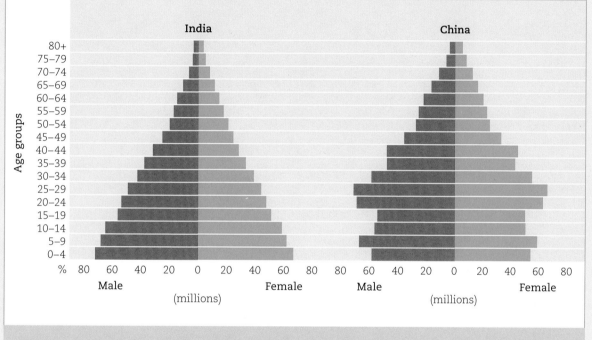

Figure 6–12   *Population pyramids for India and China, 1995*

Demographic Issues in Developed Countries

Expectations

In this chapter, you will:

■ demonstrate the need to respect the cultural and religious traditions of others

■ understand the status and roles of men and women in different parts of the world

■ predict global population changes and assess their implications

■ understand the need to consider social differences when analysing world issues

■ explain why it is difficult to make accurate predictions about human use of the Earth

In 2000, Bologna, Italy (above), had the world's lowest fertility rate, only 0.80 children per woman. If this trend continues until 2020, Bologna will have 25 people over the age of 50 for every child under five. What is happening so dramatically in Bologna is happening more slowly in many other places. This chapter examines the implications of this **population implosion**.

Different Assumptions, Different Futures

Fundamentally, there are three factors that affect an area's future population. Most obvious is the total fertility rate of the area—more births mean a higher population. Second is the life expectancy of the residents—if people live longer, the population will be greater. Third is the impact that migration has on the population of an area. The value of each of these factors is influenced by such a complex combination of economic and social conditions that population prediction becomes a hazardous task indeed. In spite of the risks, a number of international organizations, including the United Nations and the World Bank, produce world population projections—because we must know how many people there will be in the future if we are to make appropriate plans.

Typically, population projections include a range of possibilities based on different assumptions about the total fertility rate, life expectancy, and, where appropriate, migration. For example, in 1998 the United Nations projected a world population in 2050 of between 7.3 billion (called the **low variant**) and 10.7 billion (the **high variant**), with a **medium variant** of 8.9 billion. The difficulty of making an accurate and useful projection is illustrated by the fact that in 1996, just two years before this projection was made, the UN was predicting between 7.5 and 11.2 billion with a medium variant of 9.4 billion. There is a reason for the significant difference between these projections: essentially, total fertility rates dropped faster than had been anticipated by the 1996 projection.

Making Population Projections

In this chapter, we will use some detailed projections made by a scientific research organization called the International Institute for Applied Systems Analysis (**IIASA**). The IIASA reported projections for 13 regions (Figure 7–1), which can be aggregated into larger regions or the entire world. In this chapter, we are most interested in the prospects of the developed nations as defined by IIASA:

- North America (Canada, United States, Puerto Rico, Guam, Virgin Islands)
- Western Europe
- Eastern Europe
- European parts of the former Soviet Union
- Pacific members of the Organization of Economic Cooperation and Development (Japan, Australia, New Zealand).

Did you KNOW?

The International Institute for Applied Systems Analysis (IIASA) is a non-governmental research organization located in Austria. Since its inception in 1972, the institute has conducted interdisciplinary studies on environmental, economic, technological, and social issues in the context of human dimensions of global change.

The full IIASA report can be found at <www.pearsoned.ca/globalconnections>.

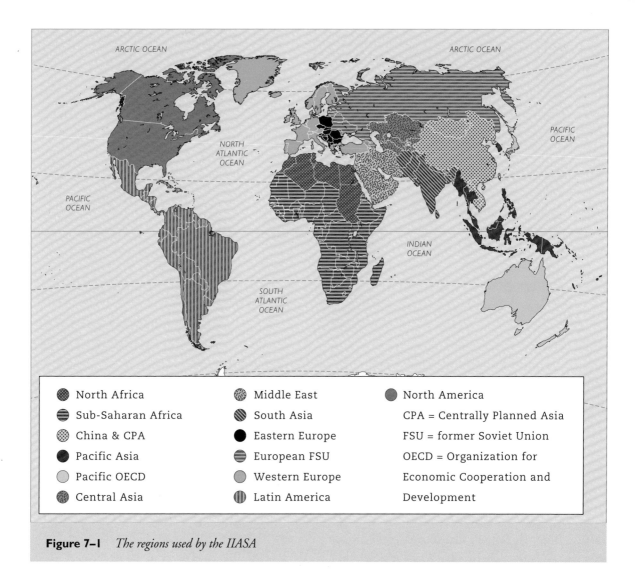

Figure 7–1 *The regions used by the IIASA*

Legend:
- North Africa
- Sub-Saharan Africa
- China & CPA
- Pacific Asia
- Pacific OECD
- Central Asia
- Middle East
- South Asia
- Eastern Europe
- European FSU
- Western Europe
- Latin America
- North America
- CPA = Centrally Planned Asia
- FSU = former Soviet Union
- OECD = Organization for Economic Cooperation and Development

IIASA Projections

The IIASA made a set of nine projections based on varying combinations of fertility and life expectancy. Since fertility predictions range from high to medium to low, as can life expectancy predictions, there are nine (3 × 3) possible combinations. As well, they built consideration of inter-regional migration into their projections. In this chapter we will concentrate on two projections in the low to medium range (Figure 7–2). The lowest projection is based on a low total fertility rate and low rate of increase in life expectancy. The moderate projection is based on medium

IIASA Population Projections for Developed Countries (in millions)

	1995 (actual)	2020	2050	2100
Lowest projection	1251	1250	1032	607
Moderate projection	1251	1340	1319	1216

Figure 7–2 *The IIASA's lowest projection suggests a massive decline in the developed world's population. Its moderate projection is for a slight decline.*
Source: International Institute for Applied Systems Analysis.

IIASA Assumptions: Summary

	Life expectancy increase per decade (years)	Total fertility rate 2000 (actual)	Total fertility rate 2000 (projected)	Total fertility rate 2030–2035 (projected)	Total fertility rate 2080–2085 (projected)
Lowest projection	1*	1.13–2.06**	1.20–1.58	1.30–1.40	1.39–1.59
Moderate projection	2	1.13–2.06**	1.50–1.94	1.70–1.85	1.89–2.09

* Except for males in the former Soviet Union, which is 0.

** Other than the United States at 2.06, the highest value is 1.81.

Figure 7–3 *These are the assumptions used by the IIASA. The projected 2000 values can be compared to the actual values for that year to check the accuracy of IIASA's predictions.* Source: International Institute for Applied Systems Analysis.

assumptions for both total fertility rate and life expectancy increase. These assumptions are summarized in Figure 7–3 and explained below.

Fertility Rate

If we examine Figure 7–3, it is relatively easy to see why we should be most interested in projections in the low to medium range. The 2000 total fertility rates (TFRs) of the regions in the developed world clearly fall between the 2000 low and moderate projections. In 2000, only one developed country, the United States, had a total fertility rate over 1.81 and 20 countries, including major ones like Germany, Poland, Italy, and Spain, had TFRs less than 1.40. (This does not include minor countries or territories like Guam and San Marino.) As well, in none of these countries has the decline in total fertility stopped. If we look into the future, it is not hard to imagine that the developed world could reach the fertility targets for the next century that would produce the lowest projection.

Life Expectancy

It is less clear at what rate life expectancies might increase. On the one hand, medical science is constantly coming up with advances that prolong life. On the other, we cannot predict how quickly these advances might occur, and there is always the possibility of a new outbreak of disease that might affect virtually the entire world. Nor can we make any meaningful predictions about the impact on life expectancies of healthier (or less healthy) lifestyles or more (or less) pollution. As amateurs in this field, we can do no better than to accept what experts at IIASA think these life expectancy increases will be.

Migration

Migration projections are the same for all of the possible projections, and are shown in Figure 7–4. Not surprisingly, almost all of the migration that is anticipated for the 21st century will be from developing regions to the developed regions. The average 3.4 million people moving to the developed world each year are included in each of the projections.

Inter-regional Migrations (in thousands)

From	To North America	Western Europe	Pacific OECD	Middle East	Total
Africa					
North Africa	90	250	20	15	375
Sub-Saharan Africa	115	150	40	5	310
Asia—East					
China & CPA	270	50	50	—	370
Pacific Asia	400	50	100	10	560
Asia—West					
Central Asia	10	30	—	—	40
Middle East	15	30	10	—	55
South Asia	300	100	80	15	495
Europe					
Eastern Europe	50	100	—	—	150
European FSU	50	150	25	—	225
Latin America	700	90	25	5	820
Total	2000	1000	350	50	3400

CPA = Centrally Planned Asia   FSU = former Soviet Union

Figure 7–4   *Predicted annual inter-regional migrations. Regions are as defined by the IIASA (Figure 7–1).*
Source: International Institute for Applied Systems Analysis.

Where World Population Is Headed

If we accept the lowest projection, we can anticipate that by the year 2100, within the life span of your children (or perhaps we should say your child), the population of the developed countries could drop by more than 50 per cent to barely 600 million. The distribution of this population is shown in Figure 7–5. As you can see, North America's population will rise slightly and then decline to about 250 million from the current 300 million. A disproportionate share of this impact is more likely to be felt in Canada than in the United States because our total fertility rate is lower.

The Pacific OECD region's population will start out fairly stable at around 150 million before declining to about 70 million. Most of this decline will occur in Japan, which has a much lower total fertility rate than Australia and New Zealand.

It is Europe that will be most affected by this low total fertility rate, also called the **birth dearth**. Europe's population has already started to decline slightly. This decline will accelerate throughout the century as the children of today's smaller families have small families of their own. Europe's projected 2100 population of about 290 million is about the same number of people who live in Russia, Germany, and France today.

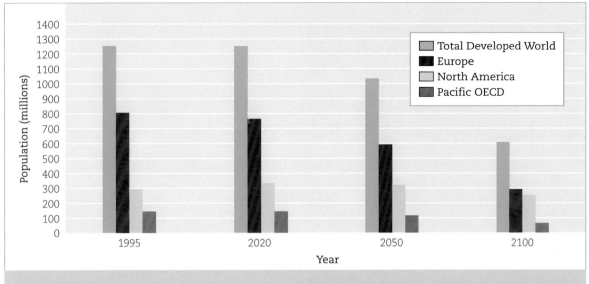

Figure 7–5 *If the IIASA's lowest projection is correct, the developed world's population will drop precipitously in the 21st century.* Source: International Institute for Applied Systems Analysis.

Implications of the Birth Dearth

Only since the 1990s have concerns over a possible population implosion surfaced. Social scientists are working diligently to understand the likely effects that these population changes will have, while political leaders, at best, have barely begun to consider the problems that will occur. Five of the major effects are described below.

1. Family Structures

If the trend to very small families continues (and there is no reason to think it will not), the citizens of Bologna and much of the world can look forward to family structures that are very different from those we are used to. Many families will have no brothers and sisters, no aunts and uncles, and no cousins (Figure 7–6). The existence of such tiny families will alter the character of family life as we know it. This has already happened in China because of the one-child policy. In one generation, Chinese families have

Figure 7–6 *A one-child family in Anhui, China: Could this be a typical 21st century family?*

gone from very large to very small. As a result, the phenomenon of "little emperors" has become common. The single child, especially a boy, comes to be spoiled not only by his parents, but by his grandparents as well.

Part of the move to lower fertility rates has been an explosion in the numbers of what are called **DINKs** (*D*ouble *I*ncome, *N*o *K*ids couples). Social scientists are concerned that as DINKs age, many may end up as **LINKs** (*L*ow *I*ncome, *N*o *K*ids). These people would live their lengthy elderly years in relative poverty with no one to care for them. Without family members to assist, these people will put even more pressure on governments. Other potential family problems emerge, as well. Lone children of such couples might find themselves overwhelmed by the responsibility of trying to look after parents (and, perhaps, grandparents) without help. In the absence of traditional families, friends and co-workers may come to play family-like roles for many people.

2. Aging Populations

Perhaps the most profound effect of the birth dearth will be a dramatic change in the age structure of the population. As a result of the post—World War II baby boom, countries such as Canada spent a half-century with a culture dominated by younger people. The next century is likely to be dominated by the elderly. Figure 7–7 shows a sequence of projected population pyramids for Spain until the year 2050. Spain, which had the lowest total fertility rate in the world in 2000, shows the direction in which dozens of countries are going. In fact, if predicted trends continue to 2100, half of Europeans will be over age 60. Between 1990 and 2030, the World Bank expects the number of people over age 60 to go from 500 million to 1.5 billion.

Never in human history has there been a large society where so many people are elderly. As a result, we have no experience in dealing with this new reality. The most obvious impact will be

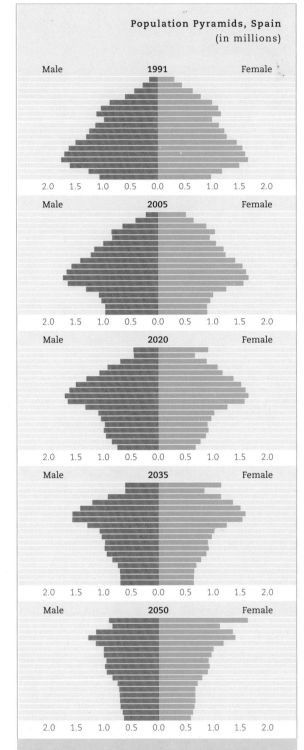

Figure 7–7 *Spain's projected population development may be typical of that of developed countries in the 21st century: a steeply declining population with, by 2050, the largest segment of the population being women over 85 years.* Source: US Census Bureau, International Data Base

the need to spend vast amounts of money to meet the special needs of older citizens—in particular, for pensions and health care.

All developed countries have government and private **pension plans** to provide incomes for older people. In the past, these plans were relatively affordable because the working population was much larger than the retired population. For example, in 1955 there were nine working Americans for each person receiving government Social Security payments. By 2030, there will be only two workers for each retired person. Perhaps it is not surprising that in the 2000 US presidential elections, a major plank in the platform of each major candidate dealt with ways of ensuring that the Social Security system would not go bankrupt.

Three solutions are possible in the face of exploding older populations:

- Pension benefits can be significantly lowered, which would have the most impact on LINKs.
- Eligibility for pensions can be restricted based on income. This has already happened in Canada, where Old Age Pensions are "clawed back" from people who have income from other sources greater than a certain amount.
- Contributions to pension programs, in the form of premiums or taxes, can be increased both now, to prepare for the population change, and in the future.

This last approach has already started in Canada, where contribution rates for the Canada Pension Plan were substantially increased in 1999 because of fears that the plan would run out of money. The possibility of inter-generational conflict looms as younger people rebel against focussing so much of their lives on providing financial and moral support for the huge number of older people. Similar issues exist in providing adequate health care for these people.

3. Labour Shortages

The expression "Freedom 55" started as an insurance company's advertising slogan. Soon, however, it entered the Canadian vernacular as a powerful image—the desire to retire earlier than the conventional age of 65 (Figure 7–8). In fact, for many Canadians and residents of other devel-

Figure 7–8 *In general, older people are more active and healthier than they were in the past. This trend may help to offset the cost of health care.*

oped countries, early retirement has become a reality. This move to earlier retirements may be short-lived, however, and may benefit only people of your parents' and grandparents' generation. The reason is that, as our population ages, there will be too few people to do the work of society. The shortage of workers will continue to worsen because people typically will spend more years in school than was the norm in the past.

There is some evidence that this **labour shortage** is already starting to happen. For example, there have been ongoing shortages of workers in fields such as computer engineering, nursing, manual labour, and teaching in many countries. Germany's robust economy has been maintained only because, over the years, the country has been able to import millions of "guest workers" from countries such as Turkey and Iran. The legal situation in the United States is different, but the economic impact of the labour shortage is similar. The US has about six million people who are in the country illegally. The workers who are part of the illegal population are an essential, if not officially acknowledged, part of the economy. Illegal workers, primarily from Mexico and other Latin American countries, fill service and agricultural jobs in many parts of the United States (Figure 7–9). Since the US economy was considered to be at full employment levels in the late 1990s and early 2000s, these illegal workers could not have been replaced. Without them, the US economy would have been seriously harmed.

Over the next century, developed countries will need to accept hundreds of millions of immigrants if they are to have enough workers to maintain their economies. A number of problems about this idea emerge. In Canada, we are used to accepting large numbers of immigrants in relation to the size of our population. In fact, we take pride in our tradition of multiculturalism. However, this is not the case in much of Europe and in Japan. These countries have no strong tra-

Figure 7–9 *US Border Patrol arrests illegal migrants at the US–Mexico border, Tijuana, Mexico. Despite the money and efforts expended by the United States to keep out illegal immigrants, hundreds of prospective migrants attempt to cross the border every day.*

dition of accepting large numbers of immigrants and integrating them into society. Further, if tens or hundreds of millions of immigrants were to move to Europe and Japan, what would happen to the cultures of these countries? It is not hard to imagine that many such countries will end up with a minority of their residents being of native descent. In countries that have taken many immigrants, such as France, intolerance is common. The governments in France, Austria, and other countries have significant opposition parties advocating strong anti-immigrant policies. It is entirely uncertain whether the people of these countries would be willing to accept substantial numbers of immigrants.

4. Economic Effects

Our economy is based on the concept of never-ending growth. This growth has two components. One is the demand for additional goods and services that comes from a population that is getting wealthier. The other is the need to provide for a population whose size has been growing explosively for decades. If there is a population implosion, not only does the second component disappear; in fact, there could be substantially fewer people for whom to provide. This should not be a problem in the first half of the 21st century, as the world's population will continue to increase—by the lowest estimates, by more than one billion. Further, many people in developing countries will become increasingly affluent. The problem will become more noticeable in the second half of the century, as the population significantly declines and the possibility arises that growth in material wealth may be limited by environmental and resource constraints.

5. Shift in World Power

The Security Council is the United Nations' most important agency for solving international crises, for example, by sending out peacekeeping missions. It has 15 members, of whom five are permanently on the Council. As well as being permanent, these five (United States, Russia, China, United Kingdom, and France) have veto power over any resolution being voted on by the Security Council. They were given this extraordinary power when the UN was formed at the end of World War II because they were clearly the most powerful nations in the world. But how should world power be distributed in 2050, when all the permanent Security Council mem-

bers are likely to have declining populations and only 12 per cent of the world's population live in the developed world? Will countries like India, Indonesia, Brazil, and Nigeria come to be seen as major world powers, replacing Russia, United Kingdom, and France (Figure 7–10)?

Benefits of Declining Populations

While the impending population implosion presents some startling challenges for the world, there is considerable good environmental news attached to the idea of a smaller-than-anticipated world population. Fewer people mean less resource use and less waste. Also, since population declines will be focussed in the world's wealthiest countries, there will be fewer people of the very sort who use the most resources and produce the most waste. We can understand the impact of these changes by looking at the demographic assumptions that underlie predictions about global warming in the future. These predictions were based on an assumed population of 11.3 billion in 2050. If there are instead seven to nine billion people, there will be an obvious difference in the amount of global warming.

Most Populated Countries, 2050 (millions)

Rank	Country	Population	Rank	Country	Population
1	China	1431.0	11	Ethiopia	117.6
2	India	1363.0	12	Philippines	107.8
3	United States	346.0	13	Dem. Rep. of Congo	106.0
4	Indonesia	272.0	14	Vietnam	104.1
5	Pakistan	251.9	15	Egypt	96.2
6	Brazil	219.0	16	Iran	88.4
7	Nigeria	204.5	17	Turkey	85.2
8	Bangladesh	180.5	18	Germany	80.0
9	Russia	136.9	19	Thailand	72.1
10	Mexico	130.9	20	France	64.2

Figure 7–10 *The world's 20 most populous nations, 2050 (predicted).*
Source: UN Population Reference Bureau Data Sheet, 2001.

Why Is the Birth Dearth Happening?

There are many reasons why birth rates have collapsed in dozens of countries and show no signs of stabilizing, let alone increasing to even replacement levels. At no time in human history has a society's birth rate increased after it has significantly declined. You should be familiar with most of these reasons, since they are simply the reasons for demographic transition that have continued beyond the point at which birth rates and death rates coincide. They include two of the most profound characteristics of modern life: urbanization and industrialization.

The Role of Women

What is most critical in the ongoing decline of birth rates is the role of women in society, which has changed dramatically and continues to change. Women today are better educated and have higher career aspirations than ever before. Their attitudes towards married life are different. They marry later and are more likely to divorce. In a growing number of cases, they choose not to marry at all. As well, they have greater access to effective methods of birth control than did women in the past.

The birth dearth is occurring as a result of the decisions made by individuals about the direction that they want their lives to take. You are likely at the point in your life when you are starting to make decisions that will affect your future career and family life. Consider the example of Laura Forbes, 35, who is making those decisions now.

After graduating from university, Laura worked as a teacher for a number of years before deciding that she wanted to move into educational administration. To do this, she decided at age 32 to return to university for two years to get the master's degree that she would need to be successful in her career. While there, she met her future partner.

After finishing her degree, Laura was able to get contract work with a provincial education department. She was told that in a couple of years she would likely get a permanent job with her employer, instead of having to rely on a series of contract postings. In a permanent job, she would be eligible to get maternity leave and be guaranteed her job on her return. At the same time, her doctor was telling her that if she wanted a child, it would be best for her and for her baby if she were to become pregnant in the next six months, while still in her mid-30s.

Laura is left facing an obvious conflict between her desire to advance her career and her desire to have a family. Her dilemma is typical of those faced by many women in developed countries—how to combine the desire to have a successful and rewarding career with the longing to have a family. When she thinks about her situation, Laura realizes two things. One is that, when she picked her career goals, she did not really understand the conflict in which she would find herself. The other is that the working world has not changed, to any significant extent, to meet the needs of women who want a family. What is clearer is that Laura and her partner are unlikely to have more than one child and, hence, will contribute to Canada's birth dearth.

Can We Prevent a Population Implosion?

This is a key question, and one that is difficult to answer because it is a new problem. Obviously, people would need to be encouraged to have more children. Policies designed to do this are called pronatalist. There are many possible **pronatalist strategies**. Some governments provide cash payments or offer tax benefits to parents. For many years after World War II, Canada provided monthly grants called "baby bonuses." Now, lower-income families receive "child tax credits." The relatively small payments available to Canadians have had no demonstrable impact on birth rates in Canada.

A German politician has proposed much larger payments. Under his scheme, a family would receive the equivalent of $480 per month for each child under the age of four. Providing payments at this level could prove enormously costly—if they had the desired effect of significantly increasing the number of German babies.

Some pronatalist strategies are designed to address the pressures that prospective parents feel. For example, more generous short-term and long-term parental leaves could be provided. Employers can provide more flexible workplace arrangements, including on-site daycare and allowing more employees to work from home. Even reducing the cost of post-secondary education might encourage people to have more children.

To date, there is little clear evidence that pronatalist strategies work. Sweden provides considerable evidence that, in fact, they may not. The

> ## Did you KNOW?
>
> A generation ago, families with four children were common. Today, when many students go on to university, educating four children could easily cost $160 000, an amount beyond the capabilities of most families.

Swedish government has a proud tradition of providing the highest level of family support in the world. It has been estimated that Sweden provides about three times more financial support to families than does the United States, which has a much higher total fertility rate. In 1990, Sweden had the highest birth rate in Western Europe, with a total fertility rate of 2.12. By 1998, in spite of its pronatalist policies, Sweden's TFR had fallen to 1.42. This decline began during the early 1990s, when economic conditions were poor, and continued through the late 1990s, when the economy had recovered.

What Will Happen?

No one knows whether the current birth dearth will continue for the next 100 years. We lack the expertise to make a dependable prediction because nothing like this has ever happened. Some authorities feel that society has fundamentally changed, that people are now so focussed on meeting their immediate needs that their longer-term desire to have children loses out. Such influences as the changed role of women and changes in the world of work mean that larger families are a thing of the past.

If we want to know what will happen in the decades to come, we will have to be able to anticipate the decisions that will be made by people

like Laura Forbes and like you. The possibility of a population implosion in some parts of the world does not mean that we no longer need fear the impact of a population boom. Rather, both of these events will happen in different parts of the world at the same time. The result is likely to be a demographic tension between countries with rising and falling birth rates. International organizations like the United Nations and World Bank will be faced with meeting the often conflicting needs of those nations fighting to limit their populations, as well as those needing to increase theirs. How well this can be done will be critical to human progress in the 21st century.

Chapter Questions

Knowledge and Understanding

1. a) How might the information in this chapter affect your career choice? Why?
   b) Consider how your career choice may affect your family choices and how your family choices may affect your career.

2. a) Describe how the health needs of countries like Canada will change as the population implosion occurs.
   b) What evidence is there that this is already happening?

3. In recent years, there has been a tendency towards earlier retirements. In the future, this is likely not to be the case. Give two different reasons why working until an older age will make sense in the future.

Thinking and Inquiry

4. Describe one social and one economic influence of each of the three factors that affect the accuracy of population projections.

5. Comment on the statement, "The birth dearth is essentially a women's issue."

6. What changes in the organization of the work world would be necessary to meet the needs of women (and men) who want children?

7. Explain why solving the demographic tensions of the next century is not as simple as moving people from overpopulated regions of the world to underpopulated regions.

Communication

8. a) Graph the total fertility rate data in Figure 7–11.
   Hints:
   - Create a different graph for each "world," i.e., use five graphs in total, each with four lines.
   - Use a dashed line to show the 2000 to 2050 projection.
   - Label each country's line.
   - Add a line to show the replacement level for total fertility. Label this line.
   b) Describe the patterns you see. What do these patterns suggest about the world's future population, both in total and in the different "worlds"?
   c) Why does the total fertility rate drop several years before the population growth rate?
   d) Why might the total fertility rate projections for several countries increase between 2000 and 2050?

Application

9. a) Estimate approximately how many immigrants Europe and Japan (Asian OECD) would need to accept in order to maintain their current populations.
   b) What impact would this immigration have on the cultures of these countries?

10. Not all areas of the developed world will be affected by the population implosion in the same way. Discuss the impact on each of the following:
    - Canada
    - United States
    - Russia and Eastern Europe
    - Western Europe and Japan
    - China

11. a) Consider how life in the future (in the time period from 2030 to 2050) will be different from life today. Brainstorm with a group of four or five of your classmates.
    b) Write a short story (300 to 500 words) to illustrate a specific point that was discussed in your group.
    c) Share your story with the other people in your group.

Total Fertility Rates, 1960 to 2050

	1960	1980	2000	2050 (predicted)
First World				
Canada	3.8	1.7	1.64	1.70
France	2.8	1.9	1.75	1.70
Japan	2.0	1.8	1.41	1.70
United States	3.5	1.8	2.06	2.22
Second World				
China	5.7	2.9	1.82	1.80
Cuba	4.2	2.0	1.60	1.70
Poland	3.0	2.3	1.38	1.70
Russia	2.6	2.0	1.25	1.54
Third World				
Brazil	6.2	4.0	2.13	1.70
Chile	5.3	2.8	2.20	1.70
Malaysia	6.8	4.2	3.29	2.24
South Korea	6.0	2.7	1.72	1.70
Fourth World				
Ecuador	6.7	5.1	3.18	2.03
India	5.9	4.7	3.11	2.02
Indonesia	5.5	4.4	2.61	1.75
Pakistan	6.9	6.8	4.56	2.02
Fifth World				
Bangladesh	6.7	6.4	2.85	2.00
Ethiopia	6.9	6.9	7.07	2.78
Haiti	6.3	5.3	4.50	2.04
Sierra Leone	6.2	6.5	6.08	2.75

Figure 7–11   Sources: 1960, 1980 data: Woodstock Development Database/Demography, Wesleyan University; 2000 data: *CIA World Factbook, 2000*; 2050 data: US Census Bureau International Programs Centre.

8 Population Migration

Expectations

In this chapter, you will:

■ compare the economic and social hopes of selected groups

■ analyse the causes and results of recent refugee situations

■ analyse the impact of human migrations on natural and human systems

■ conduct an independent inquiry related to a geographical issue

■ identify applications in the local community for conclusions reached in the inquiry

Image above: Family at Canadian citizenship ceremony

Chances are good that some of your classmates have recently moved to Canada from another country, like the Moroccan family in the photo above. Perhaps you are descended from immigrants. Immigrants or descendants of immigrants make up 98 per cent of the Canadian population. Since 1990, approximately 200 000 immigrants have arrived in Canada annually.

Immigration Trends to Canada

Where immigrants come from to Canada has changed dramatically over time. Complete the following activity to see the changing pattern.

1. a) Using the information in Figure 8–1, construct a graph, placing the four time periods along the horizontal axis and the percentage of immigrants on the vertical axis.
   b) Draw a divided bar graph for the four time periods. Use a different colour for each.

2. a) Describe the pattern for each of the eight regions/countries.

b) If present trends continue, from which regions/countries will most new immigrants migrate to Canada?
c) Suggest reasons why the pattern has changed over this time period.

3. Why do people migrate to Canada? Consider conditions in (i) their place of birth; (ii) Canada.

4. How might Canada be affected if we had no immigration?

Canada's Immigrants (percentages)

Place of Birth	1961–1970	1971–1980	1981–1990	1991–1996
United States	6.4	7.4	4.2	2.8
Central and South America	2.2	6.8	9.7	7.3
Caribbean and Bermuda	5.7	9.6	6.6	5.5
United Kingdom	21.3	13.3	5.8	2.4
Other European countries	47.7	22.7	20.0	16.6
Africa	3.3	5.8	5.9	7.3
Asia and Middle East	12.2	32.9	46.9	57.1
Oceania and Other	1.2	1.5	0.9	1.0

Figure 8–1 *Immigrant population in Canada by place of birth and period of immigration*
Source: Statistics Canada Web Site, <http://www.statcan.ca/english/Pgdb/People/Population/demo25b.htm>,extracted December 4, 2001.

Why People Migrate

What causes people to migrate? We need to look at conditions in the country from which the immigrants come and in the country to which they are moving. The conditions in the "sending country" that cause people to move away are known as **push factors**. These may include low wages, shortages of food, overcrowded living conditions, political persecution, high crime rates, wartime conditions, or lack of economic opportunity. Environmental changes, such as the degradation of agricultural land or the depletion of forests or water, are push factors that often cause mass migrations to more ecologically stable areas.

Conditions that attract migrants are called **pull factors**. These may include high wages, good educational opportunities, havens from political or religious persecution, high standards of living, or plentiful resources such as fresh water, forests, wildlife, or agricultural land.

Types of Migration

Population migration is the movement of people, individually or in groups, from one place of residence to another. When people migrate, they may settle permanently in a new location, or they may settle only to migrate again later. For thousands of years, humans have been moving from one location to another, and as a result, now permanently occupy all the world's continents except Antarctica. Migration may be classified into four categories.

Ecological Migration

South of the Sahara Desert, a semi-arid zone called the Sahel, an Arabic word meaning *desert shore*, stretches more than 4000 km across seven countries (Figure 8–2). Successive droughts since the early 1970s, plus the over-exploitation of the grasslands, forests, and water resources, are lowering the water table, degrading the soil, and causing the vegetation to disappear. As a result, the Sahara Desert is expanding into the Sahel. This desertification is forcing the people who live there to move away. The movement of

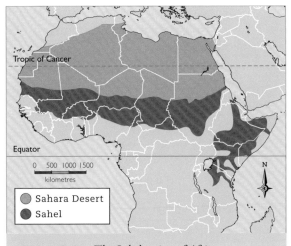

Figure 8–2 *The Sahel region of Africa*

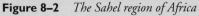

Did you KNOW? Mass migrations to warmer climates occurred during the last glacial advance, which was at its maximum about 20 000 years ago in North America and Europe.

people from one place to another because something they depend upon for life disappears from, or moves out of, their environment is called **ecological migration**.

Today, groups of people usually participate in ecological migration because of a negative change in their environment. In the future, global warming could cause the greatest human migration ever. People living in low-lying islands or coastal plains may see their homes disappear beneath rising sea levels, while people from dry southern climates may move into far northern parts of the world as warmer climates make these areas more suitable for human habitation.

Voluntary Migration

Between 1800 and 1914, approximately 70 million people left Europe and migrated, of their own accord, to Canada, the United States, Australia, Argentina, and other countries. This is an example of **voluntary migration**; that is, the movement of people of their own free will from one place to another. As a result of this voluntary migration, Europe was able to alleviate serious population pressures.

Involuntary Migration

Between 1450 and 1870, about 11 million people were forced out of Africa as slaves by Europeans. In the 1930s and 1940s, as Nazi Germany mounted its campaign against European Jewry, many Jews fled to safe havens like Spain, England, and the United States. In the late 1990s, war in Rwanda, the Congo, and the former Yugoslavia forced people to flee their homes (Figure 8–3). The movement of people against their will is known as **involuntary migration**, and is often associated with persecution or the fear of persecution. Many of today's refugees have had to leave their homelands because they fear persecution owing to their political beliefs, race, or ethnicity.

Illegal Migration

On many occasions over the last decades, migrants from China have tried to enter Canada illegally, some hidden in the hulls of decaying cargo ships. Many thousands of Mexicans have avoided border patrols and illegally entered the southern United States. Workers from Bangladesh have crossed the border into India in order to find jobs and improve their standard of living. The movement of people without the sanction of immigration laws is known as **illegal migration**. It is a relatively new phenomenon, and arises from people's desire for improved economic opportunities and from the desire of a country to limit access (illegal immigration exists only if there are laws to prevent migration).

Figure 8–3 *A Rwandan family flees with their belongings in the face of civil war and tribal violence.*

International Migration

The United Nations estimated that in the year 2000, more than 100 million people were living outside their country of birth or citizenship. This number includes not only permanent immigrants, but also temporary migrants, who often provide an indispensable labour force in their host countries. The largest international migration takes place between developing countries, where most of the world's population is concentrated.

International migration is, for the most part, voluntary. However, the rising number of victims of forced international migration has compelled most developed countries to tighten their policies regarding refugees seeking political asylum. Governments have to be particularly aware of the trends in international migration because they know that migrants have dramatic effects upon the cultural, economic, and political conditions within their countries. As well, since the attack on the World Trade Center in New York on September 11, 2001, receiving countries are more aware of security threats from terrorists who pose as law-abiding refugees or migrants.

Consequences for Sending Countries

Migration has a profound effect on both the countries that migrants leave and the countries that they adopt. When people leave a country, the pressure caused by stiff competition for few employment opportunities can be alleviated. For example, in Eastern Europe and Egypt, there are often more highly educated graduates than the domestic market can absorb. When these highly trained people leave the country, it is easier for those remaining to find employment. Emigration also relieves pressure on housing that is often scarce, especially in urban areas. When frustrations caused by lack of employment or housing are relieved, the opportunities for political unrest are lessened. Furthermore, both well-trained and unskilled workers who have migrated send valuable hard currency home to their relatives, and this is a boost to the local economy. The World Bank has estimated that global remittances from international migration reached over US$71 billion in 1990. Sometimes migrants return to their native country and bring back new skills and knowledge that can benefit the economy of their homeland.

Very often, however, sending countries lose their most educated and their most enterprising business people to emigration. These citizens leave in search of better opportunities for themselves and their children. The special demands for skilled technicians and workers who cannot find employment in Canada is one reason for the so-called "brain drain" to the United States. This trend is especially hard on developing countries because these are the very people the country needs to build its educational, judicial, commercial, political, and medical infrastructures. Furthermore, when these people migrate, they take their financial assets with them. The sending country thereby loses an important source of money for investment within the country.

Consequences for Receiving Countries

Countries receiving migrants benefit in many ways. Immigrants often bring with them skills that are in great demand in their new country. For example, Canada welcomes tool-and-die makers, stonemasons, art restorers, chefs, and diamond cutters, among many others. Immigrants provide much-needed labour, both skilled and unskilled. They were an important source of labour for European countries that rebuilt their economies after World War II. Immigrants act as a ready market for goods produced in their new country. They are needed not only as a work force, but also as taxpayers to support the increasing old-age populations of developed countries. In some countries, the mix of many immigrant cultures helps to break down extreme nationalistic feelings, and contributes to a unique ambiance within the country as a whole.

Countries that welcome newcomers find that their immigration policies often cause fear among citizens who object to the loss of jobs caused by increased competition from immigrants. In some cases, this loss may be real. Immigrants, however, do not generally take the jobs of citizens. They take the jobs that others do not want to perform, namely the "3D" jobs—dirty, dangerous, and difficult. Unfortunately, the perception that immigrants cause job losses sometimes leads to unfounded animosity towards newcomers. Sometimes even violence occurs against migrant groups if the economy of the receiving country is

experiencing serious recession, inflation, or unemployment (Figure 8–4). Immigrants are often used as scapegoats when complex economic or social problems develop. Citizens may also object to the costs of integrating immigrants into their society. These costs are borne by taxpayers, and provide for health care, temporary shelter, language instruction, and other social services. Although newly arrived immigrants may initially require considerable support as workers, in time they contribute more in tax dollars than they ever took in the form of benefits in the first place. They also create jobs.

Figure 8–4   *Rioters in the town of El Ejido, southeastern Spain, burned a barricade during several days of anti-immigrant violence sparked by the alleged stabbing of a Spanish citizen by an immigrant, February 2000.*

Refugees in Crisis

"The camp in which we are staying has tents row upon row. The continuous rain has turned the ground into a muddy field, making it difficult to walk. There is a shortage of wood, so we are often cold, and it is not always possible to have hot meals even if we can get food. The international aid agencies send food but there is never enough, and we have to fight for our share.

"Our lives were not always like this. Before the war came to my country, I went to school, played with friends, and looked forward to the future. But all that seems so far in the past. Soldiers took my father, grandfather, and older brother one night and we haven't seen them since. My mother was raped when enemy soldiers came through town. As soon as the soldiers left, we fled our home and left all our possessions behind. We travelled at night to avoid the patrols until we came to this refugee camp. The old and the sick suffer the most here because there is not enough medical care.

"Do I have a future? I am so tired and sad that I almost don't care anymore...."

—A fictitious account based on various reports

Each year, thousands of people in the world face a prospect similar to what is shown in Figure 8–5. In 2000, the United Nations High Commissioner for Refugees (UNHCR) estimated that there were approximately 12 million refugees (Figure 8–6). When people leave their home country to save their lives, they are called **refugees**. Refugee movements are caused by many factors, among them threats of violence from civil war or terrorism; authoritarian government controls; religious, racial, or ethnic persecution; environmental scarcities; and declining socioeconomic conditions. Refugee camps are often established near the border in nearby countries as the refugees wait for an end to the events that forced them to leave.

Figure 8–5 *In 2001, drought, starvation, and the threat of retaliation for the terrorist attacks in the United States forced thousands of Afghans to flee to refugee camps like this one in neighbouring Pakistan. They joined over two million others who had fled a civil war that had lasted more than a decade.*

Global Refugees in 2000

Region	Number of Refugees
Africa (except North Africa)	3 421 399
Americas	666 602
Asia and the Pacific (includes India, China, Japan, Indonesia, Australia)	982 397
Europe	2 715 167
CASWANAME* (includes North Africa, Middle East, Southwest Asia, Central Asia)	4 362 452
Total	12 148 017

*The UNHCR'S regional designation for Central Asia, Southwest Asia, North Africa, and the Middle East

Figure 8–6 *Where the refugees were in the world, 2000.* Source: Table 1, "Indicative Number of Refugees and Others of Concern to UNHCR for the year 2000," Population Data Unit, PGDS/UNHCR Geneva, April 11, 2001.

If people are forced to move from their homes but not outside the borders of their country, they are more properly known as **internally displaced persons (IDPs)** rather than refugees. There are more internally displaced people in the world than refugees. These people are usually more at risk of persecution than refugees who have fled the country because they are still under the jurisdiction of the government that may have forced them to leave their homes.

Asylum seekers enter a country claiming to be refugees, even though they may come from a country that is not experiencing war or a natural disaster. Frequently, asylum seekers must undergo legal investigation by the host country to determine whether they fled out of fear for their safety, or out of a desire to improve their economic position. If they fled for the latter reason, the host country usually rejects their request for asylum since they do not meet the requirements for refugee status.

Much of the assistance to refugees comes from various United Nations organizations. In 1950, the UN General Assembly established UNHCR to begin operations in 1951. The role of this branch of the United Nations is to help people legally defined as refugees by providing them with international protection and by helping them to resettle in new countries or repatriate to their original homes. This role has expanded today to include people classed as "others of concern" such as asylum seekers, IDPs, and refugees who have returned home but still need help in rebuilding their lives. In 1990, there were about 15 million people "of concern" to the UNHCR. By 2000, that number had increased to just over 22 million, or one out of every 269 people on Earth.

Did you KNOW?

In 1951, the UN Convention Relating to the Status of Refugees was written to be the primary instrument of international law concerning refugees. This Convention and its 1967 Protocol guide the UNHCR and set the legal standards for refugee protection around the world. As of 1999, 134 countries had signed the Convention, the Protocol, or both.

The UNHCR tries to assist refugees by providing three "durable solutions" to their problems. The preferred solution is **voluntary repatriation**. If conditions in the home country improve to the point that refugees no longer believe their lives or liberty are in danger, they may safely return home. The second solution is **local integration** of refugees into countries of first asylum. A country of first asylum usually borders on the refugees' home country, and is the first country to which refugees flee. The government in the country of first asylum allows the refugees to integrate into the local communities in which they are staying. The UNHCR tries to link refugees with kinship groups or other populations with whom they have linguistic or other cultural ties. The third solution is **third-country resettlement**. When repatriation to the refugees' home country is not possible and the first-asylum country refuses local integration, the final option is to find a third country willing to accept the refugees (Figure 8–7). Such was the case in the 1970s after the war in Vietnam when many refugees from Vietnam, Laos, and Cambodia were settled in the United States and Canada.

Most of the world's refugees do not find durable solutions to their problems. The majority have been granted temporary asylum in neighbouring countries but have not been able to integrate into those societies. Instead, millions live in refugee camps with squalid conditions, poor job prospects, limited mobility, and poor educational opportunities. Sometimes refugees are subjected to attacks by citizens of the host country who object to their presence. Not infrequently, refugees are forcibly returned to their home country because the country of asylum is

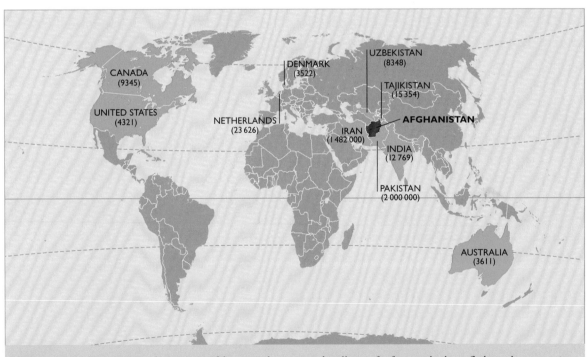

Figure 8–7 *Since 1979, the wars in Afghanistan have created millions of refugees who have fled to other countries. The 10 countries receiving the most Afghan refugees as of 2000 are shown on the map.*
Source: Table 4, "Indicative Refugee Population and Major Changes by Origin and Country of Asylum, 2000." *Provisional Statistics on Refugees and Others of Concern to UNHCR for the Year 2000,* Population Data Unit, PGDS/UNHCR, Geneva, April 11, 2001.

unable to cope with large numbers of people who come uninvited. In countries with economic stability and adequate resources, however, the influx of refugees can be a positive occurrence.

The environmental problems that already exist in many of the host countries, such as deforestation, water contamination, and soil erosion, are usually exacerbated by large influxes of refugees. Preserving or repairing the environment in host countries has become an important part of the UNHCR's agenda. A wide variety of approaches is being used: satellite imagery and remote sensing to assist in planning; alternative fuels, such as solar cookers, kerosene, and peat; reforestation; implementation of proper sanitation facilities; and the use of less damaging agricultural practices.

In addition to the United Nations, a large number of NGOs provide assistance to refugees and immigrants around the world. Some of these include Amnesty International, Canadian Centre for Victims of Torture, International Organization for Migration, National Network on Immigrant and Refugee Rights (USA), European Network on the Integration of Refugees, Refugee Council of Australia, and Les Sans-papiers (France).

Did you KNOW?

In 1954, the UNHCR created the Nansen Refugee Award, named after Fridtjof Nansen, who received the Nobel Peace Prize in 1922 for his work as League of Nations High Commissioner for Refugees. This annual award includes a prize of US$100 000 to enable the recipient to pursue refugee assistance projects in consultation with the UNHCR. In 1986, the people of Canada were the recipients.

Illegal Immigration

Most countries are willing to offer asylum to refugees whose survival has truly been threatened by war, terrorism, or ethnic or political persecution. It is often difficult, however, for governments to distinguish genuine refugees from "economic" refugees, that is, those people who have immigrated solely for the purpose of improving their standard of living. People who leave countries in turmoil are not always refugees in strict legal terms, and since the international migration of people searching for jobs has steadily increased over the last 50 years, immigration officials are often suspicious of the true motives of those claiming refugee status.

International law recognizes the right of every nation to determine how many non-citizens it will allow to enter, stay, and work within its boundaries. Countries have immigration laws (and usually large governmental departments to administer them) in order to determine those who are legal immigrants and those who are not. Immigrants may be illegal for several reasons, including the following:

- They may have entered illegally by avoiding border patrols or by using false documents at border crossings.
- They may have entered legally, but work without a proper permit.
- They may have entered legally, but remain in the country after their visa has expired or their application for asylum has been rejected.

Countries find it difficult to determine the number of illegal immigrants within their borders because these immigrants are not registered in tax or employment records, and of course they avoid contact with government agencies for fear of detection. Some countries do not even attempt to provide realistic figures because they see themselves only as "stepping stones" for migrants on their way to other countries. For example, many Latin American countries are only stops-along-the-way for illegal immigrants heading for the United States. Some countries deliberately record figures that are too high in order to obtain international financial assistance; others record figures that are too low to give the impression to would-be illegal immigrants that the country is not an easy one to enter.

Why is illegal immigration a problem? Illegal immigrants are viewed as having "jumped the queue," that is, they entered the country without waiting their turn. If illegal immigrants are tolerated, they are viewed as having been rewarded for not following the immigration laws of the host country. Since they are unable to work legally, they may pursue criminal activities in the underground economy. Employers often exploit them, hiring them for low wages in sweatshop conditions because they can't complain to the authorities. Since they are willing to work for less, employers hire more of them, thereby excluding legal workers from jobs. Because illegal immigrants are not part of "the system," they may not pay taxes, but most likely take advantage of public services such as education, medical treatment, or welfare. This places an extra tax burden on citizens and legal immigrants.

Smuggling People Is Big Business

Most human smuggling is conducted by transnational organized crime groups operating in China, India, Pakistan, Thailand, Sri Lanka, Nigeria, Brazil, Russia, the United States, Mexico, Canada, Australia, and countries in Western Europe. It is estimated that more than 400 000 people are smuggled into the European Union alone each year. These crime syndicates offer "package deals" that include counterfeit documents, airline tickets, spaces in cargo containers, contacts, and the use of safe houses at various points en route. The fee per individual varies from $5000 to $50 000, depending on the package and the destination country. Fees for entrance into the United States are among the highest, and many of the routes to the USA are through Canada and Mexico.

For these large sums of money, illegal migrants put themselves in the hands of criminals who direct them across borders, sometimes under the most appalling conditions. You may be familiar with news reports of dead or dying illegal immigrants hidden inside shipping containers on the back of trucks or on the decks of cargo ships heading into port. In 2000, 58 migrants from the Chinese province of Fujian were found suffocated in a container truck that arrived in the United Kingdom.

How Countries Deal with Illegal Immigration

Countries use a variety of methods to limit illegal immigration. First and foremost are enforcement measures along borders and at specific border points (Figure 8–8). Although they are expensive to maintain, and sometimes not particularly effective, they do cut down on other types of smuggled goods besides human cargo.

Did you KNOW?
In the underground economy, neither the employer nor the employee tells the tax department about the transaction . Underground activities include illegal immigrants who work, people who barter goods or services, and illegal activities such as drug trafficking, theft, and fraud.

Figure 8–8 *Traffic backs up on a busy day at the Canada–US border crossing in Point Edward, Ontario.*

They also send out the message that a country's borders are under control and outsiders must enter by legitimate means. Border controls and patrols, however, cannot control those who enter legally but then go underground when their visas expire.

Governments usually have policies to deal with illegal immigrants who are already in the country. A work permit system operates under the premise that a newcomer must show a valid permit to be employed. In reality, many migrants work in the underground economy. This is when "employer sanctions" are useful: if employers hire illegal immigrants, they may be prosecuted. It is hoped that the penalty incurred by the employer will far outweigh the economic advantage of hiring illegal immigrants.

Some countries adopt a policy of **amnesty** towards illegal immigrants as a means of bringing to light the number of "hidden" people within their borders. Illegal immigrants are encouraged to declare themselves, without fear of prosecution, in order that they may be counted among

the country's legal citizens. The government usually sets conditions for amnesty, such as no criminal record or at least five years of residence within the country. Once illegal immigrants become legal citizens, they are less likely to be exploited in the workplace, and their standard of living and state of health will improve. But why would a government declare an amnesty for illegal immigrants? Once they become citizens, they and their employers are then obliged to pay income tax, and make contributions to pension plans and health and unemployment insurance.

Not all illegal immigrants choose to accept amnesty. Some are reluctant to register with the government for fear of being deported, especially if they have come from a country where there is good reason not to trust the government. Others who are engaged in criminal activities refuse to declare themselves because they do not want to be identified by the police. Whatever the reason, however, illegal immigrants have only one chance to come forward, as governments usually adopt amnesty as a one-time-only policy. If adopted every few years, amnesty would tend to increase illegal immigration. Why? Because people would enter a country illegally, knowing that if they wait until the next amnesty is offered, they could become citizens much more easily than if they wait their turn to enter legally.

When the Canadian government first offered a general amnesty to illegal immigrants in 1973, almost 18 000 people came forward and were granted citizenship. Ten years later, when estimates of illegal immigrants living underground reached over 50 000, the government again offered amnesty to those who had no criminal record and had resided in the country for more than five years. Over 4000 people applied and were granted landed immigrant status. In 2001, when it was estimated that approximately 200 000 illegal immigrants were living in Canada, government critics and immigration lawyers again called for amnesty. Elinor Caplan, then Minister of Immigration, responded by stating that illegal immigrants were queue jumpers who undermined the integrity of Canada's generous immigration system. She declared that the government did not want to reward people who were working illegally, not paying taxes, and possibly engaging in criminal activity. It would not be fair to the hundreds of thousands of would-be immigrants who patiently followed the rules when trying to enter Canada.

Illegal Immigration into Canada

A report written for the Canadian Immigration Department in 2000 stated that China would be the source of the most problematic migration to Canada in the foreseeable future. The government estimated that between 1990 and 2000 alone, approximately 15 000 Chinese citizens entered Canada illegally. Most came from Fujian, an impoverished province located north of Hong Kong on China's southeast coast, with a history of economic migration. When 600 Fujians arrived in four rusty cargo ships in 1999 seeking refugee status, the government sent almost half of them back to China. Of the 200 who were released pending refugee hearings, 150 disappeared in spite of facing deportation if caught. A 1999 survey indicated that Canadians were split on the issue of deportation, with 49 per cent for and another 49 per cent against. A survey of the Chinese-Canadian community at the time indicated that over 90 per cent favoured immediate deportation of these "queue jumpers." As far as China is concerned, illegal immigration is not the issue: it is a "brain drain" to countries such as Canada whose strict visa policies and liberal refugee laws are viewed as the cause of illegal immigration.

The smuggling of illegal migrants is a big business, and it is growing. The Fujian smugglers, known as "snakeheads," charge large sums of money for passage and documents, and then charge interest until the amount is paid off. This financial burden forces illegals to work long hours under very poor conditions—usually in restaurants or garment factories, on farms, or sometimes in brothels as prostitutes. The snakeheads often threaten the migrants or their loved ones in China if the money is not forthcoming.

Many of the illegal migrants come to Canada so that they can eventually make their way into the United States. The United States has complained to Canada about the flow of illegal immigrants, and now has stringent rules about proper identification and proof of citizenship from people crossing from one country to the other. One of the suspects arrested in September 2001 after the terrorist attack on New York was under a Canadian deportation order. Since that day, more stringent checks of people crossing the border have been instituted in an effort to prevent possible terrorists and illegal immigrants from entering the United States from Canada.

Illegal Immigration into the United States

The United States faces a serious problem of illegal migration along its 3141-km border with Mexico. Most of the estimated six million to 12 million illegal aliens in the USA are thought to be Mexicans. The United States has tried to stem the tide of economic migration by building a high fence along the whole land portion of its southern border, by equipping its 11 000 border patrol officers with high-tech equipment such as night-vision goggles and ground sensors, and by using aircraft, four-wheel drive vehicles, and dogs. Although the border patrols are good at catching illegals, there is no punishment when they are caught. They are usually sent back to Mexico, from where they will try to cross again on a different night and at a different location. Some migrants pay the smugglers, or "coyotes," anywhere from $500 to $1000 to lead them at night through the weaker points of the border. If they can avoid detection as well as the perils of the desert, they hide out in safe houses until they are transported to jobs throughout the country. Some Mexican villages are almost empty of men of working age because so many have left to find jobs in the United States.

The governments of Mexico and the United States have been trying to resolve this problem for many years. One solution may be the granting of amnesty for up to four million illegal Mexican immigrants and the creation of a new category of migrant called guest workers. This category was used during the 1960s, 1970s, and 1980s in Germany. A migrant was allowed to work in Germany, but neither the worker nor any children born in the country were granted citizenship.

Rural–Urban Migration

The migration of population from rural to urban areas began in Britain during the mid-18th century. It was a gradual but direct result of industrialization and the mechanization of agriculture. Farmers migrated from rural areas to find work in factories that had been built near sources of power such as waterfalls and coal deposits. Rural depopulation continued with the advent of new agricultural machinery that eliminated much of the need for manual labour on the farms. Cities and towns grew up as workers in the manufacturing industries began to congregate near their workplaces. The newly urbanized areas continued to attract people who provided services for the growing concentrations of workers living near the factories. This pattern of rural-to-urban migration became more pronounced worldwide as industrialization became a global phenomenon. (See Chapter 9 for more information about urbanization.)

Today, the process of urbanization in the world's developing countries occurs at what seems like lightning speed compared to the urbanization that took place in developed countries. What took 200 years during the 18th and 19th centuries has taken just over half a century in many of today's developing countries. The United Nations has estimated that 40 per cent of urban population growth in developing countries is a result of rural–urban migration. In fact, there are more people in the world participating in rural–urban migration than in international migration.

As is the case with international migration, there are push and pull factors at work as rural

Factors in Rural–Urban Migration

Push

Subsistence farms do not provide enough food or income to support grown children, who migrate to the city looking for work. Men must often leave their families for months at a time to earn money in the city.

Sometimes countries have policies that favour urban over rural areas. For example, a government may protect goods manufactured in city factories by imposing import taxes on foreign goods. But at the same time it may keep the price of agricultural products low so that city dwellers have cheap food, in an attempt to maintain social stability in the cities.

Rural areas of most developing countries offer a poor living. The UN estimates that 60% of the developing world's poorest people live in areas affected by desertification, waterlogging, salinization of soil, and overgrazing and overcultivation.

Government policies may create problems. In the 1980s, Brazil encouraged farmers to resettle in cleared areas of the tropical rain forest. After a few harvests, the soil was so depleted that the settlers had to abandon the land and move to the city.

Pull

Urban areas offer more employment opportunities in a wider range of economic activities.

Educational opportunities are more readily available in cities.

Medical care is more readily available in urban areas.

Urban areas offer a wider range of opportunities and lifestyles, a factor that is particularly attractive to young people.

Figure 8–9 *Push and pull factors associated with rural–urban migration*

populations in developing countries migrate to cities (Figure 8–9).

The effects of rural–urban migration in developing countries are many and far-reaching. For example, it is the better-educated people in rural communities who tend to migrate to cities, where they are in a better position to learn about opportunities and also to recover the costs of moving. If they have friends or family in the city, they are more likely to be offered financial aid until they are settled. Poorer people in rural areas usually do not migrate. They do not have the money to move, and their social contacts in the city, if any, are less likely to be able to support them until they find jobs and places to live.

The trend towards rural–urban migration in developing countries has often led, surprisingly, to the revitalization of rural villages. Rural families frequently receive financial help from family members who have moved to the city to work. The influx of money sent home by migrants provides a new source of income in rural areas, and so improves the economic standards of rural citizens.

Over the past 50 years, the number of women participating in rural–urban migration in developing countries has been increasing. In countries such as the Philippines and Thailand, more women than men are moving to urban areas. The growth of labour-intensive industrialization and the development of service industries in cities are providing many job opportunities that did not exist in the past for women, giving them an increased level of independence. Women also gain when men migrate to the city. The women who are left behind benefit both from the men's remittances and also from increased independence in running the household.

The downside of the migration of women to cities is that many of the jobs are temporary and poorly paid, and provide little security. Because the women are not organized, they may have to work in unsafe or unhealthy conditions. Some women may be exploited sexually or forced into prostitution. Despite these negative aspects, migration provides improvement and empowerment for many women in developing countries.

Rural–urban migrants exhibit great energy, skill, and talent as they carve out new lives in urban areas of developing countries. Most migrants are absorbed into the economic and social fabric of cities, and are not necessarily thrust into poverty when they arrive. Furthermore, rural poverty is not usually transferred to the cities with migrants. Rural–urban migration leads to the circulation of people, goods, ideas, and money, and contributes to the health of developing countries.

Replacement Migration

It is projected that over the next 50 years, the population of most developed countries will diminish, while the median age of each population will increase. You learned in Chapter 7 that these conditions result from low fertility rates and the increased longevity of citizens. Even if fertility rates increase, there will not be enough people to replace the aging population and the consequent loss of working-age people—that is, unless developed countries adopt a policy of **replacement migration**. In 2000, the United Nations' Population Division released a report describing replacement migration as the international migration needed to offset the overall aging of a population, the decline in the population of working-age people, and the decline in the size of population in general.

Developed countries with declining populations will have to decide in the near future whether replacement immigration is a viable option, and if so, how much immigration they should allow. Consider the examples of Germany and the United States. Figure 8–10 gives the United Nations' predictions for the amount of replacement immigration for each country in order to maintain the size of its total population, and the size of its working-age population, at year 2000 levels in the year 2050.

If governments decide that replacement immigration is not an option, they will have to change their policies regarding the appropriate age for retirement, the level of health care for the elderly, and the amount of tax imposed on workers. Otherwise, there will not be enough people to fill the jobs that are necessary for the proper functioning of some countries' economies, or money to help maintain the aging population.

Replacement Migration Levels

	To maintain total population at year 2000 levels	Total migrants by 2050	To maintain working-age population at year 2000 levels	Total migrants by 2050
Germany	344 000 annually	17 million	487 000 annually	24 million
United States	128 000 annually	6.4 million	359 000 annually	18 million

Figure 8–10 *UN estimates of replacement migration levels for Germany and the United States*
Source: United Nations.

Chapter Questions

Knowledge and Understanding

1. Describe, with specific examples, the four categories of migration.

2. Explain, using specific examples, the push and pull factors associated with migration.

3. What are "3D" jobs, and why do some immigrants take them?

4. Differentiate, using specific examples, among the terms refugee, internally displaced person, and asylum seeker.

5. a) What are the three "durable solutions" used by the UNHCR?
   b) Demonstrate the role played by the UNHCR in a current refugee situation.

Thinking and Inquiry

6. Individuals who migrate tend to fall into specific categories. These include:
   a) Age: most migrants are adolescents or young adults.
   b) Skills: people with higher-level rather than lower-level skills tend to migrate.
   c) Marital status: most immigrants are single adults rather than married individuals.
   d) Gender: more males than females tend to migrate between countries.
   Explain the reasons for the behaviour of people in each category.

7. "The most significant consequence of immigration is the alteration of the cultural, ethnic, racial, and political make-up of the receiving country." Discuss, using specific examples to support or refute this statement.

8. In 1986, Canada was awarded the Nansen Refugee Award by the UNHCR. Investigate why Canada received this award.

9. Research the activities of an NGO involved in refugee assistance. You may use one that is mentioned in this chapter or one of interest to you. Consider such things as the location of their offices, the guiding principles of the organization, the countries in which they operate, the types of activities in which they are involved, their source of funding, where the workers/ volunteers come from, etc. You may wish to start with the Canadian Council for Refugees (see <www.pearsoned.ca/globalconnections> for more information.

10. Research the media to find one or more recent incidences of illegal migration into Canada, the United States, Australia, or Western Europe. Examine such aspects as where the migrants were coming from, why they left, why they selected their country of destination, conditions en route, and what happened to them when they arrived at their destination.

11. Do you think it feasible for either Germany or the United States to allow the levels of immigration shown in Figure 8–10 over the next 50 years? Explain.

Communication

12. Create two maps to show the sending and receiving countries of refugees. This may be done by hand, or by using the GIS application ArcView. Your teacher will suggest which approach to use and provide you with the appropriate data.

13. Construct a chart to show the pros and cons of immigration for receiving and sending countries.

14. a) Briefly outline Canada's current immigration policies.
    b) Do you think these policies are fair to prospective immigrants and Canadians? Explain your response.
    c) If given the opportunity, how would you change these policies?

Application

15. Should governments offer amnesty to illegal immigrants? Evaluate the pros and cons, and come to a conclusion on this question.

16. Should economic refugees be considered legitimate refugees and therefore allowed into Canada? Support your answer.

17. In spring 2001, *Time* magazine published a report in which it posed the following question:

"The Canadian border separates the United States from 31 million people; the Mexican border divides the USA from 97 million—or 440 million, if you count all the way to Chile. Which border is more important, and which has more impact?"

How would you answer this question? Explain your point of view.

9

Urban Issues

Expectations

In this chapter, you will:

- analyse the impact of urban growth on natural and human systems

- explain how selected natural and human systems interact

- predict global population changes and assess their implications

- use geographic terms correctly in written and oral communication

- analyse cause-and-effect relationships in geographic data

- use maps to analyse change over time

Our earliest cities arose from food surpluses. The first agricultural revolution and the introduction of farming relieved some people of the need to produce food. Humans could now settle in small villages and specialize in non-agricultural activities, such as building. This bronze statuette, which shows King Shulgi of Ur (now Iraq) carrying a basket of building materials on his head, dates from the third millennium BCE.

Cradles of Civilization

"Cradles of civilization" is a metaphor often used to describe those regions where humans first lived together in organized, non-migratory societies (Figure 9–1). Freed from the need to grow their own food, people could engage in a wide variety of activities, such as making pottery, leather goods, jewellery, textiles, and weapons. These goods were exchanged for food products, or traded for products from other villages. Trade was the catalyst for the spread of ideas and spiritual beliefs, and of knowledge about how to make products, grow and use different crops, write, and keep records. The outward spread of knowledge and influence from a cradle of civilization is known as **cultural diffusion**.

As villages, towns, and cities developed, the distance between them was determined by two factors: population density and transportation technology. When population density was low, towns grew up farther apart. This happened because the population was not big enough to support an array of services in many towns. As a result, towns were few and far between. When population density was high, towns were located closer together. With more people demanding services, more towns sprang up to supply the demand. As a result, they were located near one another.

When the main mode of travel was walking, towns tended to be built close together. Rural people seeking products and services were able to walk from their farms to the towns and back in one day. As a result, towns sprang up close to their rural customers and, consequently, close

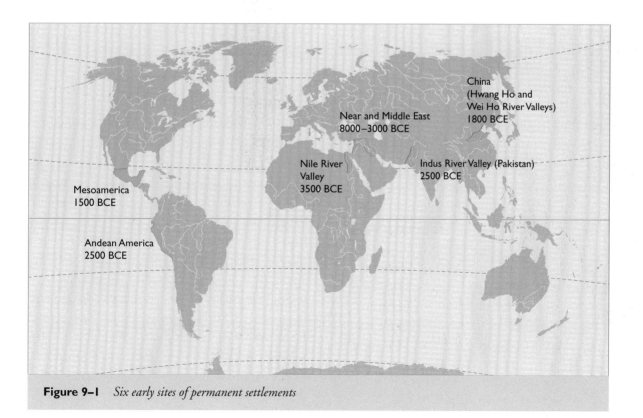

Figure 9–1 *Six early sites of permanent settlements*

together. As faster modes of travel developed, towns sprang up farther apart because people could travel farther in the same amount of time.

Later towns often developed in places where services—such as marketplaces, civil administration, churches, or gristmills for grinding grain—could be provided most economically. But this was practical only when there were enough people to buy or use the services. The minimum number of customers required for an urban service to succeed economically is known as the **threshold population**. A particular service could not be offered until its threshold population was in place.

Different services require different threshold populations. A low-order good or service is one that requires a small threshold population. For example, a gristmill needed only a small number of farmers to survive. For this reason, it was quite usual to see one built in every small town.

A high-order good or service requires a high threshold population. A university, for example, requires the fees of many students to remain economically viable. Because they must have a high threshold population from which to draw students, universities are located in only a few communities that serve very large areas.

People will travel only so far to take advantage of a service or to buy a product. If the product is particularly desirable, they will travel long distances to acquire it. This distance is referred to as the **range** of the product or service. Urban communities grew to become important centres, or remained static in their development, based on the size of the threshold population and product range. In other words, a hierarchy of urban communities developed based on the types of services they provided.

Towns soon developed to fulfill military, political, religious, or trading functions for both urban and rural citizens. With the advent of industrialization, some towns and cities, while still providing the services mentioned above, grew up for entirely different reasons. They grew up to provide housing, services, and transportation for people mining and processing raw materials, and to assemble and distribute manufactured products that were mass produced. Because of these functions, they were known as industrial cities. Industrial cities developed in essentially two different ways. Some developed close to sources of raw materials or energy. These cities grew as workers moved to live close to their workplace. Other cities developed from already existing towns because the skilled labour force and market were already present.

Functions of Cities

A city may grow up and thrive for just one reason, or any number of reasons. Consider the following cities. Singapore came into being, and continues to function, as a port city because of the presence of a large, well-protected harbour on a major sea route. Sudbury, Ontario, developed into a mining city because of the presence of a mineral resource (nickel). Because Moscow plays a special role as the centre of Russia's government, this role has attracted other functions and made the city into an important urban centre. Cities may have one or many functions that lead to their establishment and continue their growth. The functions and activities on which a city depends for its existence are known as the community's **economic base**.

Did you KNOW?

In the 1930s, the German geographer Walter Christaller defined settlements that provide goods and services as Central Places. His Central Place theory related the size and spacing of towns and cities to peoples' shopping behaviour. He defined a hierarchy of settlements of different sizes. These settlements were ranked from smaller to larger, according to the number and variety of goods and services they offered.

Cities provide services and produce goods for people. If these goods and services bring money into the city from the surrounding area or "hinterland," they are classified as **basic activities**. These basic activities serve as the economic base for the city. For example, a bank's head office in Toronto provides services for customers across Canada and in other parts of the world. People in the hinterland purchase the head office's services; money comes in to Toronto and supports the city. On the other hand, if the goods and services are produced for, and purchased solely by, the residents of the city, they are classified as **non-basic activities**. Let's take the example of a local branch of a bank in Toronto that provides services for bank customers in the city only. The money paid for services rendered at the local bank comes from within the city; the services rendered do not bring in money from the hinterland.

Cities are usually distinguished by their basic activities. That is, they are noted for activities that *bring money into the community* rather than for the activities that *generate money within the community*. This is because the proportion of money generated by workers engaged in non-basic activities is similar from city to city. Some cities that are particularly well known for their basic activities are Los Angeles, California (a centre of show business); Frankfurt, Germany (a financial centre); and Ottawa (a centre of government).

Some cities become so large and powerful within their countries that they are known as **primate cities**. A primate city contains a disproportionate share of the country's wealth, population, and political power in relation to the second- and third-largest cities in the country. London, UK; Paris, France; and Addis Ababa, Ethiopia, are examples of primate cities.

Global Patterns of Urbanization

Two hundred years ago, less than 5 per cent of the world's 980 million people lived in urban communities. As the Industrial Revolution began its spread across the world during the 1800s, people began to leave farms and villages to settle in cities in order take advantage of greater opportunities in urban labour markets and higher wages offered by new types of jobs. By 1900, almost 14 per cent of the world's population lived in urban areas. The United Nations predicts that at current rates of urbanization, urban dwellers will be equal to the number of rural dwellers in the world in the year 2007.

There is a problem in defining the term *urban*. Different countries use different numbers to describe their urban areas. Canada and Australia count settlements of 1000 people or more as urban; Italy uses a minimum of 10 000 people; and Japan uses a minimum of 50 000 people. The UN, recognizing that each country knows best how to distinguish between its urban and rural places, accepts each country's individual definition. This means we must be cautious when interpreting urban statistics.

Rural Versus Urban

What percentage of the world's population today is rural and what percentage is urban? What are the trends for the future? Complete the following activity to discover the answer to these two questions.

1. Examine the data for 2000 and estimates for the year 2030 in Figure 9–2.

   a) Describe the anticipated change in the number of people living in urban places in developed countries.

   b) Describe the anticipated change in the number of people living in urban places in developing countries.

   c) Compare the results of your answers in parts (a) and (b).

2. Examine the data for 2000 and estimates for the year 2030 in Figure 9–2.

   a) Describe the anticipated change in the number of people living in rural places in developed countries.

   b) Describe the anticipated change in the number of people living in rural places in developing countries.

   c) Compare the results of your answers in parts (a) and (b).

3. Compare the anticipated population changes in developing countries between 2000 and 2030 for both urban and rural populations.

4. For the year 2000, examine the urban populations for developed and developing countries in Figure 9–2. Then look at the percentages in Figure 9–3 for these countries' urban inhabitants. What do you notice about the actual size of the populations compared to the percentage of urban dwellers for both types of countries?

5. Examine Figure 9–3 for the year 2000 and estimates for 2030. Is the percentage change greater for developed or developing countries? Explain why.

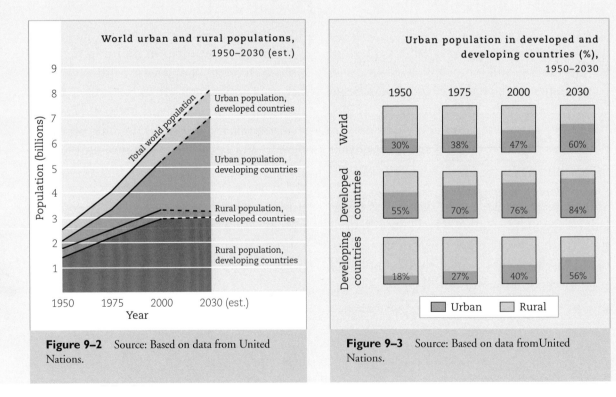

Figure 9–2   Source: Based on data from United Nations.

Figure 9–3   Source: Based on data from United Nations.

As you might expect after completing the previous activity, different countries around the world are urbanizing at different paces. Examine Figure 9–4. In the 50 years between 1950 and 2000, the percentage of the population of North America living in urban areas rose by 13 per cent. Latin America and the Caribbean, on the other hand, experienced a rise of 34 per cent. Now look at Africa and Asia in the year 2000, and calculate the projected percentage increases in urbanization for the year 2030. Compared to the anticipated changes for the same time period in other major areas, would you say that these are rapid rates of urbanization?

As more and more people in the world move to cities, two questions arise. First, what size of city have people been moving to, and second, what size of city will they be moving to in the future? You might be surprised at the answer, especially if your first reaction is to say, "The bigger the city, the more people will settle there!" Take a look at Figure 9–5. What do you see for the cities in 2000 compared to 1975? What are the projected changes for the year 2015?

Growth of Urban Populations (%)

	1950	1975	2000	2030 (est.)
North America	64	74	77	84
Latin America and the Caribbean	41	61	75	83
Europe	52	67	75	83
Oceania	62	72	70	72
Africa	15	25	38	55
Asia	17	25	37	53

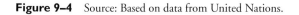

Figure 9–4 Source: Based on data from United Nations.

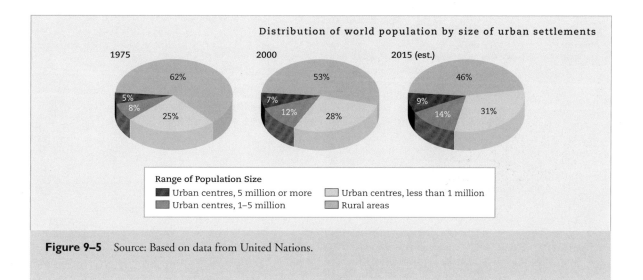

Figure 9–5 Source: Based on data from United Nations.

You may be under the impression that developed countries, because they have well-developed economies, efficient transportation systems, high levels of education and health, and modern services and conveniences, must have great numbers of large cities. In fact, this is not the case. The number of cities of one million or more residents is currently greater for developing countries, as is the number projected for 2015. Figure 9–6 shows how the numbers of these large cities compare between developed and developing countries.

Included in the global number of cities over one million are a number of urban settlements known as megacities (such as Tokyo, Figure 9–7). In the 1970s, the United Nations used the term **megacity** to refer to any urban community with

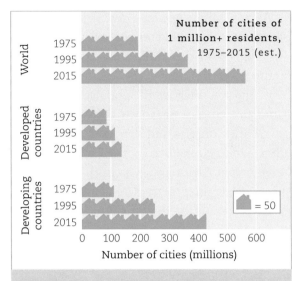

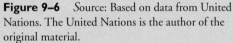

Figure 9–6 *Source:* Based on data from United Nations. The United Nations is the author of the original material.

Figure 9–7 *Tokyo, Japan. In 2000, the megacity of Tokyo had more than 26 million people. Canada's entire population at the time was about 31 million people. How would you like to live in such a megacity?*

Populations (in millions) of the World's Megacities (10 million+ inhabitants), 1950–2015 (est.)

	1950 City	Pop.		1975 City	Pop.		2000 City	Pop.		2015 City	Pop.
1	New York	12.3	1	Tokyo	19.8	1	Tokyo	26.4	1	Mumbai (Bombay)	28.2
			2	New York	15.9	2	Mexico City	18.1	2	Tokyo	26.4
			3	Shanghai	11.4	3	Mumbai (Bombay)	18.1	3	Lagos	23.2
			4	Mexico City	11.2	4	São Paulo	17.8	4	Dhaka	23.0
			5	São Paulo	10.0	5	New York	16.6	5	São Paulo	20.4
						6	Lagos	13.4	6	Karachi	19.8
						7	Los Angeles	13.1	7	Mexico City	19.2
						8	Calcutta	12.9	8	Delhi	17.8
						9	Shanghai	12.9	9	New York	17.4
						10	Buenos Aires	12.6	10	Jakarta	17.3
						11	Dhaka	12.3	11	Calcutta	17.3
						12	Karachi	11.8	12	Manila	14.8
						13	Delhi	11.7	13	Shanghai	14.6
						14	Jakarta	11.0	14	Los Angeles	14.1
						15	Osaka	11.0	15	Buenos Aires	14.1
						16	Manila	10.9	16	Cairo	13.8
						17	Beijing	10.8	17	Istanbul	12.5
						18	Rio de Janeiro	10.6	18	Beijing	12.3
						19	Cairo	10.6	19	Rio de Janeiro	11.9
									20	Osaka	11.0
									21	Tianjin	10.7
									22	Hyderabad	10.5
									23	Bangkok	10.1

Figure 9–8 Source: Based on data from United Nations. The United Nations is the author of the original material.

a population of eight million or more. By 1990, the definition had been changed to refer to urban communities with a minimum of 10 million inhabitants. Until the end of the 20th century, cities this large were unprecedented. Just over 100 years ago, London, England, was the only city in the world with a population greater than five million. Today there are 19 cities with more than 10 million, and this number is expected to rise (Figure 9–8). As you might expect, megacities have the same problems faced by smaller urban communities, but on a much larger scale.

Urban Changes Worldwide

The terms urban growth and urbanization, although they sound similar, actually describe two different ideas. **Urban growth** refers to a measure of the actual number of people added to a city's population. For example, between 1981 and 1996, Toronto's urban growth was 1 133 365 people; its population increased by this number through natural increase and immigration. **Urbanization**, on the other hand, refers to the proportion of a country's total population living in towns and cities. For instance, when we say that by 1991, 76.6 per cent of Canada's population was urban, we are measuring urbanization, not urban growth. Keeping this distinction in mind, let's examine some urban changes in both developed and developing countries.

Developed Countries

In most developed countries today, when people or businesses move, they usually move between (or within) urban communities rather than between rural and urban communities. Urban populations in developed countries are in a constant state of flux, and several trends are noteworthy (see Figure 9–9).

In the years following 1950, people who could afford to buy new houses, particularly in North America, moved away from central parts of cities into the suburbs. In the United States in 1950, for example, 70 per cent of the urban population lived in central areas of cities. By 1990, however, less than 40 per cent lived there. This **decentralization** occurred for a variety of social, political, and economic reasons, including widespread ownership of motor vehicles. Racial problems in inner-city areas in the United States propelled many people to the suburbs, plus the promise of newer housing and educational and recreational facilities. Industries also moved to the suburbs. Spacious industrial parks that had easy access to transportation routes, plus the cheaper cost of land, were attractive to old and new businesses alike. In fact, this **suburbanization** process was enabled in great part by the building of expressways that allowed people to live in the suburbs but still work in central city locations.

After 1990, however, suburbanization slowed down. In some cities, the trend was reversed, and people began moving back into central parts of the city. Problems that were once associated

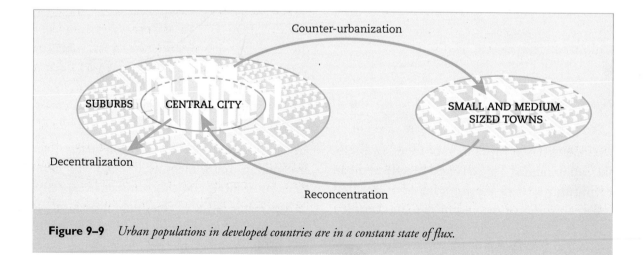

Figure 9–9 *Urban populations in developed countries are in a constant state of flux.*

with downtown areas, such as traffic congestion, overcrowded schools, and the rise of crime, began to develop in the suburbs. It wasn't long before people began to consider inner-city addresses desirable once more, especially as developers began to renovate former warehouses and office buildings into lofts, studio apartments, and luxury condominiums.

Another urban population change began to occur in the 1970s in Japan, the United States, Britain, and other developed countries. This trend saw people moving from suburban and central city locations to small and medium-sized towns and rural areas. **Counter-urbanization** was attractive because social problems such as crime and homelessness seemed to be fewer; land costs, taxes, and labour costs for business were lower; and the lifestyle in smaller communities seemed less hectic. One trend follows another, and there are indications in several developed countries that counter-urbanization is being followed by **reconcentration**. At the beginning of the 21st century, it appears that people and businesses are moving back into the cities and their surrounding suburbs. This comes as a result of recent investment by large cities such as New York, London, and Tokyo in rebuilding their **infrastructure** and in revitalizing parts of their downtown areas. The globalization of the national economies of developed countries has led many cities to revitalize these areas in order to offer a wide variety of business services to national and international customers.

Developing Countries

Urban change occurs differently in developing countries than in developed countries. In developing countries, urban population growth takes place before widespread economic and infrastructure development. Rural migrants flock to cities because they are desperate for employment and a better standard of living, but the

industries that supply jobs do not exist. A disproportionate number of these migrants are teenagers and young adults, who are responsible for high rates of natural increase. When a city's population grows faster than the number of jobs or housing units available to sustain it, the result is **over-urbanization**. Too many people, large-scale unemployment, and lack of housing lead to sprawling squatter settlements on the outskirts of cities. These urban settlements lack proper sanitation facilities, decent shelter, schools, and hospitals, as well as basic social services.

Urban change in developing countries is extremely diverse. It takes place for many different reasons, and trends are difficult to define. In Central and South America, domestic industries, in an effort to compete on an international scale, have moved to the outskirts of cities in search of cheaper labour and land on which to expand. This trend has caused massive urban growth or "sprawl," not to mention the loss of farmland. In sub-Saharan Africa, cities such as Kinshasa and Freetown have fallen into serious states of disrepair due to civil war, government mismanagement, and the stress of rapid population growth. In Central Africa, settlements of people seeking refuge from political conflict have grown up almost overnight. These settlements are sometimes referred to as refugee cities. In Asia, small urban centres, which have grown because of high birth rates and rural poverty, are frequently more rural than urban in character. They are called urban places because they perform some governmental administrative functions.

Urban Problems Worldwide

The United Nations Development Program surveyed mayors around the world about 14 categories of problems facing cities today.

1. Identify at least 10 major urban problems. Compare your list to the one used by the United Nations (Figure 9–10). Which problems did you not identify? Why might you have missed these?

2. The percentage of mayors who identified each problem as severe is shown in Figure 9–10. Now imagine that you are the mayor of your community and the UN has asked you to rank these 14 problems in order of their severity. Use 1 as the most severe and 14 as the least severe. Compare your list with those of your classmates.

3. a) Now imagine that you are the mayor of a large city in a developing country. Rank these 14 problems in order of their severity.

   b) How does your list differ from the list you made in question 2? Explain any differences.

UN's Top 14 Urban Problems

1.	Unemployment (52%)
2.	Insufficient solid waste disposal (42%)
3.	Urban poverty (42%)
4.	Inadequate housing stock (34%)
5.	Insufficient solid waste collection (31%)
6.	Inadequate water/sanitation facilities (28%)
7.	Inadequate public transportation (26%)
8.	Traffic congestion (22%)
9.	Poor health services (22%)
10.	Insufficient civil society participation (21%)
11.	Inadequate education services (19%)
12.	Air pollution (17%)
13.	Urban violence/crime/personal safety (14%)
14.	Discrimination (against women, ethnic groups, poor) (7%)

Figure 9–10 *The percentage of mayors who identified the problems as severe in their cities is shown in brackets (they were allowed more than one choice). Seventy per cent of the mayors who ranked unemployment as a severe problem also ranked poverty as severe.*

Urban Problems in Developed Countries

Urban problems in both developed and developing countries cannot be studied in isolation. Unemployment, poverty, problems associated with the elderly, loss of tax base, decaying neighbourhoods, decentralization, lack of affordable housing, air pollution, traffic, solid waste disposal, and all the other problems that beset urban areas are interconnected in an intricate web of cause and effect.

Economic Problems

One of the major problems facing cities in developed countries has been called the **fiscal squeeze**. This means that there is never enough tax money to pay for all the services that cities need to run efficiently. Why is this so?

The problem stems from the fact that, over the last half century, developed countries have moved from industrial to post-industrial economies in which most people work in businesses that provide services (see Chapter 11). As developed countries have moved from industrial to post-industrial economies, their cities have undergone tremendous change, or "urban restructuring." One aspect of urban restructuring is that traditional manufacturing industries—and their related activities, such as warehousing and transportation—have moved away from inner cities to the suburbs, often leaving decaying neighbourhoods behind. As residential and commercial taxpayers leave for the suburbs, the tax base in the central city decreases. So, not only is there less money to pay for services; there is also less money to maintain and repair older roads, out-of-date water and sewage lines, and crumbling public buildings. Add the costs involved in providing increasing levels of service to an aging population and to new immigrants, and cities really begin to feel the squeeze! A problem for many cities, such as those in Ontario, is that they are able to tax only the value of properties and not the incomes of residents. This limits their ability to raise money.

Since the mid-1970s, cities such as New York, Toronto, Frankfurt, Liverpool, and Rome have had serious economic problems. These cities experienced a decline in the quality of their infrastructure because they were unable to come up with the money to repair roads and bridges, sewers, power lines, and water treatment plants that were built 50 to 100 years ago. The solution? Raise taxes, or find other levels of government to pay for these services. No wonder municipal politicians are constantly put in a position where a great deal of compromise and negotiation must take place to try to solve their cities' economic problems. Starting in the 1990s, the US federal government came to the rescue of many of the country's largest cities by spending billions of dollars on infrastructure improvements.

Social Problems

Another serious urban problem in developed countries is poverty. A study of poverty in Canada in 2000 by the Canadian Council on Social Development found that 20 per cent of urban dwellers were living below the poverty line. According to a study done in the United States during the 1990s, people living in the inner city are more than twice as likely to be poor compared to people living in the suburbs. You have already learned that manufacturing and retailing jobs have moved to the suburbs along with great numbers of people since the 1950s. Low-income residents remained behind. With the loss of businesses and jobs associated with industry, and the lowering of the tax base, the core of some cities started to decay. Urban decay, lack of employment opportunities, poor housing, and overcrowded conditions usually lead to a cycle in which one generation after another remains locked in poverty (not the same as deprivation). Overcrowded living conditions and poor diet contribute to absenteeism at school and work, which in turn leads to limited educational achievement and lower incomes. An environment of high unemployment, low wages, lack of successful role models, and general despair creates a continual cycle of poverty.

Even when the economy is strong, some residents of inner cities still face problems. Redevelopment often occurs, pushing up rents faster than wages. The combination of low incomes and high rents causes many families to lose their homes. The number of homeless people has also increased since the mid-1980s because of cutbacks in welfare programs. The homeless are now much more visible in the cities of Canada, the United States, Japan, Australia, and Western Europe, and include men and women of all ages, as well as an increasing number of children (Figure 9–11). In fact, it is estimated that about one-quarter of Canada's homeless are children.

A major problem in many cities is the shortage of affordable housing. Budgeting experts say that people should not spend more than about 30 per cent of their income on housing costs. People working for low wages find that 30 per cent of their salary is not enough to cover housing costs. Their choice is either to spend more on housing (leaving them less for essentials like food), or to end up homeless. Lack of affordable housing has contributed to homelessness in many cities.

In most developed countries, the proportion of elderly people living in the city is greater than in rural areas. The United Nations has projected that the proportion of people 65 years and older in developed countries will increase from about 14 per cent to about 20 per cent in 2025. This means the number of elderly in cities will rise tremendously. This aging population will require many adjustments to cities' housing and services, among them improved walking routes, better public transit, more affordable housing, and residences providing assisted living, not to mention increased health and social services.

Figure 9–11 *A homeless person bundles up on a heating vent as he tries to keep warm in frigid temperatures in Toronto.*

It was stated in the beginning of this section that urban problems are interrelated. Can you now see how the fiscal squeeze (economic problem) might be connected to the problems of the elderly (social problem)?

Environmental Problems

The concentration of so many people in cities leads to numerous environmental problems. In some cases, these problems present a real risk to life. Since many cities in North America have not developed effective rapid transit systems, people take their cars to work. When the number of vehicles running on a highway exceeds its capacity, gridlock and excessively long travel times are the result. The large amounts of pollutants produced by traffic congestion are a threat to young and old alike, especially to those with respiratory difficulties. The "heat island effect" created by large cities in the summer only exacerbates the problem: large expanses of buildings and paved streets heat up, increasing the temperature while decreasing the humidity. As the

Did you KNOW?

To help alleviate the problem of affordable housing in Canada, the Toronto Disaster Relief Committee has proposed a "1 per cent solution." All levels of government would spend 1 per cent more of their existing total budgets on housing than they now do. In 2001, the three levels of government spent about 1 per cent of their current budgets on housing and support services for people who needed housing, so an increase of 1 per cent would double the amount they spent.

You can find out more about the 1 per cent solution at <www.pearsoned.ca/globalconnections>.

heated air rises, it carries the pollutants upward to form a smoggy haze over the city.

The mayors who were surveyed about the most serious problems facing their cities placed the disposal of solid wastes in the number two spot. Our throwaway society produces huge amounts of garbage, and most cities today are facing a garbage disposal crisis. Some cities incinerate their garbage, but this produces greenhouse gases. Some recycle bottles, cans, paper, and plastic, but these programs are usually not extensive enough. A combination of landfill, incineration, and recycling is probably the best that most cities can achieve for the present. Most cities have landfill sites in rural locations nearby, but rural residents don't like having someone else's garbage "in their backyard." Toronto has filled all its nearby landfill sites; since none will be built in the foreseeable future, it has tried to find new ones in other regions (see Chapter 15).

Urban Problems in Developing Countries

As in developed countries, the economic, social, and environtmental problems of developing countries are interrelated.

Economic Problems

You learned in the previous section that urbanization in developing countries usually takes place before there is enough economic development to support it. The economies of developing cities lack jobs that offer decent wages. Rural migrants who come to the cities looking for a better life often find themselves working in the informal sector of the economy (Figure 9–12). This sector encompasses a wide range of activities—shining shoes, selling souvenirs, working in roadside repair shops, writing letters for others. It also includes prostitution, begging, and even scavenging on garbage dumps (an important way of recycling, in some urban centres of the developing world). It is estimated that more than a billion people worldwide make their living from such occupations. Unfortunately, the poor wages and unreliable nature of these jobs lead to chronic poverty for the people who undertake them.

Figure 9–12 *The informal sector of the economy in the cities of developing countries includes a wide variety of activities, such as selling goods at this open-air stall in Jaipur, India.*

Many children work in the informal economy. Very often, industries in the formal sector sub-contract work to families who carry out the work in their homes. Here, the children routinely work with other family members because everyone is expected to contribute to the family's income.

Developing countries are often noted for the huge gap that exists between the rich and the poor. There is usually a very small wealthy population, a large poor population, and a small middle class. A few very wealthy people live in exclusive enclaves in the most desirable areas of cities, but not very far away are the overwhelming number of poor people living in squatter settlements or slums.

In cities with low levels of economic development, it is difficult to build a tax base adequate to offer services to city dwellers, especially those living in poverty. An inadequate tax base cannot finance the building of schools, hospitals, transportation systems, and roads, or fund social services for the poor. Furthermore, it is difficult—if not impossible—to tax so many people working in the informal sector of the economy.

Social Problems

As in developed countries, the social problems of cities in developing countries are associated with too many people living in poverty—in squatter settlements located on the outskirts, and in slums in more central parts of cities. **Squatter settlements** are built illegally on land for which the inhabitants pay no rent to the owner; slum dwellers, on the other hand, pay rent for their housing. Living conditions are similar in both types of settlements. Squatter housing is built on the cheapest land in the city (Figure 9–13)—steep slopes, swamps, bare rock, or in the case of Cairo, in cemeteries. It consists of the most rudimentary type of shelter: hovels made of corrugated tin, cardboard, discarded plastic sheeting, wooden boards, and in some cases, even mud. Squatter settlements have been known to spring up on vacant lots or in vacant buildings overnight, or sometimes during a national holiday before the landowner can react. So swiftly are they erected that no infrastructure of services can be put in place—no sewers, running water, electricity, or streets.

Efforts to eradicate slums and squatter settlements have resulted in even more misery for poor urban dwellers. In the past, cities like Manila, Caracas, and Bangkok forcibly removed hundreds of thousands of people from their slum and shantytown dwellings and destroyed their homes. Since the displaced residents had nowhere to go except to new squatter settlements elsewhere in the city, it became evident to governments that this practice was pointless—people still need places in which to live, even if conditions are wretched. Furthermore, these communities act as reception areas for newly arrived migrants, who can usually find some support from experienced residents. Low-income squatter communities that provide affordable shelter, community support, and informal jobs are called "slums of hope." In time, some of these settlements have services such as electricity and communal water supplies that residents have helped install by providing the labour. In some of Brazil's *favelas*, residents have been trained as builders to repair damaged buildings and to construct makeshift electrical and water systems.

A World Bank project, "Cities Without Slums," helps to upgrade living conditions in

Did you KNOW?

In Chile, squatter settlements are known as "mushroom cities"; in Turkey, "communities built after dark and before dawn"; in Brazil, *favelas*; in Colombia, *barrios*; in Indonesia and Malaysia, *kampungs*; and in India, *bustees*.

Figure 9–13   *Many of the urban poor in Hong Kong, where land is scarce, live on rickety houseboats in the harbour.*

slums by providing education and health care for residents and by supporting local small-scale businesses. The aim is to improve the lives of 100 million people throughout the developing world by 2020.

Many social problems are rooted in such extreme poverty. Even with attempts to provide medical care and sanitation, incidences of the diseases of poverty—such as malnutrition—are increasing. Poor urban dwellers are also exposed to road accidents or deviant social behaviour associated with living in overcrowded, degraded living conditions. There are no community organizations to help residents, no access to birth control, and no government welfare services. The rates of illness and infant death are high. Often referred to as "slums of despair," these areas of urban poverty offer few opportunities of escape.

Environmental Problems

When natural disasters are reported on television, it often seems as if the poorest people in the world are the victims. There is some truth to this observation. Not only do the poorest people live in badly constructed dwellings offering little shelter, but they also live in the most undesirable sites in the city. These sites are susceptible to environmental damage, and when natural disasters or industrial accidents occur, the poor are more affected than wealthier people. Rickety hovels perched on steep hillsides collapse under mudslides during heavy rains; cardboard houses blow away in hurricanes; squatter settlements are flattened during earthquakes; homes in low-lying areas are carried away in floods; and thousands of people are poisoned in flimsy shelters next to industrial sites. Underlying all environmental

Figure 9–14 *Largely unplanned growth to accommodate its 20 million residents and the absence of environmental controls on factories have made Mexico City one of the world's worst cities for air pollution.*

problems that plague urban areas in developing countries is the fact that governments simply do not have the money to solve the problems of so many urban poor.

Air pollution in cities in developing countries is often worse than in developed countries. Rapid population growth results in tens of thousands of poorly maintained trucks, cars, and buses pumping pollution into the air. Added to that are the unregulated emissions from charcoal cooking fires, coal-fired electrical power stations, petrochemical industries, and the effects of the heat island (Figure 9–14). The combination of lead, carbon dioxide, carbon monoxide, nitro-

gen oxides, and other toxic chemicals in the air causes severe respiratory disease and takes a toll on human health and productivity.

The United Nations determined in 2000 that access to clean water by urban populations in Africa, Asia, and Latin America and the Caribbean declined by 1.2 per cent between 1990 and 2000 (Figure 9–15). Further, about

Did you KNOW?

Time magazine stated in the 1980s that if fecal matter glowed, Mexico City would not need street lamps.

Changes in Water Supply and Sanitation (Africa, Asia, Latin America, and the Caribbean, 1990–2000)

	Water Supply				Sanitation		
	1990	2000			1990	2000	
	Percentage	Percentage	Change		Percentage	Percentage	Change
Urban	92.4	91.2	−1.2		70.8	80.0	+9.2
Rural	60.7	68.9	+8.2		26.1	32.5	+6.4

Figure 9–15 Source: Adapted from UN Economic and Social Council, Commission on Sustainable Development, 8th session 24 April to 5 May 2000, Report of the Secretary-General, *Progress made in providing safe water supply and sanitation during the 1990s* (E/CN.17/2000/13).

91 per cent of the urban populations of these countries has access to drinkable water. The remaining 9 per cent represents millions of people who are still using contaminated water. People living in affluent areas have clean water piped into their homes, but poor people must fetch their water, and many governments consider a water tap within 100 m of one's dwelling as adequate (Figure 9–16). Often, the tap runs for only a few hours a day, forcing residents to stand in line for long hours to get a small quantity of treated water. The lack of potable water (water that is drinkable) in cities in developing countries is a leading cause of disease and infant mortality.

The infrastructure supplying clean treated water is usually connected with the infrastructure dealing with the disposal of human waste. Although the increase in the availability of sanitation looks encouraging, much of the sewage in poor urban districts still runs into drainage ditches beside the roads, and then flows untreated into rivers and streams that people use for drinking water. Even if there are sewers to collect human waste, water from sinks and bathtubs, and chemical waste from factories, many of these pipes are not connected to sewage treatment facilities.

Figure 9–16 *A group of women and children pump water from a well on Marina Beach, Bangalore, India.*

The Urban Future

What does the future hold for urban areas in developed and developing countries? Although it is difficult to predict the future, we have a pretty good idea about what policies are needed to improve the lot of urban residents.

In developed countries, facilities and services will have to be provided for growing numbers of elderly people. Adequately paying jobs and affordable housing must be created to allow people to live and work in central city areas, thereby curtailing decentralization and urban sprawl. The improvement of mass transit systems, stricter emission standards for motor vehicles, and programs for the reduction of industrial pollutants must be put in place to combat environmental pollution. All these policies depend upon governments' ability to supply the money from a sufficiently large tax base. Politicians will have to come up with innovative ways to develop city economies that will allow the building of larger tax bases.

In developing countries, steps will have to be taken to curtail rapid urban growth. Policies that restrict rural–urban migration may not be successful because most urban growth is a result of natural increase. Rural development schemes will have to encourage people to stay in their rural homes. Birth control education will have to be disseminated more widely to urban and rural residents alike to reduce the number of potential rural migrants, as well as children born into urban poverty. Many development agencies see education and empowerment of women as a major tool in achieving this aim (Figure 9–17). But the question remains: will developing countries adopt policies that create urban jobs, alleviate urban poverty, develop urban infrastructure, and make city governments more responsive to local needs?

Figure 9–17 *A woman and her daughter tend the family store in San Francisco de la Cruz, a squatter settlement outside Lima, Peru.*

Chapter Questions

Knowledge and Understanding

1. Define the terms:
   a) economic base
   b) basic activities
   c) non-basic activities

2. Why are the largest and fastest-growing cities located in the developing world?

3. Differentiate between the terms urban growth and urbanization.

4. Describe the urban changes that are taking place in
   a) cities in developed countries
   b) cities in developing countries

5. a) Summarize the economic, social, and environmental problems facing cities in developed countries.
   b) Summarize the same types of problems for cities in developing countries.

6. a) Describe the living conditions in squatter settlements.
   b) Reference was made in this chapter to "slums of hope" and "slums of despair." Differentiate between these two types of neighbourhoods.

Thinking and Inquiry

7. Examine Figure 9–8.
   a) On a world map, locate and label the megacities that existed in 2000. Use a different colour or symbol to locate and label the four additional megacities of 2015.
   b) What is the number of megacities in developed countries for each of the four years?
   c) What is the number of megacities in developing countries for each of the four years?
   d) What differences do you see? Explain why this trend is occurring.

8. It was mentioned in this chapter that the US federal government is spending money to improve the infrastructures of cities. Find out what the Canadian federal government is doing. Do you think these initiatives will be successful? Explain.

9. Investigate a major economic, social, or environmental problem in your community or one nearby.
   a) What are the causes of the problem?
   b) What is being done to solve the problem? Do you predict that these actions will be successful? Explain.

10. Compare a population distribution map of the world with a map of the location of major urban centres. What relationship do you see?

11. A UN study found that 13 of the 15 cities with the worst air pollution in the world are in Asia. How would you explain this?

12. In some developing countries, the movement from rural to urban environments is mainly male; in others, it is mainly female. What are the social implications of such movements?

13. On page 36 of Chapter 3 it was stated that after the Industrial Revolution, as people moved from rural areas into urban ones they lost their direct contact with the land, and their knowledge of and respect for nature diminished. Do you think this is the case today? Support your point of view.

Communication

14. a) The number of homeless people is increasing in Canadian cities. What are the causes of homelessness in Canada?
    b) What can or should be done to deal with this problem?

c) Write letters to a municipal, provincial, and federal politician suggesting things that should be done to reduce this problem. The contents of your letters should reflect knowledge of the jurisdictions of each level of government.

15. Construct a flow chart to show how the 14 factors in Figure 9–10 are interrelated. If you were a mayor of one of these cities and were given a large sum of money to help alleviate these problems, which ones would you deal with first to make the best use of the money? Explain your choices.

16. A number of organizations assist poor urban dwellers in developing countries. One such organization, Sleeping Children Around the World, raises money in Canada and has bed kits made up in developing countries for homeless children. Examine the work of this or another organization, and create a visual and oral report for presentation to the class.

Application

17. a) Conduct an Internet search for urban problems in developed and developing countries.
b) Make a list of the problems for cities in both developed and developing countries.
c) For each type of country, categorize the problems according to the 14 listed in Figure 9–10.
d) Which problems received the most coverage for each type of country?
e) Does the coverage of these problems match your rankings in the activity on page 134 of this chapter? Explain.
f) Select one problem and research the solutions that are offered.

18. a) Read Rohinton Mistry's novel, *A Fine Balance*, which has a pivotal scene describing the eradication of a slum. Write a response to what happened to the slum's residents.
b) Why did the government take this action?
c) Describe the nature of the community that developed in spite of poverty.

Unit 3: Economic Issues

10

Food and Agricultural Issues

Key Terms

famine
starvation
malnutrition
undernutrition
Green Revolution
high-yield variety (HYV)
loss of genetic diversity
biotechnology
genetically modified
   organism (GMO)
organic farming
corporate farming
aquaculture
land reform

Expectations

In this chapter, you will:

■ consider the interde-
pendence of ecology
and economics

■ analyse how agricul-
tural trends affect natu-
ral and human systems

■ explain how new
technology affects
employment and
resource management

■ evaluate the sustain-
ability of trends in the
consumption of Earth's
resources

■ evaluate the role of
NGOs and community
initiatives in managing
resources wisely

■ effectively use infor-
mation from a variety
of primary and second-
ary sources

In 1984, people watching televisions in the developed
world saw horrifying images of the famine in Ethiopia. This was not the
world's first famine, nor the worst that had ever occurred. But it was the
first time that famine had been brought "live" into the living rooms of
Europe and North America, giving hunger issues a new place in the
consciousness of Western nations.

The World Responds

Bob Geldof, a minor Irish pop star, wondered what he could do to help the suffering people of Ethiopia. His first action was to organize the production of a record called *Do They Know It Is Christmas*, which featured the singing of many of his friends in the British pop industry. He hoped to raise £72 000 with this recording, but was astonished to find that it quickly became the largest-selling record in British history. Similar recordings were made by Canadian and US artists, with similar success.

While Geldof was pleased with this response, people were still dying in Ethiopia. His next idea was to organize Live Aid, the world's first global rock concert/telethon. Concerts were held in stadiums on the same day in London and Philadelphia, and involved virtually every major rock performer and band in the Western world (including groups that had broken up years before). The concerts were shown worldwide, and viewers were encouraged to phone and give money for famine relief. When all the money was counted, Live Aid had raised more than $150 million.

The Nature of Hunger—A Vocabulary

While Live Aid did shine the spotlight on hunger, it also contributed to a serious misunderstanding in the minds of most people. Hunger problems in the world came to be seen as synonymous with famine. In fact, fewer than 10 per cent of hunger deaths are caused by famine. To better understand the problems of hunger, you should become familiar with its vocabulary.

Famine can be defined as a temporary failure of food production or distribution systems in a particular region that leads to increased mortality due to starvation and diseases that result from lack of food. Famines can result from either natural causes (for example, a drought or serious plant disease that causes crop failure) or human causes (for example, a civil war).

Starvation is an extreme form of hunger in which people suffer from a total lack of energy and essential minerals. The body wastes away as tissue is consumed to provide protein and energy.

To a doctor, **malnutrition** is a condition in which damage to health is caused by a diet that includes either too much or too little of one or more essential nutrients over an extended period. By this definition, obesity and high blood pressure could be considered diseases of malnutrition since they are sometimes caused by excesses in diet. Generally, though, when we consider international development issues, we are typically focussing on diets that lack nutrients. This form of malnutrition is called **undernutrition**. There are more than 50 different forms of malnutrition. Some of the more important diseases of undernutrition in developing countries are summarized in Figure 10–1.

You can learn about current famines at
<www.pearsoned.ca/globalconnections>.

Name of Disease	Caused by Deficiency Of	Characteristics of Disease
Kwashiorkor	Protein	Loss of muscle mass Damaged immune system Edema (swelling), particularly of belly
Scurvy	Vitamin C	Anaemia, weakness Gum disease Bleeding skin sores
Pellagra	Niacin and tryptophan (an amino acid)	Scaly skin sores Diarrhoea Mental illnesses
Anaemia	Iron	Lack of energy Weakened immune system
Keratomalacia	Vitamin A	Blindness
Beriberi	Vitamin B_1	Damage to heart and nervous system
Marasmus	Calories, protein	Disease of starvation

Figure 10–1 *These are just a few of the many diseases of undernutrition.*

Chronic persistent hunger is responsible for more than 90 per cent of hunger-related deaths. It does not get very much attention in the media because it does not make for "good television" in the way that a famine does. Chronic persistent hunger kills indirectly, by the many diseases of undernutrition and by weakening people who are then killed by diseases like diarrhoea and measles, which would be no more than inconveniences to stronger, better-fed people. In 1996, about 840 million people lived in this condition, with about 35 000 people dying each day. A substantial majority of these were children.

Historical Agricultural Development

How do we produce our food? Compare the photographs in Figure 10–2. There are some clear differences but, fundamentally, they all show the same thing—food production in the world today.

As you learned in Chapter 4, the development of agriculture is probably the single most important advance in human history. Without the ever-increasing production of food that has occurred in the 10 000 years or more since the first agricultural activities were carried out, our huge population growth and cultural development could not have occurred. Over the millennia, two developments have contributed to our growing food supply.

The first development was the expansion of agriculture into more areas of the world. For example, the opening of the grasslands of North America for farming between 1840 and 1915 greatly increased the world's food production capacity. The world's last major agricultural expansion was the Virgin Lands scheme in the Soviet Union between 1953 and 1964. It brought 3.6 million hectares under the plough for the first time. We have now reached the point where there are no significant areas to plant for the first time.

The second development was the more effective use of the land we already farm. Throughout history, a series of technological breakthroughs has increased food productivity dramatically.

The first agricultural revolution happened independently 8000 to 10 000 years ago in several parts of the world, including the Near East, China, and South America. Subsequent technological and social changes have had profound impacts. The dates that follow indicate when these innovations were first used, generally in

Figure 10–2   *Traditional and modern forms of agriculture and animal husbandry. Clockwise from top-left: ploughing a rice paddy in Lao Cai, Vietnam; working a rice field in Hokkaido, Japan; raising free-range pigs in Surrey, England; factory farming pigs in Dauphin, Manitoba.*

Europe. The expansion of their use to other parts of the world sometimes took centuries and, in some cases, still has not happened. For example, modern ploughs are still not in use in many parts of Africa and Asia.

- *3000–4000 BCE* The scratch plough was developed to replace hoes and foot ploughs for planting. The scratch plough was essentially a sharpened stick with handles to give direction and a frame to allow attachment to an animal. It enabled a farmer to use the power of domestic animals rather than having to rely only on human muscle power. While the scratch plough was a significant improvement on the technology that had existed before, it could only be used in light, dry soils with few roots, conditions that existed in relatively arid areas like the Near East.

- *500–900 CE* A more powerful plough was developed that included a knife blade that could cut roots and a board that pushed the cut soil to the side, creating an open furrow. This plough allowed previously forested land—with wetter, heavier soils—to be farmed. The power of this plough was further increased by the development of the horse collar that allowed a horse to pull harder without choking itself. As well, harnesses were invented that allowed more than one animal to be attached to a single plough. The horse-shoe was also invented around this time, and gave the horse better traction. The time period when these innovations occurred is often called the second agricultural revolution.

- *1600–1870 CE* In this period, significant improvements were made in just about every aspect of agriculture. Improved machinery was developed, including more robust ploughs and steam-powered tractors and threshers. Crops from one part of the world came to be widely grown in another. For example, corn and potatoes were brought from North America to Europe, and wheat from Europe to North America. Larger farms were created, and farms started to specialize more. Farmers started selective breeding of animals like cows and pigs to produce more meat. Artificial fertilizers and specialized forms of animal feed came into use. Each of these innovations significantly increased agricultural productivity. These new forms of agriculture were introduced to many parts of the world in this period. Among the most important of these regions were the US Midwest and the Great Plains of North America. There is some confusion among experts about what to call this time period. For some, it is the third agricultural revolution, while for others it is the second, since they do not recognize the previous period as a "revolution."

- *1945–1970* This period was marked by the Green Revolution, which will be discussed in detail later in this chapter.

- *1990–present* Two innovations mark the most recent period. One is the growing influence of biotechnology. This has been called, by some, the second Green Revolution. The second innovation is a growing corporatization and globalization of farming. Both will be discussed later in this chapter.

> ## Did you KNOW?
>
> The *acre*, a unit of land measurement, came to be used at the time of the second agricultural revolution. It was originally defined as the amount of land that one horse could plough in a day using the new inventions of this time.

The Nature of Agriculture

In Canada, we are used to having a reliable and relatively inexpensive supply of food. In fact, we have come to take this bounty for granted. Our complacency is not surprising: since fewer than 4 per cent of Canadian workers are farmers, very few of us have direct experience of farming. If we start with the premise that most of us do not know very much about agriculture, then it would be a good idea to start at the beginning.

Agricultural Resources and Limitations

Agriculture depends on the interactions among a number of natural systems (see Figure 10–3).

Climate

The first natural system, climate, contributes two variables to the equation of how successful farming will be in a particular area. One variable is the amount of solar energy (or heat) that is available. This factor explains why bananas can be grown in the Caribbean, but not in North Bay. The amount of heat is described by measures like the length of the growing season or the number of agricultural degree-days (this is calculated by summing the number of degrees each day's average temperature is over 5.5°C).

The second climatic variable is the amount of moisture available. Most often this is measured in terms of precipitation levels. It is more accurate to consider the relationship between the amount of precipitation and the demand for moisture as measured by the amount of evapotranspiration (the movement of water from the soil to the atmosphere by evaporation from the soil and transpiration from plants). The potential for evapotranspiration increases with higher temperatures, which means that in cooler locations, a smaller amount of precipitation will allow for more plant growth.

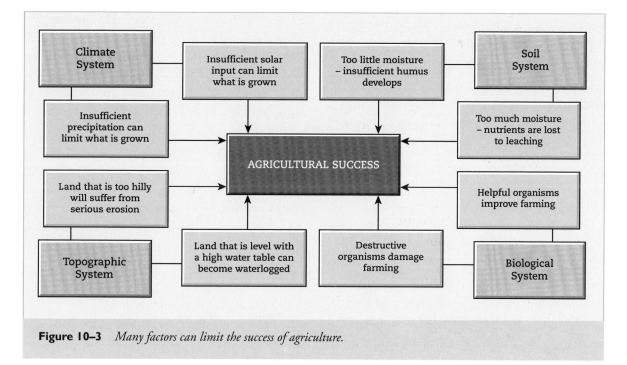

Figure 10–3 *Many factors can limit the success of agriculture.*

Soil

The second natural system that is fundamental to agriculture is the soil system. Soil is a complex substance that includes minerals, living organic materials like earthworms and bacteria, and decaying materials like rotting plants, water, and air. While all these must be present in a soil, the amount of decayed organic material is the most critical factor in determining its fertility. The richness of this material, called humus, is closely tied to the amount of plant growth that occurs and to the availability of moisture. If there is a shortage of moisture, the amount of plant growth, and hence humus, will be less than it might otherwise be. The soil that develops in these conditions will be relatively infertile. If there is an excess of moisture, fertility will be reduced because vital soluble nutrients will be leached out of the soil.

Topography

The third system that has an impact on agriculture is the topographic system. In general, level land is best for farming. If an area is too hilly, there is the potential for the loss of vital topsoil through erosion. On the other hand, land that is very flat, especially if it has fine soil materials and a high water table, could be too wet for farming.

Biology

The fourth important system is biological. Some organisms are highly beneficial for farming. Earthworms, for example, improve the movement of air through the soil, while bees are vital for effective plant pollination. Other insects are highly destructive. For example, the Old Testament describes a "plague of locusts" as one of the worst disasters possible. The growth of unwanted plants, generally called weeds, can also interfere with the productivity of agriculture. Animal diseases, like the foot-and-mouth epidemic that affected the United Kingdom in 2000 and 2001, can devastate an industry.

Correcting Deficiencies

Few places in the world have the perfect combination of conditions for farming: a long growing season, not too much and not too little moisture, rich soils, level land, and just the right mix of biological conditions. Unfortunately, most areas suffer from one or more deficiencies. For thousands of years, people have worked to overcome the shortcomings of the land that they farm. For example, if an area lacks sufficient moisture, and water from streams or lakes is available, farmland can be irrigated. Irrigation was used in Egypt and Iraq more than 4000 years ago and is still being expanded today to increase food production in arid areas (Figure 10–4). For each of the deficiencies mentioned above, adjustments have been made. These are summarized in Figure 10–5.

Types of Agriculture

Agricultural activities can be categorized in two ways. In the first, farming can be described as directed towards either subsistence or cash cropping. *Subsistence farmers* grow crops and raise livestock to meet the immediate food needs of their families. Typically, subsistence farmers produce many different agricultural products, often using quite small acreages. Any surplus production may be sold or traded to meet other needs of the family. This is the dominant form of agriculture in developing countries. In contrast, the produce of *cash-crop farmers* is sold on the open world and local markets. These farmers specialize in producing only a few products, even if they have very large farms. They may not use any of the products they grow or raise—it would not be unusual for a dairy farmer who produces hundreds of litres of milk every day to buy dairy products at the local supermarket.

The second way to describe agriculture is as either intensive or extensive. *Intensive agriculture* involves farming a relatively small amount

Figure 10–4 *Irrigation is typical of adjustments that people make to improve the productivity of agricultural areas.*

Agricultural Deficiency	Human Adjustment
Growing season too short or too cool	Grow a crop with a shorter growing season Develop varieties that mature more quickly Provide additional energy input (e.g., in greenhouse)
Insufficient moisture	Provide irrigation Use growing methods that preserve moisture (reduce evaporation) Develop crops that require less water
Infertile soils	Add natural fertilizers (e.g., manure, compost) Add chemical fertilizers Use appropriate plant rotations
Hilly terrain	Build terraces Use cropping practices that minimize erosion
Low-lying, wet terrain	Choose crops that tolerate or need abundant water (e.g., paddy rice) Tile (drain) soils
Shortage of beneficial insects	Introduce them (e.g., ladybugs and bees can be bought on the Internet)
Excess of harmful insects	Use chemical insecticides Introduce predator insects Use cropping methods that limit insects Grow genetically modified, insect-resistant crop varieties
Excess of weeds	Use chemical herbicides Manually remove weeds Grow genetically modified plant varieties that work with herbicides Use cropping methods that minimize weeds

Figure 10–5

of land in a concentrated fashion with the use of a great deal of labour and, often, other inputs. Typical forms of intensive farming in Canada would include fruit and vegetable growing, vineyards, livestock feedlots, where animals are penned in a small field area and fattened, and hog factory farms. *Extensive farming* uses large amounts of land with limited amounts of labour and other large inputs. Examples in Canada would include prairie grain and oilseed farming, ranching, and most forms of mixed farming. While we have talked about two distinct models of agriculture here, in reality, various forms of farming exist on a continuum between subsistence and cash cropping and between intensive and extensive farming (see Figure 10–6).

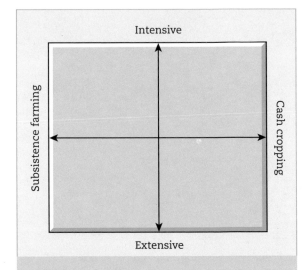

Figure 10–6 *Every type of agriculture in the world can be found somewhere on this plane.*

The Green Revolution

The United States has an interesting history of private philanthropy. For example, in the 1890s, a man named Andrew Carnegie was regarded as the Bill Gates of his time—the world's richest man. Carnegie owned many large steel mills at a time when steelmaking was the world's glamour industry. He was a fierce competitor and ruthlessly exploited his workers. At the same time, there was a remarkably charitable side to the man. He believed that it was a sin to die wealthy, and set out to give away his wealth. Most significant of his gifts was the establishment of almost 3000 public libraries all over the world, including 156 in Canada.

What does Carnegie's example of generosity have to do with agriculture and food production? Directly, nothing; but Carnegie was not the only formidable businessman who was also a great philanthropist. John D. Rockefeller, the founder of Standard Oil (now Exxon Corporation), also created a foundation to give away much of his wealth to benefit humanity.

Over the years, the Rockefeller Foundation has supported many valuable projects, but none is as remotely important as its role as the initiator of the Green Revolution.

The **Green Revolution** began in 1945 when the Foundation, at the request of the Mexican government, established an agricultural research station in Mexico to develop more productive varieties of wheat that could be used to feed the rapidly growing population of the country. The basic idea behind this initiative was that the selective breeding methods that had greatly improved agricultural productivity in the developed world could be used with equal success in developing countries.

Dr. Norman Borlaug, who would eventually win the 1970 Nobel Peace Prize for his efforts, was the head of the research station. Borlaug and his colleagues wanted to produce **high-yield varieties (HYVs)** of wheat that could be used to increase food production in Mexico and eventually throughout the developing world.

You can read more about the history of the Green Revolution at
<www.pearsoned.ca/globalconnections>.

Compared to the varieties that were then being grown in Mexico, the new varieties they developed had three things in common:

- They were smaller in size (see Figure 10–7). At first glance, it might not be obvious what advantage smaller plants would have. Dwarf plants focus more of their energy growing their seeds (the part of the plant that we ultimately eat) and less on growing their stems, which are useless to humans for food.
- They responded better to the use of farming inputs like fertilizer and irrigation.
- They grew faster. In suitable areas, a variety that grows faster allows the same land to be used for more than one crop per year.

The success of the wheat project in Mexico encouraged efforts to develop high-yield varieties of rice. This was done at the International Rice Research Institute (IRRI) in the Philippines. Ultimately 16 research institutes, each specializing in some crop or aspect of food production in the developing world, were operating under the umbrella of the Consultative Group on International Agriculture (CGIAR).

Successes of the Green Revolution

In the decades after World War II, experts were predicting massive famines as the world's population exploded. There was a very real possibility of a Malthusian catastrophe, with millions of deaths. The Green Revolution went a long way towards preventing such an event. Importantly, it also gave the countries of the developing world time to work their way through much of the demographic transition (see Chapter 5). This reduced the population pressures and food supply problems that these countries faced.

In just a few years, grain production doubled and, in some cases, even tripled. From 1967 to 1968, India produced 17 million tonnes of wheat, an amount more than 40 per cent higher than the previous record (Figure 10–8, on the next page). In fact, the growth in wheat production was so large and happened so rapidly that there was nowhere to store the excess—schools in some areas had to be temporarily closed to be used as granaries. Between 1966 and 1997, Asia's production of rice increased by 116 per cent. Worldwide, food production increased 20 per cent more quickly than did the population. On average, prices for wheat and rice declined by 70 per cent in real terms (after the impact of inflation has been eliminated). This meant that all but the poorest people had better diets than before.

Figure 10–7 *In northern India, dwarf wheat crops like this one increased grain supplies and helped saved millions of people from malnutrition.*

Figure 10–8 *The Green Revolution produced surpluses of wheat and rice in many developing countries, dramatically increasing the availability of food.*

Concerns About the Green Revolution

While no one disputes its role in boosting world food production and preventing famines and chronic hunger, concerns have been expressed about a number of aspects of the Green Revolution:

- The Green Revolution used a modern Western model for agriculture that involves the use of costly inputs like chemical fertilizers, pesticides, and irrigation. Many farmers, especially poor farmers on small plots, could not afford these inputs. This meant that while their wealthier neighbours benefited greatly from the Green Revolution, the poorest farmers were often harmed (Figure 10–9).

- The Green Revolution initially focussed on farming in the areas that were best suited to agriculture—those with the most fertile soils and reliable rainfall. This research was of little help to people who lived in arid and semi-arid regions. The residents of these areas were, and are, among those with the least reliable food supplies. It was not until many years later that research stations were created in India and Syria to improve farming in such countries.

	Before the Green Revolution		After the Green Revolution	
	Poor farmer	Wealthier farmer	Poor farmer	Wealthier farmer
Yield (units per hectare)	20	20	20	50
Price (per unit)	10	10	7	7
Income per hectare	200	200	140	350

Figure 10–9 *The Green Revolution actually harmed the poorest farmers, since they could not afford to take advantage of the new varieties of crops.*

- The Green Revolution led to a dramatic **loss of genetic diversity**. A few highly developed varieties of wheat, rice, and other grains came to replace the hundreds of native varieties that previously had been grown. This specialization has allowed weeds and animal pests to flourish. This problem arises because an insecticide will kill all insects except a few individuals who happen to be immune to the effects of the chemical. The descendants of these resistant individuals will flourish in the absence of their natural competitors and predators. The response to these infestations has been the increased application of powerful pesticides and herbicides that have only made the situation worse.

- The Green Revolution produced a system of agriculture that is not as environmentally sustainable as traditional agriculture. While traditional mixed cropping had been carried out successfully for centuries, yields from HYV crops have declined significantly in only a few decades. Rice yields that peaked in India at about 11 tonnes per hectare in the late 1960s had dropped to the range of four to five tonnes per hectare by 2000. These decreasing yields occurred because HYVs have caused a decline in soil fertility that cannot be entirely made up by the addition of chemical fertilizers, and because of growing losses due to animal and plant pests.

- Some observers have even questioned the motives behind the creation of the Green Revolution. They suggest that self-interest drove the developed countries to fund it. There are several reasons for this belief. One is that the governments of the developed countries feared the possibility of communist revolutions, like that in China, driven by food shortages. They were also concerned about the possible repudiation of the debts owed to the wealthier countries by the developing world (see Chapter 14). The other reason is that the creation of Western-style agriculture opened huge new markets for the makers of fertilizers, pesticides, farm equipment, and other products, almost all of which came from companies in developed countries.

Did you KNOW? A pre-Columbian irrigation system in Peru was recently restored for use after lying dormant for more than 600 years.

Food Production Issues for the Future

By one important measure, the Green Revolution peaked in the mid-1980s. This was when increases in the per capita world production of grain ended (Figure 10–10). Since then, this vital measure has slowly but steadily declined. This is just one of the concerns about the world's food supply that must be addressed in the years to come. The more important concerns will be considered in the remainder of this chapter.

Biotechnology and Farming

Some diets, especially those that are dominated by rice, tend to be deficient in two important nutrients: iron and vitamin A. Nearly two billion people in the world suffer, to varying degrees, from iron deficiency, while almost two million children each year are at risk of going blind because of vitamin A deficiency. A richer, more varied diet (or vitamin pills) would eliminate such deficiencies, but these are not viable options for millions of poor people. Recent remarkable breakthroughs in **biotechnology**—the application of biological processes to agricultural and industrial purposes—may go a long way towards eliminating these problems.

The Promise of Biotechnology in Food Production

Swiss scientists spent more than 10 years and $150 million to produce new varieties of rice that would provide people who rely on this grain with sufficient vitamin A and iron to prevent deficiencies of these nutrients. Vitamin A–rich "golden rice" was produced by modifying the genetic material of rice with two genes from a type of daffodil and one from a bacterium. The resulting variety of rice is high in beta carotene, a nutrient that the body can convert to vitamin A and so prevent blindness. A similar approach was used to produce an iron-rich variety of rice.

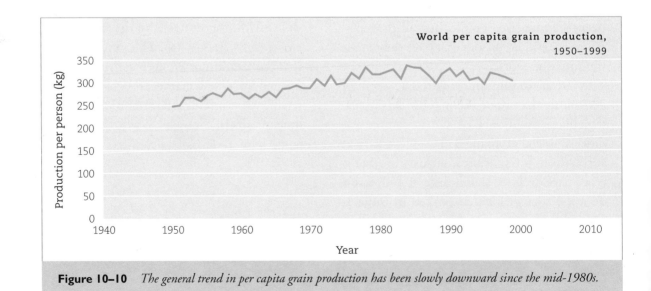

Figure 10–10 *The general trend in per capita grain production has been slowly downward since the mid-1980s.*

While the scientists' objective might have been similar to that of the Green Revolution, the methods they used were completely different. Green Revolution scientists used crossbreeding between two varieties of plants, hoping to pass the genes for desirable qualities from each parent to the offspring. Biotechnologists, on the other hand, attempt to move a desirable gene from one organism to another. They can move genes (and the characteristics they carry) between entirely different plant species and even between animals and plants.

The new species that are created as a result of this research are called **genetically modified organisms (GMOs)** or transgenic organisms. Their potential has prompted some observers to suggest that we may be entering a second, biotechnology-driven Green Revolution.

More nutritious golden rice is just one example of the benefits that can be produced by genetic modification. Crops of GMOs are already widely grown, particularly in the United States and Canada. These crops—varieties of soybeans, corn, cotton, and canola in particular—were created to have tolerance to certain herbicides, to be resistant to insects, or both. In 1999, there were almost 45 million hectares of transgenic crops in the world (Figure 10–11). This is an area about as large as Newfoundland and Nova Scotia combined.

You might wonder why growing herbicide-resistant crops is so popular. The reason is simple. Fighting weeds is one of the most difficult challenges that a farmer faces. Many herbicides can only be used with certain crops or at certain points in the growing cycle, or may be effective only against certain types of weeds. This means that multiple, costly applications of different herbicides might be necessary during the growing season. These applications cause an increased risk of environmental and health damage because of the use of so many chemicals. Agricultural chemical companies had developed broad-spectrum herbicides that could kill just about every plant, but these were of little use to farmers once the crop had started to grow.

Biotechnological research had a solution to this problem. Scientists were able to take the appropriate gene from the relatively rare plants that were resistant to two of these herbicides and introduce them into soybeans and other crops. The result was a crop that could be sprayed with these herbicides as needed, killing virtually all the weeds that might threaten the crop.

World GMO Crop Areas Planted, 1999	
Crop	Area (million ha)
Soybean	24.3
Corn	12.5
Cotton	4.1
Canola	3.8
Potato	<0.1
Squash	<0.1
Papaya	<0.1

Selected Traits of GMO Crops Planted Worldwide, 1999	
Desired trait	Area (million ha)
Herbicide resistant	31.5
Insect resistant	10.0
Both herbicide and insect resistant	3.3
Virus resistant	<0.1

Figure 10–11 *Transgenic crops are already widely grown in North America and are being increasingly grown in other parts of the world.* Source: Department of Life Sciences, Colorado State University.

You can learn more about the growing use of biotechnology in agriculture at <www.pearsoned.ca/globalconnections>.

To create crops that were resistant to insect infestations, scientists took a gene from a soil bacterium called *Bacillus thuringiensis* (Bt, for short), modified it, and introduced it into the plant. The new gene allows the Bt-modified plant to produce a toxin that kills specific types of insects and yet is harmless to non-target insects and to people or animals that might eat the plant or its fruit. The use of Bt-modified plants has allowed farmers to reduce their use of insecticides drastically. One study of US cotton farmers calculated that in 1998 insecticide use was 450 000 kg less than it would have been if Bt cotton were not available.

Figure 10–12 *GMOs have become the subject of lively debate in the editorial pages of the world's newspapers.*

Concerns about Biotechnology in Food Production

While the creation of GMOs has had some impressive benefits and promises more for the future, few subjects have proven as controversial in recent years (Figure 10–12). The debate has become so heated that opponents have dubbed GMOs "Frankenfoods." This controversy has arisen for many reasons, ranging from the scientific to the ethical. It also has a strong regional bias, as concerns about transgenic crops and animals are much greater in Europe than in North America.

One of the major fears expressed by GMO critics is that the use of Bt-modified and similar transgenic crops may result in the creation of multitudes of "super bugs" that are resistant to the effects of pesticides. This fear is based on the fact that there will always be a tiny number of individual insects who will be immune to the toxic effects of Bt crops. In the normal scheme of things, these resistant individuals would make up only a tiny percentage of the total population,

but without competition they will flourish and their numbers will explode. Similar concerns have been expressed about the creation of "super weeds" that would be resistant to potent herbicides.

The United States Department of Agriculture has recognized the threat of "super bugs" by requiring that farmers who grow Bt crops maintain 20 per cent of their acreage in non-Bt crops. The intent of this rule is to ensure that sufficient numbers of non-resistant insects will survive so that they will outnumber, and genetically swamp, the resistant bugs. Critics fear that this approach may not work, and point out that such laws do not exist in every country where GMO crops are (or will be) grown.

Another concern about GMO technology involves the ownership of the agricultural advances that are created. While charitable groups funded the Green Revolution to benefit the world's poor, private companies are carrying out most GMO research. Their primary goal is to provide the maximum possible return for their shareholders, rather than to solve the world's agricultural and poverty problems. For example, at least one company has created what has been called "terminator technology." To understand how this technology works, we have to consider the source of the seeds that farmers plant.

Traditionally, farmers saved a portion of seeds from the previous year's crops. Now, if farmers want to plant a variety with special characteristics developed using either transgenic or traditional crop research, they must purchase special hybrid seeds from a seed company. In subsequent years, they can replant seeds from these hybrid varieties, but over several years, the plants gradually lose their desirable qualities as they naturally crossbreed with other varieties. At this point, the farmer has to buy more hybrid seeds. Farmers growing wheat, rice, soybeans, cotton, and other important crops have followed this routine for years.

Seed companies have always realized that there would be huge commercial benefits if farmers had to buy seeds every year, but until the development of transgenic terminator seeds there was little they could do to achieve this goal. Terminator plants have been engineered in such a way that they kill their own seeds. If terminator technology is added to plants that have other desirable characteristics like herbicide resistance, farmers have no choice but to buy new seeds each year.

Critics of this technology make two very different points. They view it as an unethical way to do business, since they feel that the technology exists only to increase profits. They liken it to an auto maker choosing to produce a car that will stop working on a certain date. They also worry about the safety of introducing genetic material into the environment that is programmed not to reproduce. They fear that the terminator gene could escape into the gene pool, with potentially catastrophic results.

Supporters of terminator plants feel that it would be impossible for terminator genes to escape, since they cannot reproduce. In fact, they feel that adding terminator genes to a plant that has been genetically modified for another purpose—for example, Bt-modified plants—creates a safer situation, since transgenic genes cannot escape into the gene pool.

Those who oppose GMOs also feel that not enough research has been done to prove the safety of transgenic food products. They fear unknown health effects that may not occur for years. A major concern in North America is that consumers may not even know that they are eating genetically modified foods. Unlike most countries in Europe, Canada and the United States do not have labelling rules that would allow purchasers to determine whether the products that they are buying contain GMOs. This difference in attitude towards labelling illustrates the fact that Europeans have been far less accepting of GMOs than North Americans.

Loss of Genetic Diversity

One serious concern for the future is the loss of genetic diversity that is occurring in agriculture. So much emphasis has been placed on producing "the best" in commercial terms that thousands of varieties of crops and domestic animals have disappeared. The Food and Agricultural Organization of the United Nations estimates that 75 per cent of the genetic diversity of agricultural crops was lost in the 20th century.

The Irish potato famine in the 1840s illustrates the concerns that many people have about this loss. Only two varieties of potatoes were grown in Ireland at the time, and neither was immune to a particular plant disease that destroyed the entire crop. The loss of this staple food meant that over one million people died in just a few years. A similar, although less dramatic, example of the loss of genetic diversity occurred in Florida orange groves in 1984. The outbreak of a disease called citrus canker was made much worse because most growers produced only a few varieties of oranges for the juice industry, all of which were canker-susceptible. If more varieties of potatoes and oranges had been grown in these two situations, including some that were resistant to the disease, the damage would not have been so serious. The maintenance of the largest possible genetic stock is also important for the ongoing success of selective breeding programs and genetic engineering initiatives, since both rely on the availability of the widest possible range of desirable qualities.

A significant number of individuals, groups, and agricultural colleges have embarked on schemes to protect endangered varieties of plants and agricultural animals. They do this by collecting and storing seeds, sharing seeds with others, raising commercially obsolete animal varieties, and providing information about the problem to the public, farmers, and governments.

Organic Farming

Organic farming has developed largely as a response to the many concerns that consumers have about the safety of the products of conventional agriculture. They worry about pesticide residues on crops and about the routine, preventive use of antibiotics in livestock. They also fear that GMO products have not been adequately tested. To answer these concerns, a small but growing number of farmers in developed countries have decided to grow their crops in a more natural fashion.

While there are no commonly accepted definitions of what organic farming is (or is not), organic farmers try to replace the use of chemical fertilizers, pesticides, and GMOs with more natural practices, such as crop rotation and planting two or more crops in the same field.

Corporate Farming

The economics of farming are changing, particularly in the developed world. With these changes, a lifestyle that goes back for centuries is being lost. The family farm is the traditional model for farming. It is an economic and social unit that involves one family's farming and living off the productivity of a modest amount of land. Most often, a family farm is passed down from generation to generation.

Increasingly, farming at this scale is proving to be uneconomic. Larger farm units have considerable economic advantages compared to smaller ones. This means, though, that an entire way of life is threatened as large-scale **corporate farming** comes to replace family farming. Corporate farming can take many forms. For example, in Manitoba and southwestern Ontario, huge hog farms with thousands of animals now dominate pork production, but have raised fears about contamination of groundwater. While a family may own one of these larger, corporate farms, the lifestyle involved is quite different.

The other way that world food production is being corporatized is by the expansion of the influence of huge companies that supply inputs to farming (such as seeds and fertilizers) and that market agricultural products. The influence of huge commercial entities on farming is not new. Perhaps best known are the powerful companies that operated in Africa, Asia, and Latin America starting in the late 1800s. Most notorious, perhaps, was a banana company called United Fruit Company, which had immense political power in countries like Guatemala and Costa Rica. In 1954, United Fruit was even involved with the US Central Intelligence Agency (CIA) in the overthrow of an elected Guatemalan government that United Fruit felt threatened their dominance in the country. Today, huge agribusinesses continue to exercise immense and growing economic and political power.

Alternative Farming Methods

Two forms of food production that do not use conventional farming methods, but are likely to provide more food in the future, are hydroponic farming and aquaculture.

Hydroponic Farming

Hydroponic farming allows agricultural activities to be carried out in environments where plant growth would otherwise be impossible. In a hydroponic environment, virtually every growing condition can be controlled. For example, water and fertilizer are provided in precise amounts. Also, since soil is not used, the possibility of soil-borne diseases and pests is eliminated. Hydroponic farming is used in Canada to produce crops like cucumbers and tomatoes, even in the winter. In desert areas, hydroponic methods are used in large greenhouse structures to produce a wide variety of crops using the minimum amount of water possible.

Aquaculture

When we think of food production, we tend to focus on farming, but it is important to remember the important role that fishing plays as a source of protein for the world. Unfortunately, overfishing has damaged most of the world's major fisheries to the extent that their productivity has been seriously compromised. In some cases—Canada's Atlantic ground fishery being an excellent example—fish stocks have not recovered to earlier levels in spite of dramatic restrictions on the amount of fish that can be caught.

To many observers, the problem is that traditional fishing follows a hunting-and-gathering model and that, as on land, this model provides only a limited carrying capacity. **Aquaculture**—an agricultural model for fish production in which fish are raised on fish farms—is becoming more

common, and offers the possibility of a significantly enhanced fish supply (Figure 10–13). In the developed world, this "aquacultural revolution" means cheaper prices for popular fish varieties like salmon and trout. In developing countries, it offers the promise of a much healthier diet. At the same time, there are concerns about aquaculture. For example, fish are being genetically engineered to grow faster, and there are concerns about these fish escaping and interbreeding with wild fish and diminishing genetic diversity.

Land Reform

In Chapter 6, you learned about the remarkable success of population control in the Indian state of Kerala. A critical factor in this success is that Kerala was able to institute effective land reform many years ago. When **land reform** occurs, land (or at least the right to use land) is distributed to benefit all residents in a country, and not just the rich.

Figure 10–13 *Baby fish produced in this hatchery in Ringwood, Ontario, are cultivated in fish farms until they are ready for market.*

Those who benefit include landless farm workers, sharecroppers (who farm land owned by someone else and share a substantial part of the proceeds with the landowner), and landowners whose holdings are not large enough to support their families.

Land reform has not been the norm in most developing countries. For example, in Guatemala, the 10 largest landowners control 93 per cent of the country's land, while 85 per cent of farmers own no land at all. Needless to say, land reform tends to be very popular with the poor and intensely unpopular with the rich landowners who have so much to lose. In some cases, like that of Guatemala in 1954, attempts to introduce land reform have led to the overthrow of governments in violent revolts.

Agricultural Subsidies

For many years, the world's agricultural markets have been distorted by a wide range of government agricultural supports, particularly in the European Union and the United States. At times, wheat from the European Union has been sold in developing nations in Asia at prices that were lower than the price of transporting the grain to these markets. This underpricing obviously puts farmers in the poorer countries at a tremendous disadvantage, since their governments are not able to provide competitive financial support. Canadian farmers have been harmed because the Canadian government has tended to be less generous with supports than European and US governments.

At a time when free markets have become the rule in the world, it may be hard to understand why agricultural markets remain so controlled.

The reality, however, is simple. While the governments of the European Union nations and the United States might wish to reduce, or even eliminate, the support they give farmers, they lack the political will to take on the powerful agricultural lobbies in their countries. This situation is perhaps best shown in France, where attempts to reduce subsidies have been met with national farmer strikes that have tied up the country's transport systems. A secondary factor is the belief among some, particularly in Europe, that a country should support its farmers so that it can maintain the ability to feed itself.

Role of Women in Agriculture

Women produce more than 50 per cent of the world's food. In the regions where food shortages are worst, sub-Saharan Africa and South Asia, this proportion increases to as much as 80 per cent in some countries (Figure 10–14). Yet women often have little, if any, control over this important part of their lives, since men make the decisions even if they may not do much of the work.

Some authorities suggest that the solution to the world's food problems lies in acknowledging the role that women play in food production and ensuring that they have the knowledge and power they need to be more successful. For example, women must gain more control over decision making and have access to more education and better health care. They must be able to borrow money so they can purchase land and provide inputs, such as machinery and fertilizers, for their farms. If women are empowered in this manner, the result will be substantially more food.

Figure 10–14 *A wheat harvest near Ramnagar Fort, India. In many countries, especially in the developing world, women provide most of the labour in agriculture yet have little control over decision making.*

The Future of Food Production and Distribution

Each year, farmers and governments in North America and Western Europe face the combined problems of overproduction and depressed commodity prices. Prices are so low that farmers face financial ruin and must rely on huge subsidies from their governments to survive. At the same time, many millions face death from hunger-related causes. To many people, this contradiction illustrates that the world does not have a food shortage. Rather, they feel that we have a dysfunctional economic system—one that does not allow a vital commodity to move from producers to those who desperately need it.

The solution to this problem is that we must reform the way in which food is produced and sold in the world market. It is easy to say this, but not so easy to suggest exactly how such a vital goal might be accomplished. In reality, each of the problem areas described in this chapter must be addressed separately. The solutions must be found at many levels—individually, regionally, nationally, and internationally. The problems of food production and consumption did not develop overnight, and they are likely to take many years to solve.

Chapter Questions

Knowledge and Understanding

1. Explain the differences and similarities in meaning among the following terms: famine, starvation, malnutrition, undernutrition, and chronic persistent hunger.

2. Describe, with specific examples, how technological breakthroughs increased food production in the years up to 1870.

3. In this chapter, it was stated that agriculture depends on the interactions among a number of natural systems. Describe each of these systems.

4. Make a diagram like Figure 10–6 in your notebook. On this graph, locate each of the following types of farming operations with a small "x." Label each point.
   a) a 1000-ha cattle ranch in Alberta
   b) nomadic goat and sheep herding in North Africa
   c) a 0.2-ha family farm in Bangladesh
   d) a vineyard in southern France
   e) a 75-ha southern Ontario dairy farm
   f) a 300-ha corn and soybean farm in Iowa

5. a) Make a point-form summary of the events and importance of the Green Revolution.
   b) Why have some of the benefits of the Green Revolution been lost in recent years?

Thinking and Inquiry

6. a) Consider the dietary deficiency diseases listed in Figure 10–1. How are these avoided (for the most part) in countries like Canada?
   b) Why are these solutions not practical in most developing countries?

7. a) Most agricultural areas of the world suffer from one or more deficiencies in the natural systems that support farming. List these deficiencies.

b) Work with three or four classmates to investigate some of these deficiencies. Each of you should choose one of the deficiencies to research. In your investigation, look for examples of both traditional and modern methods of addressing the deficiency. Share your findings with the members of your group.

8. How would you respond to each of the concerns about the Green Revolution that are expressed in this chapter? Give reasons for your responses.

9. When a natural disaster strikes a developing country, developed countries often send food aid. This food aid, however, can disrupt the local economy. The price of locally grown food drops because free food is available, and farmers lose their income as a result. How should donor countries like Canada deal with such situations?

Communication

10. One way to measure the adequacy of the food supply in a country is to compare the amount of food energy available to the amount needed for good health. To examine the world pattern of food adequacy, you will create and analyse either a hand-coloured or ArcView map. (Your teacher will suggest which approach you will use and provide full instructions.)

11. Investigate eight food issues for the future, using a jigsaw approach. Research one of the topics below and present your findings to other members of the class who have studied other issues and who will present their findings to you. Your teacher will give you details about how to do this.
    a) organic farming
    b) corporate farming
    c) loss of genetic diversity
    d) hydroponic farming
    e) aquaculture

f) land reform

g) agricultural subsidies

h) role of women in agriculture

For links to begin your research, go to
<www.pearsoned.ca/globalconnections>.

Application

12. Philanthropy still plays a role in world development. Using the Internet, investigate how each of the following very rich people has contributed to making the world a better place in which to live.

a) Ted Turner

b) George Soros

c) Bill Gates

d) another very rich person of your choice

13. a) How are transgenic crops and animals created?

b) Create a summary of the advantages of and concerns about GMOs by completing Figure 10–15.

c) On balance, do you personally feel comfortable about eating GMO products? Do you think you have enough information to make an informed choice? Explain.

14. The United Nations has given you the task of making recommendations to solve the following situation: The developed countries have an excess of food, and the developing countries have a shortage of food. What do you think can or should be done? Explain your recommendations.

Advantages of GMO Revolution	Concerns About GMO Revolution

Figure 10–15

11

Economic Issues

Expectations

In this chapter, you will:

■ identify ways in which countries and regions are becoming more interdependent

■ evaluate factors that compound hunger and poverty problems in a country

■ analyse the conse- quences of past colo- nialism and present-day economic colonialism

■ analyse causes of eco- nomic disparities in the community

■ understand how employment and quality of life are linked to the global economy

Image above: New York Stock Exchange

In every country, there are wealthy as well as poverty-stricken people. The relative proportion of one group to the other, however, can vary vastly from one country to another. This chapter examines the causes of the economic chasm between the rich and the poor. It looks at how powerful economies dominate weaker ones and at the basic economic theories underlying government policies.

Changing Economies

The proportion of the GDP created by primary, secondary, and tertiary activities is commonly used to measure economic development in a country. Primary industries are resource-based activities such as agriculture, mining, forestry, and fishing. Secondary industries include manufacturing and construction. Tertiary industries include everything else.

Complete the following activity to learn about what happens to this distribution of economic activities as a nation's economy develops.

1. For this exercise we will be using standard X/Y graph paper with an important difference. We need to deal with three values that must total 100 per cent. It is possible to show three values on this apparently two-dimensional graph (see the example in Figure 11–1). Remember that GDP from primary industries is shown on the X axis, while the GDP from secondary industries is shown on the Y axis. At points A, B, and C, the total of primary and secondary GDP is 100 per cent. That means that anywhere along the line through these points, the tertiary GDP value (T)

is 0 per cent. Along the line through D and E, the sum of primary and secondary GDP is 50 per cent. This means that the tertiary value on the line through D and E must be 50 per cent. Similarly, along the line joining F and G, the tertiary value must be 80 per cent. In simplest terms, as you move towards the graph's origin (0,0), the percentage of tertiary GDP increases.

2. Figure 11–3 on the next page summarizes the changes in GDP by economic sector for the countries of our Five-World model. On a full page of graph paper, plot the economic changes for each country in a manner similar to that used for Canada in Figure 11–2. Plot the members of each "world" in a different colour.

3. Examine the graph you have created. What economic changes does it suggest as a country progresses from Fifth World to First World? Explain why you think this might happen.

4. How might economic planners in less developed countries use knowledge of these changes?

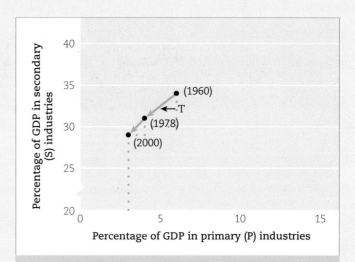

Figure 11–1 *Graph of economic development: Percentage of GDP in primary (P), secondary (S), and tertiary (T) industries*

Figure 11–2 *Changes in Canada's economy: Percentage of GDP in primary (P), secondary (S), and tertiary (T) industries. What happens to the structure of a country's economy as development occurs?*

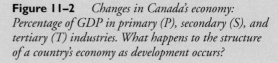

	% of GDP from Primary Industries			% of GDP from Secondary Industries			% of GDP from Tertiary Industries		
	1960	1978	2000§	1960	1978	2000§	1960	1978	2000§
1st World Countries									
Canada	6	4	3	34	31	29	60	65	69
France	10	5	3	38	37	24	52	58	73
Japan	13	5	2	45	40	38	42	55	60
United States	4	3	2	38	34	28	58	63	70
2nd World Countries									
China†	39	31	17	38	46	50	23	23	34
Cuba	n/a	n/a	n/a	n/a	n/a	n/a	n/a	n/a	n/a
Poland	26	16	3	57	64	32	17	20	66
Russia	21	17	7	62	62	38	17	21	56
3rd World Countries									
Brazil	16	11	9	35	37	32	49	52	59
Chile***	11	10	8	38	29	34	51	61	57
Peru***	26	14	8	29	36	38	45	50	55
South Korea	40	24	5	19	36	44	41	40	52
4th World Countries									
India	50	40	27	20	26	27	30	34	46
Indonesia	54	31	17	14	33	47	32	36	36
Malaysia	37	25	12	18	32	40	45	43	48
Pakistan	46	32	27	16	24	23	38	44	50
5th World Countries									
Bangladesh	61	57	26	8	13	25	31	30	49
Ethiopia	65	54	52	12	13	11	23	33	37
Haiti	n/a	n/a	31	n/a	n/a	19	n/a	n/a	50
Sierra Leone**	34	39	43	28	22	27	38	39	30

n/a = no data available

§ stats for Canada, France, Japan, South Korea, Ethiopia, Haiti from
1996; stats for US from 1990; stats for Russia, Ethiopia from 1999

** 1960 stats not available; 1965 stats used

*** 1978 stats not available; 1977 stats used

† 1960 stats not available; 1965 stats used. 1978 stats not available; 1986 stats used

Note: The figures in the 2000 columns do not always add up to 100% because of rounding.

Figure 11–3 *Graph these data, following the model for Canada shown in Figure 11–2.* Sources: Data for 1960 and 1978 from World Bank, *World Development Report 1982.* The World Bank: Washington, DC; data for 2000 from World Bank, World Development Indicators database, July 2001. The World Bank uses agriculture for primary industries, industrial for secondary industries, and service for tertiary industries.

Stages of Economic Development

From the preceding exercise you now have a better understanding of what happens as a country develops, but perhaps not what might cause one country's economy to grow while another's stagnates. Many attempts have been made to explain why this happens. Perhaps the best known of these is the model for economic growth proposed by Walt Rostow in the 1960s. Rostow suggested that a country goes through five stages as its economy develops.

Stage 1: Traditional Society

Countries in this stage have an economy dominated by subsistence agriculture. Because of this, they have a severely limited potential for both economic and population growth. Social and economic progress are limited by natural controls such as droughts and outbreaks of disease. Government structures often feature absolute monarchies or dictatorships, and are inflexible because they are used to operating in conditions that change very little over centuries. Examples of traditional societies include Britain before about 1750, Canada before 1880, and many of today's Fifth World countries.

Stage 2: Establishing the Preconditions for Takeoff

At a certain point, and for a variety of reasons, a country will reach a stage where it is able to start the transition to a more complex, advanced economy. This happened first in Great Britain at the beginning of the Industrial Revolution in 1750. The transition was somewhat different in Britain than in the nations that reached this stage later. The conditions that prepared the country for economic takeoff had to be developed in Britain because there were no external models to follow. When the remainder of Western Europe (and, later, other countries) moved to this stage, they could choose among a variety of examples to follow.

Rostow believed that the takeoff stage could be reached only if a society was able to achieve a surplus of wealth, which he called savings, that could be invested in vital economic sectors like transportation, communications, and natural resource exploitation. The achievement of these conditions suggests that the society is starting to develop a sense of national purpose. Part of this development is the creation of more effective, responsive central governments. Many Western European nations were at this stage in the late 1700s and early 1800s. Canada was there in the mid-1800s. Some Fifth World and many Fourth World countries are now at this stage.

Stage 3: Economic Takeoff

This is the stage at which a country's economy starts to change dramatically in response to the introduction of important technological innovations. Agriculture changes from primarily subsistence to primarily commercial. Manufacturing becomes a more important part of the economy. The tertiary sector of the economy expands in response to the growth of cities and the number of paid workers who become customers for service providers. Great Britain reached this stage first, in the very late 1700s. Countries like France and the United States were there by 1860, with Canada reaching takeoff by 1900. Many Fourth World and poorer Third World nations are at this stage now.

Stage 4: The Drive to Maturity

After a country's economy takes off, there is an extended period of sustained growth. Economic gain outpaces population growth, so per capita wealth increases. The economy becomes more diversified with a continued expansion of manufacturing and a variety of services. Modern, efficient production methods come into use. An increasing percentage of the nation's wealth is invested in developing the economy. Historically, a country's economy would reach maturity about 50 to 60 years after its takeoff. Hence, Great Britain's economy reached maturity in the 1850s, with France and the United States following around 1910 and Canada by the 1950s. More recently, economies like those of Hong Kong, Singapore, and South Korea were able to reach maturity more quickly than was the norm before World War II.

Stage 5: High Mass Consumption

In this final stage, many people have incomes that are greater than necessary for buying essentials such as shelter, food, clothing (Figure 11–4). As a result, there is a growing demand for additional consumer goods and services. The society is also wealthy enough to invest in social programs such as improved health care systems and educational opportunities. This stage occurred first in the United States in the 1920s; Canada followed shortly after. Mass consumption economies developed in Western Europe and Japan in the years following World War II.

Rostow's model presents only one explanation for variations in the economic development and quality of life of different countries. His model describes development as he saw it in Europe and North America. Elsewhere, economic development may not occur in the same way.

Figure 11–4 *Left, picking tea in Assam, India; right, a shopping mall in Bangalore, India. Economic growth, from the stage of the traditional society to the stage of high mass consumption, fundamentally changes the way in which people live.*

Historical Colonialism Past and Present

Colonialism dominated the world's economic system for more than four centuries until the second half of the 20th century. Its impact was so profound that, even today, it affects the economic, social, and political systems of much of the world. If we are to understand the economic progress and problems of most of the developing world today, we have to go back many years to look at the beginnings of the colonial period, which can be tied to the need to establish reliable trade routes between Europe and East Asia.

Until the middle of the 15th century, trade for spices and other commodities was conducted overland via the famous Spice Road. In 1453, the Byzantine Empire, centred in Constantinople (now Istanbul), collapsed and travel over the Spice Road became difficult. Europeans therefore sought to discover sea routes to India, the islands of southeast Asia, Japan, and China. Spain and Portugal quickly became dominant in these explorations. Columbus's first voyage to America on behalf of Spain occurred in 1492; by then, Portuguese explorers had already sailed to South Africa and India. There was a fear that the rivalry between these nations, as they expanded their expeditions and trade, might lead to war.

The remarkable solution to this problem was the Treaty of Tordesillas in 1494. This treaty, which was brokered by the pope of the day, defused the rivalry by dividing the non-Christian world arbitrarily between the two countries at a north–south line about 2100 km west of the Cape Verde Islands (which are off the west coast of Africa). The fact that this treaty totally ignored the rights of all the people affected by it indicates the central belief of colonialism—that the colonies existed only to meet the needs of colonizers.

Many European countries challenged the claims of Spain and Portugal and established their own colonies. Some, like Sweden, Belgium, and the Netherlands, had only a few, while others, like France and Great Britain, developed immense empires that were many times the size of the mother country (Figure 11–5). While most empires were created by European countries, the United States and Japan scrambled to develop empires near the end of colonial period in the late 19th and early 20th centuries. In the case of the United States, this meant taking control of countries like Cuba and the Philippines that had been part of the disintegrating Spanish Empire until the end of the 19th century. In the 20th century, Japan expanded its control into areas of Korea and China.

To many observers, World War II occurred as a result of the desires of Germany and Japan to expand their economic control over ever-larger areas of their neighbours. Germany used its proclaimed need for *lebensraum* (living space) to justify its invasion of the Soviet Union. Japan had no particular desire to go to war against the United States. Their attack on Pearl Harbor in 1941 was an attempt to neutralize the power of the US Pacific Fleet, so that Japan could invade and take control of the rich oil fields of the Dutch East Indies (now Indonesia).

Did you KNOW?

Under the Treaty of Tordesillas, Spain got the area to the west of the north–south line, which opened the door for it to develop its immense empire in the Americas. Portugal got the eastern part of the world, which led to the development of its colonies in Africa, India, and China (Macau). An anomaly to this pattern is that Portugal colonized Brazil, since Brazil's easternmost point crossed the magic line. This is why Brazil is the only country in Latin America with Portuguese as its official language.

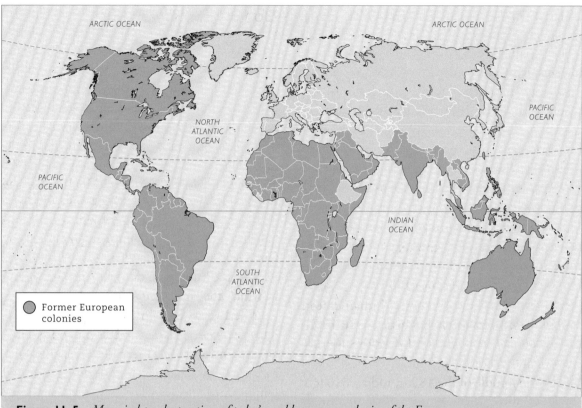

Figure 11–5 *Many independent nations of today's world were once colonies of the European powers.*

The colonial period (Figure 11–6) can be divided into two distinct periods, roughly identified as pre– and post–Industrial Revolution. In the earlier period, colonies were principally seen as sources of useful products that were not available at home. For example, Canada supplied Great Britain with furs and lumber, while the southern United States provided cotton and tobacco. Colonies also provided novel products like coffee, tea, spices, and even potatoes.

While colonies provided useful and at times essential products, during the first colonial period they often were not as profitable as they might have been. The solution to this problem was the introduction of a system that tied colonial possessions more closely to the imperial power. Under the **mercantile system** of the 17th and early 18th centuries period, colonies were considered to exist only for the economic benefit of the mother

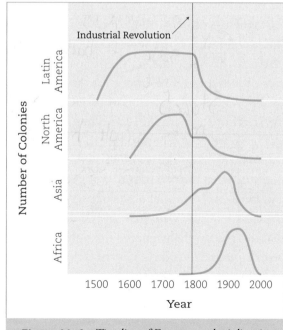

Figure 11–6 *Timeline of European colonialism in different countries*

country. This meant that not only was the colony a source for raw materials; it also was seen as a captive market for the manufactured goods produced in the mother country. This rigid system did not allow the colony to operate in its own economic interests. For example, it was not allowed to sell its raw materials to the highest bidder or to buy the cheapest manufactured goods, since all trade had to be with the colonial master.

The colony was also prevented from competing with the mother country. This was the case with India's cotton industry. India had been a major producer and exporter of hand-woven cotton cloth before the Industrial Revolution. In fact, for many years Great Britain had had to impose a duty on the import of Indian cotton cloth to protect its domestic textile industry. To prevent competition, Britain forced the destruction of India's cotton industry. The result was that by the middle of the 1800s, India no longer exported cotton textiles and, in fact, imported one-quarter of all the cotton clothing produced in Britain.

Concession Companies

One of the important ways that European countries developed their empires was by establishing **concession companies**. Countries created dozens of these corporations to trade in particular parts of the world, or to trade in particular products. In many cases, the companies were also given the responsibility to act as the government in remote parts of the empires. Many of these companies, like the Anglo-Belgian India Rubber Company, are little more than minor historical footnotes; but some, like Canada's Hudson's Bay Company, are remembered as vital parts of the histories of the countries and regions in which they operated (Figure 11–7).

The British East India Company was perhaps the most famous concession company of all. Founded in 1600, its charter gave it a monopoly to trade in India, Southeast Asia, and China until 1833. "The Company," as it was often called, had tremendous power. It operated its own fleet of armed transport ships and fortified trading posts. It was responsible for the infa-

Figure 11–7 *Inuit women haul a sled loaded with pelts from the wharf in Pangnirtung, NWT, to the Hudson's Bay Company warehouse, August 1946. Yes, this concession company is The Bay, the same company whose stores you may visit at your local mall.*

mous opium trade from India to China that helped to pay for the tea that the East India Company sold successfully in Britain and elsewhere. More importantly, the company's political activities did much to expand the British Empire. At home, its financial success provided much of the wealth that spurred Britain's early economic takeoff.

In some ways, these concession companies could be likened to the high-flying, hi-tech companies of our time. Each was tied to the economic growth of its day, in both a positive sense and a negative one. Great fortunes were there to be made, but company stock prices could rise or fall to ridiculous levels and investors could lose everything. For example, the South Sea Bubble stock collapse in 1720 was so infamous that it is still remembered today, almost three centuries later.

Impacts of Colonialism

The largest colony in the Commonwealth of Nations—today's British Empire—is Bermuda, with a population of only about 60 000. Obviously, the great colonial empires are gone, but their impacts continue. While some impacts of colonialism were positive (for example, Canada inherited its governmental and legal systems from Britain), most impacts proved negative in the years after these countries achieved independence. These are some of the ongoing economic, social, and political effects of colonialism.

- Traditional **land tenure** practices were destroyed. In many parts of the world that became colonies, the concept of private ownership of land had been unknown and land resources were shared. This was the situation in Canada, for example. The European system in which land was privately owned was introduced. Private ownership implied that a few people could own a great deal of land, while many others would not own enough to support themselves, and some had no land at all.
- Frequently the best land came to be owned by concession companies or European settlers, often in the form of large **plantations**. The local population was pushed off this land. These dispossessed farmers were then used as cheap labour on the plantations and in other industries. This practice was widespread in Africa.
- Land that had been used to grow food for local people came to be used for growing crops that would be sent to the mother country. These **cash crops** varied widely from colony to colony but included such commodities as tea, coffee, sugar, bananas, cacao (used to make chocolate), jute (used to make rope, sacking, and mats), cotton, and silk. The result of this change was that some areas that had been self-sufficient in food became dependent on imports.
- The growth of local manufacturing was delayed and distorted by artificial trade controls. The case of textile manufacturing in what is now India and Bangladesh is an excellent example of this. The trade, taxation policies, and manufacturing restrictions on the Thirteen Colonies led directly to the American Revolution in 1776.
- Colonial mining, forestry, and agricultural and manufacturing developments paid little, if any, attention to environmental protection. Environmental problems continued in many countries long after independence.
- Foreign political systems were imposed on colonies. Rarely did these systems recognize and respect the traditional political systems of the

colony. A good example can be seen in Canada, where there has been a long history of conflict between the federal government and those of various Aboriginal groups. In recent years, the federal government has started to work more closely with hereditary or elected chiefs and to accept the validity of Aboriginal legal traditions, such as healing circles (Figure 11–8).

- Colonial powers were unable to supply enough of their own people to manage, control, and protect their colonies. As a result, they established elite groups among the local residents. These elites were trained to take less important administrative jobs and to serve as enlisted men in the army. Members of these elites often ended up running the former

colonies when they became independent countries, whether they were representative of the population or not. For example, an army sergeant-major named Idi Amin became the murderous dictator of Uganda.

- Countries were created from land areas that did not match traditional tribal or cultural boundaries. National boundaries were drawn on maps to meet the needs of competing colonizers. This situation is most clearly seen in Africa. For example, the Yoruba were a highly organized people living in many small kingdoms throughout what is now southwestern Nigeria and Benin. Owing to colonialism, today's Yoruba in Nigeria commonly speak English, while those in neighbouring Benin commonly speak French. An argument can

Figure 11–8 *The Aboriginal healing circle brings together all those concerned about the wrongdoer and involved in the offence. Community elders, the families affected, police, and a judge attempt to reach an agreement on the most appropriate consequences for a wrongful act.*

be made that the historical conflict between the English and French in Canada has its roots in our colonial history.

- Colonizers imposed their culture and language on the people living in the lands they took over. This action had both positive and negative impacts. The colonial languages—for most of the world, English, Spanish, or French—provided a common form of communication in a country that might have many languages (such as India, which has 14 major languages and over 1000 minor languages and dialects). In many countries, the colonial language has even become the official language because it was often the only common language in the new country. Cultural imports also have proven important. For example, cricket is a popular pastime in places as diverse as the West Indies, India, Australia, and South Africa. On the other hand, the dominance of the colonial culture can make the local cultures appear inferior. Local people who speak the colonial language and have European-style educations often end up dominating the political and business life of the country. The globalization that is occurring today only serves to make this situation worse.
- Colonizers built an infrastructure that served their commercial needs. Roads, railways, and ports were built to develop raw materials and service export industries. Often these did not serve the most populated areas.

Current Economic Colonialism

The old form of colonialism has been eliminated, but various forms of informal imperialism have replaced it. For example, in the Cold War decades immediately after World War II, as part of their battle to dominate the world, both the United States and the Soviet Union supported many client states among the former colonies. In return for financial and military aid, the developing nation was expected to support the policies of its benefactor (e.g., in the United Nations) and to develop its economy following the patron's model. In some cases, countries would even shift from one sphere of influence to the other as the superpowers fought for dominance. For example, in 1956 when the United States, followed by Britain, decided not to guarantee a loan to Egypt to cover the costs of building the Aswan High Dam, the Egyptian government accepted an offer from the Soviet Union for aid.

After the breakup of the Soviet Union in 1989 and the rise of the free-market or capitalist system, this new form of imperialism took on a different face. In the absence of a political challenge, economic dominance became more important. This dominance has some things in common with colonialism, but in some important ways it is quite different. These features are summarized in Figure 11–9.

Colonies' Role	Colonial Period	Post-colonial Period
Source of raw materials	Yes	Yes
Source of manufactured products	No, competition not wanted	Yes, because of cheap labour supply
Market for manufactured goods	Yes	Yes
Chief beneficiary	Colonial power	Transnational corporation

Figure 11–9 *In the post-colonial period, the chief beneficiaries of economic activities in the former colonies are not the colonial powers, but transnational corporations.*

Economic Systems

Over the past century, economic decision making by the world's nations has occurred along a continuum between two extremes (Figure 11–10). At one extreme is a **free market economy**, while at the other is a **command economy**. In a perfect free market, the price of all goods and services is determined by the relationship between supply and demand. In a command economy, on the other hand, the supply and price of goods and services are determined entirely by the government as part of a totally planned economy.

In reality, there have never been countries that have had either a free market economy or a command economy in their purest forms. Governments of all types have learned that, in spite of the political philosophies under which they operate, they will end up with a **mixed economy** that combines elements of both free enterprise and government intervention. Some mixed economies have a limited role for free markets, while in others, the market is dominant and the role of government is minimized.

The leaders of the former Soviet Union found out soon after the Russian Revolution in 1917 that they could not have the perfect command economy that they had envisioned. The Soviet government attempted to run the country in this way, for example, by taking over landowners' estates, but within just a few years, the country was facing a severe food shortage. The government had to compromise its principles and give farmers the right to grow food on small private plots and to sell this production at market-determined prices. Similarly, the governments of countries like Canada and the United States, whose economies are nominally free market, have found that the market cannot be relied on to provide all goods and services. Some activities, like operating the military, maintaining a police force, and protecting endangered species, are best provided by governments.

The fundamental question when we think about mixed economies is exactly how large a role government should play. This is hardly a new question. Adam Smith, the founder of modern economics, published a famous book in 1776 called *The Wealth of Nations*, which advocated the idea of **economic liberalism**. His contention was that mercantilism should be abolished and the economic system should be allowed to operate without government intervention. The economic ideas of Smith and his disciples remained dominant in the Western world until the early 1900s.

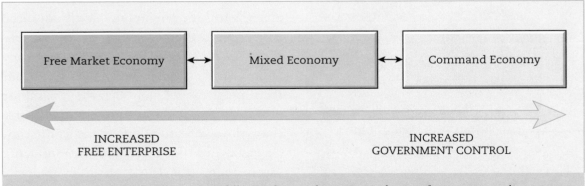

Figure 11–10 *All the world's economies fall somewhere on the continuum between free enterprise and government control.*

Keynesian Economics and Progressive Governments

The economic collapse of the Great Depression of the 1930s forced the emergence of a new economic direction. During this time, when unemployment reached record levels, a British economist named John Maynard Keynes proposed that the only way to ensure the economic growth that would end the Depression was to have substantially fewer unemployed people. Further, he said that governments had a key role to play in ensuring that employment was high. They could do this by increasing their spending during poor economic times to provide jobs for people.

Keynesian economics became central to the policies of many governments as they fought against the hardships of the Depression. Perhaps best known of these efforts was the New Deal, which President Franklin D. Roosevelt instituted in the United States (Figure 11–11). The New Deal provided jobs by spending many billions of dollars on projects like dam building and highway construction. Similar policies were adopted in Canada and elsewhere. During and after World War II, the influence of Keynesian economics expanded and led to a changed understanding of the role of government.

Between the 1940s and the 1980s, the governments of most developed countries came to be seen as agents of social and economic change. Governments of this type are sometimes called **progressive governments**. Taxation was seen as having two main roles. In countries with free market economic policies, taxes were collected to pay for important government functions like providing for schools and paying for the military. In addition, progressive governments used taxation as a way to redistribute incomes from richer to poorer citizens. For example, in Canada from 1957 on, a system of equalization payments was established that transferred money from the richer provinces like Ontario, Alberta, and British Columbia to the rest of the country.

In many countries, this era was marked by a great expansion in the scope of social programs offered. In much of Western Europe, this meant the creation of a "womb-to-tomb" social safety net. In contrast, the United States implemented relatively fewer social programs. The United States is still the only economically advanced nation that does not have a system of government-paid health care for all citizens. As in many areas, Canada is somewhere in between—our social programs are more elaborate than those of the United States but less comprehensive than those of most European countries. Unemployment (now Employment) Insurance was introduced in 1941. Medicare gradually developed between 1947 and the 1960s, and the Canada Pension Plan began in 1967.

Figure 11–11 *US President Roosevelt priming the New Deal pump. Does this cartoon represent a free-market or progressive slant?*

Neo-liberal Economics

By the 1980s, criticism of progressive economics had become common, starting in the United Kingdom and the United States. Concerns focussed on the amount of national debt that countries had accumulated as, for many years, their governments spent more than they had collected in taxes. Both of these countries elected leaders (Margaret Thatcher in the United Kingdom; Ronald Reagan in the United States) who strongly favoured a return to a freer market economy and to a reduced role for government in many aspects of life. They felt that the policies of restrictive trade practices and subsidies that had been given to non-competitive industries had badly distorted the efficient operation of the world's economy. In addition, they asserted that growth was also reduced by the amount of money taken out of the economy by government, in the form of taxes, to pay for social services and other government expenditures.

This trend, which has spread to much of the developed world, has come to be known as **neo-liberalism** since it is a newer form of the ideas of Adam Smith. The name has led to considerable confusion, since the political parties most supportive of this approach have been conservative in nature (and, in some countries, in name too). In the United Kingdom, the chief proponent is the Conservative Party, while in the United States it is the Republican Party. In Canada, it was originally the Progressive Conservative Party (PCs). The Reform Party, later to become the Canadian Alliance, was created because of a feeling in the country (and particularly in Western Canada) that the PCs were not sufficiently neo-liberal in their views.

The impact and philosophy of neo-liberalism can be seen in the actions of neo-liberal governments. One of the most dramatic moves by British Prime Minister Margaret Thatcher (Figure 11–12) was her decision to close many government-

Figure 11–12 *Margaret Thatcher, British prime minister from 1979 to 1990, was renowned, like Ronald Reagan in the US, for neo-liberal policies.*

supported, uneconomic coal mines. For many years, these mines had provided thousands of jobs in economically depressed parts of the country, but had lost millions of pounds each year. Keeping these mines operating made sense in a world where the government took responsibility for keeping people employed, but could not be supported in a neo-liberal one. The move to neo-liberalism can also be seen in a wide variety of steps that are designed to reduce the influence of government.

- Several jurisdictions in North America and Europe have moved to **privatize** the production of electricity by selling off government-owned utilities.
- In Ontario, a major toll highway, Highway 407, was sold to a private company to be operated as a profit-making business.
- In Canada, the United Kingdom, and other countries, governments have withdrawn from earlier commitments to provide social housing for people who cannot afford to secure

housing in the open market. The result has been an increase in the number of people who live on the street or in overcrowded, substandard housing.

- In the United States in 2001, President George W. Bush created an Office of Faith-based Programs to work with religious groups to provide social programs that previously were supplied by the government. Critics claimed this was an attempt to begin dismantling the social safety net.

As the appeal of neo-liberalism has grown, even political parties that have traditionally been more progressive in their views have adopted neo-liberal ideas. This has been the case with Canada's Liberal Party, which had formed the government throughout most of the years when deficit-spending ideas dominated. During the 1990s, the Liberal government of Canada scaled back its support for social and economic development programs. More dramatic is the case of Britain's Labour party. Labour governments had always been strongly interventionist in the economy and in favour of the state taking over (nationalizing) certain industries like steelmaking and coal mining. This policy changed dramatically with the election of Tony Blair's government in 1997. His government, which he called New Labour, was markedly less committed to governmental involvement in the economy than earlier Labour governments. In fact, its policies were not very different from those that would have been adopted if a Conservative government had been elected.

Internationally, the most significant impact of the neo-liberal revolution has been the move towards **economic globalization**. In the past, economic restrictions, such as tariffs and quota systems, reduced the amount of economic integration among nations. Today, the world can be seen as having one economic system with increasingly easy movement of goods, production, capital, and resources. You can see this economic globalization in the things that you buy each day such as clothing, sporting goods, and food products. You can also see it in the stories about Team Canada trade missions that are designed to promote the sale of Canadian products around the world. Finally, you can see it in newspaper articles about factories closing in Canada with their production being moved to other countries.

Central to this trend is the elimination of economic barriers among nations, most importantly restrictions on trade. (See Chapter 12 for more information on economic globalization.) Accordingly, the last few decades have been marked by the growth of free trade between and among countries in many parts of the world. Most obvious of these agreements was the expansion of the European Community, now the European Union (Figure 11–13). For Canada, this trend has meant a free trade agreement with, first, the United States and, later, with Mexico and the United States. Beyond this, there have been significant attempts to include Canada in free trade agreements that would involve, in one case, the nations of the Americas, and in the other, the countries of the Pacific Rim. It would not be an exaggeration to suggest that we may be moving towards a world in which free trade is virtually universal.

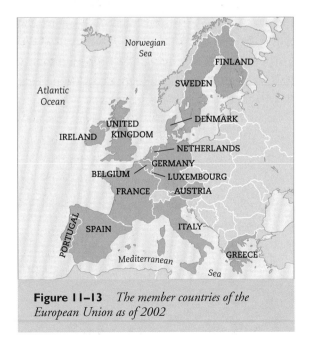

Figure 11–13 *The member countries of the European Union as of 2002*

Neo-liberalism and the Developing World

The dramatic shift to neo-liberalism in the developed world has had an impact on the developing world as well. Whether this impact has been negative or positive depends on the political leanings of the observer. In reality, it is too early to be sure whether the benefits of free market economics outweigh the costs. Proponents of neo-liberalism feel that the elimination of trade and other barriers will allow developing countries to speed their transitions towards economic maturity. In theory, the removal of barriers will guarantee developing countries a market, since their inexpensive labour allows them to price their products competitively. On the other hand, opponents of globalization contend that the elimination of barriers is designed to help transnational companies by allowing them to move their production to less developed countries that have cheap, unregulated labour and low environmental standards. For opponents, globalization is no more than an excuse for sweatshops and high profits.

What Will Happen Next?

Is neo-liberalism here to stay, or will the world's governments adopt some form of "neo-progressive" economic policies in the future? Only time will tell. Clearly in the early years of the 21st century, neo-liberal thought is on the rise; but its critics point out the shortcomings of this approach, in particular, the fact that many societal needs cannot be provided by a free-market economy. For example, the number of homeless people in the cities of Canada and other industrialized countries has grown. These are people who have fallen through the cracks of the new economic system. They are not able to compete successfully in a competitive economy and, at the same time, have lost many of the social supports that they had when more progressive government policies were in place.

Perhaps the real test for neo-liberal governments will come as they are challenged by poor economic times. The mid- and late 1990s, when there were many neo-liberal governments in the Western world, was a time of unprecedented economic growth. Proponents of free markets said this was evidence that their policies worked. Opponents, on the other hand, said that the growth would have happened in any case, and without the costs to society of reduced government programs.

Neo-liberal governments, like that of the United States under President George W. Bush, were faced with a particular challenge as a result of the terrorist attacks on the United States on September 11, 2001. In addition to the horrific loss of life, there was tremendous damage to the US economy and that of many other countries, including Canada. Worst affected initially was the air travel industry, including both airlines and aircraft manufacturers. Airlines in the United States and elsewhere announced major service reductions, laid off many thousands of employees, and called for billions of dollars of aid from governments to help them survive. Governments that truly believe in allowing the market to work would not provide support, even in such exceptional circumstances. They would allow competition within the reduced scope of the air travel industry to decide if some companies would disappear or merge. The fact that support was made available indicates that governments are prepared to compromise on theoretical beliefs if they believe that circumstances dictate such a response.

Chapter Questions

Knowledge and Understanding

1. Give evidence, from our economy and lifestyles, to show that Canada is in Rostow's stage 5 (high mass consumption).

2. Imagine that a developed Western nation is facing a period of economic decline. What might this government tend to do if it believes in
   a) Keynesian economics?
   b) neo-liberal economics?

3. a) Using Rostow's work as an example, define what is meant by a "model."
   b) What are the advantages and disadvantages of using a model to describe a complex reality?

4. Explain why the terms neo-liberalism and neo-conservatism mean basically the same thing.

5. Briefly summarize, in your own words, the impacts that colonialism has had on former colonies. For each impact, suggest why, after 40 or more years of independence, these effects of colonialism are still causing problems in these countries.

6. Suggest how colonialism and concession companies aided the economic takeoff of imperial nations and hindered that of colonies.

Thinking and Inquiry

7. a) Create a table to summarize the characteristics of the five stages of Rostow's model of economic growth.
   b) Canada and Australia reached the stage of high mass consumption before their economies reached full maturity. Why is this not a surprise if you consider the nature of the economies of these countries?

8. While it is true that all countries have mixed economies, there are some countries that have very limited free markets for both goods and services, while there are others in which the role of government in the economy has been minimized. Identify three countries in each category that have:
   a) limited free markets
   b) a balance between free markets and an involved government
   c) a limited role for government

   (Hint: A good place to begin your research is the CIA World Fact Book. Check it out at <www.pearsoned.ca/globalconnections>.)

9. a) How might having more elaborate social programs put Canada at a competitive disadvantage compared to the United States?
   b) In what ways might more comprehensive social programs give us a competitive advantage?
   c) How have Canadian governments responded to this challenge?

10. Many countries that used to have command economies have abandoned them. These include the countries that were formerly part of the Soviet Union (including Russia), the countries of Eastern Europe, and China.
    a) Choose one of these countries and research how the change from command economy was accomplished.
    b) Describe how this process has resulted in some people "winning" and others "losing."

Communication

11. What impact has colonialism had on the level of development of former colonies? One commonly used measure of social development is the UN Human Development Index (HDI). Complete a mapping exercise of HDI values, using either a paper base map or ArcView. (Your teacher will provide you with full instructions.) What relationship is there between those countries that were colonies and those with low HDI values? What pattern do you see?

12. Choose a country in Africa, or elsewhere, that was formerly a colony. Research its history during three eras: pre-colonial, colonial, and post-colonial. Prepare a poster or paper to show this history and to show how this country was affected both by the process of colonization and by the process of de-colonization (independence). In your research, consider at least the following themes: government, economic development, social development, and cultural patterns.

13. Interview a person born before 1950 to discover how the impact of globalization (see page 182) has changed life in Canada. Compare your findings with those of others in your group. Present a short oral report to show the social and economic impacts.

Application

14. a) Suggest reasons why relatively small countries like Great Britain and the Netherlands were able to develop huge empires.
    b) Research the reasons why this happened. Were your thoughts on this question accurate?

15. a) Identify one country for each stage of economic development according to Rostow's model. Give evidence to support your choices.
    b) Is Rostow's model still valid for describing economic development in the 21st century? Why or why not? (Hint: Consider the impact of economic and financial globalization.)
    c) Work with one or more classmates to suggest how Rostow's model could be modified to better fit the economic characteristics of the 21st century.

16. Imagine you are a government official in an actual former colony that is in Rostow's stage 1 of economic development. Your mandate is to prepare the country for the "take-off" stage. What steps would you propose? Consider the following:
    a) How did countries like South Korea, Singapore, and Japan make this transition?
    b) Where on the spectrum shown in Figure 11–10 would you want the economy to be?
    c) What importance would you place on programs like education, health, and environmental protection?
    Present your recommendations in a two-page report.

17. Do you agree with the statement on page 178 that the new beneficiaries of economic activities in the former colonies are transnational corporations? Use the Internet to select two or more transnational companies as evidence for your response. Share your findings with your group in an oral or written report.

Growth of Economic Globalization

Expectations

In this chapter, you will:

- identify different methods of grouping countries, including economic affiliation

- identify the social, economic, cultural, and political aspects of globalization

- explain the effects of trade policies and agreements on the environment

- analyse the economic consequences of past colonialism and present economic colonialism

- understand how quality of life and job prospects are tied to the global economy

- make judgements or predictions based on reasoned analysis

Can you guess where the photo above was taken? (Osaka, Japan; but this street might be anywhere in the world.) Each year, *Fortune* magazine publishes a list of the **Global 500**, the 500 largest companies in the world based on their annual revenues. What do you know about international big business? Take the quiz on the next page (based on the 2000 Global 500) and find out.

Quiz: The 2000 Global 500

See how many of these questions you can answer without doing any research:

1. What company headed the Global 500 list?

2. What other companies were in the top five places?

3. What country had the most companies on the Global 500? How many of the companies did this country have?

4. What other countries were in the top five in terms of the number of companies they were home to?

5. What company in the world had the largest profits?

6. What was the rank of the largest Canadian company? What is the name of this company?

7. How many of the Global 500 companies were in Canada?

8. Name as many of these as possible.

9. How many of the Global 500 were located in developing countries?

10. Which of the following companies are or are not on the Global 500? The Gap, Wal-Mart Stores, L'Oréal, BMW, Royal Bank of Canada, McDonald's, Toys 'R' Us

The answers to these questions can be found on page 199. You can check the current Global 500 at <www.pearsoned.ca/globalconnections>.

Transnational Corporations

If you are like most people, you probably got only a few of the answers to these questions right. Most of us give little thought to the huge companies that dominate our economic life. At the same time, this ignorance should be somewhat disturbing, since these companies have enormous influence in the world. In the past, such large companies were often called **multinational companies** because they operated in several, or even many, countries. Increasingly they are being called **transnational companies**, as many of them operate across the world and are becoming less clearly identified with any particular nation. Some important features of the largest companies of all are shown in Figure 12–1 on the next page.

When you examine these statistics, you may marvel at the enormous economic scale of these companies. In fact, their economic power rivals that of many nations! A reasonable comparison can be made between the revenue of some companies as shown in the Global 500 list and the economies of some countries with gross domestic products (GDPs) of similar size (Figure 12–2). For example, each year, the amount of income generated by General Motors is comparable to the size of the entire economy of Bangladesh with 130 million people, affluent Sweden, or oil-rich Venezuela.

Similar comparisons can be made between smaller companies on the Global 500 list and other countries. For example, Coca-Cola's revenues of US$34 billion are similar to the GDPs of Ghana and Ethiopia, the latter of which has a population of over 65 million people. The Walt Disney Corporation's revenues of US$23 billion are more

World's Top 20 Companies Based on Revenues (from the Global 500 list)

Rank	Company	Main Type of Business	Country	Revenue ($US billions)	Profit ($US billions)	Employees (thousands)
	Johnny Depp					
1	General Motors	Motor vehicles	USA	176.6	4.5	386
2	Wal-Mart Stores	Retailing	USA	166.8	6.3	1140
3	Exxon-Mobil	Oil	USA	163.9	17.7	123
4	Ford	Motor vehicles	USA	162.6	3.5	365
5	Daimler-Chrysler	Motor vehicles	Germany	160.0	7.4	467
6	Mitsui	General trading	Japan	118.6	0.3	11
7	Mitsubishi	General trading	Japan	117.8	0.2	11
8	Toyota	Motor vehicles	Japan	115.7	4.5	215
9	General Electric	Diversified financial	USA	111.6	12.7	313
10	Itochu	General trading	Japan	109.1	−0.8	5
11	Royal Dutch/Shell Group	Oil	Netherlands	105.4	12.7	96
12	Sumitomo	General trading	Japan	95.7	0.3	8
13	Nippon Telegraph & Telephone	Telecommunications	Japan	93.6	−0.6	224
14	Marubeni	General trading	Japan	91.8	0.02	5
15	AXA	Insurance	France	87.6	3.7	92
16	IBM	Computers	USA	87.6	8.1	316
17	BP Amoco	Oil	UK	83.6	11.9	80
18	Citigroup	Diversified financial	USA	82.0	13.5	230
19	Volkswagen	Motor vehicles	Germany	80.1	N/A	324
20	Nippon Life Insurance	Insurance	Japan	78.5	3.6	60

Figure 12–1   *The 20 largest companies in the world in 2000 had their headquarters in only five countries. There are no close equivalents to Japan's enormous general trading companies in North America or Europe.*

Country/ Company	GDP/Revenue (US$ billions)	Country/ Company	GDP/Revenue (US$ billions)	Country/ Company	GDP/Revenue (US$ billions)
Bangladesh	187	Hong Kong	158	Norway	111
Chile	185	Portugal	151	Ukraine	110
Sweden	184	Greece	149	Nigeria	110
Venezuela	183	Algeria	143	*Itochu*	109
General Motors	177	Denmark	128	Morocco	108
Wal-Mart Stores	167	Czech Republic	121	*Royal Dutch/Shell*	105
Exxon-Mobil	164	*Mitsui*	119	Petoria	
Ford	163	*Mitsubishi*	118		
Daimler-Chrysler	160	*Toyota*	116		
		General Electric	112		

Figure 12–2   *The "economies" of the largest companies (shown in italics) measured by their revenues, compared with the GDPs of some nations. The economic power of these companies is intensified by the fact that all their efforts are focussed on one goal—increasing their size and profitability.*

than the GDP of Bolivia, while revenues of Toys 'R' Us, The Gap, and L'Oréal can be compared to the GDPs of Jamaica, Latvia, or Madagascar.

Most of the Global 500 companies are located, as one might expect, in the United States, Japan, and countries of the European Union. Figure 12–3 shows the distribution of some of the head offices of the Global 500 companies. Not only are more than 90 per cent of these companies located in these three parts of the world; almost all of the very largest companies are here. In 2000, 98 of the 100 largest companies were American, Japanese, or European. Canada's situation is typical of developed countries outside of the USA–Japan–EU economic hub. In the 2000 list, with one exception (Nortel Networks), all of Canada's largest companies ranked at or below 345 on the Global 500.

One striking feature is how few of the companies on the Global 500 list in 2000 had their headquarters outside the First World. Only 19 companies were found in the developing world—not even half as many as in Germany alone. The reality is that most giant companies in developing countries exist for one of two reasons. First,

a significant number were created only to market oil-producing nations' output, often by selling the oil to giants like Mobil-Exxon and Shell. In 2001, Global 500 national oil companies were in China, Brazil, Mexico, Russia, Venezuela, India, and Malaysia. Second, many companies are created by governments to promote economic development. In China, for example, the relatively large number of Global 500 companies, at least by the standards of the developing world, were created by the Chinese government in an attempt to modernize an antiquated economic infrastructure. In many ways, these Chinese companies are more like Canadian Crown corporations such as Canada Post and Via Rail than conventional, privately owned enterprises.

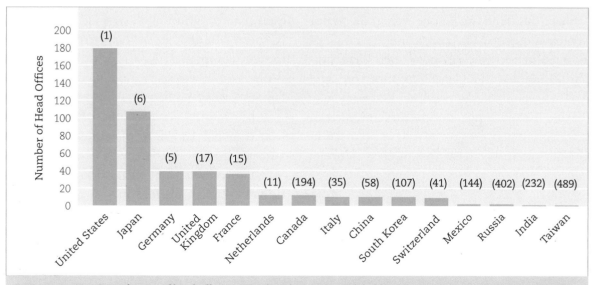

Figure 12–3 *Distribution of head offices in 15 selected countries (Global 500 ranks shown in parentheses). Clearly, the distribution does not reflect the population of the host countries. Can you suggest what factors influence distribution?*

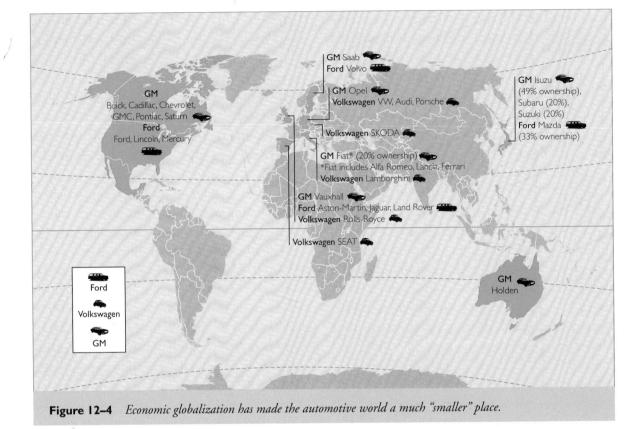

Figure 12–4 *Economic globalization has made the automotive world a much "smaller" place.*

One of the most important characteristics of transnational companies is the international scope of their operations, which is contributing to the gradual breakdown of national identities. Perhaps this trend can best be seen in the motor vehicle industry. Most people are not aware of how few motor vehicle manufacturers there actually are in the world. General Motors, Ford, and Volkswagen provide an excellent example (Figure 12–4). A major impact of the large number of acquisitions and mergers that have occurred in the auto industry is the loss of clear national identities for brands of automobiles. You may be surprised to find out that such famous British brands as Jaguar and Aston Martin are part of the Ford empire, while the legendary Italian marques, Lamborghini (Volkswagen) and Ferrari (General Motors), are at least partly owned by foreign companies. As a result of this trend, BMW was able to sell a modern version of the famous British Mini.

The "family connections" of two closely related models can show the complexity of the auto industry. During the 2001 model year, Volvo introduced their S40 and V40 models to Canada. At first glance, buyers might assume that their new Volvos were made in Sweden. In fact, Volvo no longer makes cars at all. In 1999, they sold their car-making division to Ford. Volvo cars are now made by a Ford division called Volvocars. The S40 and V40 are actually made in the Netherlands, in a factory that is a joint venture by Ford with the Japanese automaker, Mitsubishi. But Mitsubishi is partly owned by Daimler-Chrysler. The S40/V40 is, in reality, produced cooperatively by two traditional rivals, Ford and Daimler-Chrysler. To complicate matters further, the identical car is sold as a Mitsubishi in some parts of the world and as a Volvo elsewhere.

Another feature of transnational corporations in the 21st century is the enormous scope of their operations. What products do you associate with the General Electric Company? Probably products like refrigerators and electrical equipment come immediately to mind, but GE's manufacturing goes far beyond this. It also makes aircraft engines, locomotives, generating station equipment, plastics, medical imaging equipment, and even nuclear reactors. This list tells only part of the story. GE's operations now extend far beyond manufacturing. More than half the company's revenues come from a division called GE Capital, which provides a wide range of financial services to millions of customers.

Questions About the Growth of Transnationals

The growth in the number and size of transnational corporations has proven very controversial. Those who support the growth of huge transnational corporations maintain that this growth is an inevitable and desirable outcome of an effectively operating free market. They point out that this development provides many benefits for the peoples of the world. These benefits include:

- The provision to consumers of an ever-widening range of products and services at affordable prices. This allows more and more people of the world to enjoy the benefits of everything from consumer goods to entertainment and pharmaceuticals.
- An overall increase in world economic growth

that will make everyone wealthier by providing more jobs and greater economic production. This benefit has been described as "a rising tide that lifts all boats."
- A stimulus for the economic development of developing nations.
- A faster and more equitable sharing of the most recent technological breakthroughs.

Critics of the growth of transnationals reply with the following arguments:

- The growth of transnationals encourages the worst aspects of globalization. There could be a loss of local cultural identities as the products of US, European, and Japanese companies become commonly used everywhere. In particular, US cultural domination could erode cultural identities, since US companies dominate the market for entertainment and consumer products.
- Corporations are becoming so large that they are beyond the control of governments. Whose laws apply when a company's operations extend far beyond the borders of any country? An interesting example of this problem occurred in 2001 when the European Union turned down a potential takeover of Honeywell International by General Electric. What made this decision odd was that both of these companies were US-owned.
- Rather than making everyone richer, the growth of transnationals will benefit the developed world far more than the developing world. Most of the best jobs and the profits will go to the former. The latter will get only low-paying jobs and the possibility of environmental damage.
- The operation of transnationals produces economic uncertainty. These companies "shop around" for the best places in which to do business. This means they can play one country against another in their search for the cheapest labour or the weakest environmental standards.

Growth of Free Trade Agreements

Key to the growth of economic globalization has been an explosion in the number and extent of **free trade agreements**. The increase in the number of these agreements is shown in Figure 12–5. The expansion of free trade in the world allows much larger free markets to exist; that, according to supporters, promotes greater worldwide economic growth and prosperity. Barriers to investment and the movement of technology disappear, and artificial limits to growth are eliminated. Opponents fear a loss of national sovereignty and the loss of a country's ability to protect its culture, environment, labour standards, and social programs.

It is not a coincidence that most of the growth in free trade agreements occurred at the same time (beginning in the early 1990s) as the rise in influence of neo-liberal economic thought, which strongly believes in the effectiveness of free market economies. Before this time, most governments felt that their role was to manage the economy and ensure something close to full employment. An important way to achieve this goal was by establishing high tariffs and non-tariff barriers to protect local industries. Non-tariff barriers to trade included such measures as purposely complex rules for imports and local-content requirements for government purchases. So, during the first half of the 20th century, attempts to promote free trade were limited. The mass of free trade agreements that arose in the latter half of the century were drawn up to eliminate tariffs and other barriers to trade.

The first major region to move towards free trade was Western Europe. The process started in 1958 with the signing of the Treaty of Rome, which liberalized trade in goods and services and paved the way for a fuller free trade agreement that was signed in 1971. The original members of the European Community (EC) were Belgium, France, Germany, Italy, Luxembourg, and the Netherlands.

Since then, the EC, now known as the European Union (EU), has expanded both in

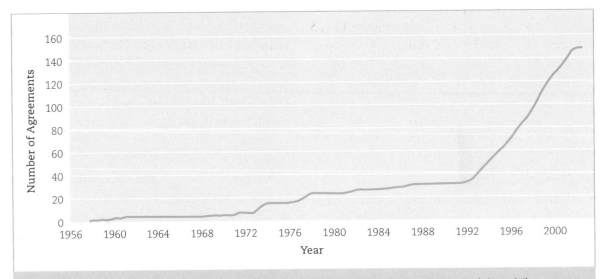

Figure 12–5 *An explosion in free trade agreements began around 1992. Most of these were bilateral (between two nations), often involving small countries, although some, like NAFTA, affected hundreds of millions of people.*
Source: World Trade Organization.

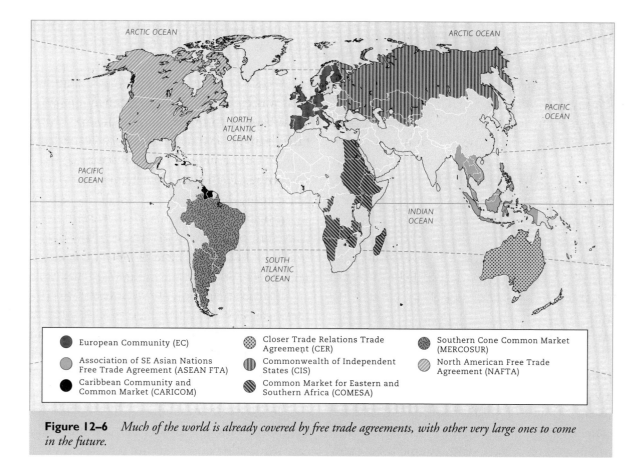

Figure 12–6 *Much of the world is already covered by free trade agreements, with other very large ones to come in the future.*

Legend:
- European Community (EC)
- Association of SE Asian Nations Free Trade Agreement (ASEAN FTA)
- Caribbean Community and Common Market (CARICOM)
- Closer Trade Relations Trade Agreement (CER)
- Commonwealth of Independent States (CIS)
- Common Market for Eastern and Southern Africa (COMESA)
- Southern Cone Common Market (MERCOSUR)
- North American Free Trade Agreement (NAFTA)

size and purpose. Denmark, Ireland, and the United Kingdom joined in 1973; Greece in 1981; Portugal and Spain in 1986; and Austria, Finland, and Sweden in 1995 (see Figure 11–13 on page 182). As the new century began, several formerly Communist countries in Eastern Europe were trying to join. The Union's purpose has also expanded beyond that of a free trade agreement. A common currency, the Euro, has been introduced that has replaced most national currencies. In addition, the EU is creating a rapid-response military force that can be used instead of national armies for peacekeeping and peacemaking missions.

The EU also has negotiated bilateral free trade agreements with many countries. Some of these agreements were with potential new members of the EU (like the Czech Republic, Poland, and Hungary). Others were with European countries that wanted closer trade relations with their huge neighbour, but did not want to become members of the EU (like Switzerland and Norway), while others were with countries and peoples that the EU wanted to aid (like South Africa and the Palestinian Authority). Regional free trade agreements have also been made in many other parts of the world. The more important of these are shown in Figure 12–6.

Did you KNOW?

New members may join the European Union only if all current members agree. In 2001, Irish voters turned down a planned expansion because they feared that the economic health of the Union could be harmed if the poorer countries of Eastern Europe were allowed in.

Did you KNOW?

Freer trade exists between Canada and the United States than between the provinces. For example, marketing boards regulate the supply of milk, poultry, and eggs by allotting quotas to farmers by province. Quebec farmers have 47 per cent of the milk quotas, and British Columbia has to import milk, despite having farmers who could easily produce enough milk for the local market.

As well as the multilateral regional trade agreements shown in Figure 12–6—which involve groups of several countries—there are dozens of bilateral agreements. In total, much of the world is already part of one or more free trade agreements.

The next stage in the process seems to be discussion of the possibilities of even wider free trade zones. In addition to the expansion of the EU, discussions have been held about a Pacific Rim free trade agreement and a free trade agreement for the Americas. It is not hard to imagine that eventually the entire world may be united in some sort of free trade. In fact, this is the long-term intention of the World Trade Organization (WTO), the international organization responsible for managing and liberalizing trade in the world.

Free Trade and Canada

Canada's history is rife with disagreements over whether we should have free trade, in particular with the United States. Early in our history, from 1854 to 1866, we did have a limited free trade agreement with the United States. But Canada's first prime minister, Sir John A. Macdonald, won an election in 1878 based on his National Policy, and free trade was abandoned. This policy was designed to protect Canadian manufacturers from American (and other) competition. In 1911, Prime Minister Wilfrid Laurier ran for re-election on a campaign that would have allowed freer trade with the United States. He lost, indicating that Canadians of that time were still not comfortable with the idea of free trade with their neighbour. Twenty years later, during the Great Depression, even more protectionist trade policies were put in place in a futile attempt to minimize the impact of the Depression by protecting local producers.

Since the 1930s, it was the Conservative and (later) Progressive Conservative parties that, historically, favoured more unfettered trade relations with the United States; in recent years, freer trade has found a place in Liberal administrations. This fact points out the confusion that exists with respect to the use of terms like liberal, conservative, neo-liberal, and neo-conservative, in particular when we consider them in relation to political parties that may use these words in their official names.

Canada's move towards free trade began with the signing of the **Auto Pact** in 1965. It is an example of **sectoral free trade**, since it involved only one specific part of the economy. The Auto Pact was a profoundly important document in Canada's economic history. In many ways it was a type of free trade, but in one important respect it was not. The Auto Pact effectively eliminated the border for the products of the "Big Three" car manufacturers (General Motors, Ford, and Chrysler). No longer were cars like the Mercury Montcalm and Pontiac Laurentian produced only for the Canadian market. Instead, auto plants in Canada and the United States were used to make a particular model for both countries. It was a form of free trade agreement in the sense that barriers to trade were eliminated, but the agreement included one additional component that certainly did not reflect a free trade bias. The Canadian government feared that, in a completely uncontrolled free trade environment, all auto assembly might end up in the United States. To prevent this, they insisted on a rule that would require at least one vehicle to be assembled in Canada for each car that was sold in Canada. Because of this clause in the Auto Pact, it might be most accurate to describe the agreement as **managed free trade**.

At the time, few would have predicted what a bonanza the Auto Pact would be for Canada. The Big Three found that assembly of automobiles in Canada made good sense. Labour costs were lower in Canada than in the United States and quality was high. Auto production in Canada grew significantly, with southern Ontario becoming the eastern section of the world's greatest auto production region. By the late 1990s, Canada was exporting one million more motor vehicles than it was importing. Most people know that Canada is a major exporter of natural resource products like grains and lumber, but they have little sense of how important the auto industry is (see Figure 12–7).

Next came the **Free Trade Agreement (FTA)** with the United States. In the 1988 general election, Brian Mulroney's Progressive Conservative Party campaigned in support of free trade with the United States. The FTA came into effect on January 1, 1989, with all bilateral tariffs and other trade restrictions to be removed by 1999. Trade disputes were to be settled using a mechanism that ultimately could lead to decisions being made by the World Trade Organization (WTO). The Auto Pact ended in 2000 as a result of a challenge made to the WTO by foreign carmakers, who felt that the Big Three had an unfair advantage in selling cars in North America.

The third step in the process was the extension of the FTA to include Mexico to create the **North American Free Trade Agreement**

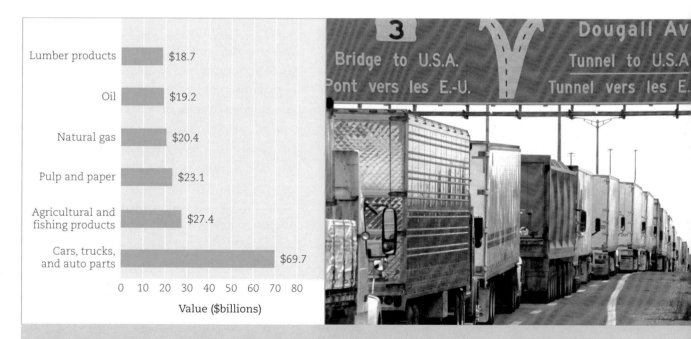

Figure 12–7 *The value (in Canadian dollars) of Canada's exports, 2000. A major problem has developed at the border crossings in Southern Ontario—how to get so many trucks carrying vehicles and auto parts across the border quickly.* Source: Adapted from Statistics Canada Web site, <www.statcan.ca/english/Pgdb/Economy/International/gblec04.htm>, extracted Mar. 22, 2002.

(NAFTA) in 1994. At first glance, this larger agreement would not seem to be of vital interest to Canada, since Canada–Mexico trade has never been very large. In reality, the extension of free trade southward offers both opportunities and risks to Canada. Mexico has a large and growing market of more than 100 million people who are becoming wealthier. Hence, it is an attractive new market for Canadian businesses. On the other hand, there is always the possibility that Canada may lose jobs to Mexico, where wage rates are a fraction of those in Canada.

Canada has also signed bilateral free trade agreements with Chile and Israel in an attempt to stimulate trade with these countries and expand opportunities for Canadian companies in these markets. The trade treaty with Chile can also be seen as a step towards a broader Free Trade Area of the Americas (FTAA) agreement. At three meetings, the first in Miami in 1994, leaders of all of the nations of the Americas (with the exception of Cuba, which is not a member of the Organization of American States, the US-dominated organization that organized the initiative) met to develop a huge free trade zone that would come into effect in 2005. The third meeting of heads of government occurred in Quebec City in 2001 at the Summit of the Americas. Because of growing concern over globalization, these meetings have been met with increasingly large and vocal protests (Figure 12–8).

You can examine the FTAA from the perspective of its supporters and its opponents at <www.pearsoned.ca/globalconnections>.

There also is a plan to develop an immense free trade agreement among the 21 countries along the Pacific Rim that are members of the Asia–Pacific Economic Cooperation (APEC) group (Figure 12–9). The plan is to have free trade among all the developed countries in APEC by 2010, with full free trade among all members by 2020. If this free trade agreement does become a reality, it would be by far the largest in the world. As with the FTAA, plans for Pacific Rim free trade have provoked significant protests, including those at an APEC meeting in Vancouver in 1997.

In the contemporary world there are few issues that have proven as controversial as the move to increased economic globalization. The fight against economic globalization has focussed on the growth of transnational corporations and the expansion of free trade. The protest against transnationals is evident in campaigns against companies that are seen as operating sweatshops and that use child labour to produce clothing, shoes, and other goods in developing countries. It can also be seen in attacks made on the franchises of companies like McDonald's and Starbucks during anti-globalization protests in North America and Europe. The fight against the expansion of free trade can be seen in wide-scale demonstrations and in hundreds of anti-globalization Internet sites. Critics contend that any benefits that may come from free trade will not make up for the costs that may follow. For Canada, these include the fear that our culture and health care systems are threatened and that the gap between the rich and the poor can only grow larger.

Figure 12–8 *For dozens of heads of government, Quebec City provided a beautiful setting for a meeting to discuss the creation of a Free Trade Agreement of the Americas. For anti-globalization demonstrators, the event meant facing more tear gas than had ever before been used in Canada.*

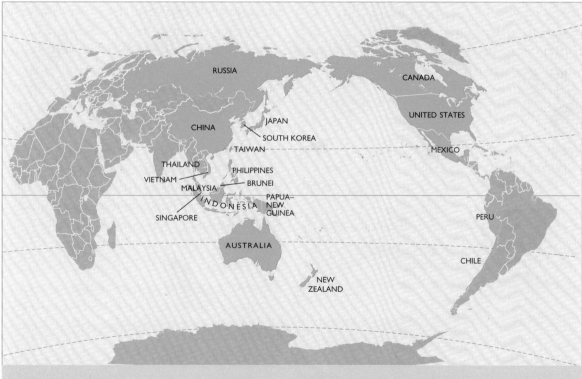

Figure 12–9 *These nations, the members of APEC, are to be linked by a free trade agreement between the years 2010 and 2020.*

Chapter Questions

Knowledge and Understanding

1. a) Why is a comparison between a company's sales and a nation's GDP a meaningful one?
   b) What does this comparison suggest about the amount of influence that a large company might have when it comes into conflict with smaller nations?

2. Examine the statistics in Figure 12–1 and answer the following questions.
   a) What kinds of businesses are most common among the largest companies in the world?
   b) Why have companies in these fields grown so large?
   c) What do the profit statistics suggest about the state of Japanese business today?
   d) Why have you heard of some of these companies and not others?

3. a) How are the trade agreements of NAFTA and the countries of the European Union similar?
   b) In what ways are they different?
   c) Could the NAFTA develop to be more like the European Union?

4. Create a table to summarize the arguments in favour of and in opposition to economic globalization.

Thinking and Inquiry

5. a) Use an atlas to compare the distribution of Global 500 headquarters among the world's countries to the distribution of the world's population. What differences do you see between these patterns? Why are these differences a problem?
   b) Give two reasons why countries like the Netherlands, Belgium, Italy, the United Kingdom, and France have so many large companies.

6. Investigate the current status of the FTAA and APEC free trade negotiations. What progress has been made in implementing these agreements and in meeting the concerns of free trade critics?

Communication

7. Construct a metaphor that an opponent to economic globalization might use to counteract the pro-globalization comment, "A rising tide lifts all boats." Compare your metaphor to that of a classmate. Within the context of globalization, was each understandable to the other person?

8. On their Web site, which you can access through <www.pearsoned.ca/globalconnections>, a citizens' group called Action for Community and Ecology in the Regions of Central America summarizes its opposition to the FTAA with the dramatic statement:

   > "FTAA = MAI* + NAFTA = DEATH
   > Death to democracy, indigenous rights, environment, human rights, labor unions, women's rights, sovereignty, healthcare, education, food safety, culture, LIFE"

   Work with two or three other students to investigate this statement. Each person should investigate at least two of these concerns. Prepare a poster to describe your findings. Be sure to include arguments both in support of and in opposition to this group's feelings.

   *MAI (Multilateral Agreement on Investments) was an attempt, now abandoned, to reduce barriers to international investment and to protect the rights of investors.

Application

9. In this chapter, you saw how complex the interconnections are in the auto industry and how the number of brand names is actually much greater than the number of auto companies. Similar situations exist in other industries as well. Research one of these and produce an organizational diagram showing the relationship between ownership and brand names. It might be easiest to look at some area of consumer spending like packaged foods, clothing production and retailing, soft drinks, or brewing. You should be able to research this topic by visiting the Web sites of major corporations, using business publications, or both.

10. Some people feel that the operations of transnational corporations in developing countries are almost completely exploitative (e.g., sweatshop manufacturing). Others feel that they are a useful aid in the economic growth of these countries. They provide vital jobs and foreign income that will allow these countries to advance. With which of these sides would you agree? Explain your view.

11. Has free trade been good for Canada or not? Research the impact of free trade on Canada and try to determine if it has, in your opinion, been a good thing. You might want to consider the impact of free trade on such issues as the growth of the GDP, the number and quality of jobs created, and the environment. The report of your findings should be 300 to 400 words in length and should include a bibliography.

12. Not every country in the Organization of American States favoured the idea of the FTAA. The Brazilian government was only lukewarm towards the idea because they were afraid of losing the advantages of MERCOSUR and their dominant position in this regional free trade area. The Venezuelan government was openly hostile to the notion because they feared that they could not protect their identity and independence. Are such concerns valid? Will a point be reached when free trade exists across the entire world, or will this aspect of economic globalization decline in importance as economic protectionism re-emerges? Write a brief paper (400 to 500 words) to address these questions. Besides giving your own opinions based on your current knowledge of the situation, describe any additional information you feel that you might need to obtain to make the most reasoned position possible.

Answers to Quiz, page 187

1. General Motors; **2.** Wal-Mart Stores (2), Exxon-Mobil (3), Ford (4), Daimler-Chrysler (5); **3.** United States (179 companies); **4.** Japan (107 companies), Germany (39), United Kingdom (39), France (36); **5.** Exxon-Mobil ($17.7 billion); **6.** 194—Nortel Networks; **7.** 12; **8.** Nortel Networks (194), George Weston (345), CIBC (361), Royal Bank (374), Trans-Canada Pipelines (399), Seagram (418), Bank of Montreal (444), Bank of Nova Scotia (446), Sun Life (466), TD Bank (468), Power Corporation (488); **9.** 19—China (10), Brazil (3), Mexico (2), Venezuela (1), India (1), Malaysia (1), South Africa (1); **10.** All are on the list.

13

Economic Disparity in the World

Expectations

In this chapter, you will:

■ identify the social, economic, cultural, and political aspects of globalization

■ compare statistics about quality of life in developed and developing countries

■ analyse the causes of economic disparity

■ understand the interdependence of countries in the global economy

■ analyse the economic consequences of past colonialism and present economic colonialism

■ use statistical methods to analyse information

Most observers agree that economic globalization has created more wealth in the world. Unfortunately, the economic growth has not been shared equitably among all nations and peoples. While the wealthier nations (like Singapore, above) have seen their economies grow, poor countries have not. This chapter explores the implications of the growing gap between rich and poor nations.

Growth in Economies: Five Worlds

1. Figure 13–1 summarizes the growth in gross domestic product for a sample of countries in the Five Worlds, including Canada. Create two graphs with these data.

   a) First, create bar graphs to show the data in columns 2 and 3. Use a different colour or pattern (for example, dashed lines) for the countries in each world. Label each pair of bars with the country's name.

   b) For the second graph, plot the data in columns 1 and 4 using bar graphs. Colour and label the lines as in (a).

2. Using columns 2 and 3, calculate the average growth of the countries in each world between 1960 and 2000.

3. What do the results that you obtained in question 2 suggest about the nature of growth in each of the Five Worlds?

4. What significance is there to the fact that growth is shown as percentages, rather than dollar amounts? [Hint: Which would you prefer—60 per cent of $1.00 or 1 per cent of $1000?]

5. Ethiopia's economy grew during each time period between 1960 and 2000, and yet its 2000 per capita GDP is below its 1960 level (expressed in the more valuable dollars of 1985). Similar, although less extreme, situations exist in other countries. Why? [Hint: Remember that the 1980 to 2000 changes are calculated in local currencies.] What impact would this have on the level of prosperity of these countries?

Growth in GDPs

		1	2	3	4
First World	United States	9895	155%	156%	33 934
	Japan	2954	341%	154%	34 402
	Canada	7258	195%	135%	20 874
Second World	Romania	431	330%	85%	1 507
	China	567	171%	229%	791
Third World	South Korea	904	342%	329%	8 712
	Chile	2885	135%	194%	4 521
Fourth World	Indonesia	638	201%	175%	729
	Pakistan	638	174%	163%	453
Fifth World	Haiti	924	112%	64%	570
	Ethiopia	257	125%	103%	108

Column 1 – GDP per capita in 1960, expressed in 1985 US dollars

Column 2 – Increase of GDP from 1960–1980 based on US dollars

Column 3 – Increase of GDP from 1980–2000 based on local currency

Column 4 – GDP per capita in 2000, expressed in US dollars (2000)

Figure 13–1 *Growth in gross domestic product for selected countries, 1960 to 2000.*
Source: Based on data from Center for Economic and Policy Research.

Global Economic Disparity

As you have seen in the previous activity, a glaring fact of economic life is the enormous **economic disparity** that exists in the world. For the world's poor, the situation has been described as "a race to the bottom." The United Nations has reported that per capita incomes in 100 countries, with a combined population of 1.6 billion, have dropped from the maximum levels ever reached. This decline has not been just a recent phenomenon. Remarkably, almost 20 countries, from Armenia and Tajikistan to Nicaragua and Sudan, reached their maximum per capita income in 1960 or before, with 50 more reaching theirs in the 1960s and 1970s.

By the end of the 1990s, the world found itself in the sad situation in which its 13 richest countries had per capita GDPs of more than US$20 000, while the 26 poorest countries had per capita GDPs of less than US$350 per year (Figure 13–2). While 200 million people saw their incomes fall between 1965 and 1983, the situation was even worse between 1980 and 1993, when more than five times that many experienced a decline in income.

At the same time, there has been a much smaller number of economic winners, some of whom have enjoyed remarkable success. The traditional "fat cats" of the world, like most of the members of the **Organization for Economic Co-operation and Development (OECD)**, have maintained their growth. A few countries, such as the so-called "Asian tigers" (Taiwan, South Korea, Singapore, and Hong Kong), have produced a model for growth and prosperity that the developing world has tried in vain to copy (Figure 13–3).

Figure 13–2 *Haiti, one of the 26 poorest countries, had a per capita GDP of US$1800 in 2000.*

Figure 13–3 *Hong Kong, one of the "Asian Tigers," had a per capita GDP of US$25 400 in 2000.*

A graph of income distribution in the world clearly illustrates the situation (Figure 13–4). This graph makes an interesting and important distinction between urban and rural populations in India and China. Similar distinctions could be made in most countries, although the number of people involved would not be large enough to register on this graph.

The Nature of the Problem of Disparity

Less than 20 per cent of the Earth's GDP is produced in the developing world, and yet this is where 80 per cent of its people live. In the next 25 years, the Earth's population is likely to increase by about two billion. Of these people, 97 per cent will be in the developing world, and the vast majority of them will be poor. Such poverty produces a great reduction in opportunities for human development.

As a result of drastically different rates of economic growth, the gap between the world's rich and poor has grown steadily wider. Income disparities can be measured using a statistical tool called the **Gini index**. Gini values can range from 0 (which means that income is distributed perfectly evenly among everyone) to 1 (which means that all income is owned by one person). Depending on the source, Gini index values are sometimes given as decimals (for example, 0.66) and sometimes as whole numbers (for example, 66.0). Gini values can also be shown graphically (Figure 13–5). In 1988, the world's Gini index was 0.625. By 1993, it had risen to 0.66. Since then, it has continued to increase.

In addition to the problem of global disparity, significant economic disparities exist within each nation. These disparities are worst in developing countries, with Gini coefficients in many countries exceeding 0.60 (Figure 13–6). The UN uses a Gini value of 0.4 as a warning level that a country's economic disparities are

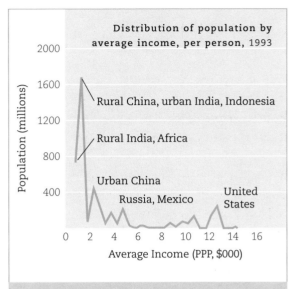

Figure 13–4 *Average income is calculated in terms of purchasing power parity (PPP), that is, by comparing the cost of similar items, such as food, among countries.* Source: Branko Milanovic, "True world income distribution, 1988 and 1993." Washington, DC: World Bank.

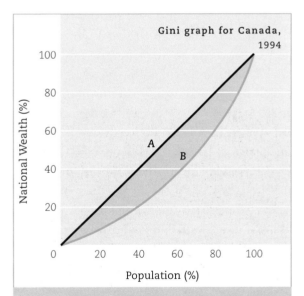

Figure 13–5 *The diagonal line A represents a perfectly equal distribution of the country's income in which each fifth (quintile) of the population gets one-fifth of the income. The other line, B, represents the distribution of income in Canada in 1994. The data for this curve are shown in Figure 13–6. The shaded area between the two lines shows the amount of income inequality.*

Income Disparities							
	Gini Index	Lowest Quintile (poorest)	Low-Middle Quintile	Middle Quintile	High-Middle Quintile	Highest Quintile (wealthiest)	Year of Data
Canada	31.5	7.5%	12.9%	17.2%	23.0%	39.3%	1994
Bangladesh	33.6	8.7	12.0	15.7	20.8	42.8	1995/6
Brazil	60.0	2.5	5.5	10.0	18.3	63.8	1996
China	40.3	5.9	10.2	15.1	22.2	46.6	1998
Italy	27.3	8.7	14.0	18.1	22.9	36.3	1995
United States	40.8	5.2	10.5	15.6	22.4	46.4	1997

Figure 13–6 *Examples of income disparities in selected countries.*
Source: The World Bank Group.

becoming excessive. The people in the most desperate circumstances are the many who are poor in an already poor country.

Dire poverty has been defined as a per capita GDP of less than US$1.00 per day. Compare this amount to how much you might spend to go to a movie, or to buy a new pair of jeans. If we look within specific countries, we can come closer to understanding the human cost. In India, for example, 47 per cent of the population lives on less than US$1.00 per day, while another 40 per cent lives on between US$1.00 and US$2.00. This means that 700 million people have to survive for a day on less than you might spend for popcorn at a movie theatre. The situation is much worse in Zambia, where 85 per cent have less than US$1.00 per day and another 13 per cent have between US$1.00 and US$2.00.

Supporters of economic globalization contend that an important reason why some countries are poor is that they are isolated from the world's economic system. They say globalization will bring much greater prosperity to these countries. Opponents respond by saying that globalization will only make a bad situation worse.

Causes of Disparity

The causes of the world's economic disparities are complex. In contrast to the countries of the First and Third Worlds, and a few Second and Fourth World countries, most of the developing nations have not been able to fund an economic takeoff as described by Rostow. (See Chapter 11 for more about Rostow's theory of economic growth and how colonialism helped countries of the First World to fund their own development.) The reasons for economic disparity will be discussed here and in other chapters of this book. As you look at the reasons that follow, remember that disparity is often a product of poor or

Did you KNOW?

The assets of the Earth's three richest people are similar to the combined GDP of the world's poorest nations, which have a total population of 600 million people. The average income of the citizens of the wealthiest group of countries is 37 times as great as that of the poorest countries. This value doubled between 1990 and 2000.

unfair decisions in the past, rather than a result of fundamental differences in the resource base of different countries. The obvious solution for the future would be to make better decisions.

Impact of Colonialism

Most developing countries were, at one time or another, colonies. Colonization produced distortions in the economic structures of these countries that still have a huge impact, even though they may have been independent for a half-century or more. (The impact of colonization was discussed in Chapter 11.)

Population Growth

In general, developing countries have experienced (and are still experiencing) substantially higher rates of population growth than the developed world. This means that economic growth in developing countries has provided at best a miserable level of existence for more and more people, rather than a higher standard of living for a more stable population. (The population problems of developing countries were discussed in Chapter 6.)

Foreign Debt

In 2000, developing countries owed US$2.5 trillion to creditors in developed countries. (One trillion is one thousand billion!) These debts were so great that many debtor nations, after paying the interest on their loans, had little left to invest in vital economic development, education, and health care. (The reasons for, and problems of, international debt are examined in Chapter 14.)

War

The poorest countries, especially those in Africa, have often had to deal with the devastation of wars and civil unrest arising from tribal conflicts and the ambitions of warlords (Figure 13–7, on the next page). Some civil conflicts, like those in Colombia, Mozambique, and the Democratic Republic of the Congo, have been going on for decades. An argument can be made that, in the years after World War II, the world could be divided into a "zone of war" (which included most of Africa), where conflicts continually stifled efforts to improve the economy, and a "zone of peace," where economic growth occurred in an atmosphere free of the constant threat of conflict. Frequently, in a "zone of war," a rebel group will overthrow the government only to have to focus its energies (and money) on protecting itself from the next insurgency. (World conflict is examined in Chapter 22.)

Leadership Issues

Many of the poorest countries in the world have had to deal with leaders who had little interest or skill in improving the economic lot of the citizens of their countries. Far too often they have used their positions to steal millions—and in some cases, billions—of dollars for their own use.

When leaders emerge who put the interests of their country ahead of those of the international business community, they face fierce opposition. For example, the United States has imposed strict economic sanctions on Cuba since Fidel Castro's government nationalized (took over without payment) the assets of US companies in the early 1960s, after the United States refused to buy Cuba's sugar. It is generally believed that the Central Intelligence Agency (CIA), the United States' main international information-gathering and espionage body, was responsible for the 1973 overthrow of the democratically elected government of Salvador Allende in Chile because it feared that his socialist government might adopt policies similar to those of Castro's Cuba.

Figure 13–7 *Liberians watch as Monrovia, their capital city, burns, May 1996, following a battle between rival factions in a decade-long civil war.*

Trade Inequities

The Group of Eight (G8) nations (with the exception of Russia) have traditionally used tariff and non-tariff barriers to restrict imports from developing countries. For example, the tariffs placed by these countries on cloth and clothing produced in Africa and the Middle East are four times as high as the tariffs on similar products from other G8 countries. At the same time, the G8 nations subsidize their agricultural products so that they are often as cheap or cheaper than commodities from developing countries. Trade policies in the developed world that are fair to all would help poorer countries to reach their economic potential without relying on direct aid from richer countries.

Local Control

Citizens of developing countries complain about the lack of local control that they feel over their own affairs. They point out that far too many critical decisions are made outside their countries by the United Nations, the World Bank, and the International Monetary Fund, by the governments of First World nations, and by the management of transnational corporations.

> **Did you KNOW?**
>
> The G8 members include Canada, the United States, the United Kingdom, France, Germany, Japan, Italy, and Russia. These nations— except for Russia, which did not join until the mid-1990s—are the main holders of developing country debt.

Addressing the Problem

In simplest terms, the solution to inequity lies in addressing the problems listed on the previous two pages.

- For most colonies, political colonialism disappeared only to be replaced by economic colonialism, with the demands of huge corporations coming to replace those of imperial powers. A way must be found for developing nations to run their economies for their own benefit. This is much more difficult to do than it might seem. Typically, a country that relies for income on the export of one or two commodities produced by transnational companies, or on factories using cheap labour to export manufactured products to G8 countries, needs the income from the company more than the company needs that particular country.

- Demographic transition is continuing at a reasonable rate in most developing countries. Rates of natural increase have declined significantly and continue to decline in the great majority of countries. Populations that are growing at a slower rate will allow developing countries to use more of their resources to improve the quality of life of their people. However, as you will see in Chapter 25, when an epidemic such as AIDS kills millions, including many of the most productive members of society, an entirely new set of problems is created.

- For many years, various types and amounts of development assistance have flowed from developed to developing countries. Some of this aid has proven successful, while in many cases the results have been disappointing. In the future, larger sums of money and more effective forms of aid will be needed. (Development assistance will be considered in the second half of this chapter.)

- It is generally agreed, in both the developed and developing worlds, that the levels of debt owed by developing countries are unsustainable. (Read Chapter 14 to learn more about efforts to reduce, or even eliminate, this debt.)

- The governments of the developing world are demanding a greater voice in the vital decisions that affect them. For example, most of the governments of Africa agreed in 2001 to work towards the creation of an African Union that would be modelled after the European Union. The creation of such a large and powerful economic and political bloc would make it easier for African governments to stand up to foreign interests during negotiations over international debts and globalization rules.

- Developing countries need leaders who are prepared to work for the national good rather than for their own interests. Mobutu Sese Seko, the former president of the Democratic Republic of the Congo (Zaire), for example, was believed to have amassed a personal fortune of over US$3 billion during his term of office. Meanwhile, by 1994, the per capita GNP of the population had fallen 70 per cent from the 1958 figure.

Development Assistance

Governments, NGOs, and private individuals have recognized the need to support the world's poor. But how successful have their efforts been?

The Marshall Plan: A Standard for Foreign Aid

Development assistance (often called **foreign aid**) has been used for over a half-century to address the problem of global economic disparity. After World War II, Europe lay in ruins, and the United States and the Soviet Union were already starting to compete for influence in the post-war world. In 1947, General George C. Marshall, the US Secretary of State, proposed a remarkably generous reconstruction plan for Western Europe. Over the next few years, the United States gave the non-communist nations of Europe US$13 billion to aid their recovery from the war. Similar generous aid was given to Japan. The cost of the Marshall Plan was very high—between 2 and 3 per cent of the total US gross national product (GNP) for several years.

It was no surprise that the Marshall Plan was successful. While Western Europe had been devastated by war, there was an enormous amount of know-how to rely on, along with a centuries-long tradition of economic leadership. Unlike many developing countries today, an infrastructure had existed, even though it needed repair.

While the Marshall Plan was a very generous act, the United States was not being totally altruistic. Making the products that Europe needed to rebuild helped US industries convert from wartime to peacetime production and helped to prevent a serious economic downturn. As well, an economically rebuilt Europe became a good customer for US products. Beyond these benefits, the Marshall Plan ensured that as much of Europe as possible would remain non-communist. In fact, international assistance became a major weapon in the Cold War between the Soviet Union and the West that was to dominate world relations for the next four decades.

Reasons for Providing Development Assistance

There are many reasons why a country might want to offer development assistance to its less wealthy neighbours. Some of the most important follow.

Humanitarian Motives

Countries in Europe and North America have a strong Christian and humanitarian tradition of giving aid. There is a belief that the rich countries have a responsibility to help poorer countries. Similarly, wealthy Islamic countries like Saudi Arabia and the United Arab Emirates provide a great deal of humanitarian aid to poorer Muslim countries.

Economic Motives

Giving aid may benefit the economy of the donor country. In many cases, aid is given in kind (that is, as material such as food or industrial equipment) or is linked directly to purchases from the donor. For example, Canada may give aid in the form of wheat from Saskatchewan or provide the funding to purchase transportation equipment from Ontario.

Political Motives

Aid may be given to foster strong relationships between the donor and the recipient (or not given, to punish a country that a donor might disagree with). When describing the president of one Latin American country that received US aid during the Cold War, President Lyndon Johnson allowed that, given the harsh and corrupt rule of the man, he could be described as a "bastard," but, Johnson added, "He is our bastard."

Assistance is often linked to former colonial relationships. This has even influenced the way in which Canada gives aid. We have a stronger record of giving aid to former British and French colonies than to other developing countries. In giving such aid, Canada talks about having "special relationships" with members of the Commonwealth and La Francophonie. The prime requirement for belonging to either of these organizations is that a country was a former colony of either the British or French empires.

Development Assistance After the Marshall Plan

The Marshall Plan created a model for development assistance for the next half-century. In fact, the chancellor of Austria called for a "Marshall Plan for the South" in 1959. (The reason for calling the world's developing nations the "South" was described in Chapter 3.) This proposal was followed, in 1960, by a call from the World Council of Churches for the world's richer countries to give 1 per cent of their GNP for aid. Eventually, a UN Commission led by Canadian Prime Minister Lester Pearson decided that the target for development assistance should be set at 0.7 per cent. This laudable target remains today, but is rarely reached.

Overall, foreign aid was relatively successful in the three decades between the early 1950s and the early 1980s. Evidence of this success can be seen in the growth in income, increased life expectancy, and the decline in fertility rates and infant mortality that occurred virtually everywhere in the developing world. Most impressive of all was the impact of the Green Revolution, which dramatically increased food production and reduced the potential for a Malthusian population decline. (The Green Revolution was discussed in Chapter 10.)

While the 1960s were described as the "Decade of Development," the 1980s came be known as development's "Lost Decade." Donor countries' confidence in the benefits of foreign aid started to drop significantly and continued in the 1990s. This decline coincided with decreased development assistance (Figure 13–8, on the next page) and with reduced levels of both economic and social growth in many recipient countries. There are several reasons why development aid in the latter part of the century was not as successful as it was in the preceding years.

The Cold War

The immediate needs of the Cold War took precedence over the need to focus on the elimination of poverty. An example of this is the attention paid to the Koreas in the years after the Korean War, which lasted from 1950 to 1953. While US aid was paying for 60 per cent of South Korea's defence spending and providing 66 per cent of its investments, communist-bloc aid was providing 45 per cent of the entire economic activity of North Korea.

Promoting Development

The problem of promoting growth in the developing world after World War II proved to be a lot more complicated than in Europe. There, the problems were clear. The war had destroyed physical infrastructure—factories, mines, railways, homes—but not the underlying economic structures, government traditions, and advanced human resources. In the developing world, the problems were much more complex and the solutions less clear. A modern economic system had to be built from scratch, not just rebuilt. Of primary importance was the need to deal

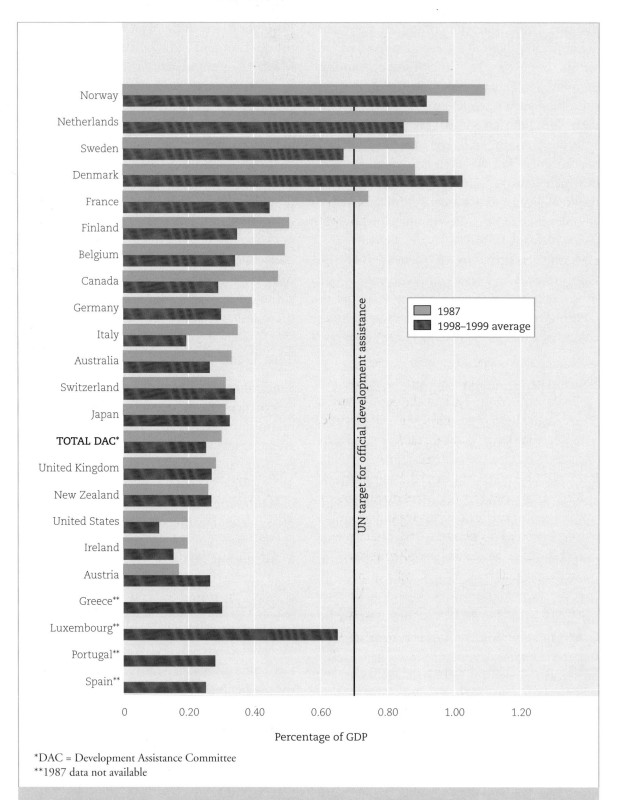

Figure 13–8 *Development assistance by OECD countries that are significant aid donors, 1987–1999.*
Sources: 1987 Development Assistance Committee Report, OECD, 1988; 1998–1999 Average Development Assistance Committee Report, OECD, 2000

with the economic, political, and social problems that colonialism had caused. This was a daunting task, since it was impossible to know how these countries might have developed if colonialism had never existed.

A Flawed Model

Fundamentally, most development assistance in the last half-century has used a flawed model for growth, that is, a top-down, centralized approach that is insensitive to local needs and differences. Two examples will illustrate the problem.

- *Case 1*—Foreign aid donors look at a poor country and determine that there are food deficiencies. They know that the donor country's farmers produce a surplus of food, so a perfect match seems to exist. The donor nation can help its farmers by buying surplus food from them and giving it to the poor country. Experience has shown that it is not this simple. When the donated food reaches the needy country, two serious problems emerge (Figure 13–9). One is that the food aid rarely reaches those who need it most—the rural poor. In most cases, the food aid stays in the cities, often going to people there who could survive without it. The second problem is that the sudden availability of the food aid, particularly in the cities, distorts local markets for agricultural products. Demand for locally produced food declines, which in turn causes reduced prices for the products of the country's farmers. These depressed prices hurt those who are most in need. In some cases, donor countries will provide foodstuffs unfamiliar to people in recipient countries—only because there is a surplus of a particular commodity in the donor country. In one case, children became ill after eating milk powder. Their mothers did not know that they should have mixed the powder with water.

Figure 13–9 *Donations of relief supplies are intended to ease emergencies in poor countries, but distribution to those in greatest need often remains a problem.*

- *Case 2*—A donor nation with a diverse manufacturing industry decides to build a hydroelectric power generating station in a developing country. This decision is applauded at home because the materials needed to build the station will be purchased in the donor country and the donor country will be seen to be helping a less developed country. The problem with many past projects is that they were built without considering the long-term effects. For example, the Akosombo Dam on the Volta River in Ghana was built in 1965 to supply electricity for foreign-owned companies that were promised cheap power to make aluminum. The dam created the largest reservoir in the world at the time, and displaced more than 80 000 people. Many of these families are still living in poverty, and suffering from bilharzia and river blindness, caused by organisms living in the reservoir.

Canada's Uneven History of Development Assistance

For many years, Canada was regarded, in foreign aid terms, as a North American version of a Scandinavian country. This was clearly a compliment, as the Scandinavian countries were the most generous foreign aid donors. Canadians took pride in the fact that one of their prime ministers, Lester Pearson, played a central role in establishing the 0.7 per cent of GDP aid target, and that Canada was one of the more generous aid donors. While Canada never reached the 0.7 per cent target, for many years in the 1980s, considerable progress was made towards it. More recently though, Canada's foreign aid has dropped steeply, and aid efforts have lost focus.

One incident illustrates the confused approach that Canada takes towards foreign aid. In 1995, an earthen dam collapsed in a remote region of Guyana. The dam had been built to hold waste from the Omai gold mine that was owned by Cambior, a Canadian mining company. When the dam broke, it released vast quantities of cyanide-laden water into the Essequibo River, which was both a vital source of drinking water for many people and the most important source of fish in the country. Canadian development assistance played two quite contradictory roles in this incident. On the one hand, in support of a Canadian company, funds from the **Canadian International Development Agency (CIDA)** had been used to train the workers at the Omai mine. At the same time, Canadian aid had been used to fund the activist indigenous groups that had opposed the Omai mine at every step and had predicted that the dam would collapse.

The ambiguous nature of Canadian aid is even shown by a name change in the government department responsible for CIDA. For many years after World War II, it was called the Department of External Affairs. In response to the neo-liberal economic forces of the 1990s, the name was changed to the Department of Foreign Affairs and International Trade. The renaming reflected a change in attitude about the purpose of Canada's international relations.

The Role of NGOs Worldwide

Not all aid is given by governments and multilateral bodies like the United Nations and the World Bank. A significant amount of aid is provided by **non-governmental organizations (NGOs)**, which are non-governmental, non-profit organizations that operate internationally in fields such as development programs and human rights. There are many hundreds of NGOs in the world. Some are world famous, such as the Red Cross, while others are very small and known only to those who work with them or who benefit from their work. CIDA works with NGOs and often helps to fund them. A visit to the CIDA Web site will allow you to connect with dozens of Canadian NGOs (Figure 13–10).

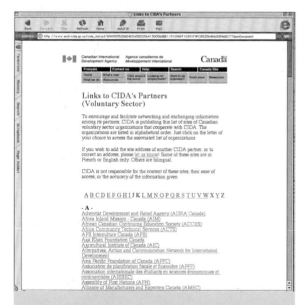

Figure 13–10 *CIDA's Web site offers links to many of its partner NGOs. CIDA's home page can be accessed through <www.pearsoned.ca/ globalconnections>.*

What Will Happen Next?

If we are to understand the future of development aid, we must understand some of the factors that influence policy decisions in this area.

Aid Fatigue

There is a growing feeling in the world that foreign aid does not seem to accomplish very much. After a half-century of development assistance, much of Africa seems worse off than it was before the aid began. There are concerns that much aid money is wasted, that it goes to support a vast, bureaucratic "aid industry," and is used politically in both donor and recipient countries. To support their argument that **aid fatigue** has set in, observers point to the fact that only muted protests were heard in countries like Canada when aid expenditures were cut in the 1990s.

Business Interests Versus the Civil Society

In both the developed and developing worlds, a battle is being waged between business interests and what has been called the **civil society**. The latter is a largely unorganized group that includes many NGOs and independent citizens concerned about labour rights, the environment, human rights, and social development. The most public face of the civil society has been seen in protests at a variety of anti–free trade demonstrations in North America and Europe. Many business supporters view the idea of giving aid as a distortion of the free market system that has been proven not to work. They feel that the best hope for poorly developed countries lies in the economic growth that will occur if the free market system is allowed to operate. In contrast, supporters of the civil society feel that more and better aid must be given.

Calls to Eliminate Development Assistance

Surprisingly, it is not the governments of developed countries, tired of paying development aid, who are saying that development aid should be reduced, or even eliminated. Rather, it is activists in recipient nations who are suggesting this. The only exception to this stance would be aid provided after emergencies such as earthquakes or wars. Activists have several reasons for making this remarkable statement. They point out that too much aid today is tied to Structural Adjustment Programs (SAPs), which require governments receiving loans to cut government services, sell off government assets, boost production of cash crops, and allow foreign competitors into the country. (Structural Adjustment Programs are examined in Chapter 14.)

Opponents argue that SAPs often do more harm than good to social development. They also point out that most aid does not reach the poorest of the poor—in 1998 and 1999, only 23 per cent of the US$61 billion of aid in the world went to the poorest nations. Too much aid is tied to meeting the needs of the donor rather than the recipient. For example, activists point out that aid given in the form of products from the donor country or cash that is used merely to pay debts owed by developing countries to the donor are of little help. In both cases, the aid money ends up going back to the donor country. The final argument against aid is that it leads to a sense of dependency in developing countries.

Whatever the developing nations decide about development assistance is sure to have an important impact on economic disparity in the world.

Learn more about aid in the 21st century at
<www.pearsoned.ca/globalconnections>.

Chapter Questions

Knowledge and Understanding

1. a) Summarize the causes of the large economic disparities that exist among countries in the world.

    b) Suggest how each of these causes can be addressed in the future.

2. Give evidence to support the statement that since World War II "The rich get richer and the poor get poorer."

3. Give two different reasons why it is more helpful for aid to be given as cash than as material.

4. Examine the editorial cartoon in Figure 13–11. What is the significance of the images chosen by the cartoonist? List the main ideas from this chapter that the cartoon expresses.

5. Give at least three reasons why US aid to Western Europe and Japan at the end of World War II was so much more generous than any aid that was given to the rest of the world.

Thinking and Inquiry

6. We tend to take the concept of continuous growth for granted. Why is this so? Were you surprised to learn that most of the world's countries are poorer now than they were at some point in the past? Why or why not?

7. Explain why Gini index values for individual countries are lower (generally between 25 and 60) than the Gini index for the entire world (higher than 66).

8. a) Examine the data shown in Figure 13–8. Group the countries according to their pattern of foreign aid assistance over the 12-year period shown.

    b) What do these groupings say about attitudes towards aid during this time? [Hint: The early 1990s was a time of economic recession in the OECD, while the late 1990s was a time of great economic growth.]

Figure 13–11   *The horn of plenty—a "cornucopia."*

Communication

9. a) Create separate Gini-curve graphs for each of the countries (except Canada) in Figure 13–6. Refer to Figure 13–5 on page 203. Note that to plot line B, the lowest quintile (20%) of Canada's population has 7.5% of income; 40% of the population has 20.4% of income (7.5% plus 12.9%); 60% of the population has 37.6% of income (20.4% plus 17.2%); 80% of the population has 60.6% of income (37.6% plus 23%).

b) Which country has the most equitable distribution of income? Which country has the least equitable distribution of income?

10. Complete the foreign aid mapping exercise that your teacher will give you. You will do this activity either on a paper base map or using ArcView GIS software.

Application

11. Should economic globalization have a purpose? There are three possible answers to this question:

i) No. Globalization is a value-free concept. It is no more than the free market operating in an unfettered way.

ii) Yes. Globalization should operate in such a way as to diminish poverty in the world.

iii) Yes. Globalization should both diminish poverty and reduce the gap between rich and poor.

Choose one of these statements and explain why you agree with it.

12. Battlefield casualty hospitals, like the one shown in the movie and TV show *MASH*, use a triage system to decide which patients should get immediate assistance when the number of wounded exceeds the capacity of the hospital. Casualties are put into one of three groups:

i) those likely to survive with or without medical aid

ii) those likely to die even if they get medical aid

iii) those likely to die without medical aid, but likely to survive with it.

Only those in group (iii) would receive immediate aid. It has been suggested that a similar system should be put in place to decide on recipients for foreign aid, since the amount of aid available is far less than what is needed.

a) How might a triage system work with aid?

b) Identify two countries that would likely be put into each group.

c) Do you agree that such a system should be used? Explain your answer.

13. A question that is often asked is: "Why should Canada give away huge amounts of money for foreign aid when there are so many serious problems at home?" What factors should a Canadian consider before trying to answer this question?

14. Assume that you have been put in charge of the aid efforts of the Canadian International Development Agency and that you have been assigned the job of ensuring that Canadian development assistance is as effective as it can be. State at least six specific reforms that you would introduce to achieve this goal.

International Debt Crisis

Expectations

In this chapter, you will:

■ understand how some economies are affected by decisions made elsewhere

■ understand how quality of life and job prospects are linked to the global economy

■ evaluate the effectiveness of short- and long-term solutions to geographic problems

■ evaluate and communicate the views of different stakeholders in a geographic issue

■ evaluate the effectiveness of international strategies

In the last chapter you learned about the growing gap between rich and poor nations. This chapter explores one of the worst aspects of economic disparity: the plight of those peoples (like the Bolivian miners, above) who have seen the value of their country's exports drop while their debts to the developed world have increased beyond hope of repayment.

A Difficult Dilemma

What would you do if you found yourself in the following situation?

As a student, you took out loans each year to pay for your post-secondary studies, so that at graduation you were $20 000 in debt. After working for someone else for a couple of years, you decided to start your own business. The bank liked your business plan and lent you $50 000 to start your company. You did not like the idea of being $70 000 in debt, but you were sure that your business would be profitable and you could pay off your loans while building a better future for yourself and your family.

After two years of disappointing sales, you came to realize that your operation was just too small to be successful. The only way to rescue your business was to expand. The bank agreed, and decided to lend you another $120 000 for expansion. The only way that you could get the loan was by putting up all of your business and personal assets as collateral (loan security). If you are not able to pay back your loan, you could lose your business, your truck, and your furniture.

Unfortunately, your expansion occurred at the same time as a serious downturn in Canada's economy that was accompanied by much higher interest rates for loans. You now find yourself owing the bank more than $180 000. Even though you have paid almost $70 000 in interest since you left school, you have paid less than $10 000 off the principal of the loan. The interest alone is more than $2200 per month. Sales are slow, and you just can't pay! What should you do?

One possibility is that you could cut your operating costs. For example, you could lay off one of your two workers. You feel badly about this. The person you would fire is a single parent, a good worker, and jobs are difficult to find, but you feel you do not have much choice. If things do not improve you might even have to declare personal **bankruptcy**. This is a legal process that cancels your debts, but it means you would lose your ability to borrow more money for several years.

The Burden of International Debt

An individual has the option of bankruptcy when debts become unsustainable, but under the provisions of international law, a country deeply in debt does not have this choice. Sadly, there are dozens of nations in the developing world that are in exactly this situation. Their debts far exceed their ability to pay, and the future promises only greater debt. By 1998, developing countries owed the staggering sum of almost US$2.5 *trillion* (thousand billion)(Figure 14–1), with this amount increasing at a rate of about 5 per cent per year. Debt service charges or interest in 1998

were almost US$300 billion per year. Countries in all parts of the developing world (Figure 14–2) owe this debt.

> **Did you KNOW?**
> Laws are based on precedent. There is no clear precedent regarding what might or should happen if a country refuses (or is unable) to pay its debts.

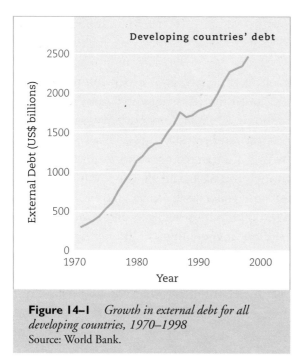

Figure 14–1 *Growth in external debt for all developing countries, 1970–1998*
Source: World Bank.

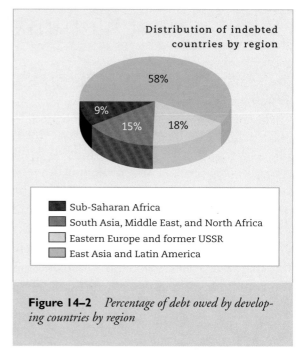

Figure 14–2 *Percentage of debt owed by developing countries by region*

Three types of lenders hold this debt: in 2000, 57 per cent was owed to private lenders like commercial banks, while 27 per cent of the debt was in the form of **bilateral** loans, that is, money lent directly from one country to another. The remaining 16 per cent of debt was held by international agencies like the **World Bank**. The source of loans varies throughout the developing world.

Private lenders consider some regions, like Latin America and the Caribbean, to be "safer" places in which to make loans. These regions are considered better risks by bankers for the same reason that some private borrowers are considered safer than others—the lender feels that the loan has a better chance of being repaid.

There were two main reasons why banks felt that loans to regions like sub-Saharan Africa were too risky. First, because it was the poorest region of the world, there were questions about the ability of the region's nations to pay off substantial loans. Second, the region had (and has) a reputation for political instability. Frequent civil wars and violent overthrows of government do not inspire confidence among bankers. As a result of this lack of confidence, the poorest areas of the world get less than one-quarter of their loans from private lenders, and must rely more heavily on bilateral loans and international agencies like the World Bank.

Effects of Debt

Being deeply in debt has an enormous impact on a poor country. Nowhere is this truer than in the poorest continent of the world, Africa. A summary of the debt situation in this region is given in Figure 14–3. A careful analysis of these data is needed if we are to understand the importance that debt plays in African countries.

Did you KNOW? A bilateral relationship exists between two countries. A multilateral relationship involves more than two countries.

HDI Rank

First, we can confirm from the table that Africa is, in fact, the poorest and least developed region in the world. The United Nations' **Human Development Index (HDI)** is a measure of the quality of life in a country using life expectancy at birth, the adult literacy rate, and per capita GDP. The nations of sub-Saharan Africa make up most of the bottom 25 per cent of this list.

Total and Per Capita Debt

Next is the question of how much debt these countries face. While a country's total debt is important, it tells only part of the story. The populations of these African countries vary enormously, from just over one million (Guinea-Bissau) to more than 120 million (Nigeria). As a result, the per capita debt is much more significant than the total debt. The other thing to consider is the relationship between the size of the debt and the poverty of these countries. To most Canadians, a debt of a few hundred dollars per capita does not seem like very much, but in some of these countries, the per capita debt is several times as much as the annual per capita income. If you know that per capita income in many of these countries is less than one-fiftieth that of Canada, you will have a better understanding of the significance of their debts.

Debt and Social Development

	HDI Rank (of 174)	Total Debt (US$ million)	Debt per Capita (US$)	Debt to Exports (%)*	Spending on Debt Service (% GNP)	Spending on Education (% GNP)
Angola	160	12 173	1014	236	33.0	4.9
Burkina Faso	172	1 399	131	274	2.1	1.5
Burundi	170	1 119	172	806	3.4	4.0
Cameroon	134	9 829	687	356	6.5	2.9
Ethiopia	171	10 352	169	898	1.8	4.0
Ghana	129	6 884	372	172	7.7	4.2
Guinea-Bissau	169	964	803	1733	4.1	3.2
Ivory Coast	154	14 852	1024	246	13.5	5.0
Mauritania	147	2 589	1036	318	11.6	5.1
Nigeria	151	30 315	251	184	3.4	0.7
Senegal	155	3 861	429	187	7.0	3.7
Sierra Leone	174	1 243	254	745	3.2	1.9
Sudan	143	16 843	595	2448	0.7	0.9
Zambia	153	6 865	708	438	6.4	2.2
Zimbabwe	130	4 716	403	148	16.6	7.1

*Debt-to-export ratio relates the debt service cost to the yearly export earnings. For example, in the case of Angola, for every $100 worth of goods it exports, the debt service costs are $236.

Figure 14–3 *Debt and social development in selected African countries, 1998.* Source: Jubilee 2000.

Debt-to-Exports Ratio

An important statistic in understanding international debt is the ratio between a country's debt and the value of its exports. There is an obvious reason for this relationship. Loans are typically given in **hard currencies**, like British pounds, Japanese yen, and (especially) US dollars. Payments must be made in these currencies. Just as you must have a source of income to pay your bills, a country must have a source of hard currency—from exports—to pay for its debt. Some African countries, with debt-to-export ratios of greater than 700 per cent, find that they cannot pay even the interest on their debts, even if they use all of the country's export earnings for this purpose. Far too often, African countries have found themselves involved in civil wars that have essentially eliminated exports.

Debt Servicing

The next statistic to consider is how much the country spends to service its debt. This is expressed in Figure 14–3 as a percentage of the country's gross national product. While there is no clearly defined limit beyond which a country should not go, the simple fact is that the more a country spends on debt payments, the less it will have for other needs.

Two important points should be noted here.

- Some countries, like Angola and Zimbabwe, are paying an enormous amount of their limited wealth to keep up with the interest on their debts.
- The other, much less obvious, point is that some countries, like Sudan, cannot pay enough to cover even their debt service costs, let alone the loans themselves. The level of their debt was increasing by the amount of the unpaid interest.

Spending on Education

The final statistic in Figure 14–3 is the amount of money the country is able to spend on education. In most countries, a comparable amount would be spent on health care. Experience has shown that money spent on education and health care is vital to the economic and social development of a country (Figure 14–4). Unfortunately, many African countries find themselves spending more money on servicing their debt than they do on either education or health care.

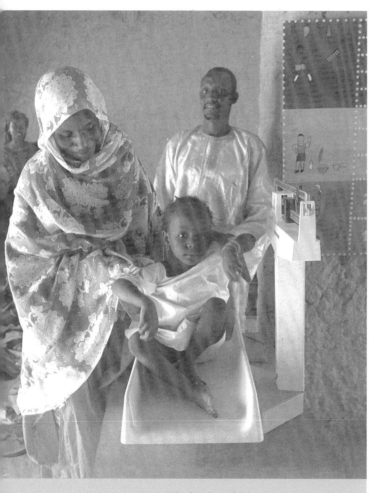

Figure 14–4 *The burden of debt payments can seriously affect the number of social and educational programs, like this one in Mali, that the government of a poor country can afford.*

How the Debt Crisis Happened

The great international debt crisis did not occur as a result of any single event. Rather, it can be linked to a sequence of interconnected events that happened over several decades. None of these events, in and of itself, caused the debt crisis, but each contributed to the creation of an economic environment within which the crisis became inevitable.

- *Loans, not grants.* In 1957, US Secretary of State John Foster Dulles announced that future US foreign aid would be in the form of loans rather than grants. The logic behind this decision was that the loans would be used for investments in developing countries, and would generate sufficient wealth to more than pay for themselves. Other countries followed the United States' lead and changed from a grant model for aid to a loan model. From the perspective of the developed world, this approach might have made sense, but for poor nations it meant that they had to accept loans if they wanted to get aid. Many of these loans were given with below market level interest rates, but they were still loans, not grants.
- *Abolition of US gold standard.* In the early 1970s, the United States went off the gold standard. This meant that the value of the dollar was no longer tied directly to the value of gold. The result was a great deal of uncertainty in world financial markets. Since the international price of oil was quoted in US dollars, the Organization of Petroleum Exporting Countries (OPEC) felt that the lower value of the dollar was costing them a great amount of money. In response, they increased the price of oil by 70 per cent. Additional significant oil price increases occurred in 1979. These price jumps were a big problem for a wealthy country like Canada. For the nations of the developing world, they often proved economically devastating.
- *Explosion of petrodollars.* Because of the massive increase in the cost of oil, the OPEC nations in the 1970s had vast sums of money to invest. They deposited this money in banks in North America, Europe, and Japan. These banks had to find customers to borrow this cash. In fact, according to what are called fractional reserve requirements in a bank, $1 billion in deposits allowed as much as $30 billion in loans. The world's developing countries became more than willing customers for loans that had low but floating interest rates. In reality, a major reason why these countries had to borrow money was to pay for the oil they needed, which was now dramatically more costly. When a country uses loans to pay for day-to-day needs like oil, little capital is left over for economic development. These oil purchases, of course, enriched the oil exporters even more.
- *Spiralling inflation.* Things might have worked out better for the developing countries except for one other complication. During the 1970s and early 1980s, the world experienced spiralling inflation that drove up interest rates. Loans that might have been affordable when the cost of borrowing was 5 per cent became totally unsustainable with rates between 10 and 15 per cent.

Did you KNOW? For many years before the 1970s, one ounce of gold was worth US$35. After the gold standard was eliminated, the value of gold increased to many hundreds of dollars. As the value of gold increased compared to the US dollar, the dollar lost some of its value.

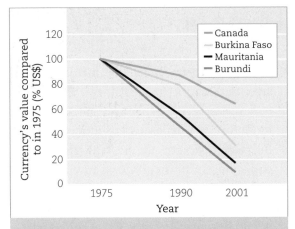

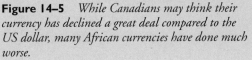

Figure 14–5 *While Canadians may think their currency has declined a great deal compared to the US dollar, many African currencies have done much worse.*

■ *Declining currency value.* To make matters worse, throughout this whole period, as the economies of debtor nations declined, their currencies lost value compared to hard currencies like the US dollar and the Japanese yen (Figure 14–5). If the currency lost half its value compared to US dollars (and many lost much more than that), the debt load doubled in terms of local currency.

■ *Falling commodity prices.* To add to the growing economic mess, the price of many of the commodities that the developing countries relied on for export earnings, principally agricultural, forestry, and mining products, declined during the 1970s and early 1980s. Hence, these countries had to pay higher prices for their imports (especially oil) with less income.

While these conditions were largely beyond the control of the developing countries, their governments also contributed to the crisis. The availability of cheap credit encouraged many of them to go on a spending spree. Rather than using the loans to invest in useful development projects, the governments spent money on consumer goods, military hardware, and hydro-electric dams that might not have been the most pressing need at that stage of these countries'

economic growth. Corrupt leaders in far too many countries, like Sukarno in Indonesia, Mobuto in the Democratic Republic of Congo (then called Zaire), and Marcos in the Philippines, stole billions of dollars of the loans for themselves, their families, and cronies (Figure 14–6). The debt created by corrupt leaders is called **odious debt**.

Threat of Defaults

By 1982, the borrowing and spending spree had ended. Starting then, and over the next 20 years, many countries had reached the point where they could no longer pay even the interest on their loans. Countries like Argentina, Brazil, and Mexico threatened to default on their debts.

Now a new variable was added to the equation. Banks in North America, Europe, and Japan had lent so much money to the developing world that their very existence would be threatened if defaults became common. In reality, if these banks were to go bankrupt, the financial stability of the developed world would be in serious jeopardy.

Debt Rescheduling

The governments of the rich countries had to choose between forcing the already heavily indebted poor countries to accept additional financial aid, or running the risk of devastating their own economies. The choice was an easy one. Typically, the support took the form of additional loans or the rescheduling of existing loan payments so that they could be paid off more slowly. These measures were taken either directly by the government of a country in the form of bilateral aid, or as **multilateral** aid from agencies like the World Bank and the International Monetary Fund (IMF). In either case, the result was higher debt charges to be paid and a greater total debt load.

Generally, this multilateral aid came with many strings attached for the recipient countries:

Figure 14–6 *The hundreds of pairs of shoes owned by Imelda Marcos, wife of the former president of the Philippines, became an international symbol of the odious debt that occurred in many developing countries.*

- They had to devalue their currencies, since this would discourage imports and stimulate exports. Since their debts were in foreign currencies (mainly US dollars), they became much greater in terms of their own currencies.
- They were forced to increase their export earnings so that they would have as much foreign currency as possible. For most countries, this meant accelerating the rate of rain-forest destruction, the degradation of vital agricultural resources, or the growth of destructive mining practices.
- They were also required to restrict their social and education spending so that they would have more money available for loan payments. These cutbacks had an obvious impact on the rate at which countries could develop.

- They were not allowed to use foreign currencies to import critical necessities, like food and medicines.

The result of all of these restrictions was that most of the residents of the poorest debtor nations of Africa and Latin America experienced a significant decline in their standards of living in the 1980s. For example, in Mexico the average income, adjusted for inflation, dropped by more than 40 per cent between 1982 and 1988, while the cost of a selection of basic foodstuffs for a family of five increased from 46 per cent of the minimum wage to 161 per cent between 1983 and 1992. In most developing countries, only the richest citizens avoided this squeeze between falling incomes and rising costs.

Debt Relief for Developing Countries

By the last half of the 1990s, it had become apparent to just about everyone, debtor and lender alike, that the international debt situation was unsustainable. The immense debt of many developing countries would not, and could not, ever be paid. The only possible solution was some form of **debt relief**. What the amount and nature of this relief should be has proven to be highly controversial. Some people believe the relief should be only enough to ensure that a debtor nation is able to pay off its remaining obligations. For others, nothing less than the complete elimination of the debt of the poorest countries will do.

Highly Indebted Poor Countries Initiative

One approach to debt relief is the **Highly Indebted Poor Countries (HIPC)** initiative. This is a program created by the World Bank and the International Monetary Fund, and was the first serious international attempt to reduce the debt faced by the poorest countries of the world. The basic idea of the HIPC program was agreed to by the governments of the world in 1996 and strengthened in 1999. It applied to only the 41 poorest nations in the world, who had a debt of US$201 billion in 1999 (Figure 14–7).

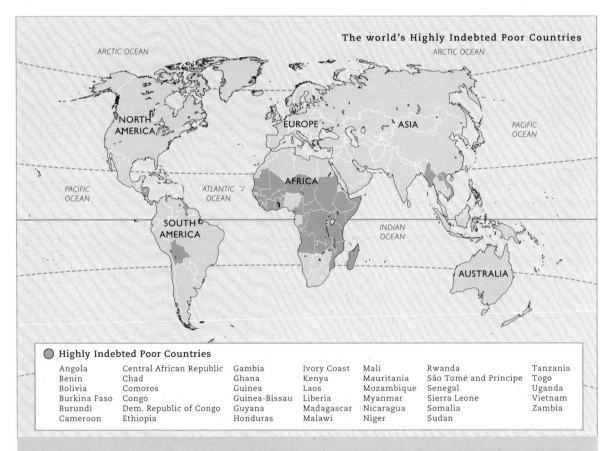

The world's Highly Indebted Poor Countries

⬤ Highly Indebted Poor Countries

Angola	Central African Republic	Gambia	Ivory Coast	Mali	Rwanda	Tanzania
Benin	Chad	Ghana	Kenya	Mauritania	São Tomé and Príncipe	Togo
Bolivia	Comoros	Guinea	Laos	Mozambique	Senegal	Uganda
Burkina Faso	Congo	Guinea-Bissau	Liberia	Myanmar	Sierra Leone	Vietnam
Burundi	Dem. Republic of Congo	Guyana	Madagascar	Nicaragua	Somalia	Zambia
Cameroon	Ethiopia	Honduras	Malawi	Niger	Sudan	

Figure 14–7 *The 41 developing countries classified by the International Monetary Fund as Highly Indebted Poor Countries in 1999.* Source: International Monetary Fund.

The HIPC program is complex and demanding on the debtor country. The HIPC initiative begins only when the debtor nation meets a set of very specific criteria. At the beginning of the process, a country must agree to implement a **Structural Adjustment Program (SAP)** that has been approved by the World Bank/IMF. The SAP requires the country to make the sort of controversial adjustments (such as restricted social spending) described in the previous section.

After three years, the country reaches the "decision point." At this point, the World Bank/IMF decides whether the country needs further assistance. If it does, a plan will be established over the next three years to reduce the amount of the country's debt to a sustainable level. To get the aid, the debtor nation must be able to convince its commercial and bilateral creditors—that is, foreign banks and governments—to offer similar debt relief. By 1999, only 10 of the HIPC nations had been assessed, and only US$3 billion in debt relief had actually occurred.

Jubilee+ Campaign

To many, the HIPC initiative is based on a fatally flawed premise—that the main purpose of debt relief is to re-establish a country's ability to pay its debts. Instead, they feel that debt relief should occur so that poor countries can use their limited wealth to fund their economic and social growth.

An international campaign, called the Jubilee 2000 Campaign, was begun in 1990 with the goal of marking the new millennium by having all US$230 billion owed by the 50 poorest countries forgiven. It was spearheaded by the world's major faith communities. In spite of considerable lobbying, including presenting creditor governments with petitions signed by more than 20 million people, Jubilee 2000 did not reach its goal. The campaign continues as the **Jubilee+ Campaign.**

Did you KNOW?

The Jubilee 2000 Campaign took its name from the Bible (Leviticus 25: 10-14). Jubilee refers to an old Judeo-Christian tradition of forgiving debts every 50 years, when the "Year of Jubilee" happens.

You can read an analysis of the HIPC initiative and the Jubilee+ Campaign at <www.pearsoned.ca/globalconnections>.

Proponents of the Jubilee approach give three main reasons for their revolutionary approach to debt relief:

- Fundamentally, they feel that the debt of developing countries is ruinous. Ethically, they cannot accept a situation that condemns a majority of the world's citizens to poverty. They want to see a program of debt elimination that focusses on the needs of debtors and not creditors.
- They point out that the debtor nations have already paid more than a fair amount for loans that were often forced on them. As evidence, they note that between 1980 and 1992 debtor nations paid US$1.6 trillion to their creditors, and yet saw their indebtedness rise from US$567 billion to US$1.4 trillion.
- They say that it is not fair to make the current citizens of debtor countries pay for debts that may be more than two decades old. In a great many situations, these loans may have been used unwisely or even illegally and should be considered odious debt.

Canada's Role in Debt Forgiveness

As a member of the Group of 8 (G8) nations, Canada is a small but significant creditor country. Debts owed to Canada were estimated to be $1.2 billion in 1999. Most of this debt was owed to the Export Development Corp-oration and the Canadian Wheat Board. The money had been lent to poorer countries so that they could buy Canadian grain and other products. Supporters of the Jubilee approach argue that the loans have already provided substantial benefits for Canada—yet another reason why this debt should be forgiven.

Canada's attitude to debt forgiveness can be seen in two different ways. First, Canada has a recent history of forgiving bilateral international debt. In 1989, the Canadian government cancelled debts totalling $672 million that were owed to Canada's main foreign aid agency, the Canadian International Development Agency, by Commonwealth and Francophonie nations. While this might seem like a very large sum, it actually cost $67 million, since the original loans were given with substantial concessional terms. This means that the loans did not have to be paid back in full. Canada has given debt relief to other countries, such as Egypt ($239 million) and Ivory Coast ($64 million). This relief came in lieu of other forms of governmental development assistance. Debt cancellation for Rwanda, Liberia, Ethiopia, and the Democratic Republic of Congo has been announced, but will come into effect only when a greater measure of security has returned to these conflict-ravaged nations.

Another way in which Canadian government leaders have been leaders in debt forgiveness is by trying to encourage the other members of the

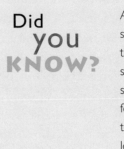

IMF and World Bank to make the HIPC initiative more generous. Canada's approach to debt forgiveness could be described as "broader, quicker, and deeper," which means that, in comparison to the existing HIPC agreement, we would like to see it involve more countries, follow a more rapid process, and provide more significant debt relief to eligible countries.

The Future of Debt Forgiveness

While most international observers, along with the governments of both developed and developing countries, can agree about the problems of debt, there is much less agreement about what should be done about it. Even among the members of the World Bank and the IMF, there is substantial disagreement. For example, in 2001, the US House of Representatives did not support a budget proposal that would have helped pay for the US contribution towards the HIPC initiative—an initiative that many people find woefully inadequate and shortsighted. Only time will tell if a level of debt relief can be found that will meet the needs of the debtor nations and, at the same time, be acceptable to creditor nations.

Chapter Questions

Knowledge and Understanding

1. Identify similarities and differences between the hypothetical situation of the person in the chapter opening ("A Difficult Dilemma"), and the situation in many developing nations today.

2. a) Identify the parts of the world most affected by international debt problems.
   b) Explain why these problems are much worse in these areas than elsewhere.

3. a) Chart and briefly describe the reasons why the international debt became so large.
   b) Compare the role played by developed and developing countries in the growth of this debt.
   c) Consider the various factors that have contributed to the international debt crisis. What information suggests that at the time these events were occurring, the developed nations gave little thought to the impact they might have on developing nations?

4. a) Create an organizer to compare the HIPC and Jubilee approaches to debt relief.
   b) Do you think that the HIPC approach is fair to debtor nations? Why or why not?
   c) Do you think that the Jubilee approach is practical? Explain.

Thinking and Inquiry

5. a) Canada owes billions of dollars. Should we be worried about the debt of distant countries when we are, ourselves, deeply in debt?
   b) Much of Canada's debt is owed to Canadians, for example, as Canada Savings Bonds. How is this situation different from the debt situation in developing countries? How does this difference affect the problem of our debt?

6. a) Multilateral aid from the World Bank/IMF had many strings attached. Discuss the impact of the conditions that were placed on this aid.

   b) What conditions do you think should be placed on countries that accept foreign aid?

7. a) Why is the level of a country's exports important in understanding that country's ability to support its debt?
   b) Think of four different problems that are caused if a country must spend too much of its wealth on debt repayment.

8. There is an old expression that says, "If you owe your bank $10 thousand and can't pay it back, you have a problem. But if you owe $10 million and can't pay it back, the bank has a problem." What is meant by this expression?

Communication

9. "While the ethical reasons for the Jubilee+ Campaign are admirable, this approach is totally impractical in the modern world." Do you agree with this statement or not? Explain.

10. Your teacher will provide you with an expanded version of the data in Figure 14–3 and will tell you whether to do the following exercise on a paper base map or using ArcView GIS.
    a) Examine the data carefully to decide how you would classify countries' debts as "severe," "serious," or "moderate."
    b) Apply your criteria to the countries of Saharan and sub-Saharan Africa.
    c) Locate and shade each country on a base map of Africa according to its category.
    d) How did your categorization of the most indebted nations compare to the HIPC list?

11. Write a formal letter to either the prime minister of Canada or the president of the World Bank, or to the editor of your local newspaper, expressing your views on debt relief. Your letter should be about 200 words in length and focussed clearly on the problem of international debt and your reaction to it.

Application

12. a) Define the term "odious debt."

    b) Describe at least three ways in which odious debt can occur.

    c) For each of your answers to (b), decide whether the nature of the debt justifies its forgiveness. Explain your conclusions.

    d) Do lenders have a special responsibility to ensure that their debts do not lead to additional odious debt for a nation? Explain your views.

13. Choose one country listed in Figure 14–3, and research to find out how its debt was incurred, its economic status, its recent political history, and how likely it is to be able to repay its debt.

14. Using the Internet, research the current status of debt relief in the world. Find out Canada's present attitude towards debt forgiveness.

15. Work with two other students to discuss the following situations. One student represents Canadian bankers, one the Jubilee+ Campaign, and the third, the Government of Canada.

    ■ An African HIPC complains that it is spending 33 per cent of GNP on debt service.

    ■ An Asian Fourth World country is angry because its past leaders created huge odious debt.

    ■ A large South American country threatens to refuse making interest payments on its growing debt.

Unit 4: The Earth in Balance

15

Land Issues

Expectations

In this chapter, you will:

■ understand the inter-dependence of ecology and economics

■ understand how human-induced changes in natural systems reduce their capacity to support human activity

■ evaluate the impact of current methods of rais-ing or harvesting a resource (monoculture)

■ identify current global issues related to sustain-ability and environmen-tal threats

■ evaluate the sustain-ability of selected trends related to consumption of Earth's resources

■ collect and analyse data, using field tech-niques, to find patterns and relationships

Environmental issues are often very complex and interrelated. Because environmental problems (such as **salinization** of farmland, above) almost always have significant economic implications, resolving these issues becomes even more difficult. Unit 4 will explore a selection of environmental issues to reveal how they are interconnected. This chapter begins by examining three issues related to land.

Nothing Is Quite As Simple As It Seems!

Try this little quiz. For each question decide whether you agree, partially agree, or disagree.

1. I think they should do something about global warming.
2. Pollution levels should be lower than they are today.
3. We don't take the problem of smog seriously enough.
4. We need more politicians who are environmentally aware.
5. Cars should be made that have better fuel efficiency.
6. Ontario should eliminate its nuclear power plants.

Chances are that you agreed with many, if not all, of these statements. If so, the obvious next question is, "What do you intend to do about these environmental problems?" Consider just a few possible contradictions.

- You think that "they" should reduce global warming, but "they" is really "us." Reducing global warming requires changes to your lifestyle that you may not find acceptable.
- You think that we should have less wasteful vehicles, but the only thing between you and that hot sports car or SUV may be the relative poverty you experience at this stage of your life.
- You think that politicians should pass laws that protect the environment more. But you may end up voting for the party that promises to cut your taxes and promote economic growth.

The conflict between good intentions and personal ambitions is just one of the reasons why, like the weather, everyone talks about protecting the environment, but rarely does anything about it.

Land Degradation

If asked to name the most important environmental problems facing the world today, most of us would immediately mention global warming, air pollution, endangered species, or perhaps an issue like dealing with nuclear waste. What rarely comes to mind is **land degradation**. Yet, it can be argued that land degradation affects more people and living things, more seriously, than any other environmental problem. This ignorance is not altogether a surprise, since the problems of land degradation are not always visible. Also, land degradation is a rural problem, and most of us live in cities.

While global warming and endangered species are relatively new concerns, the problems of land degradation have been known for more than 2000 years. The Greek philosopher Plato said:

> Attica (Athens) was no longer cultivated by true herdsmen, who made husbandry their business, and were lovers of honour, and of a noble nature. As a result Attica had become deforested, the soils depleted, and there are remaining only the bones of the wasted body—all the richer and softer parts of the soil having fallen away.

You can read the UN report on land degradation at <www.pearsoned.ca/globalconnections>.

Land degradation is any deterioration of the productive capacity of soil for either present or future use. It is closely linked to poverty in the sense that, as the degree of degradation increases, crop and animal yields decline and people have both less to eat and less to sell to support themselves. Even as agricultural advances occur, the benefits may be lost as the total agricultural capability of a region is reduced by land degradation.

The United Nations recognizes four categories of degradation: erosion, chemical deterioration, physical deterioration, and desertification.

Erosion

Erosion can remove of the nutrient-rich topsoil layer by either water or wind. Water erosion can occur in any climate zone of the world, while wind erosion occurs most commonly in arid and semi-arid climates. Most erosional activities are subtle and not readily noticed. For example, a stream flowing with water that looks "muddy" is transporting eroded topsoil. The UN has estimated that an average of 17 t of soil is lost every year from each hectare of cultivated farmland in the world. This amount can be compared to the load of a good-sized dump truck. Erosion has many effects, including some that may not be obvious at first glance (Figure 15–1).

When more severe erosion occurs, we may see changes in the landscape. This is called **terrain deformation**. In the case of water erosion, large or small gullies maybe cut in farmers' fields (Figure 15–2) or mass movements (landslides) may occur. With wind erosion, we may see dunes or deflation hollows, which are depressions created when the wind removes topsoil from a

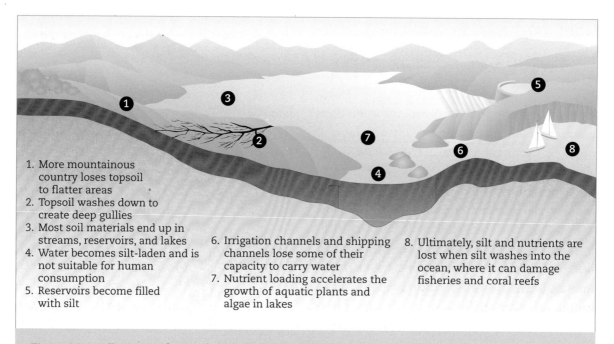

1. More mountainous country loses topsoil to flatter areas
2. Topsoil washes down to create deep gullies
3. Most soil materials end up in streams, reservoirs, and lakes
4. Water becomes silt-laden and is not suitable for human consumption
5. Reservoirs become filled with silt
6. Irrigation channels and shipping channels lose some of their capacity to carry water
7. Nutrient loading accelerates the growth of aquatic plants and algae in lakes
8. Ultimately, silt and nutrients are lost when silt washes into the ocean, where it can damage fisheries and coral reefs

Figure 15–1 *Erosion involves much more than the removal of soil from land areas to the ocean.*

Figure 15–2 *Gullies in farmland caused by water erosion*

previously level area. The land may also be "overblown," that is, covered by wind-eroded materials from somewhere else.

Chemical Deterioration

Chemical deterioration can take four forms. The most important of these is loss of soil nutrients. Vital nutrients (especially nitrogen, phosphorous, and potassium) can be lost in two main ways. If an area has an excess of precipitation, nutrients can be leached or washed away. Leaching occurs in much of Canada (the exception is the southern Prairie provinces where there is a slight to moderate moisture deficit), but the seriousness of the problem here is much less than in humid, tropical areas. In these areas, the severely leached soils have an orange-red colour that indicates the dominance of oxides of aluminum and especially iron in the soil. These compounds are not soluble and cause the soil to become very hard. This problem frequently occurs in tropical rain-forest areas, like much of

Brazil, that have had their vegetation cleared to allow farming. Leaching is made worse if a dense layer of vegetation does not protect the soil. For a few years after the land is cleared, yields are high because some organic materials remain in the soil, but the leaching soon destroys the fertility of the soil. The second way in which soil nutrients are lost is by the growth of crops, particularly if the same crop, with the same nutrient needs, is grown each year.

A second type of chemical degradation is salinization, an increase in the concentration of salt in the soil, to the point where the soil becomes toxic for plant growth (see the photograph on page 230). While salinization can occur naturally if the water table is close to the surface in an arid area, it can be greatly accelerated by poorly managed irrigation techniques. The water being used for irrigation dissolves salts that will be left in the soil when the water evaporates from the soil's surface. If these salts are not flushed from the soil into drainage ditches, the salt concentration will eventually reach a dangerous level. Significant areas of formerly highly productive irrigated farmland have to be removed from production when salt levels get too high. About one-eighth of all irrigated land in the world has been degraded by severe salinization, with as much as another third being somewhat affected. Salinization is a particular problem in parts of the United States, China, the Middle East, and Australia.

The other two forms of chemical deterioration are less common. Land can become acidified by the use of excessive fertilizers or because of drainage problems. Finally, land can be polluted by emissions from nearby industries, or by the dumping of liquid or solid waste.

Physical Deterioration

The productivity of land can also be reduced by **physical deterioration**. There are three ways in which this happens. Soil can be compacted by the use of heavy machines or by the trampling of herds of animals. Waterlogging—for example, after floods recede from an area—can also damage land. The third form of physical damage is subsidence, or sinking, of land. It can be caused when a significant amount of water is removed from the water table.

The relative significance of all these forms of land degradation is shown in Figure 15–3.

Land Degradation Worldwide		
Type	Amount of arable/pasture land affected (million ha)	Total degraded area affected by this factor (%)
Loss of topsoil	504	70.0
Terrain deformation	96	13.0
Loss of nutrients	40	6.9
Salinization	28	3.9
Compaction	25	3.5
Pollution	8	1.1
Overblowing	4	0.6
Waterlogging	4	0.5
Acidification	2	0.3
Subsidence	1	0.2

Figure 15–3 *For comparison's sake, Canada has about 125 million hectares of farmland. The United Nations has estimated that about 15 per cent of the Earth's productive land has been significantly affected by some form of land degradation.* Source: Adapted from United Nations Development Program.

Figure 15–4 *Cattle attempt to graze on desertified land near Lake Chad in Niger, Africa.*

Desertification

Desertification is a special type of land degradation. It differs from those mentioned previously in that it refers to the results of degradation rather than the causes. Desertification occurs when human activities reduce the productivity of an arid or semi-arid area to the point that it resembles a desert. It would be a mistake to picture such land as we usually think of deserts—that is, sand dunes spreading outward from an existing desert. Rather, desertification creates desert-like conditions and destroys the agricultural capability of the land around populated areas (Figure 15–4). As much as 40 per cent of the world has climates dry enough that they face the possibility of desertification. This situation puts over one billion people at risk.

Causes of Land Degradation

While land degradation can be caused by natural factors, overwhelmingly it occurs as a result of human activity. These causes fall into five main categories:

- *Deforestation.* When land is cleared for agricultural use, particularly in tropical rain forests, soil is exposed to serious erosion and leaching.
- *Overgrazing.* Sheep and goats graze even more heavily than cattle, and can destroy vegetation beyond its ability to recover. As a result, soil is exposed to erosion and leaching.
- *Unsustainable agriculture.* If carried out too intensively to allow soils to renew themselves,

agriculture reduces nutrient levels and, in dry areas, can result in salinization. Such farming is considered to be "agricultural mining" and is not sustainable in the long run. The most obvious factor is monoculture, the practice of growing the same crop year after year. This happened in the Canadian Prairies during the 1930s. Even if chemical fertilizers provide nutrients, the soil will still degrade because it will lose the structure provided by humus.

- *Overuse of vegetation.* In most developing parts of the world, people rely on trees and shrubs for fuel and for building materials. If the population density of an area is too high, overuse of vegetation can have an impact similar to that of overgrazing and deforestation.
- *Urban/industrial pollution.* In heavily industrialized urban regions, pollution can foul the soil of adjacent farms and make them unusable for farming.

The relative importance of these causes of soil degradation is shown in Figure 15–5.

Impact of Land Degradation

There is a powerful correlation between land degradation and poverty. Unfortunately, documentation of the importance of land degradation is not readily available. The first comprehensive worldwide study of the problem was not completed until 1991 and has not been repeated. We do not even have enough data collected over time to see how quickly land is being damaged and lost from production. Estimates suggest that somewhere between five million and 12 million hectares of land are lost from production each year. Productivity of the land being used declines with degradation. For example, salinization and waterlogging can reduce the yields from irrigated fields by between 30 and 80 per cent. In total, estimates of food production that will be lost because of land degradation of all sorts between 1985 and 2010 are 19 to 29 per cent. Another estimate suggested that

Causes of Land Degradation

	Deforestation	Overgrazing	Unsustainable Agriculture	Overuse of Vegetation	Urban/Industrial Pollution
Africa	14%	49%	24%	13%	*
North/Central America	11%	24%	57%	7%	*
South America	41%	28%	26%	5%	—
Asia	40%	26%	27%	6%	*
Australasia	12%	80%	8%	*	*
Europe	38%	23%	29%	*	9%
WORLD	29%	35%	28%	7%	1%

* indicates amount less than 0.5%

Because of rounding, rows may not total 100%.

Figure 15–5 *The table shows the distribution of the various causes of land degradation by region and worldwide, 1995.* Source: United Nations Population Information Network.

Effects of Land Degradation

	Amount of degraded land	Most important types of degradation	Countries most affected
Africa	41%	Loss of topsoil (76% of degraded land) Loss of soil nutrients (9%)	Burkina Faso, Burundi, Ethiopia, Madagascar, Lesotho, Morocco, Rwanda
North and Central America	13%	Loss of topsoil (75%) Terrain deformation from water erosion (16%)	Costa Rica, El Salvador, Panama
South America	13%	Loss of topsoil (39%) Loss of soil nutrients (26%) Terrain deformation from water erosion (12%)	Brazil
Asia	29%	Loss of topsoil (71%) Terrain deformation (16%) Salinization (7%)	China, India, Thailand, Vietnam
Australasia	22%	Loss of topsoil (95%)	
Europe	23%	Loss of topsoil (61%) Compaction (15%)	

Figure 15–6 *Unfortunately, those parts of the world most affected by land degradation are those least able to afford the lost agricultural productivity.* Source: Adapted from 1991 data from United Nations Population Information Network.

this degradation would result in a loss of about 14 million tonnes of grain annually—or about half the amount needed to feed the population growth of the world during this time.

Not all parts of the world are equally affected by land degradation. On a global basis, about 26 per cent of agricultural land is degraded to some extent, but the range of degradation is from 13 per cent in the Americas to 41 per cent in Africa (Figure 15–6).

Did you KNOW?

During the 1980s and 1990s, famines in Ethiopia and Sudan were routinely blamed on drought and civil wars. Rarely did observers acknowledge the contribution of land degradation to these tragedies.

Solid Waste Management

What is your postal code? Check Figure 15–7 to see how many old dump sites there are in your part of Ontario. Does this number surprise you? Now try zooming in a little. Figure 15–8 shows the number of dumps in each of the postal code areas of Toronto. The total number of dumps here is particularly surprising if you remember that more than 2.3 million people live in the "M" postal code area and that almost all of the land here has been developed for some urban use. If you live in Toronto, how many dumps are in your neighbourhood? How would you know exactly where they are?

Should you be worried about what is in these dumps? Some say there is little to worry about, that most of the garbage will have decomposed over the years, but this is not the case.

Distribution of Closed Dump Sites in Ontario

First Letter of Postal Code	Number of Dumps
K	1186
L	877
M	860
N	1446
P	1232
Total	5601

Figure 15–7 *Old dump sites are widespread across Ontario.* Source: Dr. Richard Anderson, Geography Department, York University.

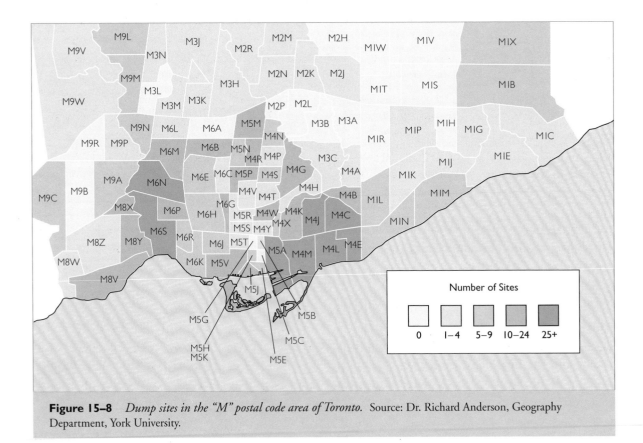

Figure 15–8 *Dump sites in the "M" postal code area of Toronto.* Source: Dr. Richard Anderson, Geography Department, York University.

Anthropologists have done excavations at the now closed Fresh Kills landfill in New York City, the largest landfill site in the world, and discovered that decades-old newspapers are still readable, while food wastes are easily identifiable.

Our society's (and perhaps your own) reaction to these old dumps illustrates a lot about our attitude towards garbage disposal or, as it is more properly called, **solid waste management**. For most of us, out of sight is out of mind. At the beginning of the 21st century, members of the city council of Toronto had to think about what the city was going to do with its solid waste. Its major landfill, in Maple, just north of the city, was close to full and a long-term alternative had to be found.

At first, the solution seemed to be to ship the garbage by rail to an abandoned open-pit mine near Kirkland Lake, Ontario. While many political leaders in northeastern Ontario favoured this plan (it would provide much-needed economic growth in the region), there was opposition from residents who feared the potential of environmental damage from the new landfill. The proposed deal collapsed when, in spite of assurances from both sides that the plan was ecologically sound, neither the city nor the landfill company was prepared to accept the financial responsibility if something were to go wrong. Toronto's short-term alternative was to send its garbage to an existing landfill in eastern Michigan. Residents there tried to oppose this plan but could not, since the landfill was already in operation. Also, provisions of the North American Free Trade Agreement require that US and Canadian garbage be treated in the same way.

In the longer term, Toronto decided to introduce a waste diversion plan that, if successful, would eliminate 100 per cent of all household wastes from landfills by 2010—a significant increase from the 27 per cent that was being diverted in 2001. Toronto residents would have to divide their waste into three streams. The materials currently collected in recycling boxes (aluminum and steel food-and-beverage containers, some types of plastic, newspapers, corrugated cardboard, boxboard) would be collected together. Organic materials (kitchen scraps, dirty diapers, plant waste) would be collected in a separate container. All other wastes would be collected in garbage bags. A waste diversion scheme like this requires the construction of a sophisticated and costly facility, but eliminates the cost and environmental risks associated with traditional landfills.

Types of Solid Waste Disposal

Different forms of waste disposal are used in different parts of the world. In North America, we have focussed on throwing away our solid waste. In rural areas, this has most often meant small, open dumps located in inconspicuous places. Larger towns and cities use carefully engineered sanitary landfills, which are designed to accept large amounts of waste while ensuring as little environmental damage as possible (Figure 15–9).

In Europe and Japan, where land is scarce, incinerators are commonly used. As with dumps, these vary in environmental quality. Older incinerators often burn waste inefficiently and produce large amounts of pollution, including extremely hazardous materials like dioxins. State-of-the-art incinerators burn at much higher temperatures and produce significantly lower levels of air pollution. At the same time, the heat generated by the burning garbage can be used for the **cogeneration** of electricity.

Waste management in developing countries is quite different. To begin with, much less waste is generated per person. Also, because of greater poverty, any waste materials are carefully picked over for anything of value: food, building supplies, and clothing.

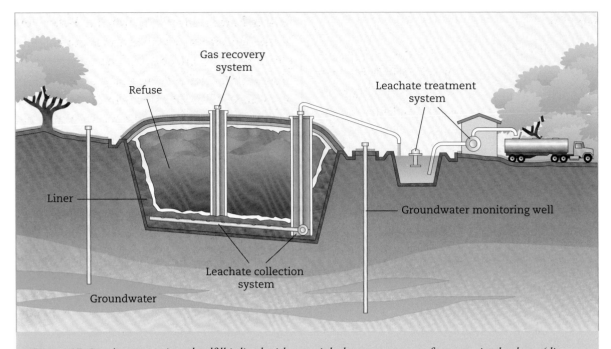

Figure 15–9 *A secure sanitary landfill is lined with materials that prevent water from carrying leachates (dissolved substances) from the refuse into underground water supplies. Pipes collect the water for transfer to a treatment plant that removes the leachates. Wells drilled nearby allow landfill operators to check for leachates in the groundwater. Pipes sunk into the landfill allow gases to escape or be collected for fuel.* Source: World Book illustration adapted from an illustration by National Solid Waste Management Association.

Better Ways of Managing Our Waste

What are our options if we want to do a better job of managing our waste? The often-mentioned 3Rs—Reduce, Reuse, and Recycle—are a good starting point.

Reduce

The idea of not producing waste in the first place is the best approach to waste management. This principle is called **source reduction**. A century ago, shoppers would go to the market with a cloth or wicker shopping bag and a number of reusable containers to pick up groceries. Relatively few commodities were packaged. (If you have shopped at a bulk food store, you have

had a similar experience.) Growth in the use of packaging occurred largely to provide convenience for consumers, to protect the product, and to make material handling and product identification easier for manufacturers and retailers.

Source reduction occurs only when the public demands it. The demand could have two impacts: companies would see that it is in their commercial best interests to meet the demands of consumers who want less packaging; and political parties would realize that they can gain votes if they propose more stringent packaging laws.

In North America, there has been relatively little public interest in source reduction. This is not the case in many European countries. For example, Germany has enacted strict packaging laws to reduce the amount of garbage that is created.

Reuse

When further reductions in waste creation are not possible, the next best approach is to reuse. As a society, we are not as good at reusing as we used to be. Thirty years ago, most people bought their milk in reusable plastic and glass containers. Similarly, soft drinks were most often purchased in glass bottles that could be used dozens of times before being recycled. In both industries, those who bottled and sold these beverages sought to replace reusable containers with one-time use plastic, cardboard, and aluminum containers. Using disposable containers was cheaper and more convenient than having to maintain a container return system. In exchange for being allowed to abandon returnable containers, the soft drink industry became a major sponsor of the first blue-box recycling systems.

One highly successful example of a returnable container system exists in Ontario—the reuse of beer bottles. Brewers Retail Incorporated (better known as "the beer store") has been reusing bottles since 1927, when a 3-cent-per-bottle deposit was imposed to encourage people to return their bottles. The return rate is more than 97 per cent, and each bottle is used, on average, 15 to 20 times before it is recycled. Such a well-developed bottle return system has put Ontario in the unfamiliar position of being a world leader in an environmental field (see Figure 15–10). Many jurisdictions in North America have a deposit system for aluminum beverage containers. These containers are recycled rather than refilled.

Reuse applies not only to containers. You probably have driven along a road on garbage pickup day and noticed useful things being thrown out: sofas, tables, toys, sporting goods, and other items. Perhaps you have even knocked on a door to ask if you could take something

You can learn more about beer bottle reuse in Ontario at <www.pearsoned.ca/globalconnections>.

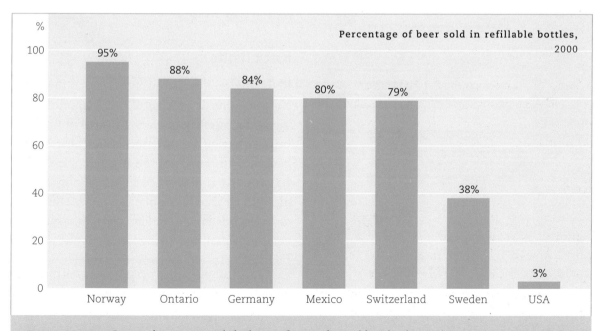

Figure 15–10 *Ontario has an extremely high rate of return for used beer bottles. At the same time an overwhelming majority of beer sold in the province is purchased in refillable containers.* Source: Container Recycling Institute.

You can see the nature of the CalMAX exchanges, and also learn more about the Edmonton compost system, at <www.pearsoned.ca/globalconnections>.

that was left for pickup. This residential version of "dumpster diving" does not happen very often, however, and most of this still-usable material ends up in the local landfill. In many parts of Canada, there has been a growth in the number of second-hand and consignment stores as sellers see an opportunity to get some money by selling what they no longer need and buyers realize that they can save money. Elsewhere, attempts have been made to link those who want to get rid of something with those who might be able to use it. A good example is the California government's CalMAX initiative (Figure 15–11). Its Web site organizes exchanges that prevent these materials from going to landfills.

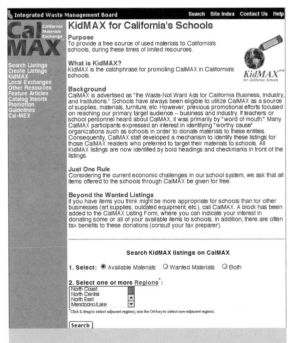

Figure 15–11 *Among other ventures, CalMAX promotes the donation of materials such as supplies and furniture for reuse in California schools.*

Recycle

When we think about recycling, we tend to associate it with blue-box programs, yet recycling has much more potential than that. Most blue-box recycling programs in Canada reduce the amount of garbage going to landfills by between 15 and 30 per cent. A different program being used in Edmonton is diverting 70 per cent of domestic waste from landfills. Edmonton is combining blue-box–style recycling with a high-tech composting system. After removing recyclables, Edmonton residents put the rest of their garbage (except for hazardous wastes) out for collection. It is taken to a state-of-the-art plant where recyclables are carefully mixed with biosolids (biosolids, or sewage sludge, are the semisolid products of a sewage treatment plant). Over a period of about one month, the mixture is aerated and screened. About one-third of the mix proves to be non-biodegradable and is sent to a landfill. The remainder is compost that can be used to improve soil quality on local farms or in gardens (Figure 15–12). Milwaukee, Wisconsin, has successfully processed and sold its sewage as fertilizer for the past 75 years.

Reconsider

Reducing solid waste disposal is not a matter of choosing one or another of the 3Rs, or of looking at the problem of waste disposal in isolation from other environmental issues. A comprehensive, integrated approach makes most sense. In many parts of the developed world, companies and families have done environmental audits to determine how to reduce their impact on the environment, often saving money in the process. Figure 15–13 summarizes the results of such an audit done by a company in Wisconsin.

Figure 15–12 *At this demonstration garden, city dwellers can learn how to make compost from kitchen and garden waste to fertilize flower beds, lawns, vegetable gardens, window boxes, and houseplants.*

Environmental Auditor's Report: Pandl's

- **Business:** Family-owned, 200-seat restaurant with 85 employees, in Milwaukee, Wisconsin

- **Waste Origin:** Food preparation

- **Waste Types:** Food wastes

- **Motivation:** Reduce waste volumes and disposal costs.

- **Strategies:** Reduce weight of dumpster by recycling restaurant waste. Reduce energy costs.

- **Original Process:** The restaurant threw virtually all wastes into the dumpster, creating 25 m^3 of waste each week.

- **New Process:** Employee training focusses on learning new habits for recycling and waste reduction. A food compost program recycles restaurant waste to an organic farmer. Compactors, bailers, and recycling bins were installed. Refrigerator Freon lines were run through a water tank; this system saves energy by cooling the Freon line while heating the water and reducing the condenser workload.

- **Results:** Dumpster wastes were reduced by 92 per cent (i.e., recycling 23 m^3 of the 25 m^3 previously produced each week). Composting reduced dumpster weight by 680 kg of food waste per pickup.

- **Savings:** US$1800–$3000 annual disposal costs (est.).

- **Capital Cost:** US$8000 for compactors, bailers, and recycling bins.

Figure 15–13 *In 1991, Pandl's received a grant of $20 000 from the state of Wisconsin for a study to determine if food waste could be used as a fertilizer. The following year, the restaurant won an award from the City of Milwaukee under its Five-Star Reduction and Recycling Program.*

Protecting Land: Canada's National Parks

Most countries of the world have come to accept the idea that they should preserve substantial parts of their land and adjacent marine areas in as natural a condition as possible. This is usually done by setting aside land as national parks. As well, countries like Canada and the United States have many parks that are under the control of provincial, state, or local governments. The first national park in the world was Yellowstone National Park in Wyoming, established by the US government in 1872. Canada's first national park, Banff, was created in 1885 and was the third national park in the world.

By 2002, Canada had added 39 more national parks and national park reserves, along with marine reserves, heritage rivers, and important historical sites. National park reserves are areas that have been designated as national parks but have not yet gone through all the regulatory steps—such as signing agreements with provincial or territorial governments—required to become full-fledged national parks. In this part of the chapter, we will consider the principles of protecting land, and the problems associated with this, from the perspective of Canada's national parks.

Canada's national parks range in size from less than 9 square kilometres to more than 44 000 square kilometres. In total, they include about 2 per cent of all of the land area in the country, or an area of 224 466 square kilometres. Some have existed for more than a century, while others are only a few years old. Some, like Banff and Gros Morne, are world famous and attract thousands, or even millions, of visitors each year. Others, like Ivvavik and Vuntut, have names that are unfamiliar to most Canadians and are visited by only a handful of people each year.

The long-term vision is that there should be at least one national park in each of Canada's 39 natural regions. In 2001, this meant that there were still 14 regions that needed a national park (some regions have more than one) (Figure 15–14). While work is progressing on the creation of these additional parks, progress is slow because agreement must be reached among many interested parties including other governments, Aboriginal groups, and forestry and mining companies.

Canada's national parks are created based on a series of principles:

- to protect representative natural areas that are of Canada-wide significance
- to provide for public understanding, appreciation, and enjoyment of the natural environment
- to maintain the parks in an unimpaired state for future generations.

While these principles are relatively simple, their application is often not. A major problem for Parks Canada is trying to reconcile these principles when they come into conflict with one another. Typically what happens is that the need to "provide public understanding, appreciation, and enjoyment" conflicts with the need to maintain the park in an "unimpaired state." While these conflicts exist in all of the parks in southern Canada that receive large numbers of visitors, they are perhaps most critical in Banff National Park.

You can learn more about Canada's national parks, and how new parks are created, at
<www.pearsoned.ca/globalconnections>.

Did you KNOW?

National parks frequently protect the most ecologically significant areas and are often larger than provincial, state, or local parks.

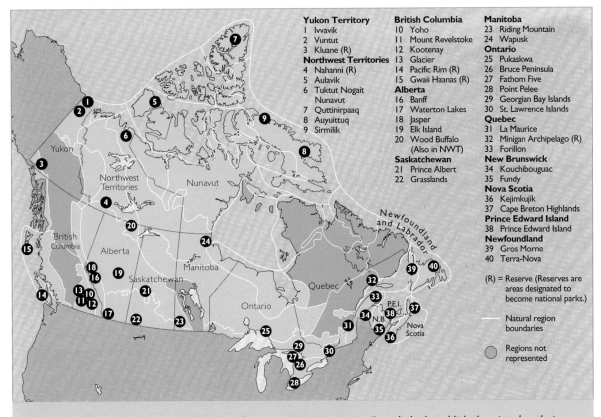

Figure 15–14 *Canada's national parks and reserves, 2002. By 2002, Canada had established national parks in 25 of the country's 39 natural regions.* Source: Parks Canada.

Park Use Conflicts in Banff National Park

Because of its great beauty and its location along the Canadian Pacific Railway and Trans-Canada Highway, Banff National Park is a major international tourist destination with many tourist facilities including the town of Banff itself (Figure 15–15, on the next page). The park receives more than five million visitors each year. In addition, millions more, along with vast amounts of freight, pass through the park on the highway and railway. Much of the park's infrastructure, like the railway and some of the hotel sites, is more than 100 years old. New facilities, such as the expansion of the 1000-room Banff Springs Hotel, have been built in the same location as earlier, smaller ones.

These tourist developments, along with the transportation corridor, are concentrated in a small area—the 6 per cent of the park that is in the valley of the Bow River. Unfortunately, this land is also vital to the wildlife of the park as a prime feeding area and movement corridor for migrations. This has meant that it is a common occurrence for elk to wander through the town (Figure 15–16) and across golf courses, or for "nuisance" bears to have to be removed from the area or, if they are repeat offenders, even killed if they become a threat in campgrounds. Each year, animals are killed crossing the highway and railway.

Banff and its adjacent parks were declared a UNESCO World Heritage Site in 1983. Those who see the preservationist role of national parks

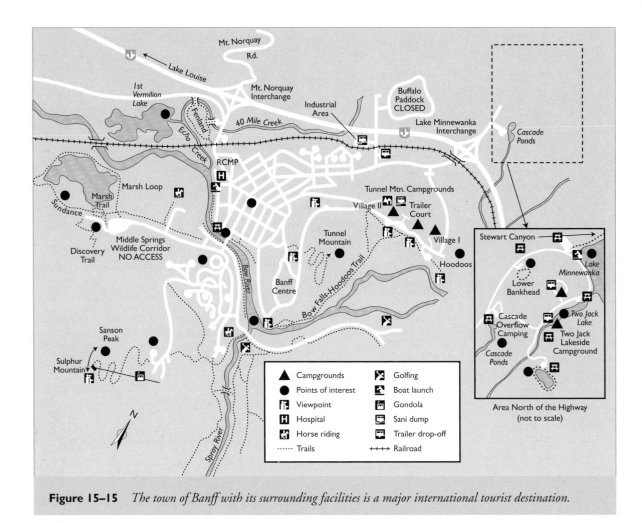

Figure 15–15 *The town of Banff with its surrounding facilities is a major international tourist destination.*

as the dominant one would like to see all human use of the park eliminated, but this wish verges on the impossible. Tourism is the centrepiece of the economy in this region and provides most jobs in the Banff–Canmore area. In addition, two vital national transportation links pass through the park. In fact, the building of the CPR through this area in the early 1880s is the reason why its great natural beauty came to the attention of the world and why it became a park in the first place. It would be extraordinarily difficult and costly to relocate these transportation routes. In all likelihood, any alternative route chosen would cause the same conflicts with wildlife.

The obvious problem for the federal government, which manages the park, is to try to find the appropriate compromise solution. A number of studies of the park were made; they concluded that the **ecological integrity** of the park was at risk and that there should be less human development allowed. To start the process of protecting the park, some facilities were to be eliminated. These include a paddock where buffalo were kept, an airstrip, and a summer camp for cadets. In addition, the population of the town of Banff is to be kept below 10 000, and no additional land is to be released for commercial purposes. To aid in protecting wildlife, Fairmont Hotels has agreed not to expand its Banff Springs golf course and its hotels in the park. The company did indicate that it would proceed with an approved seven-storey convention centre that would be an extension to Chateau Lake Louise, to the north of the town of Banff.

Only time will tell if these changes will have the desired impact on the ecological integrity of Banff. What is clear is that the kind of problems that Banff is facing are common in many other national parks in Canada and elsewhere. In the United States, this has even meant restricting recreational activities. An extreme example of this can be seen at Grand Canyon National Park, where a private individual wanting a permit to travel down river faces a 10-year-long wait. The restrictions are so strict that all human waste must be brought out by those travelling down the Colorado River.

Similar problems exist in the numerous national parks of Kenya. In this developing country, tourism revenue is, relatively, of much greater importance than it is in Canada or the United States, but the same wildlife-viewing activities that are of such importance economically are causing serious ecological damage. For example, so many tourist hotels have been built that there are serious problems with solid-waste disposal. Also, so many tourist buses and smaller vehicles compete for the best viewing locations that the normal behaviour and reproduction patterns of the animals are being affected. There is no magic answer to be found that will work in every such conflict. Rather, decisions will have to be made on a park-by-park basis.

You can learn more about the impact of tourism on Banff at <www.pearsoned.ca/globalconnections>.

Figure 15–16   *Elk lounge on the front lawn of a residence in the Banff townsite.*

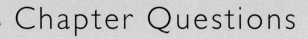

Chapter Questions

Knowledge and Understanding

1. a) Name six significant environmental problems of any type.

   b) Suggest one approach to solving each of these problems.

   c) Indicate how each of these solutions might change our lifestyle.

   d) Would these changes be negative or positive for our lifestyle? Explain. How is this sort of value judgement made?

2. Summarize the most important characteristics of each of the four types of land degradation.

3. Explain the meaning of the following statement: "The NIMBY (Not In My Back Yard) syndrome is alive and well when it comes to waste disposal."

4. Many national parks around the world face conflicts between protection and human use. Describe the reasons why this is a particular problem in Banff National Park.

Thinking and Inquiry

5. It is possible to talk about the proximate and ultimate causes of something. For example, you may feel that your favourite team lost in the playoffs because of a bad play in the final game. This would be the proximate cause of the loss. In reality, they may have lost because, in the preseason, they were poorly coached in the skills needed to make that play. This would be the ultimate cause of the loss. Using this logic, explain the proximate and ultimate causes of land degradation.

6. a) Consider the packaging that comes with the consumer products that you buy. What advantages does it have for the producer? for the consumer? What advantages are there for the company selling the product?

   b) Think about the products that you and your family buy. Give at least three examples of products in each of these two categories: those that have an appropriate amount of packaging, and those that have excessive packaging and could be packaged in a more ecologically sound fashion. In the latter case, describe how the packaging could be improved.

   c) How might changes in consumer behaviour result in different consumer packaging?

   d) How might the operations of business have to change to allow reduced packaging?

7. Investigate national park use conflicts in one of the cases listed below. Consider each in terms of the three purposes of national parks mentioned in the text. What is the fundamental reason for the conflict? What reforms, if any, have been put in place to deal with the conflict? Can a popular national park fulfill all three purposes of a national park? Be prepared to defend your conclusion in a class discussion.

   - Grand Canyon, USA
   - Yosemite, USA
   - Everglades, USA
   - Kruger, South Africa
   - Ambesoli, Kenya
   - a park of your choice

Communication

8. a) Choose a national park to research and present. The park could be in Canada or in another country. Determine the principal characteristics of your park including its size, location, and history.

   b) Investigate the characteristics of the ecosystems that are being protected by your park.

   c) Determine what threats the park may face.

   d) Present your findings in poster form, or in another form as directed by your teacher. Be sure to include appropriate illustrations as well as text.

9. a) Create a display to show the difference between ecologically sound packaging and wasteful packaging. Consider such factors as the amount of material used, the environmental impact of making the packaging, whether it can be recycled, and, if possible, how much it costs.
b) Choose an example of particularly wasteful packaging. Write a letter to the company responsible expressing your concerns about their packaging and suggesting an alternative approach that would be desirable both environmentally and from the perspective of the country. In your letter you should ask for a reply.

Application

10. a) Research the natural and human factors that intensify the severity of water and wind erosion.
b) Determine how erosion can be minimized in at least three different types of natural environments.

11. Compare the packaging methods of the beer industry in Ontario to the dairy, soft drink, wine, and liquor industries. Why has the beer industry been so successful with its container recycling compared to the others? Could they achieve similar success? How could this be done?

12. a) In 1991, McDonald's in the United States worked with an environmental group to determine how it could reduce its waste. Read this report at <www. pearsoned.ca/globalconnections>. Has McDonald's made the waste reductions talked about in this report? Research what McDonald's is doing today to reduce its waste.
b) Research waste reduction efforts by another company. This could be a large or small company involved in any kind of business.

13. Do a waste audit of your home or school. How is waste handled? What efforts are made to minimize waste in the school? Make a list of possible improvements and how these could be implemented if you find shortcomings in waste management.

14. Follow your trash: where does it go after you dispose of it—into the garbage, or into a recycling program? Assess the adequacy of the waste disposal operations in your community.

Forest Ecology Issues and NGOs

Expectations

In this chapter, you will:

■ explain how points of
view and paradigms
influence people's per-
ceptions of a location

■ evaluate the signifi-
cance of participation in
non-violent movements

■ evaluate the impact of
current methods of rais-
ing or harvesting a
resource

■ explain how strategic
lawsuits (SLAPPs) affect
public participation

■ evaluate the role of
NGOs and local initia-
tives in promoting sus-
tainable development
and resource manage-
ment

Perhaps, like many young people, you think of yourself as

an environmentalist. But how far would you go to protect a majestic

forest or a threatened animal species? Would you spend over two years

living high up in a giant tree to protect it from being cut down? That

is just what 23-year-old Julia (Butterfly) Hill did (above), starting in

December 1997.

Saving the Old-Growth Redwoods

The story begins with the remarkable redwood trees of the coastal forest of northern California and a mysterious seabird called the marbled murrelet. The hills of the California coast north of San Francisco have both abundant rainfall and a long growing season. The result is a lush temperate rain forest dominated by giant redwood trees that can reach almost 100 m in height and more than 5 m in circumference. Not surprisingly, such huge trees, in such an accessible location, proved attractive to forest companies. By the early 1990s, 96 per cent of the original redwoods, or **old-growth forest**, had been cut down. (The trees that replace the old-growth are called *second growth*.) Yet, the demand for the remaining old-growth stands continued unabated.

For two reasons, many people and NGOs (both local and national) were appalled at the potential loss of the last of these magnificent trees. One reason was an ethical sense that these forests should be preserved for their own sake. The other reason was more specific: in the early 1990s it had been discovered that old-growth redwoods were virtually the sole nesting sites in northern California for the marbled murrelet.

For many years, these robin-sized seabirds were frequently seen on the coastal waters of the North Pacific Ocean basin from Japan to northern California, but naturalists had had no success in determining where they nested. Finally, scientists in Siberia found that their murrelets did not build conventional nests but laid their eggs in mossy depressions in the branches of very large trees. These nesting sites were 20–40 m above the ground in trees that were often quite far from the sea. Research in California quickly determined that the endangered marbled murrelets had their young in the old-growth redwoods that were most in demand by logging companies.

Did you KNOW?

In other areas of the Pacific coast of the United States, the northern spotted owl, like the marbled murrelet, is an animal species at risk because of the destruction of its habitat by logging.

Role of NGOs in the Fight

The fight to save the old-growth redwoods was focussed in an area called the Headwaters Forest (Figure 16–1, on the next page). The campaign to protect Headwaters Forest was fought simultaneously in quite different ways by two groups of NGOs. One group of NGOs and their supporters were prepared to work within the system. An organization called the Environmental Protection Information Center (EPIC), for example, used the court system and pressured politicians to protect the forest. Gradually they and their allies were able to convince the federal and state governments to negotiate a way to protect the forest with the owners of Headwaters, a company called Pacific Lumber/Maxxam Corporation.

The other approach taken was more militant. Butterfly Hill was a supporter of an NGO called Earth First! Groups like Earth First! believe in an approach called **deep ecology**. They use confrontational, direct action to protect the environment and, as a rule, are not willing to accept compromise solutions. The most extreme deep ecologists consider the human race to be little more than an infection that afflicts the Earth. To them, the eventual extinction of the human species offers the best chance of survival for existing natural environments.

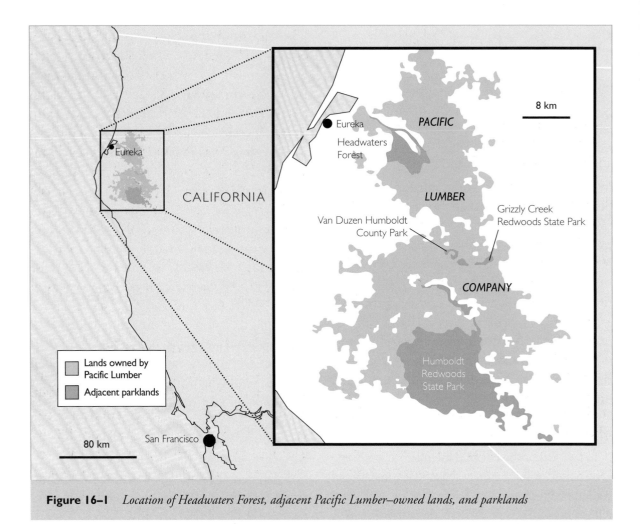

Figure 16–1   *Location of Headwaters Forest, adjacent Pacific Lumber–owned lands, and parklands*

Earth First! took action after a mudslide buried several houses in the village of Stafford, California. They felt that clear-cut logging in the hilly Headwaters Forest had caused the slide. When logging continued above the village, several members of Earth First! occupied, in turn, the upper limbs of a giant 1000-year-old redwood tree that stood on a ridge above the community. They called the tree Luna, because the occupation began on a beautiful moonlit night. Since the tree was on private property, their actions were illegal, but this did not deter them.

You can learn more about this famous "tree-sit" at <www.pearsoned.ca/globalconnections>.

Hill was the last of the tree-sitters. She expected to stay aloft for two to four weeks, but ended up staying more than 100 weeks. Although she developed a remarkably close relationship with the tree and the forest community, her stay was far from idyllic. She lived more than 50 m above the ground, on a tiny plywood platform. Food and other needs were sent up to her on ropes. The winter of 1997–98 proved to be the most severe recorded in northern California. As her protest attracted the attention of the media and the public, Pacific Lumber tried to get her to leave the tree. At night, they sometimes used loudspeakers and spotlights to keep her from sleeping. At times, a helicopter flew so close to Luna that Hill was buffeted by powerful downdrafts.

Results of the Efforts to Preserve Headwaters Forest

Both approaches to protecting Headwaters Forest yielded at least partial victories for the NGOs—and the environment. The publicity generated by Hill's tree-sit seriously damaged the corporate image of Pacific Lumber/Maxxam Corporation. Since this damage far exceeded the financial benefit that would come from cutting down Luna and the trees surrounding it, the company negotiated a compromise with Earth First! Luna, along with all of the trees within a 60-m buffer zone around it, would be preserved. In return, Earth First! paid US$50 000 to the company, with the money to be used for university forestry research. In addition, Hill promised that she would never again tree-sit on Pacific Lumber land. Hill also was given the right to visit Luna whenever she wanted.

The long, tortuous negotiations between Pacific Lumber and government, under pressure from the less extreme NGOs to protect other parts of the redwood forest, finally yielded success starting in 1996, while Butterfly Hill was still tree-sitting. An agreement was reached by which the federal and California governments purchased 6800 ha of the most important old-growth forest. Also, and very importantly, Pacific Lumber agreed to follow a mutually agreed-upon **Habitat Conservation Plan/Sustained Yield Plan (HCP/SYP)** that applied to another 90 000 ha of their redwood forest. In return for their agreement to this plan, Pacific Lumber received US$380 million from the two governments.

An HCP is a mechanism that exists under the US Endangered Species Act. It is designed to combine protection for an endangered species with the recognition that this should not come at the expense of the right of private landowners to enjoy the economic benefits of their land.

This means that not every individual in an endangered species must be protected, as long as sufficiently robust conservation measures are in place to ensure the species' survival. An SYP is a state requirement for planning the harvest of forest resources over a 100-year period. It includes the need to protect the land, rivers, and wildlife. The HCP/SYP, if approved, will protect 12 of the 13 marbled murrelet colonies in the private land outside the actual reserve, along with five of the six untouched, old-growth redwood groves still on Pacific Lumber land. These protections are to last for at least 50 years. As of 2001, the HCP/SYP for the Headwaters Reserve was in draft form and was not near final approval.

What Will Happen Next?

Not everyone was pleased with these settlements. Within Earth First!, which has the motto "No compromise in defence of Mother Earth," there were many who saw the deal made by Hill and her supporters as a sell-out. They felt that if she wanted to come down from Luna there were others to take her place. They were also very upset about the precedent of paying to protect the grove of trees around Luna. On the other side, there were many in the local community whose livelihood depended on the forest industry who were angered that any discussions were being held with Earth First!, a group they viewed as lawbreakers (Figure 16–2).

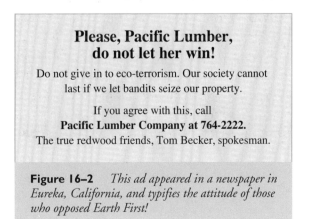

Figure 16–2 *This ad appeared in a newspaper in Eureka, California, and typifies the attitude of those who opposed Earth First!*

While some have described groups like Earth First! as eco-terrorists, there is a fringe group of environmentalists who better deserve this title. They have resorted to tactics that are collectively called **monkey-wrenching**. These range from relatively benign, if illegal, activities like removing survey stakes to slow down the building of logging roads to much more serious acts like burning down buildings and tree-spiking. Tree-spiking consists of driving long nails into a tree at the height at which a logger would cut the tree with a chainsaw. At best, the logging company would have to spend considerable time and money determining which trees had been spiked, as the nail heads rust over and become very hard to see, and then cutting these trees down in such a way as to avoid the nails. At worst, a logger could be killed if the chainsaw were torn apart when the teeth of the chain hit a nail.

Even before the Headwaters Reserve and the HCP/SYP were completely in place, there were those who said that these steps were not enough. They identified an area in the Headwaters Forest called the Hole as the next site in need of protection. By the early 2000s, Earth First!, EPIC, and other NGOs had shifted their attention to the protection of this site. The Headwaters Forest controversy is a perfect example of an environmental conflict in developed (and in many developing) countries. It is almost like a play that is performed, with only minor variations, time and time again. The *dramatis personae,* or stakeholders, were all there:

- A company trying to maximize the profit to be earned from a valuable resource.
- Members of the local community whose jobs depended on the forestry industry.
- Members of the local community whose jobs did not depend on the forest industry and whose first priority was protecting the environment.

- Active and skilful environmental NGOs with a clear agenda and experience in communicating with the public.
- Equally active and well-prepared NGOs supporting the use of the forest by the forest industry.
- A wide range of media, local and national, looking for a good story.
- Government agencies and politicians trying to find an acceptable compromise.

The final question to consider in such controversies is exactly how much land should be protected. On the one side is the extreme view that the trees are there to be used for human benefit. This view provides no protection for ancient trees or endangered birds like the marbled murrelet. At the other extreme, there are those who would protect the entire forest, but this is not practical either. The lumber produced is used to make many useful products, like decks and outdoor furniture.

As well, the forest industry provides a significant number of well-paying jobs. If the lumber were not to come from northern California, it would have to be imported, likely western red cedar from the coastal forests of British Columbia, where similar environmental conflicts exist (Figure 16–3). If the wood were imported, it would also have an economic cost, since many jobs would be lost and the United States' already negative trade balance would only be made worse.

Finding a compromise between these extremes is a difficult and uncertain task. But there is one guideline that we can use. In 1986, the UN Commission on Environment and Development published an influential report called *Our Common Future.* This report recommended that 12 per cent of the world's inhabited land should be protected from development. Even if we accept this idea, the question becomes: How do we determine the distribution of this 12 per cent within a state or province, country, continent— or even the entire world?

The Fight for Denman Island

Denman Island is a small island off the eastern shore of Vancouver Island (Figure 16–3). Because of its limited size, and the fact that it is an island, it is an effective microcosm of the larger battle that is being fought in coastal British Columbia between the logging industry and its supporters, and environmentalists who want to protect as much of the forest as possible.

1. Research the situation on Denman Island. A good starting point would be the island's Web site, which you can find at <www.pearsoned.ca/globalconnections>.

2. Identify the specifics of the conflict on Denman Island. Who are the stakeholders in this controversy? What are the issues?

3. Create a timeline to track the events on Denman Island.

Figure 16–3 *The box shows the location of Denman Island, British Columbia.*

4. What do you think would be a fair solution to the problem on Denman Island? Justify your answer.

Effective Use of Forest Resources

The word *deforestation* is now well known to most people. Stories about it appear frequently in magazines and newspapers (see Figure 16–4, on the next page). Often, though, we do not think about how deforestation is related to our lifestyle, whether we are talking about the west coast of North America or the rain forests of Brazil. On the one hand, we are concerned about the destruction of forests and the impact that this has on wildlife, the land, and river systems. On the other, we take it for granted that forest products will be available in our lives and at a price that we can afford. What we must do is overcome the divide that exists between our role as environmentalists and our role as consumers.

A good way to do this, in the case of forest products, is to ensure that the products we buy have been produced in the most environmentally responsible way possible.

Some NGOs are involved in this initiative as well. These organizations have quite different purposes from those involved in the Headwaters Forest and Denman Island disputes. The focus of those groups was on the prevention (or promotion) of forest cutting. In contrast, these NGOs concentrate on ensuring that any trees that are cut are used wisely. The membership of these groups is different as well. Typically, their members include timber buyers, environmental groups, charitable foundations, and academic forestry experts.

Figure 16–4 *Deforestation in Haiti (left) marks its border with the Dominican Republic.*

One example is the **Forest Stewardship Council (FSC)** (Figure 16–5). In 1993, 130 representatives from around the world met in Toronto to create the FSC. Its purpose is to fight deforestation by improving forest conservation, or the wise use of forests. It receives funding from foundations, governments, environmental NGOs, and from membership fees. The central focus of the FSC's efforts to protect forests is the implementation of a **forest certification** system. Forest certification is a process designed to identify forest products that have been produced from forests that are being managed according to an agreed-upon set of standards. Products that have been produced according to these standards are entitled to carry the FSC logo. With this system in place, consumers who do not want to contribute to deforestation can look for lumber products with the FSC mark. Although there are other forest certification schemes in place in various parts of the world, the FSC guidelines are the ones most widely used.

While the forest certification system appears relatively simple and straightforward in theory, in practice there are two major problems that must be overcome.

Figure 16–5 *The Forest Stewardship Council (FSC), fights the type of deforestation shown in the image above by setting the standard for responsible forestry.* FSC Trademark © 1996 Forest Stewardship Council A.C.

- The first problem is to ensure that a clear link can be made between specific trees growing in the forest and particular lumber products that appear in the marketplace. Tracing what is called a **chain of custody** ensures this connection. Logs from approved forests have to be tracked through each of the processing and transportation stages they go through until the final product reaches the consumer. By following each of these steps, the FSC can verify the end products, such as furniture or building materials, did indeed come from certified forests.
- The second problem is to make sure that there is a market for certified lumber products. Logging companies are often reluctant to go through the certification process if they are not sure whether a market exists for "green" products. On the other hand, consumers will not look for ecologically produced wood products if they never see such items in the marketplace. Certification standards, like those promised by the FSC logo, are a start in the process, but ultimately, market forces will determine the success or failure of this initiative.

For several years, the Home Depot company found itself the target of protests and boycotts from various NGOs that wanted the world's largest lumber retailer to "go green" and become a leader in the sale of certified lumber and lumber products. By the mid-1990s, officers at Home Depot had decided that it was in the corporation's interest to be associated with the Forest Stewardship Council and to work towards selling only FSC-certified products in its stores. A similar decision was made at about the same time by a major British retailer, J. Sainsbury. Home Depot's decision has both practical and symbolic importance. Practically, it provides a huge new market for "green" wood and encourages suppliers to become FSC-certified. Sources of certified lumber have to be identified (and, in many cases, developed). Manufacturers who want to sell products like doors and kitchen cabinets to Home Depot have to "go green" as well. Symbolically, it gives the message that acting environmentally can be good for business, even for one of the world's largest retailers. Now, Home Depot's competitors are faced with the choice of also selling certified products or being seen as environmentally insensitive.

Reduced-Impact Logging

The first stage in using forests wisely is to ensure that logging activities cause as little ecological damage as possible. Forest conservationists, including the FSC, are promoting the advantages of **reduced-impact logging (RIL)**. RIL systems are being developed all over the world, but especially in areas like the Amazon basin, central Africa, and parts of southeastern Asia where tropical hardwoods grow. The purpose of RIL systems is to ensure the long-term economic and ecological sustainability of forestry in an area. RIL generally includes the following features.

- An accurate study of the forest is done well before logging begins so that the logging company and government regulators know exactly how much timber can and should be removed from a particular forest tract.
- This inventory can also be used to plan the cutting to protect streams, minimize forest fire risks, promote forest regeneration, and maintain biological diversity.
- Roads and skid trails used to drag logs from where they have been cut to central locations for loading on trucks must be limited in number and as small as possible. They should be planned so as to minimize erosion.
- Trees must be cut in such a way as not to damage surrounding trees.
- Wood from trees that are cut should not be wasted. For example, trees should be cut as close to the ground as possible. As well, the cutting of

Figure 16–6 *In conventional logging (left), harvesting is not planned but uses a "hit or miss" approach. Reduced-impact logging (right) greatly decreases unwanted damage to unharvested trees and surrounding land.*

logs into planks must be planned to maximize the amount of usable lumber produced.

- Slash, the organic matter such as branches left over after logging, must be managed carefully to prevent fires.

Studies have been done that compare the impacts of RIL with those of conventional logging (CL) in tropical hardwood forests (Figure 16–6). With conventional logging, little effort is made to plan how a forested area will be logged or what roads and skid trails are needed. A logging crew goes into the forest and decides, on the spot, which trees to cut for marketing. Many other trees are damaged or destroyed in this hap-

hazard process. Since the logging process is thought of as little more than an extractive activity, little attention is paid to ensuring that the forest will recover quickly.

Foresters have found that RIL has several benefits. RIL methods waste only about 8 per cent of the volume of harvested trees, while CL methods waste 24 per cent of the wood. The more careful logging practices of RIL mean significantly less damage is done to the remaining forest—fewer than half as many trees are killed than with CL. As well, because the heavy logging machinery is used more carefully, the soils under the forest are less damaged by RIL.

At first glance, it might appear that RIL should be more expensive than CL because of the cost of planning and the extra care needed in logging. In fact, because less wood is wasted, it is estimated that the cost of RIL is actually about 12 per cent less per hectare than CL.

You can read more about RIL at
<www.pearsoned.ca/globalconnections>.

Getting SLAPPed

Working in a lawful manner to protect the environment may seem to be a simple and straightforward business. Unfortunately, some who have done this, either as individuals or as a member of an NGO, have found this not to be the case.

Scenario #1

Imagine that you are a leader of a group that was created to support the struggle for justice of a poor, small Aboriginal band in northern Alberta. This band is involved in a dispute with a major, foreign-owned company that is logging the band's land to make paper without paying the band for the lumber that is cut. Your group has organized a consumer boycott of many of the companies that buy paper products from the company. You have been able to convince more than 50 companies, including the LCBO and Mr. Submarine, to purchase bags and other paper products from other companies.

Scenario #2

Imagine that you are the president of the Canadian division of an international paper products company. Your company has purchased the logging rights to a 29 000-km^2 tract of land in northern Alberta from the provincial government. A local Aboriginal band has declared that they are the rightful owners of this land and is disputing your right to cut timber there. To make matters worse, an NGO, created to support the band, has organized a boycott by some of your customers. You have lost major customers like The Body Shop and Pizza Pizza to your competitors because they were afraid of being picketed by the NGO. What are you going to do about this situation?

As you might have guessed, both scenarios refer to the same situation. The NGO was Friends of the Lubicon (the name of the band) and the company was Daishowa, a Japanese multinational. The consumer boycott began in 1991.

If your answer to the question asked in Scenario #2 was that you would sue the NGO for interfering with your business, you are taking an action that is fairly common when an NGO or an individual challenges a private company, most commonly over an environmental dispute. Such lawsuits are called **SLAPPs (Strategic Lawsuits Against Public Participation)**. Under the law, the usual purpose of a lawsuit is to right a wrong that has been done to a person or organization. In the case of a SLAPP, the principal purpose of the suit is to stop the protest by forcing the NGO or individual to focus time and money on preparing a legal defence rather than fighting the company.

The Daishowa lawsuit against the Friends of the Lubicon was not settled until 1998. The court's decision was profoundly important in Canada's legal history. It established the right of NGOs and private citizens to protest the activities of companies by any legal means. The judge ruled that the boycott was not only legal, but also "a model of how such activities should be conducted in a democratic society." Shortly after the decision, the company agreed not to log any of the 10 000-km^2 area claimed by the Lubicon until a land claims settlement was reached between the band and the Alberta government.

Canada, unlike several US states, has no laws against SLAPPs. As a result of the Daishowa dispute, there has been a call for similar legislation here to protect those who are trying to work for conservation of the environment.

You can learn more about this dispute and the court case at <www.pearsoned.ca/globalconnections>.

NGOs and Endangered Species

What do you know about the California condor (Figure 16–7, left)? You may know that the condor is the largest bird in North America and that it is a scavenger, surviving by eating carrion. You may also know that, with the help of an extensive conservation effort, it is slowly recovering from a close brush with extinction. Now consider this question: What do you know about the valley elderberry longhorn beetle (VELB) (Figure 16–7, right)? Chances are you do not know that this large beetle is scarlet with black spots and that it lives only in elderberry thickets along the banks of streams in California's Central Valley—not far from the main habitat of the California condor. You likely also do not know that it too is an endangered species.

Here we have two animals with striking similarities. They are near neighbours, and both are considered endangered according to the US Endangered Species Act. The condor population is being increased as a result of a massive effort that costs more than $1.5 million per year. Meanwhile, the only protection the beetle has is a requirement under the Endangered Species Act that anyone destroying one patch of elderberry habitat must replace it with another. There is no requirement to prove that this replacement has not had a detrimental impact on the number of beetles.

Why is there such a difference in people's attitudes towards these two endangered species? The reason is that, to most people, the California condor is a fascinating animal. It is huge, with a wingspan of up to three metres, and a truly majestic sight as it soars over the dry mountains of southern California. When one sees a condor, there is no mistaking what it is—it could be nothing else. On the other hand, the VELB is not very big and looks like dozens of other beetles. It is hardly an animal that commands attention.

Animals like the California condor are classified as charismatic megafauna, or animals that have wide popular appeal because of their size, majesty, or appearance. They are the "superstars" of the animal world and, when classified as

Figure 16–7 *The California condor (left) and the valley elderberry longhorn beetle (right) are both endangered species—but get very different treatment.*

You can learn more about the California condor, the valley elderberry longhorn beetle, and the importance of little animals at
<www.pearsoned.ca/globalconnections>.

endangered or threatened, frequently become the focus of fund-raising efforts by environmental NGOs. In fact, an Internet search for "endangered species" combined with "organization(s)" identifies more than a dozen agencies that feature only charismatic megafauna on their home pages. These animals include wolves, rhinoceros, tigers, elephants, giant pandas, snow leopards, bald eagles, and cheetahs. It is easy to understand why these organizations feature such animals on their Web sites and in their advertising. It is less easy to determine whether this focus is desirable or not.

Supporters of this use of charismatic megafauna contend that the approach draws public attention to the need to protect endangered species in a way that would otherwise be impossible. Once people and governments begin thinking about endangered species, it becomes easier to raise money and to pressure governments to improve legal protection for them. These organizations also point out that money raised in the name of pandas, elephants, and other large animals is often used to protect the habitats in which these animals live and, hence, to protect all the animals and plants that live in these areas.

Critics of this approach suggest that concentrating on just a few attractive animals produces a warped view of the issues surrounding endangered species. People come to think of endangered species in terms of only a few animals rather than vast numbers of insects, worms, slime moulds, and bacteria that may be threatened. Many scientists contend that these invertebrates are the most important animals in the world, and that our efforts should be focussed on learning about and protecting such "noncharismatic minifauna." Instead, we think that if the number of whooping cranes or tigers is increasing, then progress is being made to protect endangered species.

Promoting Sustainability

This chapter has shown how complex and interrelated environmental issues are. Everything is interconnected, so that virtually every decision made has many implications, both expected and unexpected. We are faced with one dilemma after another. We want to protect forests, but we all use lumber and paper products and do not want to see the people who work in these industries lose their jobs. We applaud the NGOs and their supporters who rescue California condors and giant pandas, but worry that their efforts mean we are ignoring other, less spectacular animals. We are happy to see companies like Home Depot "go green," but wonder if this choice is more about gaining a marketing advantage than protecting the environment.

One of the hardest tasks that we all have is to learn how to reconcile these apparent contradictions. A good way to do this is to focus on the concept of sustainability. If an action that is to be taken promotes sustainability, then it is a "good" decision, preserving the resource or species for future generations. If it does not, it is a "bad" decision. The challenge then shifts to being able to decide whether the result of a particular decision promotes sustainability.

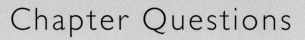

Chapter Questions

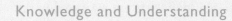

Knowledge and Understanding

1. a) Describe the role that inexpensive forest products play in our lives.

   b) Describe three ways that the average consumer can ensure that we will continue to have inexpensive, readily available forest products and still protect forests.

2. a) Explain, from both sides of the issue (producers and environmentalists), why forestry disputes are frequently focussed on areas of old-growth forests.

   b) Where in Canada, and elsewhere in the world, would we find such forests?

3. a) Explain what a SLAPP is, and indicate how the company involved can win at least a partial victory even if it loses in the courts.

   b) What action could governments take to eliminate this motivation for SLAPPs?

4. a) Identify at least 10 examples of threatened or endangered charismatic megafauna. For each, indicate what feature(s) of the animal make it attractive to humans.

   b) Why do NGOs frequently use charismatic megafauna in their promotional activities?

   c) What risks are associated with this approach to protecting endangered species?

Thinking and Inquiry

5. Identify newer forms of communications technology that are valuable in direct-action campaigns like Butterfly Hill's tree-sit. Why are they helpful?

6. a) Explain why the protection provided by laws requiring HCP/SYP-type plans is vitally important in forest and species protection.

   b) How valid is it to suggest that these sorts of management plans on private land might be more important than the protection for forest environments provided by various forms of parks and nature preserves?

7. If reduced-impact logging produces more wood and is cheaper than conventional logging explain why RIL is not done more often.

Communication

8. Research one endangered species that was unfamiliar to you before you read this chapter. Present this animal on a poster. On your poster include the following:

   ■ where the animal lives, both in terms of what country/state/province and in what sort of ecosystem

   ■ why the animal became endangered

   ■ what efforts are being taken to protect the animal

   ■ what role is being played by NGOs, governments, individuals, and companies in protecting (and threatening) this animal

   ■ what conflict (if any) exists between protecting the animal and meeting human needs.

   For more information on endangered species, go to <www.pearsoned.ca/globalconnections>.

9. Give two reasons why NGOs are most likely to target the largest, most visible companies in a particular category, like Home Depot and McDonald's, when they wish to challenge the activities in a particular industry sector.

10. One of the founders of Greenpeace, Canadian Patrick Moore, has become disillusioned by the fact that many NGOs are unwilling to seek compromises on their goals. Read the essay written by him on this topic at <www.pearsoned.ca/globalconnections>.

    Do you agree with his observations? Why or why not?

Application

11. a) Are protests like Julia Hill's and those often carried out by Greenpeace an effective way to protect the environment? Why or why not?

(For example, in 2001, Greenpeace protesters climbed the outside of the CN Tower to protest the lack of action taken by Canada and the United States to fight global warming.)
b) Are more extreme forms of protest, like monkey-wrenching, acceptable? In other words, do the ends justify the means? Explain your answer.

12. It is often difficult for a private citizen to determine the facts in an environmental or other dispute. This difficulty is understandable, since all parties in the dispute do their best to present their side of the case and to discredit their opponents. Describe a method that a person can use to analyse such a dispute intelligently.

13. In this chapter, seven stakeholders were mentioned in the Headwaters Forest case. Divide up these positions for a discussion of a typical forest dispute. Consider the arguments you will make. Do whatever research is necessary to prepare your position.

14. Investigate the operations of any NGO that is involved in either forest or endangered species protection. Determine, at least, the following characteristics of the organization:
a) its purpose
b) its history
c) its membership and funding sources
d) the location of its activities and headquarters
e) the tactics it uses
f) how successful it is in achieving its aims.

17

Water Issues

Expectations

In this chapter, you will:

■ understand how
human-induced changes
in natural systems
reduce their capacity to
support human activity

■ identify issues of
global sustainability and
environmental threats

■ evaluate the sustain-
ability of use of Earth's
resources

■ assess the effects of
environmental deregu-
lation in Canada

■ evaluate the effec-
tiveness of an interna-
tional strategy

■ use satellite images
to analyse the results of
human activities

Nearly three-quarters of Earth's surface is covered with water in the form of oceans, rivers, lakes, snow, and glaciers, such as the Columbia Icefields in Jasper, Alberta (above). Of all Earth's water, less than 5 per cent is fresh; and only a minuscule fraction of this fresh water, 0.01 per cent, is available for use. The rest is tied up in ice, or is inaccessible deep underground.

Preserving Our Freshwater Supplies

It has been estimated that the amount of fresh water on Earth could support 20 billion people, a little over three times the current population of the world. But the reality is that this water is not always located where people can easily access it. In Canada, for example, 60 per cent of rivers drain north, away from where 90 per cent of Canadians live.

Water is essential for all life. Yet, we have ignored the fact that we are polluting and wasting our fresh water, and have taken few steps to preserve it.

Surface Freshwater Pollution

Some natural events affect the quality and quantity of water. However, human activity is the main source of pollution of the world's fresh water. Agriculture, urbanization, industry, mining, forestry, and shipping are among the many activities that affect water quality.

Sewage Waste

Human and animal wastes contain germs that spread disease through water. Cholera, diarrhoea, typhoid, polio, and many intestinal parasites are water-borne, and result from poor sanitation. About 1.5 billion people worldwide do not have access to safe drinking water, and about another three billion do not have adequate sanitation, that is, the ability to dispose of their sewage safely. It is not surprising that about 80 per cent of the illnesses in developing countries result from impure water. Although sewage technology that prevents the transmission of disease is available, many communities cannot afford to put it in place (Figure 17–1).

You may be surprised to discover that in 1983 in Canada, only 72 per cent of the municipal (urban) population had some form of sewage treatment. By 1999, this figure had risen to 97 per cent (Figure 17–2). Even if cities have treatment plants, not all the water returned to the environment is treated. In some older parts of

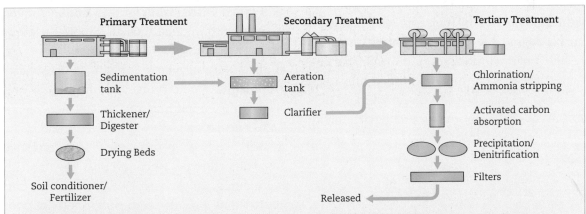

Primary: A mechanical process in which metal grating and screens remove large solids, sediment, and some organic matter.
Secondary: Biological processes (bacteria and other microorganisms) decompose the organic matter in trickle filters, aeration tanks, or sewage lagoons.
Tertiary: Chemical processes remove phosphates, nitrates, toxic compounds, metals, salts, and acids. The treated effluent may be released into water bodies or used for irrigation.

Figure 17–1   *The three stages of sewage treatment.* Source: Adapted from "How Does a Sewage Treatment Plant Work?" McMaster University, Department of Biology.

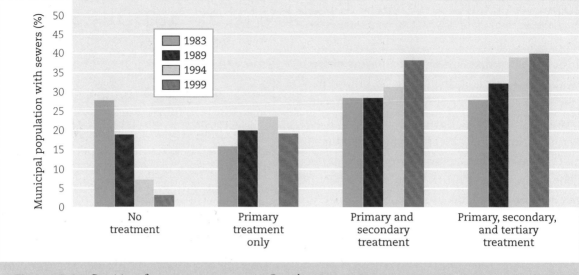

Figure 17–2 *Provision of wastewater treatment in Canada, 1983–1999.* Source: Environment Canada.

Toronto, for example, storm sewers and sanitation sewers are not separate. After a heavy rain, the sewers carry so much water that the treatment plants cannot handle the load, and much of the water is discharged untreated into Lake Ontario.

Industrial Waste

The chemical by-products of manufacturing often reach our water bodies and, as a result, pose a threat to our health. Some industrial pollutants are **biodegradable**, that is, they break down as a result of natural processes in the environment. Nevertheless, when they are flushed into rivers or lakes, care must be taken that an overload does not occur and upset the natural environment.

Did you KNOW?

A 1992 study by the World Bank found that during the 1980s, high-income countries made some improvement in the water quality of their rivers. River water quality in middle-income countries generally showed no change, and quality in low-income countries continued to deteriorate.

Other by-products, such as heavy metals like mercury, lead, copper, and arsenic, are very dangerous even in small quantities and will never biodegrade. Since these by-products can eventually contaminate underground sources of water, extra care must be taken by industry to control or eliminate them through proper waste treatment.

About nine million Canadians and 33 million Americans depend on the Great Lakes–St. Lawrence River basin for their drinking water. You would think that such an important source of water would be protected from pollution. Yet, in the 1960s, such large amounts of phosphates from laundry detergents, and phosphorus and nitrogen from industry and agriculture, entered Lake Erie that the lake was declared "dead." The growth of aquatic plants nourished by excessive nutrients created oxygen levels so low that fish were dying. In the late 1990s, when fish had returned as a result of phosphorus reduction, Lake Erie was declared "alive" again.

More serious dangers were discovered in the 1970s: over 360 industrial chemical compounds were found in the waters of the Great Lakes. Over 100 of them are toxic to humans and wildlife. In 1972, Canada and the United States signed the first Great Lakes Water Quality Agreement, and steps were taken to reduce phosphorus discharge into the Great Lakes. Then in 1985, the **International Joint Commission (IJC)**, the body set up by Canada and the United States in 1909 to deal with issues concerning the Great Lakes, identified 43 "areas of concern" on the Great Lakes that had very poor water quality, 17 of which were located in Canada. In response, the Canadian government announced its $125-million Great Lakes Remedial Action Plan (RAP) in 1989, which provided funding to clean up the Canadian areas of concern (Figure 17–3). In 1994, the federal government announced a seven-year program called Great Lakes 2000 to continue restoring sites with poor water quality and to prevent and control pollution.

For further information about Great Lakes 2000 and other programs, visit
<www.pearsoned.ca/globalconnections>.

The Sydney Tar Ponds

"Hazardous site, absolutely no trespassing" says the sign on the fence in Sydney, Nova Scotia. This is the location of the infamous Sydney Tar Ponds, North America's largest toxic waste site (Figure 17–4, on the next page). It contains over 700 000 t of toxic sludge, of which an estimated 50 000 t are contaminated with more than 15 cancer-causing compounds.

The Tar Ponds are actually a tidal estuary (river mouth that ebbs and flows with the rise and fall of tides) known as Muggah Creek, which

Figure 17–3 *Of the 17 "areas of concern" located in Canada, there are 12 in Canadian waters and five in waters shared with the United States.* Source: Environment Canada.

Figure 17–4 *The Sydney Tar Ponds have been described as North America's worst environmental disaster.*

links the site of the Sydney Steel Company (SYSCO) to Sydney Harbour. SYSCO was purchased from a failing steel company by the Nova Scotia government in 1967, and operated as a Crown corporation until 2000. Like previous companies on the site, it released toxic chemicals into the Tar Ponds. A mixture of PCBs, coal tars, benzene, kerosene, toluene, naphthalene, copper, lead, arsenic, nickel, and zinc were carelessly disposed of in Muggah Creek. Moreover, dangerous wastes leaching from a nearby unlined municipal landfill, plus raw sewage from approximately 30 outlet pipes, contribute to the lethal brew that is carried from the estuary into the ocean with the rise and fall of every tide.

Homes, schools, playgrounds, supermarkets, and restaurants surround the Sydney Tar Ponds.

For information about the Tar Ponds, go to
<www.pearsoned.ca/globalconnections>.

The City Hall is less than one kilometre away. Nearby residents report a yellow-coloured "goo" seeping into their basements, and puddles that turn fluorescent green after it rains. Residents are also convinced that the dust they are inhaling from the toxic soil could make them ill. Tests conducted by Health Canada in 2001 found that some properties contain high levels of polychromatic hydrocarbons, arsenic, and lead. Residents are frightened that their health is in danger, and those on Frederick Street, next to the Tar Ponds, want to leave. They know that Sydney has one of the highest rates of cancer, birth defects, and miscarriages in Canada. Yet, a further federal–provincial study released in December 2001 stated that the Tar Ponds were "no more dangerous than any other part of Nova Scotia" despite concerns by environmentalists about how the data had been interpreted.

When high levels of PCBs, mercury, and other compounds were discovered in the lobsters of Sydney Harbour in 1980, steps were taken to deal with the contamination in the Tar Ponds. In 1986, $34.5 million was pledged to clean up Muggah Creek and to build an incinerator to burn coke-oven by-products. Construction of the incinerator began. The project was abandoned in 1993 after $52 million had been spent because the incinerator was not designed to burn the PCBs, which were found in the sludge. Since then, the Joint Action Group (JAG) has been formed, composed of representatives from First Nations, advocacy groups, business, three levels of government, and the general public. The federal and provincial governments gave the JAG $62 million in 1999 to conduct tests and studies of the Tar Ponds, and to develop possible solutions. By 2000, the JAG had awarded contracts worth $12 million to companies for an air-monitoring program, an environmental site assessment, and a demonstration of clean-up technologies.

In 2001, the steel plant was sold to a Swiss company. Residents wonder if this will bring jobs, a clean-up of the site, or more contamination.

Pollution from Agricultural Sources

While modern agricultural techniques have greatly increased food production, they have also contributed to the pollution of surface water and groundwater. Irrigation washes away soil sediments that clog waterways, destroy fish habitats, and fill in wetlands. Manufactured chemical fertilizers become pollutants when they are washed into lakes and rivers, or into the groundwater. Nitrogen and phosphorus in lakes and ponds cause **eutrophication**, the growth and decomposition of excess vegetation that depletes oxygen in the water. Fish and other marine organisms cannot survive in excessively eutrophic water bodies. Fortunately, ecosystems can recover if the source of eutrophication is removed.

Pesticides, which include insecticides, herbicides, and fungicides, often kill organisms other than the ones they are developed to target. Designed to kill insect pests, weeds, and plant diseases, they can adversely affect soil, crops, animals, and humans, as well as water. Excessive use of pesticides has been linked to high rates of cancer and birth defects, and in Central Asia, to lower life expectancy. Although no longer used in developed countries, long-lasting toxic pesticides such as DDT, aldrin, and dieldrin are commonly used in developing nations.

Water pollution can occur from the raising of animals for human consumption. In May 2000, a torrential downpour carried water contaminated with cattle manure containing a deadly strain of *Escherichia coli* bacteria into one of the wells of the Ontario community of Walkerton. The well, located downhill from a cattle farm, drained into an aquifer covered by only 2.4 m of sand and gravel. This was not enough to filter out the *E.coli* bacteria that can kill by causing kidneys to shut down. Since problems with cattle fecal matter in the well water had been identified as early as 1978, the Ministry of the Environment had told local officials to chlorinate the water and monitor for bacteria. Nevertheless, seven people died, and 2300 became ill from drinking the town water.

Groundwater

Only a very small proportion of precipitation becomes groundwater. This is water that filters downward through the soil under the force of gravity, collecting in rock fissures and cavities, and eventually flowing through rock and sediments located deep underground. These groundwater "reservoirs" are known as **aquifers**. There are two types:

- *Open aquifer:* water percolates through permeable (porous) soil, rock, and sediments and enters the aquifer from above.

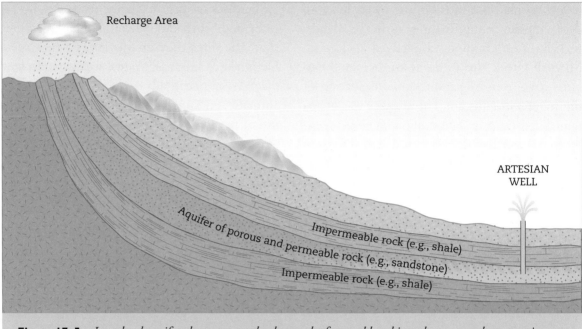

Recharge Area

ARTESIAN WELL

Aquifer of porous and permeable rock (e.g., sandstone)

Impermeable rock (e.g., shale)

Impermeable rock (e.g., shale)

Figure 17–5 *In a closed aquifer, the water may be thousands of years old and is under pressure due to gravity. Because of this water pressure, an artesian well flows without the need for pumps.*

Closed aquifer: water is prevented from entering from above because the aquifer is confined by rock or sediments, such as shale or clay, with low porosity and low permeability (Figure 17–5). Water in a closed aquifer may be **fossil water**, several thousands or even millions of years old. When a well is drilled into a closed aquifer, the water rises to the surface without the use of a pump. The water is forced up into the well by the pressure of the water behind it flowing down through the aquifer. This is an **artesian well**.

The Ogallala Aquifer

In the United States, the Ogallala (or High Plains) Aquifer is an important source of water.

> **Did you KNOW?**
> There is about 40 times more fresh water under the ground than in all the rivers and lakes in the world.

This largely closed aquifer underlies a major agricultural area that is part of eight states, stretching almost 1300 km from north to south and 650 km from east to west (Figure 17–6). The aquifer consists mainly of sand, gravel, silt, and clay that eroded from the Rocky Mountains over 20 million years ago. Over time, these sediments soaked up water like a sponge to form an enormous underground reservoir that is now many thousands of years old. About 1000 years ago, the Ogallala was cut off from its recharging area in the Rocky Mountains. The fossil water in the aquifer cannot be replenished except by small amounts of water from precipitation, lakes, and streams that percolate into those few areas of the aquifer that are open. It is estimated that there is enough water in the Ogallala Aquifer to fill Lake Huron.

In 1950, water from the Ogallala Aquifer irrigated about 1.4 million hectares; today, it irrigates about 6.5 million hectares. In some areas, water withdrawal is up to 10 times greater than the rate of natural recharge. Consequently, in almost one-third of the region, the water level in the aquifer has declined by as much as three metres. In some regions, the decline has been as great as 15 m. Despite conservation measures such as the introduction of more efficient methods of irrigation and the planting of crops that require less water, the Ogallala Aquifer continues to drop. New sources of water will be needed if the High Plains area is to remain one of the world's major agricultural regions, producing wheat, alfalfa, soybeans, cotton, corn, cattle, poultry, and hogs. If agricultural production declines in this area because of lack of water, even people in developing countries may suffer because the United States will have less food available for export and humanitarian aid.

The aquifer is facing other problems as well. The removal of large amounts of water is causing the land above the aquifer to subside (sink) in some places. Moreover, agricultural and industrial chemicals, animal wastes, and contamination from landfills and abandoned waste sites have become major pollutants. It does not take much to contaminate groundwater. One litre of gasoline, for example, can contaminate about one million litres of groundwater.

Fossil Water in Saudi Arabia

Saudi Arabia also relies heavily on fossil water. One-third of its water comes from a combination of renewable aquifer water, desalinated water (seawater from which salt has been removed), and reused wastewater. The remaining two-thirds comes from fossil water in underground aquifers. This non-renewable resource is being used up very quickly. In the 1980s, in an effort to help the country become self-sufficient in wheat, the Saudi Arabian government provided subsidies and interest-free loans to its farmers, and guaranteed to pay them more than four times the world price for wheat. Farmers, motivated by this assistance, produced more than twice the wheat needed to meet domestic demand. By 1991, Saudi Arabia had become the world's sixth largest exporter of wheat, but at what cost? In essence, the country was subsidizing the export of its scarcest resource—water. By 1993, the government had stopped

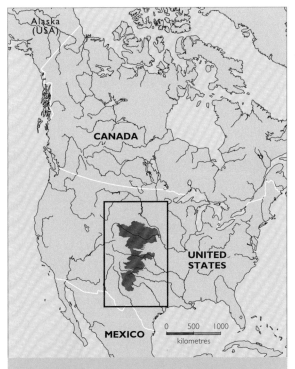

Figure 17-6 *The Ogallala (High Plains) Aquifer underlies the states of South Dakota, Wyoming, Nebraska, Colorado, Kansas, Oklahoma, New Mexico, and Texas. The aquifer was named after the town of Ogallala, Nebraska. Much of this area was in the "Dust Bowl" during the Great Depression, when years of drought resulted in massive soil erosion.*

buying wheat owing to changing market conditions and budget deficits, but today farmers are irrigating other crops with fossil water. When Saudi Arabia's fossil aquifers can no longer be tapped—and this outcome is inevitable, unless current rates of use are curtailed—the expanded agricultural sector that depends on fossil water will undoubtedly collapse. Libya, in North Africa, is in a similar position. The country is building the world's largest water pipeline to carry fossil water from an aquifer in the south to the north for irrigation purposes.

Wetlands

Wetlands are located in every major climatic zone on Earth. A global review completed in 1999 indicated that 24 per cent of the world's wetlands are found in Canada. Known by different names—swamps, bogs, marshes, peat lands, mangrove swamps, salt marshes—wetlands form a transition zone between permanently dry land and lakes, streams, rivers, and oceans. Until the latter half of the 20th century, wetlands in the Western world were generally considered useless land, and many were filled in or drained for residential, industrial, and especially, agricultural purposes.

Studies in the last 40 years have demonstrated that wetlands are very important and should be protected for several reasons:

- They are temporary water storage sites that recharge aquifers, moderate stream flow, and lessen floods.
- Their vegetation holds soil in place and anchors shorelines. For example, the roots of mangrove trees growing in swamps keep the soil in place.
- They provide habitats and breeding grounds for fish, invertebrates, birds, and mammals.
- Many are migratory stopovers for birds (Figure 17–7).
- The natural recycling of their water filters out chemicals, and circulates nutrients to plants and animals.

Figure 17–7 *Wetlands, like the Jack Miner Bird Sanctuary in Kingsville, Ontario, shown here, are essential to the waterfowl refuge management system.*

- They provide people with aesthetic environments, food, and fuel. For example, peat cut from bogs in northern Europe is dried for burning in fireplaces and stoves.

The Ramsar Convention, signed in Ramsar, Iran, in 1971, was one of the first international attempts to protect the world's wetlands. Since the Convention does not have any legal power to force countries to stop the loss of their wetlands, it uses persuasion and moral arguments to accomplish this end. By 2001, the Ramsar List comprised 1078 sites of international importance in 130 countries. Upon signing the Convention, each country must designate at least one wetland for the "List of Wetlands of International Importance." Canada signed the Convention in 1981, and currently has 36 sites with a combined surface area of over 13 million hectares on the list. Eight of these sites, including Point Pelee, Polar Bear Provincial Park, and Minesing Swamp, are found in Ontario. Unfortunately, many of the world's most important wetlands are not listed, and these productive environments are among Earth's most threatened ecosystems. This is particularly true in developing countries, where rapidly growing populations are putting pressure on governments to drain wetlands for agriculture.

Managed Water

Managed freshwater resources include small- and large-scale dams and agricultural irrigation schemes. Large-scale projects present a variety of issues related to preserving the Earth's freshwater supplies.

Large-Scale Dams

In Las Vegas, Nevada, water appears to be an abundant resource. At three of the largest hotels in the city, it "dances" to music, courses in the canals of a small-scale Venice, and flows in a

You can find additional information about the Ramsar Convention on Wetlands at <www.pearsoned.ca/globalconnections>.

miniature sea for pirate ships. But this abundance is an illusion: the city is located in the middle of a desert (Figure 17–8, on the next page). Las Vegas depends upon the management of water for its survival. The Hoover Dam on the Colorado River provides 85 per cent of Las Vegas's water, and has helped make the city the fastest-growing metropolis in the United States.

There are over 800 000 small dams and more than 45 000 large ones (dams higher than a five-storey building) in the world today. Of these, 100 are "superdams"—150 m or more high.

Benefits of Dams

- Dams provide nearly 20 per cent of the world's electricity. The power is relatively inexpensive and does not pollute the atmosphere with greenhouse gases and acid rain, as do coal and natural-gas thermal stations. The production of hydro-electricity does not produce dangerous waste products like those from nuclear power stations.
- Dams produce large amounts of electricity that attract industries requiring abundant, inexpensive power. Examples are the aluminum smelters on the Saguenay River in Quebec and in Kitimat, British Columbia. Large amounts of hydro-electric power from Niagara Falls and the St. Lawrence River were crucial to the development of southern Ontario's industrial base.
- Dams regulate the flow of water downstream to reduce flooding. The Aswan High Dam on the Nile River prevents flooding and guarantees a steady flow of water to farmers year round.
- Dams create a reservoir of water used for agriculture, industry, and other human needs. More

Figure 17–8 *The abundant greenery around Las Vegas's homes and country clubs makes the city seem like an oasis in the desert. But is this use of water sustainable?*

than 20 dams on the Colorado River provide water and power to over 21 million people through the US Southwest. Without the dams, much of the landscape would remain desert.

■ Dams create reservoirs that become artificial lakes, which in some cases provide habitats for fish, migrating birds, amphibians, and shoreline animals.

■ Dams may provide boating, swimming, fishing, and other water-based recreational activities.

■ The management of water levels below dams may allow a barge-shipping transportation system that is cheaper and more fuel-efficient than trains or trucks. For example, barge shipping on the Columbia River in the United States carries an estimated 120 000 railroad cars of goods annually.

■ Many industrialized countries import oil and natural gas for their energy needs. Dams help make countries more self-sufficient in energy.

In the past, governments in the developing world often supported large-scale projects as a means to increase food production by providing a reliable water supply for irrigation. Governments viewed dams as a way to achieve economic development through the production of electricity for use in homes and industries. Both the World Bank and many developed countries gave loans and technical assistance to build dams with related irrigation schemes and electrical projects. Today, however, enthusiasm for building large dams in developing countries is waning.

Negative Impacts of Dams

- On the economic side, there is seldom enough industry to use the power generated by such projects in developing countries. Furthermore, the payment of interest charges and the payback of loans are difficult for countries with a limited tax base. The standard of living of people who are forced to move from productive farmland and resettle on new land generally declines as a result of their loss of good farmland.

- There are always technical problems associated with dam building. Dams are often built in dry climates to regulate and increase water supply, and yet large quantities of water evaporate from the reservoirs. Sometimes the rock structure beneath the dam site is unsuitable for storing water. For example, part of Lake Nasser behind the Aswan High Dam in Egypt lies on porous sandstone that soaks up much of the water in the reservoir. And then, there is always the danger in earthquake-prone regions that the weight of water in the reservoir will trigger an earthquake.

- The social problems associated with dam building have been well documented. People's way of life, their culture, and often their spiritual focus are lost when their ancestral homes and lands are flooded, and they are forced to move to higher ground. Some find that their skills are useless in a new environment. For example, people who once fished in rivers have no skills for farming in upland regions. Many suffer from a resettlement syndrome characterized by passivity, depression, and less self-reliance.

- The damming of a river inevitably changes the ecology of the river and surrounding areas. The changed ecology more often than not results in a variety of environmental problems. Water-based animals and fish that are adapted to flowing, highly oxygenated water cannot survive in the still, low-oxygenated reservoir that builds up behind a dam. Those adapted to still-water habitats cannot survive in the controlled, fast-flowing water that empties from a reservoir. Moreover, the still, warm water behind a dam often encourages the proliferation of waterweeds, especially in tropical countries, to such a degree that sunlight is unable to penetrate below the surface. This reduction in light causes plants and organisms in the water to die, and the oxygen level to decrease such that fish cannot survive.

- Another common problem is the accumulation of sediments in the reservoir that would normally be carried downstream, where they would build up the soil in the wetlands and the delta, and fertilize the floodplain. A good example is the Nile Delta, which has become smaller since the building of the Aswan High Dam, and the farmland along the Nile River, which now requires large quantities of chemical fertilizers to replace nutrients that used to be deposited in silt carried down by the annual floodwaters.

- Dams and irrigation works in tropical areas lead to an increase in water-borne diseases. In West Africa, river blindness is caused by the blackfly, which finds the fast-flowing water below the dams an ideal breeding environment. Throughout Asia and Africa, guinea worms, mosquitoes (which carry malaria, yellow fever, and elephantiasis), and snails, which carry bilharzia (schistosomiasis), find ideal breeding conditions in the still waters of reservoirs and irrigation ditches. The people who live near dams often use the lakes and irrigation channels as toilets; this promotes the spread of bilharzia, dysentery, typhoid, and cholera.

Irrigation Schemes

Large-scale irrigation schemes are frequently associated with large dams. They can provide water for irrigating thousands of hectares of land that may then produce crops necessary for human survival. In fact, two-fifths of the world's food supply is produced on irrigated land, even though less than 20 per cent of the world's croplands are irrigated.

Despite this benefit, serious problems may result from irrigation. In hot, dry climates, much of the water stored in reservoirs evaporates, thus increasing the salinity of the water. When the water evaporates from the irrigated farmlands, it adds unnaturally large amounts of salt to the soil. The salt poisons the earth to the point that important organisms in the soil die, and crops will not grow. High levels of salinity affect about 20 per cent of the world's agricultural land, and about one million hectares of farmland have to be abandoned annually (see Chapter 15).

Some irrigation schemes have created major ecological disasters. One of the most serious concerns the Aral Sea, a saltwater lake that straddles the boundary between Kazakhstan and Uzbekistan in Central Asia. Beginning in the early 1960s, the Soviet Union diverted water from two rivers that fed the Aral Sea, at that time the fourth-largest inland body of water in the world. In an effort to make the Soviet Union self-sufficient in cotton, Moscow central planners rerouted the water from the rivers into a 1300-km canal and a vast network of irrigation ditches that would help expand existing cotton fields.

With the loss of 90 per cent of its inflow, the Aral Sea shrank to one-third its former volume, and in 1988, it split into two smaller lakes. Today, it continues to shrink, and is in danger of disappearing altogether (Figure 17–9). The remaining water has a salinity equal to that of seawater, as well as increased concentrations of toxic agricultural chemicals and human waste. The fishery that supported 60 000 jobs has disappeared, and abandoned fishing villages are found kilometres from the sea. Every year, millions of tonnes of dust laced with salt and toxic chemicals are picked up and deposited on surrounding farmland by the wind. The result is lower crop yields. The climate in the region has changed; it is now drier and hotter, and this has reduced the region's wetland areas, together with their vegetation and waterfowl.

You may well ask why dams with their irrigation schemes are not dismantled if the damage they create is so great. Unfortunately, dismantling is too expensive; it costs about as much to tear down a dam as it does to build it. Furthermore, about 20 per cent of the world's electricity now comes from hydro-electric dams, and a significant portion of the world's food supply grows on land irrigated by dam water.

Alternatives to Large Dams

Some alternatives to large dams include:

- building small dams that manage water on a local rather than regional scale
- planting trees so that rainwater is held back and has a chance to sink into the ground where it can be accessed via wells
- growing crops that require less water
- using drip-irrigation techniques that, although expensive, reduce water consumption by up to 70 per cent, dramatically increasing crop yields
- using roof-top or mountain-slope water collection

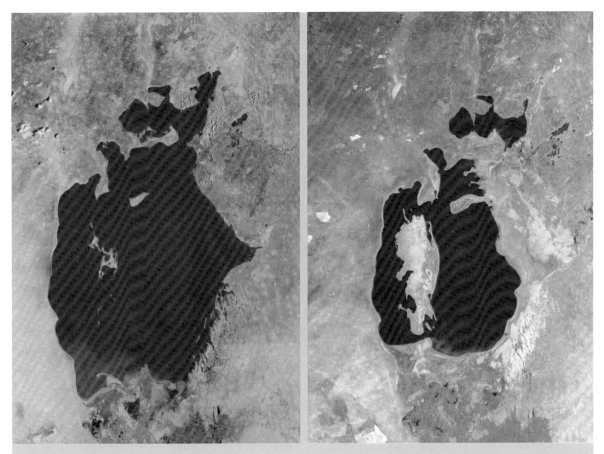

Figure 17–9 *The Aral Sea in 1976 (left) and 1997 (right). Notice the salt deposits (white) in the 1997 photo.*

- improving the efficiency of agricultural processes, since only 40 per cent of water diverted for agriculture actually contributes to food production. An example would be to keep irrigation pipelines in good repair.

Because large-scale dams and irrigation projects are the source of such controversy, the World Bank and the World Conservation Union set up a World Commission on Dams (WCD) in 1998. Its mandate was to review the effectiveness of large dams, to assess alternatives, and to develop criteria for future decisions related to the design, construction, operation, and decommissioning of dams. In the final report of the WCD, the chair of the Commission, Professor Kader Asmal, said:

…Nowhere in the Report will you read "large dams are bad." Or "good." Large dams simply are. The Report shows how, where, when, and why certain aspects of those dams have performed for better or for worse, and how we can improve decisions to develop resources for all…. The Report does not call for a moratorium. Dams should be judged on a case-by-case basis, and pass or fail according to the criteria and guidelines societies set for them.

You can learn more about the World Commission on Dams at <www.pearsoned.ca/globalconnections>.

Water Transfers

In many parts of the world, fresh water is in short supply; in other parts, it is abundant. One method of dealing with this inequity is to transfer water from one place to another. Canada and the United States share many boundary waters, and divert water on both sides of the border. But when the subject of large-scale transfers of water from Canada to the United States arises, the issue takes on another dimension.

Opponents argue that although fresh water is plentiful in Canada, it is located in the north, far away from where it is needed for human activities. As for the water in the Great Lakes, 99 per cent is non-renewable fossil water from glaciers that melted some 10 000 years ago; only 1 per cent is renewed annually by rainfall and river inflow. From this perspective, the case is made that there is much less water available for transfer to the United States than would first appear.

On the other hand, there are those who argue that since we export non-renewable oil, gas, and other minerals, why should Canada not export water that is renewed naturally? A properly managed water-export industry would provide jobs and money that could benefit Canada, especially when the spectre of global warming is threatening to render the US Southwest even more arid than it is now.

In 1994, opponents of the then-unsigned North American Free Trade Agreement (NAFTA) expressed their conviction that it was possible that Canada's fresh water might be shipped to the United States under the terms of the agreement. The Canadian government, in its efforts to counter this belief and encourage the adoption of NAFTA, produced a statement signed by Canada, the United States, and Mexico asserting that NAFTA did not give any one country a right to the water resources of another. There was nothing in NAFTA itself, however, that exempted bulk water sales between countries. As a result, opponents were concerned that once bulk sales started, they could not be stopped. Canada has not banned the export of water because bans are not allowed under NAFTA or under agreements of the World Trade Organization, of which Canada is a member. Moreover, a ban would thereby define water as a tradable commodity.

Water companies are currently allowed to export water provided the containers are no larger than 20 L (Figure 17–10).

One reason Canada does not have a common water policy is that control over water is divided between the federal government, which oversees boundary waters such as the Great Lakes, and the provinces, which have authority over all other waters within their boundaries.

Canadians are concerned about bulk water exports because of the harmful and unpredictable environmental consequences that would result from the removal of large amounts of water from lakes, rivers, or entire drainage basins. Indeed, many environmental problems in the arid portions of the United States are the result of large-scale removal and use to support the expectations of rapidly growing populations—including green lawns, swimming pools, and golf courses.

Bottled Water Exports

Province	Volume (litres)	Share (%)
Quebec	246 558 496	90.7
Ontario	16 710 533	6.1
British Columbia	7 679 841	2.8
New Brunswick	474 160	0.2
Alberta	258 127	0.1

Figure 17–10 *Canada's exports of bottled water.* Source: International Joint Commission Report, cited in "Bottled water gushing south," *Globe and Mail*, Sept. 22, 1999.

Moreover, government subsidies to US farmers have encouraged the growing of crops and cattle, activities that require large amounts of water. "Cheap" water of this sort promotes waste and does not encourage conservation. The export of Canadian water would most likely continue to discourage adapting landscaping choices to the climate of the area, building high-tech desalination plants, and using conservation methods such as low-flush toilets and more efficient irrigation systems such as drip irrigation. **Drip irrigation** uses pipes with tiny holes that take measured amounts of water directly to plants, thereby reducing evaporation while increasing crop yields.

Perhaps we should not be too worried about the sale of Canadian water to international customers. According to some experts, the cost of collecting and shipping water would far outweigh the costs of conservation techniques.

Preserving Our Oceans

The world's oceans are vast, covering 72 per cent of Earth's surface. They have been the means by which much exploration and trade have been conducted, and they have always been an important source of food. Despite their economic and ecological importance, the oceans have been sadly neglected. We dump our garbage and chemicals into them, and catch fish and whales beyond sustainable levels. We do these things even though we know very little about how oceans sustain themselves and how pollutants may be affecting marine organisms. We do know, however, that the damage we do to oceans is having a serious impact on all life on Earth.

The Fisheries

Fish from the world's oceans is the largest source of animal protein available to humans. By the 1990s, about 100 million tonnes of fish were being caught annually. Many biologists think that this amount is close to the maximum sustainable annual catch. The United Nations Food and Agricultural Organization (FAO), however, has estimated that sustainable levels may already have been reached or exceeded for about 70 per cent of fish species caught for food.

There are many examples of overfishing in the world's oceans. Canada's East Coast fishery collapsed in 1991 when the northern cod, the species that sustained the industry, disappeared. Overfishing, along with changes in the natural environment, was responsible. Then in 1994, the West Coast fishery, based primarily on salmon, collapsed for the same reasons. During the 1970s, overfishing in the North Sea brought the North Atlantic herring close to extinction. A fishing ban instituted in 1977 brought the herring back, but when the ban was lifted in 1981, another depletion occurred when the European nations could not agree on reducing the size of the catch. Large whale species, such as the blue, fin, humpback, grey, and sperm whales, are also threatened. Although the International Whaling

Did you KNOW?

Whale-watching tours, started in Japan in 1988, have become big business. The International Whaling Commission anticipates that watching whales will become more lucrative than hunting them.

Commission placed a moratorium on commercial whaling activities in 1986, Iceland, Norway, and Japan continue to catch whales for scientific purposes.

Pollution

We put many different types of pollutants into the oceans (Figure 17–11). Seventy per cent of marine pollution comes from sources that are located on land. Many coastal cities use the ocean for the disposal of urban waste because they can then avoid problems associated with land disposal. New York City used to dump its waste on the edge of the continental shelf until the late 1980s, when floating medical waste washed up on local beaches. Floating tar balls along sea routes are evidence of illegal discharges of oil from the engines of tankers and transport vessels. Routine activities such as clearing out ballast tanks, loading, and unloading often result in the accidental release of oil into the water. In 2000, a major rupture in Rio de Janeiro's sewage lines fouled beaches along the coast of Brazil (Figure 17–12). And cruise liners have been known to leave garbage and other debris in their wake.

Plastic garbage is on the rise as millions of plastic containers and other items from ship and city waste make their way into the oceans. Since plastic floats and is slow to decompose, coastlines are cluttered with plastic debris, and marine animals are dying from ingesting it. It can block

Type of Pollution	Cause or Source	Impact
Industrial/chemical pollutants (excluding long-range transport)	▪ industrial waste and urban wastewater ▪ pesticides from farms	▪ kill marine life ▪ contaminate ocean environment ▪ bioaccumulate in food chain
Nutrients	▪ municipal sewage, agricultural runoff	▪ algae blooms deplete oxygen ▪ toxic algae blooms (red tides) kill marine organisms and people
Sediments	▪ runoff from farms, forestry, mining operations	▪ carry toxic chemicals ▪ clog fish gills ▪ reduce photosynthesis
Diseases (pathogens)	▪ urban sewage, farm runoff	▪ contaminate coastal waters with pathogens that cause diseases such as cholera and typhoid
Oil	▪ land-based sources, oil tanker operations, oil spills	▪ oil slicks kill marine organisms, damage coastal environments
Litter and debris	▪ cargo and cruise ships, fishing nets, dumped garbage	▪ plastics do not break down, kill marine organisms that get caught in nets ▪ can cause disease
Pulp and paper discharges	▪ forestry industries	▪ wood fibre coats the sea floor ▪ chemicals are poisonous

Figure 17–11 *Ocean pollutants and their effects*

You can learn more about UNCLOS at
<www.pearsoned.ca/globalconnections>.

Figure 17–12 *Thousands of dead fish float in the picturesque lagoon off Rio de Janeiro, Brazil, after ruptures in two major sewage lines spilled thousands of litres of raw sewage into the ocean.*

their digestive tracts and release toxins during digestion. When plastic driftnets used in the north Pacific are lost or carelessly discarded, they may spend years floating on the currents trapping fish, animals, and birds.

A Mari Usque Ad Mare

Canada's motto, "From sea to sea," indicates the significance of oceans to our country. Canada's 244 000-km coastline is the longest in the world, and its continental shelf is the second largest at approximately 3.7 million square kilometres. In 1977, after years of enduring the indiscriminate fishing practices of other nations, Canada declared a 200–nautical mile (370-km) exclusive fisheries zone extending out from its coastlines. In so doing, Canada took upon itself the protection of over 5 million square kilometres of its coastal waters.

International Initiatives

After 22 years of negotiations among 150 nations, the **United Nations Convention on the Law of the Sea (UNCLOS)** in 1994 put into force a legal agreement for promoting peaceful uses of the world's oceans, the equitable use of the oceans' resources, and the protection of marine environments. The Convention declared that 45 per cent of the seabed with its resources was a common resource for all humanity, and as such, should be managed as a global resource.

The agreement also established **Exclusive Economic Zones (EEZs)**, within which maritime countries have the legal power, as well as the obligation, to manage and protect the resources within 200 nautical miles of their coastlines. However, although 79 of the countries that signed the Convention have since ratified it, Canada has not. This indicates that while Canada concurs with the principles of the agreement, it wishes to protect its interests by enacting its own federal and provincial laws. Meanwhile, the United States has not even signed the Convention.

Agreement of all major world nations to both sign and ratify the terms of UNCLOS is important. Without this, the future of the oceans, and the living things that rely on them, is in jeopardy.

Chapter Questions

Knowledge and Understanding

1. Describe the various types of pollution that affect fresh water.

2. Explain how aquifers are formed and why some wells are artesian wells.

3. a) Why are wetlands so important?
   b) For what purposes are wetlands drained?
   c) What is being done to protect the world's wetlands?

4. Identify two reasons for and two reasons against allowing water transfers from Canada to the United States.

5. a) What problems are we creating for the world's oceans?
   b) What initiatives have been taken to deal with some of these problems?

Thinking and Inquiry

6. Examine Figure 17–2.
   a) Describe the trend for each of the four categories.
   b) Investigate the level of sewage treatment in your community.
   c) Compare the level of treatment in your community to that in the rest of Canada.
   d) Suggest reasons why your community is ahead of, the same as, or behind the Canadian levels.

7. a) Examine the issues surrounding the Sydney Tar Ponds.
   b) Conduct research to determine:
      i) who is involved in these issues and what their positions are
      ii) the actions that have been taken and the successes and failures of these actions
      iii) the current status of the issues.

8. In using water, particularly fossil water, society must make a choice: consume the groundwater today, or conserve it for future generations, when the climate may be less favourable because of global warming. What are your recommendations? Explain your reasons.

9. Can a world population of more than 6 billion people be supported with food, energy, and water without dams? Examine the pros and cons of building dams to meet these needs, particularly large dams in developing countries. Describe your conclusions, and support your decisions.

Communication

10. In 1985, the International Joint Commission identified 43 areas of concern in the Great Lakes. Working in pairs, select two sites, one in Canada and one in the United States. Create a poster and a written presentation to show the substances creating the problem, their sources, the danger of these substances, and the actions taken (or not taken).

11. Examine the pros and cons of a large-scale dam/irrigation project in a developed country (such as the Bennett Dam in British Columbia) and in a developing country (such as the Aswan High Dam in Egypt or the Narmada Valley in India). You can consult the Web site <www.pearsoned.ca/globalconnections> for some initial information. Use a visual presentation to demonstrate to the class how appropriate the project was for each country.

12. As a class, debate the following statement: *Resolved—That water, like other commodities, should be exported in bulk as long as its export doesn't affect Canadian needs.*

13. Several institutions and initiatives have been established under UNCLOS. These include:
    - International Seabed Authority
    - International Tribunal for the Law of the Sea

- Commission on the Limits of the Continental Shelf
- Agenda 21 of the UN Conference on Environment and Development (the Earth Summit held in 1992)
- MARPOL, the International Convention for the Prevention of Pollution from Ships
- UNEP, the United Nations Environmental Program
- International Whaling Commission
- Southern Ocean Whale Sanctuary

Divide into groups. Each group can examine one of the institutions or initiatives, using the following guidelines:

a) the nature of the institution or initiative

b) its membership (where appropriate)

c) its mandate

d) recent activities

e) successes and failures (where appropriate).

Each group can prepare a visual and oral presentation to report to the rest of the class.

Application

14. a) Examine the causes and consequences of the *E. coli* outbreak in Walkerton, Ontario, in 2000 using the framework of a judicial hearing. Students will assume the following roles: judge, local water officials, medical officials, employees of a water-testing company, government representatives, local citizens, media representatives.

b) Students will research their own roles and will use this information as a basis for testimony in the hearing.

c) In light of this event, what has been done across Ontario to ensure that such a tragedy will not occur again?

d) Send a letter to the appropriate provincial officials, indicating your agreement or disagreement with actions that have been taken to prevent future contamination of water supplies.

15. Major environmental changes can be caused by large-scale irrigation schemes. Examine the Aral Sea scheme, the Colorado River water diversions, or some other project, and write a report, with visual aids, to demonstrate its positive and negative aspects.

16. In February 2002, the government of Quebec and the Crees of Quebec signed a $3.5-billion agreement that will allow Hydro Quebec to build installations on the Eastmain and Rupert rivers, and will permit mining, logging, and further industrial development on Cree territory. Write a report in which you examine and explain

a) the three decades of conflict between the Crees and the government of Quebec over development on Cree territory

b) what the 2002 agreement gives to both sides

c) what opponents say about this agreement

d) whether the deal is fair to both sides.

17. Use information in this chapter as the basis for writing an exchange of memos or e-mails between a Canadian and an American on the topic of bulk water transfers.

18

Air Issues

Key Terms

smog
ultraviolet (UV)
  radiation
persistent organic
  pollutants (POPs)
bioaccumulation
grasshopper effect
acidic deposition
critical load
temperature inversion
photochemical smog
chlorofluorocarbons
  (CFCs)
Montreal Protocol

Expectations

In this chapter, you will:

■ understand how
human-induced changes
in natural systems
reduce their capacity to
support human activity

■ explain the interac-
tive nature of selected
human and natural sys-
tems

■ identify current issues
of global sustainability
and environmental
threats

■ assess the impact of
environmental deregu-
lation in Canada

■ produce a commu-
nity action plan to con-
tribute to the
sustainability of a global
resource

The final minutes of the 1962 Grey Cup football game in
Toronto (the "Fog Bowl," above) had to be postponed because a thick
smog, a combination of smoke and fog, hid the players and the ball
from the crowd's view. Smog is just one of today's atmospheric pollution
problems. The depletion of the ozone layer, acid rain, and the build-up
of non-degradable chemicals all threaten the health of life on Earth.

The Atmosphere

From space, our atmosphere appears as a thin layer of blue covering the Earth. This atmosphere sustains all life on our planet and protects it from **ultraviolet (UV) radiation** from the Sun. It also shields Earth from the impact of meteorites that, for the most part, burn up as they pass through it.

Earth's atmosphere, a mixture of particles, aerosols (suspensions of droplets in gas), and gases, is approximately 1000 km thick. The lowest 5 km, less than the height of Mount Everest, contains 50 per cent of all atmospheric gases (Figure 18–1). The "greenhouse" gases—carbon dioxide, methane, nitrous oxide, and ozone—represent only a small percentage of the atmosphere, but play an important role in regulating Earth's temperatures. (Climate change due to intensification of the greenhouse effect is examined in detail in Chapter 20.) Like the glass walls and ceiling of a greenhouse, they trap the heat rising from the Earth, thereby maintaining temperatures suitable for life over most of the planet's surface.

The layer of atmosphere that most concerns us in this study is the troposphere, which varies in thickness from nine to 16 km above Earth's surface. It is here that weather occurs and most air pollution is found.

Human activities have had a profound effect on the atmosphere, especially since the time of the Industrial Revolution, when smoke and gases from burning coal were released, up to modern times, when airborne chemical contaminants from industrial processes have caused acid rain and opened a hole in the ozone layer.

We know that air pollution affects people's health, especially that of young children, the elderly, and those with respiratory and heart conditions. Environment Canada attributes over 5000 deaths each year to air pollution, while the Ontario Medical Association estimates that hospital admissions, emergency room visits, and absenteeism from work due to air pollution cost Ontarians more than $1 billion per year.

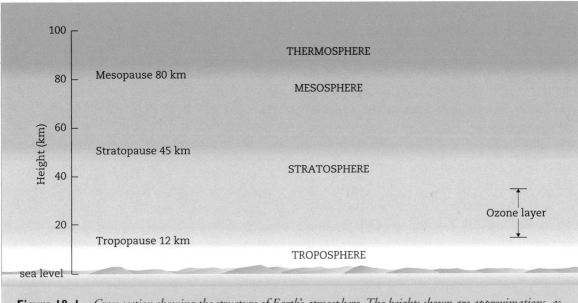

Figure 18–1 *Cross-section showing the structure of Earth's atmosphere. The heights shown are approximations, as precise heights vary with latitude and time of year.*

Poisons in the Air

Some of the most dangerous of the human-made pollutants released into the atmosphere are **persistent organic pollutants (POPs)**. These are chemicals used in pesticides and industrial chemicals such as PCBs (polychlorinated biphenyls), and are found in by-products of industrial processes such as dioxins. POPs are highly toxic and can cause cancer, reproductive problems, birth defects, damage to the immune and central nervous systems, and ultimately, death. As you learned in Chapter 17, they are also insoluble in water, very stable, and last for years in the environment before breaking down.

Through a process known as **bioaccumulation**, POPs build up in the fatty tissues of fish, predatory birds, and mammals, including humans, because these living organisms are high in the food chain (Figure 18–2). POPs often turn up far from their place of origin because they evaporate, travel through the atmosphere on air currents, and then condense in a new location. This is known as the **grasshopper effect** (Figure 18–3).

Canada and other temperate and polar countries are particularly susceptible to pollution from POPs because of slower evaporation due to low temperatures. When POPs are deposited in these regions, they become trapped in the environment and eventually enter the food chain. Not surprisingly, in Canada the highest rates of POPs are found in the Arctic.

Studies show that levels of certain POPs are nine times higher in the breast milk of Inuit women than in that of women in southern Canada. The polar bears in the Arctic and around Hudson Bay have some of the highest levels of POPs ever detected in wildlife. Their highly contaminated cubs are less fit than POP-free cubs.

In Canada, controls introduced in the 1980s reduced the use of PCBs, while stronger regula-tions established in the mid-1990s decreased the release of dioxins and furans (by-products of the pulp and paper industry) by almost 100 per cent. In 1995, the federal government created the Toxic Substances Management policy with the ultimate goal of eliminating the release of POPs into the environment. However, the United States and many countries in Latin America, Eastern Europe, and Southeast Asia still produce and release these chemicals into the environment because they are cheaper and easier to use than alternatives.

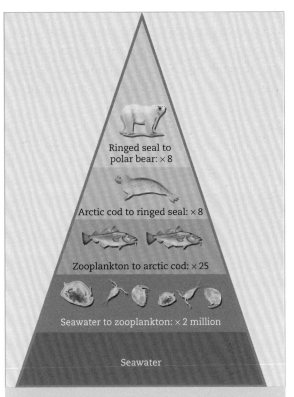

Figure 18–2 *Bioaccumulation causes PCB levels to become increasingly concentrated as they move upward in the food chain.* Source: Adapted from D. Draper, *Our Environment: A Canadian Perspective* (Toronto: ITP Nelson, 1998), p. 228; from Government of Canada, *The State of Canada's Environment* (Ottawa: Supply & Services Canada, 1991), pp. 15–18.

Efforts have also been made in other countries to eliminate POPs, although it will be years before results are seen. Northern countries have developed the Arctic Monitoring and Assessment Program to establish a database of Arctic contaminants for researchers to access. The Canadian International Development Agency (CIDA) has given Russia over $8 million to develop better environmental practices in the Arctic.

In May 2001, an agreement was signed in Stockholm by over 100 countries to control the production, import, export, disposal, and use of 12 POPs (Figure 18–4). The treaty will become legally binding only when ratified (formally approved) by at least 50 countries. This process usually takes several years; the United Nations expects ratification by 2004. One important aspect of the Stockholm Convention is that financial and technical assistance will be available to help developing countries minimize and, eventually, eliminate POPs from their environments.

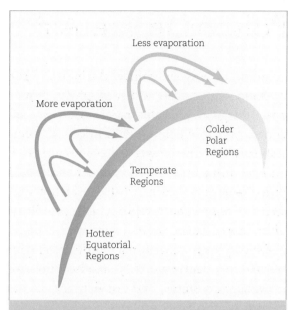

Figure 18–3 *The grasshopper effect shows how POPs evaporate and travel from their point of origin based on air circulation patterns. Because less evaporation occurs in colder regions, POPs tend to concentrate in climates such as Canada's North.* Source: © Her Majesty the Queen in Right of Canada.

Type of POP	Nature of Product	How Used
Aldrin, chlordane, DDT, dieldrin, endrin, mirex, heptachlor, toxaphene	Insecticides	▪ Synthetic substances that are sprayed on cultivated plants and crops to kill insects
Polychlorinated biphenyls (PCBs)	Industrial chemicals	▪ Lubricants, heat-transfer fluids, fire-resistant fluids used in transformers and capacitors
Hexachlorobenzene	Pesticides, fungicides Industrial chemicals	▪ Sprayed on wheat and other seeds to prevent fungus ▪ Used in fireworks, ammunition, and synthetic rubber
Dioxins and furans	Unwanted by-products of combustion and industrial processes	▪ Not used for any purpose; created in the manufacture of certain pesticides, preservatives, paper products, and disinfectants ▪ Formed when plastic, paper, wood, and certain chemical products are burned at low temperatures

Figure 18–4 *The 12 persistent organic pollutants (POPs) to be controlled under the Stockholm Convention*

Acidic Deposition

Imagine buying your French fries at your favourite chip wagon and then holding them up in the air to get your vinegar from the sky. Sounds far-fetched, but in Pitlochry, Scotland, it once rained acid rain with the pH of vinegar.

Acid rain is only one form of **acidic deposition.** Acidic pollutants may be deposited close to their source as dry deposition (acidic gas or dust) or be carried by the prevailing winds for thousands of kilometres to return to Earth as acid rain, snow, fog, or hail (Figure 18–5). Areas that are underlain by bedrock that is normally acidic, such as the Canadian Shield and the Appalachians, are very susceptible to the effects of acid deposition and may receive levels that exceed their critical load. **Critical load** refers to the amount of pollution that an ecosystem can tolerate before that pollution harms the environment. Approximately

95 000 of the 700 000 lakes in southeastern Canada are already acidified.

In many parts of the world, such as North America, Europe, India, and China, large amounts of sulphur dioxide are being released into the atmosphere from the burning of fossil fuels for energy, and especially from the smelting of sulphur-bearing metal ores. Nitrogen oxides are released during the combustion of fuels. Agriculture is also a source of atmospheric pollutants when ammonia from fertilizers and manure is released.

Many factories, smelters, and power plants have "superstacks" up to 300 m high that reduce local damage from acidic deposition by releasing pollutants high enough into the atmosphere that they do not affect the local environment. Air currents carry the pollutants to other regions,

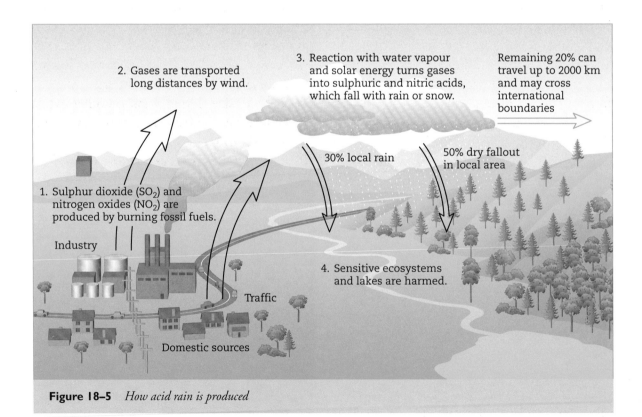

Figure 18–5 *How acid rain is produced*

Annual Emissions (millions of metric tonnes)		
Sulphur dioxide**	United States	Canada
1980	23.4	4.6
1995	16.8	2.7
2000*	15.0	3.2
2010*	14.1	3.2
Nitrogen oxides***	United States	Canada
1980	22.8	1.8
1995	21.7	2.0
2000*	20.8	2.0
2010*	20.0	2.0

*Estimates
**Sources include thermal power stations; factories; ore-smelting plants; burning of combustible products for home and commercial uses.
***Sources include cars, trucks, buses, trains; thermal power stations; other fuel-burning operations.

Figure 18–6 *Annual emissions of gases that produce acidic deposition in Canada and the United States.*
Source: Environment Canada.

often thousands of kilometres away. This creates an international political dimension to the problem. For example, studies in Norway and Sweden in the 1990s indicated that only about 11 per cent of their sulphur deposition came from domestic sources.

Environment Canada estimates that more than half of the acidic deposition in eastern Canada originates from emissions in the United States, particularly from thermal generating stations in Ohio, Indiana, Illinois, and West Virginia. The US Environmental Protection Agency, on the other hand, argues that the United States receives 88 per cent of the pollution produced at the Nanticoke generating station near Toronto, Ontario's largest coal-fired generating plant and its largest polluter. Figure 18–6 shows the annual emissions of polluting gases in Canada and the United States that cause acidic deposition.

The Atlantic provinces receive acidic precipitation from smelters in Manitoba, Ontario (Sudbury), and Quebec, while Southwestern British Columbia is affected by pollution from the United States and from local sources such as smelters and pulp-and-paper mills. The long-range, transboundary flow of pollutants has led to regional and international disputes, with parties on both sides laying blame on others while at the same time refusing to accept responsibility for their own polluting practices.

Figure 18–7 on the next page lists the effects of acidic deposition.

Did you KNOW?

A study has found that the number of blackflies in Algonquin Park is 100 times greater than it was 50 years ago. Blackfly larvae thrive in acidified lakes and rivers because they tolerate acidity better than their predators and competitors.

Effects of Acidic Deposition

Aquatic life	■ Plankton and vertebrates die when pH drops below 5
	■ Fish may be born deformed
	■ Food supply for waterfowl is depleted
	■ Aluminum leached from soil into water causes fish gills to be coated so fish suffocate
	■ Mercury and lead leached from soil make water more toxic
Terrestrial life	■ Microorganisms in soil are damaged
	■ Minerals needed for plant growth may be leached from soil
	■ Trees are damaged as protective waxy coating is removed from leaves; decreases resistance to disease, reduces germination. Major diebacks of deciduous and coniferous forests have occurred in eastern North America
	■ Reproductive rates for wildlife are reduced as habitat is degraded
Material damage	■ Corrosion is increased in automobile finishes, bronze, cement, rubber, paint, cotton, linen, and nylon
	■ Limestone, marble, and sandstone buildings and monuments are damaged (Figure 18–8)
Human health	■ Respiratory problems increase for asthmatics, children, and the elderly as sulphate particles are inhaled
	■ Water is contaminated by dissolved minerals, especially copper and lead in water pipes

Figure 18–7 *Acidic deposition has many wide-ranging effects on both living and non-living things.*

What Is Being Done?

You might think that the most obvious way to combat acidic deposition would be to eliminate the pollutants at their source by developing alternative sources of power or by installing anti-pollution equipment in factories. This is easy to say, but difficult to do because of the political, economic, scientific, and social forces that come into play when we deal with such a complex problem.

For example, the nitrogen oxide emissions from motor vehicles may be reduced by the use of catalytic converters and the regular testing of vehicle emissions, a method now used in Ontario but not in many parts of the world. Government funding for efficient and economical public transit would seem an appropriate measure, but this long-term commitment is not on the agenda of many levels of government. Politicians are subject to pressure from automobile manufacturers, oil companies, groups that want lower taxes, and people who want the convenience of driving a car.

The 1994 UN Convention on Long-Range Transboundary Air Pollution was signed by 35 countries, including Canada. With 2010 as the target year, Canada agreed to reduce its sulphur dioxide emissions by 42 per cent, the United States by 40 per cent, Britain by 80 per cent, Germany by 87 per cent, and Russia by 40 per cent below 1980 levels. Under this agreement, countries have different reduction targets based on critical load—the ability of each environment to withstand pollution.

In North America, acidic deposition worsened in the 1980s as Canada and the United States stalled on reducing emissions. In 1991, however, both countries signed the Canada–US Air Quality Agreement that set targets for reduced emissions of sulphur dioxide. Canada agreed to reduce its sulphur dioxide emissions to 3.2 million tonnes by the year 2000, and the United States agreed to reduce its emissions by 40 per cent of its 1980 levels by 2010.

The role of nitrogen in acid deposition is complex and not fully understood. Further research is being conducted, as nitrogen oxide emissions have stabilized at about 1980 levels.

Even if Canada and the United States fulfill their commitments to sulphur dioxide reduction by 2010, almost 800 000 square kilometres of southeastern Canada will still receive acid deposition above its critical load. As a result, even though some lakes are improving, the estimated number of lakes in the region damaged by acid rain will remain at 95 000.

The federal and provincial ministers of energy and environment have agreed upon a new long-term strategy to further reduce acid rain called the Canada-wide Acid Rain Strategy for Post-2000. Its primary goal is "to ensure that critical loads for acidic deposition are achieved across Canada, thereby ensuring the health of our forests and aquatic ecosystems." Although critical loads were agreed upon, targets and schedules to achieve them were not. Representatives from electrical utilities and the mining and petroleum industries did not want Canada to act unilaterally, but rather to work with the United States to set bilateral goals on both sides of the border. On the other hand, environmentalists wanted ministers to agree immediately to a schedule that would meet critical loads for acidic deposition in eastern Canada as soon as possible.

You can learn more about the Acid Rain Strategy for Post-2000 at
<www.pearsoned.ca/globalconnections>.

Figure 18–8 *Scaffolding surrounds Hadrian's Arch in Athens, Greece, as archaeologists start emergency cleaning and repairs. The 2000-year-old marble archway has turned black and is crumbling due to age, pollution, and acid rain.*

A London Smog or an L.A. Smog?

"Although broad daylight, a shadow moved darkly through the cold, dense fog in the narrow alley...." A line from a Sherlock Holmes mystery? More likely, a line from a report in a late–19th century London newspaper. The fog on winter nights in London was particularly dense and deadly on many occasions, but especially in 1880, when 2000 people died. Water droplets condensed around soot and particles of tar, then combined with sulphur dioxide from coal-burning factories and fireplaces to form sulphuric acid. Londoners were walking around in, and breathing, acid precipitation.

Usually air cools as it rises, dispersing pollutants into the atmosphere. But with a **temperature inversion**, cool air is trapped by warmer air above it, creating a stable air mass close to the ground. In 1873, in 1880, and again in 1892, a stable air mass over London trapped the smoke and its dangerous pollutants. When the fog rolled in, it combined with the smoke to form a dense yellow-black "peasouper." In 1905, the lethal combination of smoke and fog was termed smog.

Between December 5 and 10, 1952, Londoners experienced the worst air pollution disaster on record (Figure 18–9). A temperature inversion and a combination of soot, sulphur dioxide, and fog created an acidic environment that became a killer (Figure 18–10). People with respiratory diseases, young children, and the elderly were particularly susceptible. Over 4000 people choked to death on their own mucus or died from heart attacks as they tried to breathe. A study completed in 2000 by researchers in the United States estimated that some 12 000 people died in London between December 1952 and February 1953 because of the polluted fog.

In response to the London disaster of 1952, the British government passed the Clean Air Act

Figure 18–9 *In 1952, police constables in London were issued special protective smog masks. It is estimated that the pH of the smog was less than 2, about the same as that of sulphuric acid.*

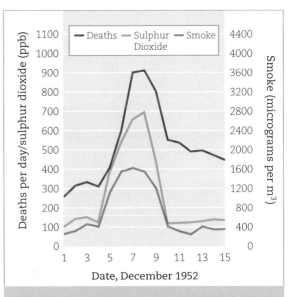

Figure 18–10 *The relationship between deaths and sulphur dioxide and smoke in the air in the London smog of December 1952.*
Source: Encyclopedia of the Atmospheric Environment.

in 1956. The act set up smokeless zones, and gave grants to homeowners to convert their coal fires to heaters that used gas, electricity, or smokeless coal. According to a recent study, London's air is the cleanest it has been for over 400 years. The exhaust smoke from motor vehicles is now the main source of London's pollution. During the occasional temperature inversion in winter, nitrogen oxides build up, causing a dangerous health hazard.

In Southeast Asia, smog is also caused by the burning of forests. Plantation companies in Indonesia, for example, clear land for cultivation in the spring by burning trees because this method is cheap and fast. In 1997, huge fires created a poisonous smog that blanketed the region, including Singapore and Malaysia, for several weeks. Local hospitals were inundated with people suffering from asthma and other respiratory diseases. This type of land clearing continues today.

For most of the world's cities, it is summer smog—formed from a combination of sunshine, high humidity, and pollutants from petroleum products burned by industry and motor vehicles—that causes concern. First identified in the early 1940s in Los Angeles, "L.A. smog" is produced from a photochemical reaction between sunlight and hydrocarbons and nitrogen oxides. This **photochemical smog** contains nitrogen oxide, nitrogen dioxide, ground-level ozone, and other compounds. The nitrogen oxides dissolve in the water of the atmosphere to form nitric acid, a component of acid precipitation. The ground-level ozone damages trees, reduces crop yields, and corrodes materials such as metal and rubber.

A variety of smog-related health effects have been documented, and include:

- irritation of eyes, nose, throat, and inflammation of lung tissue
- permanent lung damage from exposure to ozone over a long period of time
- increased risk of cancer from exposure to particles in the smog

- increased susceptibility to infections among children
- asthma attacks due to high concentrations of nitrogen dioxide.

Control of Smog

Smog can be controlled to a large extent by reducing the sources of pollutants. Since motor vehicles are the main source of the gases that produce smog, they are now equipped with catalytic converters in North America to reduce these emissions. In parts of North America, a cleaner-burning gasoline has been legislated for use. In Europe, schemes that limit the number of cars during major smog outbreaks have been introduced. For example, in Rome and Athens, cars with even-numbered licence plates drive on one day, those with odd-numbered plates on another. Another solution is more rapid transit and non-gasoline-burning cars (see Chapter 19).

Power stations and other industries that burn fossil fuels can reduce nitrogen oxides by "scrubbing" emissions from the smoke before it is released into the atmosphere. Unfortunately, the high cost of this procedure is a deterrent to many smaller industries.

Last but not least as a source of air pollution are gasoline-powered lawnmowers that, in the United States, produce as much pollution as four million cars! A switch to electric lawnmowers would reduce a significant amount of pollution—assuming, of course, that the power plants that produce the electricity equip themselves with anti-pollution devices. A switch to hand mowers would be even better.

The Ozone Layer

Could humans go the way of the dinosaurs through the use of fire extinguishers and aerosol spray cans, and as a result of junking items such as old cars and broken refrigerators? The answer is—perhaps. These common items often contain substances that could destroy the protective ozone layer in the atmosphere 15 to 35 km above the surface of the Earth.

Ozone is a substance that can both hurt us and protect us. When formed at ground level from the photochemical reaction of motor vehicle exhaust and sunlight, it can harm our health. When formed in the stratosphere, however (Figure 18–1), it protects us by absorbing harmful ultraviolet radiation that, among other things, can cause skin cancer.

Ozone forms when ultraviolet rays strike a single molecule of oxygen (O_2), causing it to split into two single atoms of oxygen. Each freed oxygen atom recombines with an intact oxygen molecule to form a molecule of ozone (O_3). The ozone molecule itself is very unstable, and breaks down into normal oxygen when subjected to UV radiation. A dynamic balance exists between the rate at which ozone is created and destroyed.

Ozone Depletion

The levels of ozone in the atmosphere alter naturally with the changing seasons and sun cycles. Scientists suspect that even material from volcanic eruptions changes the levels of this very unstable gas. Nonetheless, the processes of nature have always regulated the balance of ozone in the stratosphere. But now, human activities are upsetting this balance, and more ozone is being destroyed than created. Ozone depletion refers not only to the "holes" that scientists have observed over the North and South Poles, but also to declining levels of ozone over the entire globe.

One of the main culprits in the destruction of the ozone layer high above the Earth is the group of synthetic chemicals known as **chlorofluorocarbons (CFCs)**. These were created for use as fire retardants, propellants in spray cans, and coolants in refrigerators and air conditioners. At ground level these substances are inert because they are protected from UV radiation by the ozone layer. However, as they rise into the stratosphere and become exposed to UV radiation, they break apart, releasing their chlorine atoms. A single chlorine atom can destroy thousands of molecules of ozone; bromine may be even more harmful. Since CFCs can remain in the atmosphere for hundreds of years, damage to the ozone layer may be very long-lasting.

Other synthetic compounds that contribute to ozone depletion include:

- carbon tetrachloride, used as a dry-cleaning agent, an industrial solvent, and an ingredient in making CFCs
- methyl chloroform, used as a replacement for carbon tetrachloride; recognized as an ozone-depleting substance (ODS) in 1989
- halons, used as fire suppressants in computers, electronic equipment, and fire extinguishers
- methyl bromide, used as a pesticide; recognized as an ODS in 1991
- chlorine from rocket exhausts.

In 1985, British scientists confirmed that there was a "hole" in the ozone layer over the Antarctic. By 1998, this "hole" covered almost 26 million square kilometres and lasted for several months. It was found that the concentration of chlorine compounds in the Antarctic "hole" was 500 to 600 times greater than normal. Although not really a hole, this area of the ozone layer is significantly thinner than other parts, and appears during winter and early spring every year. In 1986, a scientist with Environment Canada discovered that the ozone layer over the Arctic was also thinning (Figure 18–11). Now, the ozone layer above southern Canada is 6 per cent thinner than it was during the 1970s.

Impact of Ozone Depletion

Ultraviolet radiation is invisible, having a wavelength shorter than visible sunlight. The Sun produces three types of UV radiation, but UV-B has the most impact on humans (Figure 18–12). It has been estimated that for every 1 per cent decrease in the ozone in the stratosphere, the amount of UV radiation that reaches Earth increases by double that amount. Environment Canada has determined that UV-B radiation over southern Canada has increased by an average of about 7 per cent since scientists began to measure it. In spring, the level increases to 12 per cent and even twice that for short periods.

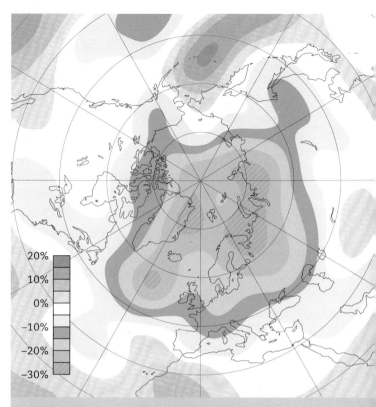

20%
10%
0%
–10%
–20%
–30%

Figure 18–11 *From March 1 to March 10, 2000, the ozone layer over the Arctic had thinned by 10 to 30 per cent.* Source: Environment Canada.

Effects of UV Radiation

	UV-A	UV-B	UV-C
Wavelength	▪ longest	▪ medium	▪ shortest
Blocked by ozone	▪ partly	▪ partly	▪ in upper atmosphere
Effects	▪ skin wrinkles ▪ premature aging	▪ sunburns ▪ skin cancer ▪ eye cataracts (can lead to blindness) ▪ weakens immune system ▪ activates some viruses ▪ reduces crop yields (e.g., canola, oats, peppers are sensitive to UV) ▪ damages phytoplankton (marine and freshwater), the basis of the food chain ▪ damages hatching fish, frog eggs, new vegetation	▪ lethal to all life

Figure 18–12 *Ultraviolet B radiation has the most impact on humans.*

The danger to human health as a result of increased levels of UV radiation can be seen in higher levels of skin cancer in Canadians. This increase was probably caused by exposure to the sun during the 1970s and 1980s before ozone thinning became so serious. With ozone thinning now an established fact, what will rates of skin cancer be in the future? What will be the effects on wildlife and plants? We do not know the answers to these questions.

What Is Being Done?

Canada is a leader in the international effort to protect the ozone layer. In 1986, it was the first country to sign the Vienna Convention for the Protection of the Ozone Layer, which established a framework for controlling the production and consumption of ozone-depleting substances (ODS). The following year, 25 countries including Canada signed the **Montreal Protocol** on Substances that Deplete the Ozone Layer. The protocol, which took effect in 1989, requires all developed countries to cut production and use of CFCs to 50 per cent of their 1986 levels by 1998. Developing countries agreed to meet the targets by 2010. By 2000, 173 countries had signed the Montreal Protocol.

All developed countries were able to eliminate the production and importation of most new supplies of ODS by 1996. Small quantities of CFCs, however, are still manufactured in a few industrialized countries for medical use. The production of these ODS is subject to the Montreal Protocol's "essential use provision," which allows production if the chemical is necessary for the health or functioning of society, and only if no feasible substitute exists. It is encouraging that Canada's ozone observatory in the Arctic has produced evidence that stopping production of most ODS has slowed the build-up of CFCs in the environment.

Some CFCs still exist in refrigerators and air conditioners manufactured before the signing of the Montreal Protocol in 1987. When old appliances are junked, the coolants are supposed to be carefully disposed of. But how are we to dispose of stockpiled supplies of CFCs? In 2001, the Canadian Council of Ministers of the Environment approved the Phase-Out Strategy for CFCs and Halons. This strategy outlines specific approaches for disposing of surplus CFCs (Figure 18–13).

Those developing countries that signed the Montreal Protocol were given an additional 10 to 15 years to phase out ODS and to make the transition to less damaging chemicals. Moreover, in 1991, the protocol established an international fund, to which developed countries contribute, to help developing countries switch from using ODS. Canada has contributed over US$5 million annually, partly in the form of technical assistance to Brazil, China, Cuba, and India.

In the 1930s, long before ozone depletion was a concern, Canada was conducting research to determine if the ozone layer affected weather patterns. For over 40 years, Environment Canada has operated a national network of monitoring stations that keep watch over the country's ozone layer. Since 1961, Canada has maintained a record of observations from ozone-monitoring stations around the world at its World Ozone and Ultraviolet Radiation Data Centre.

In 1993, the Canadian government built an observatory to study the ozone layer at Eureka on Ellesmere Island, 1000 km from the North Pole. Astronauts Marc Garneau and Steve McLean used the Brewer Ozone Spectrophotometer, developed by Environment Canada and recognized as the world's most accurate ozone-measuring instrument, to study the ozone layer from space.

Canadian scientists are also studying which crop strains are less vulnerable to UV radiation and how trees that grow at high elevations can

Phase-Out Strategy for CFCs and Halons, 2001

Sector	Approach
Mobile air conditioning (A/C)	■ Prohibit refill with CFCs as soon as possible
Mobile refrigeration	■ Prohibit refill with CFCs effective 2003
Household appliances	■ Enhance existing recovery programs ■ If necessary, add ban on converting equipment to use CFCs
Commercial refrigeration and A/C	■ Staged CFC refill ban until all equipment is covered by 2006
Chillers	■ Require conversion/replacement of CFC-containing chillers at next overhaul, effective 2005
Halons	■ Prohibit refill of portable equipment, effective 2003 ■ For fixed systems, allow one refill from 2005–2010 ■ Prohibit refills after 2010

Figure 18–13 *As with any banned substance, the small remaining supplies of CFCs and halons have become very expensive, and are a major commodity in international smuggling.* Source: Environment Canada.

resist higher levels of UV. They are also reformulating synthetic building materials to resist the effects of UV radiation.

The recovery of the ozone layer is expected to be slow, even if all nations adhere to the Montreal Protocol. Because ODS can remain in the atmosphere for 100 years or more, and because many other factors (such as increased concentrations of greenhouse gases) affect the ozone layer, improvement is difficult to predict. One hopeful projection is that ozone levels may begin to increase by 2010. Chlorine is not expected to return to its natural level in the atmosphere until after 2100.

What we do know is that society faces a hard choice between preserving the ozone layer or preserving the economic benefits provided by CFCs. The Montreal Protocol is extraordinary because nations have had to place the achievement of a common planetary goal ahead of their economic self-interest.

The Future

Can we hope to resolve the problems of acidic deposition, smog, and ozone depletion? Yes, but only with international cooperation and constant vigilance on the part of governmental and non-governmental agencies, and only if the political will of citizens around the world, not only in Canada, is marshalled to bring about the changes that are needed. Citizens must understand the environmental outcomes of unchecked emissions. We, as well as industry, must be willing to pay the substantial costs associated with putting non-polluting practices into place. Developed countries, which have created most of the problem, should also be prepared to help developing nations adopt technologies that will prevent similar environmental damage. If these steps are not taken, the future of life on Earth is at risk.

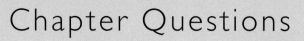

Chapter Questions

Knowledge and Understanding

1. a) What are POPs? Give examples.
   b) Why are POPs dangerous?
   c) Explain why Canada and the temperate and polar countries are particularly susceptible to POP pollution.
   d) What efforts have been made to eliminate POPs from the environment?

2. a) What parts of Canada are most affected by acidic deposition? Explain why.
   b) Draw a flow chart to show the effects of acidic deposition on aquatic life in a freshwater lake.

3. a) Differentiate between London smog and L.A. smog.
   b) What methods are used to reduce each kind of smog formation?
   c) How successful are these methods?

4. a) How can ozone both protect us and kill us?
   b) Demonstrate the impact of ozone depletion in the ozone layer on humans and the environment.
   c) What can you do to protect yourself from UV radiation?

Thinking and Inquiry

5. Developing countries do not have to phase out the production and use of CFCs for 10 to 15 years after developed countries do. Is this reasonable, since all peoples on the Earth will be affected by ozone depletion? Examine both sides of this question.

6. Chapter 1 discussed the Gaia hypothesis, according to which the conditions that make the planet habitable were created by the evolution of life. Since human activities are affecting nature in such radical ways, what might this mean for the future?

7. Magazine surveys asked US citizens if they would be prepared to pay 25 cents per gallon more for their car gasoline to reduce pollution and global warming. The results: in 1990, 36 per cent said no; in 2000, 49 per cent said no.
   a) What conclusions could you draw from these figures about difficulties in changing North American transportation patterns?
   b) What might have caused these percentages to change in this period?
   c) How do you think people might feel about this question in 2010? Explain.

Communication

8. To reduce the amount of POPs, acidic deposition, or ODS in the environment, enormous amounts of money will have to be spent. Everyone will pay more to use alternative technologies or products, even though not all places are affected to the same extent by these environmental problems. Is it fair that everyone bears the same expense, or should those industries and countries that produce the pollution pay for it? Write a letter to the editor of your local newspaper, explaining which side of the question you support.

9. In a small group, conduct a survey of at least 50 students and teachers to see how many would be prepared to pay more for gasoline (10 cents a litre, 20 cents a litre, or 30 cents a litre) to help fight the air pollution problems outlined in this chapter. Draw up charts to show your results, and summarize your findings.

Application

10. Investigate the relationship between increased UV radiation and disease.

11. The burning of coal is a major source of pollution in many cities today, particularly in developing nations. Examine one of these cities and

describe the conditions that exist, the problems that have been created, and the measures, if any, taken to alleviate the problem.

12. What lifestyle changes, such as transportation, recreational activities, or activities around the home, would you and your family have to make to reduce your contributions to:
    a) acidic deposition?
    b) smog?
    c) ozone depletion?

13. Often society has to make choices between the economic benefits of products, such as CFCs, electricity, and automobiles, and environmental damage, such as ozone depletion, smog, and acidic deposition. Work with a small group to brainstorm criteria that could be used to make these choices.

14. Obtain maps that show either the sensitivity of the local area to acidic precipitation, or acidic precipitation levels in Canada (go to <www.pearsoned.ca/globalconnections>). Use this information to develop a community action plan to address the current situation. Present your plan to the class in the form of an oral report, poster, or PowerPoint presentation.

15. In recent years, some Canadian provinces have cut government spending by reducing the size of their environment ministries. Fines for polluting have been increased as a deterrent, but the number of inspectors has decreased. Will more emphasis on voluntary compliance have effects on atmospheric and water quality in Canada? Explain your views.

19

Energy Issues

Expectations

In this chapter, you will:

- identify current global issues of sustainability and environmental threats

- explain how new technology affects employment and resource management

- evaluate student awareness of an issue by conducting a survey

- describe biases that may inform different views on geographical issues

- understand that alternative solutions to a geographical problem may exist

- collect data using field techniques and analyse the data to show patterns and relationships

- produce a case study to show the effects of resource development on an ecosystem

The way in which our society uses energy is a topic open to much debate and criticism. In developed countries, comparatively abundant and inexpensive supplies of energy contribute to people's comfortable lifestyles. In developing countries, scarce energy resources limit people's social and economic advancement.

Part of the Problem or Part of the Solution?

The 1960s and 1970s saw an upsurge in activism in North America. Civil rights demonstrations, the women's and environmental movements, and the protest against the Vietnam War marked this era. During this time a slogan emerged that became the rallying cry for a generation: "If you are not part of the solution, you are part of the problem." We can look at energy issues in a similar way. The way most North Americans use energy makes us very much part of the problem. Many important global issues of the 21st century are tied to either the provision or the use of energy. A few examples follow.

- There is a link between energy use and global warming. (You can learn more about global warming in Chapter 20.)
- In Canada, there is often a link between energy production and issues related to land ownership by Aboriginal peoples.
- The burning of fossil fuels (coal, petroleum products, and natural gas) causes air pollution that damages people's health. (Air pollution was examined in Chapter 18.)
- The movement of oil by supertankers leads to widespread fouling of the oceans from major tanker accidents and from day-to-day operations. (Water pollution was discussed in Chapter 17.)
- In the early 1990s, the Gulf War against Iraq was fought primarily to protect the oil supply of the world's developed countries (Figure 19–1).

We Canadians like to think of ourselves, above all else, as moderates. We are not comfortable being first with some new trend, but we certainly do not want to be last. Hence, it comes as a big shock to most people that we are, on a per capita basis, the world leaders in using (some would say wasting) energy.

It is understandable that Canadians would use a considerable amount of energy. As a First World country, Canada needs energy to support its advanced economy. As well, we have the second largest land area of any nation in the world, and so must use a lot of energy to move goods and people over great distances. Also, we have a demanding climate. Our homes and other buildings need to be heated in winter and, increasingly, cooled in summer. The question is whether we can justify using more energy per capita than any other country.

At the same time, a number of energy initiatives give us hope for the future. We are expanding our use of non-polluting, renewable energy sources such as wind power. Researchers are developing new ways of using energy that are less polluting than those we use now. Most significantly, there has been a growth in the number of people who have decided that they want to be part of the solution and not part of the problem.

Figure 19–1 *Towards the end of the Gulf War, when Iraq's defeat was inevitable, Iraqi President Saddam Hussein ordered his retreating forces to destroy Kuwaiti oil wells.*

A Guided Tour of the World's Energy Use

An awareness of Earth's "energy budget" is fundamental to understanding the energy issues that face Earth's population today. There are three important aspects in our understanding of energy use:

- the pattern of energy consumption in various countries
- the relationships among production, consumption, and trade in various forms of energy
- the quantity of reserves of non-renewable energy resources.

In this activity you will have an opportunity to consider a wide variety of questions about these aspects of energy use. In most cases, the information you need is given. In some cases, particularly with questions that deal with the future, your answers may be based on informed speculation. To improve the quality of your answers, you may wish to do a little research or, at least, discuss your answers with classmates or your teacher.

This overview of world energy use focusses on the commercially traded, primary energy sources: oil, natural gas, coal, nuclear energy, and hydro-electric power. Other types of energy are either currently of much less significance (for example, wind power) or are used non-commercially in a manner that makes documentation of quantities difficult (for example, the burning of dried cow dung in India)

Energy Consumption in the World

The first stop on our tour is a comparison of the relative importance of the "big five" energy sources (Figure 19–2). The most significant of these is oil. It is vital as a transportation fuel, as an energy source for industry, and for domestic and commercial heating. Natural gas and coal are next in importance; they are used primarily for industrial purposes and heating. Next is nuclear power, which is used to produce electricity. Least important of the "big five" is hydro-

electric power. It is instructive to compare the pattern of energy use in various countries and regions to that of the entire world (Figure 19–3).

Questions

1. Think about how crude oil and natural gas are moved long distances. Why do the countries of the Middle East choose to use more natural gas than oil?

2. What are the global environmental implications of the very high rate of coal use in many of the most highly populated countries? Why is this problem likely to increase in the years to come?

3. Suggest two reasons for the high level of nuclear power use in Japan, Europe, and Other Asia–Pacific countries. Give one reason why the use of nuclear power in these areas may increase in the future. Give one reason why it might decline.

4. Canada and Latin America have dramatically high values for hydro-electric use. Give two reasons why this is so.

5. Approximately one-sixth of the world's population lives in OECD (Organization for Economic Cooperation and Development) countries. OECD countries are the world's 30 most developed countries. How does their energy use compare to the energy use of less developed areas such as Africa and Latin America? Why does this situation exist?

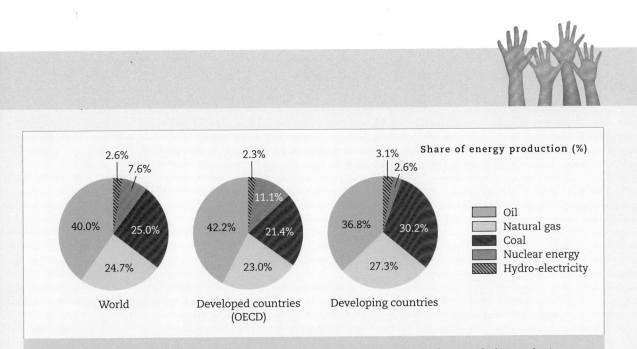

Figure 19–2 *World and regional production of energy, 2000 (units in millions of tonnes of oil equivalent).*
Source: British Petroleum.

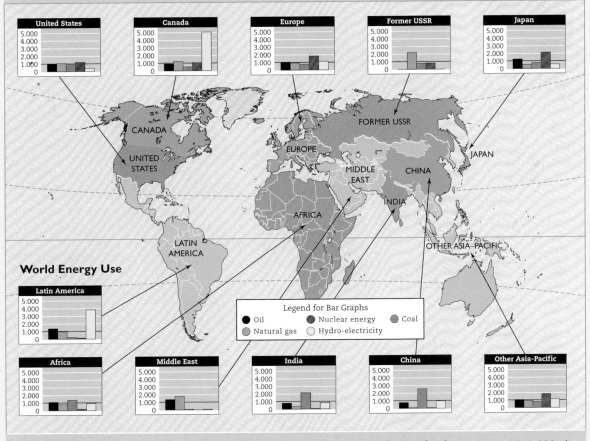

Figure 19–3 *Indices of world energy use, 2000. The world average index for use of each energy source is 1.000. A value greater than 1 indicates that the use of the energy source is greater for this region than the world average use.*
Source: British Petroleum.

OIL

The next stop on our tour is at the "gas station" where we can look at oil, our most important energy source. When we consider a non-renewable resource like oil, it is important to look at two factors: (a) the amount of production versus consumption, and (b) the level of reserves (see page 312).

Major oil-producing nations fall into two categories (Figure 19–4). Some, like the United States, Russia, and China, produce large amounts of oil and also use a great deal of oil. In fact, they may use even more oil than they produce. The second cate-

gory of countries produce far more oil than they use. This group, including countries like Saudi Arabia and Mexico, is able to export surplus oil to those nations that cannot meet their own needs.

A group of major oil exporters, the Organization of Petroleum Exporting Countries (OPEC), tries to manage the price of oil in the world by varying the level of its production and exports. Members of OPEC are Algeria, Nigeria, Indonesia, Iran, Iraq, Kuwait, Libya, Nigeria, Qatar, Saudi Arabia, United Arab Emirates, and Venezuela. The ability of OPEC to control world oil prices has been limited by the fact that there are now more large non-OPEC oil

	Oil Production (millions of tonnes)				Change in Production, 1970–2000	Share of Total Production, 2000
	1970	1980	1990	2000		
Saudi Arabia*	191.4	507.8	341.3	441.2	+131%	12.3%
USA	534.2	480.8	417.1	353.5	−34%	9.8%
Former USSR	353.0	603.2	570.5	394.4	n/a	9.0%
Iran*	191.5	74.1	161.4	186.6	−3%	5.2%
Mexico	24.3	107.8	147.1	172.1	+608%	4.8%
Venezuela*	196.5	116.3	115.9	166.8	−15%	4.6%
China	30.7	106.0	138.3	162.3	+429%	4.5%
Norway	0.0	24.5	81.7	157.5	n/a	4.4%
Iraq*	76.0	130.5	105.1	128.1	+69%	3.6%
United Kingdom	0.2	80.5	91.6	126.2	+63 000%	3.5%
Canada	69.7	82.9	92.3	126.3	+81%	3.5%
United Arab Emirates*	35.9	81.9	104.9	114.7	+219%	3.2%
Kuwait*	152.2	87.1	46.9	105.6	−31%	2.9%
Nigeria*	53.8	102.4	89.8	103.9	+93%	2.9%
Libya*	162.1	89.7	68.3	70.6	−56%	2.0%
TOTAL WORLD	**2355.3**	**3083.8**	**3164.1**	**3589.6**	**+52%**	**100.0%**
Developed countries (OECD)	660.3	817.3	892.2	1010.4	+53%	28.1%
Developing countries	1695.0	2266.5	2271.9	2579.2	+52%	71.9%
OPEC	1166.6	1340.7	1183.5	1489.4	+28%	41.5%
Non-OPEC	1188.7	1743.2	1980.6	2100.2	+77%	58.5%

*These countries are members of OPEC

Figure 19–4 *Major oil producers, 1970–2000.* Source: British Petroleum.

exporters than there were in the 1970s when OPEC was formed. These include Russia, Norway, the United Kingdom, and Canada.

The other side of the oil equation is the pattern of consumption. Since many areas of the world do not produce enough oil to meet their needs, there is an obvious need for trade in oil. Figure 19–5 summarizes the patterns of oil consumption and trade in the world.

a)	Oil Consumption (millions of tonnes)				Change in Consumption,	Share of Total Consumption,
	1970	1980	1990	2000	1970–2000	2000
USA	694.6	794.1	781.8	897.4	+29.2%	25.6%
Canada	73.0	87.6	77.7	82.9	+13.6%	2.4%
Latin America	125.5	208.3	234.0	303.0	+141.4%	8.6%
Europe	683.1	776.6	710.3	752.6	+10.2%	21.4%
Former USSR	247.1	421.0	418.7	173.1	−29.9%	5.0%
Middle East	57.0	101.6	164.7	209.0	+266.7%	5.9%
Africa	35.2	66.5	94.9	116.7	+231.5%	3.3%
Asia–Pacific	338.6	516.4	653.4	968.9	+186.1%	27.8%
TOTAL WORLD	2254.1	2972.1	3135.5	3503.6	+55.4%	100.0%
OECD	1673.4	1946.9	1919.2	2184.8	+30.6%	62.4%

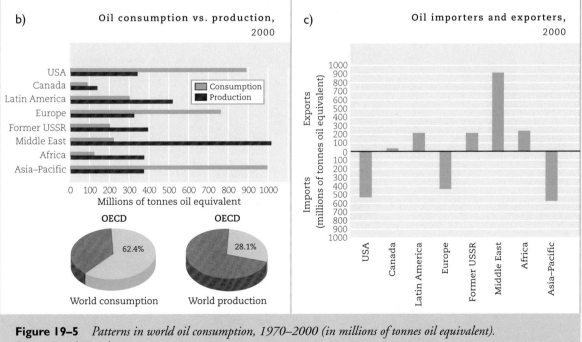

Figure 19–5 *Patterns in world oil consumption, 1970–2000 (in millions of tonnes oil equivalent).*
Source: British Petroleum.

Questions

1. Describe the distribution of oil production among developed nations, OPEC, and non-OPEC developing countries. Which of the three groups of nations has experienced the greatest growth in production between 1970 and 2000?

2. At times, countries experience severe changes in their level of oil production. Identify at least two examples (country and year) when dramatic changes occurred. Give reasons why these changes happened.

3. Which country's oil production seems to be in decline? Why might this be happening? What significance does this have for the future?

4. Which three regions have experienced the most growth in (a) percentage of oil consumption? (b) volume of oil consumption? Why has this happened? What additional data would be helpful if you wanted to better understand the growth of energy use in different regions?

5. Classify the different regions of the world as either oil importers or oil exporters. Give evidence to support your choices. Why is this pattern not surprising?

6. How have OECD nations managed to expand their economies significantly between 1970 and 2000 while increasing their oil use, on a percentage basis, relatively slowly?

7. Assume that the population of the world in 2000 was 6 billion, while the population of Canada was 30 million and that of the United States 280 million. What comments would you make about the per capita use of oil in North America compared to the rest of the world? Can this situation be ethically justified? Why or why not?

8. What are the environmental implications of the rapid growth in wealth and industrialization in many developed countries?

NATURAL GAS

Natural gas has a number of striking differences compared to oil, even though both commodities usually come from the same deposits. We see oil products, such as gasoline and diesel and lubricating oil, in use when we see airplanes flying and cars driving along the highway. The use of natural gas, however, is not as obvious. Not only is it transported in pipelines that are almost always out of sight, but it also tends to be used "behind the scenes," for example, to heat buildings or to dry substances in industrial processes. In spite of its invisibility, its costly distribution systems are vital components of many countries' infrastructures.

In general, natural gas production follows the same pattern as oil production (Figure 19–6). The differences have to do with its transportation. Natural gas cannot be moved to market as easily as oil, but it can be moved effectively by pipeline. Pipelines have allowed the export of vast quantities of natural gas from Russia to Western Europe, and from Canada to the United States. Where pipelines between gas fields and markets are impractical, natural gas is liquefied and shipped in special ocean tankers. Tankers move liquefied natural gas from a number of countries in the Middle East to Western Europe and Japan.

In many oil- and gas-producing countries, however, a supply of natural gas cannot be economically moved to market. In some cases, the gas is injected back into the ground to increase the pressure on the deposit so that more oil can be recovered. This aids in **secondary recovery** of oil. Often, though, the gas is merely "flared" (burned off) to get rid of it.

a)	Natural Gas Production* (millions of tonnes oil equivalent)				Change in Production, 1970–2000	Share of Total Production, 2000	Share of Total Consumption, 2000
	1970	1980	1990	2000			
USA	546.1	501.7	462.8	500.0	–8%	22.9%	27.2%
Canada	53.4	69.1	89.4	151.0	+183%	6.9%	3.2%
Latin America	26.8	55.1	76.6	119.2	+436%	5.4%	5.3%
Europe	93.3	204.2	195.1	259.1	+178%	12.0%	19.1%
Former USSR	166.2	365.4	684.6	607.0	+265%	27.8%	22.8%
Middle East	18.0	34.0	91.1	188.7	+948%	8.7%	7.9%
Africa	2.6	20.8	60.1	116.6	+4385%	5.3%	2.4%
Asia–Pacific	14.5	63.8	134.9	239.0	+1548%	11.0%	12.1%
TOTAL WORLD	**920.9**	**1314.1**	**1794.6**	**2180.6**	**+137%**	**100.0%**	**100.0%**
OECD	684.7	778.9	767.8	962.6	+41%	44.2%	54.9%

* Excluding gas flared or reinjected into the ground

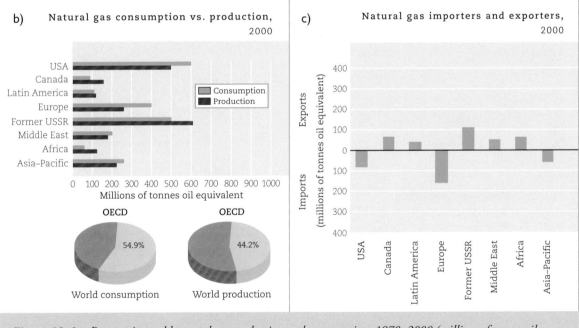

Figure 19–6 *Patterns in world natural gas production and consumption, 1970–2000 (millions of tonnes oil equivalent).* Source: British Petroleum.

Questions

1. Compare the pattern of oil production and consumption to that of natural gas production and consumption. What similarities and differences do you see?

2. In addition to being wasteful, the flaring of gas is environmentally destructive. Why?

3. Speculate on why shipment of liquefied natural gas is not more common. Research this question on the Internet. Was your speculation correct?

COAL

Two generations ago, most Canadians heated their homes with coal (and had a coal pile in a corner of their basement!). Few Canadians today have ever seen a piece of coal, although Canada produces a substantial amount. Most of the country's coal is mined in isolated locations in Alberta and British Columbia, and then exported to Japan. In eastern Canada, a considerable amount of coal is imported

a)	Coal Production (millions of tonnes oil equivalent)			Change in Production, 1981–2000	Share of Total Production, 2000	Share of Total Consumption, 2000
	1981	1990	2000			
USA	459.4	561.4	570.7	+24.2%	26.7%	25.8%
Canada	18.0	38.2	37.2	+106.7%	1.7%	1.3%
Latin America	8.6	24.5	42.3	+391.9%	2.0%	1.2%
Europe	441.5	399.2	241.4	–45.3%	11.3%	15.9%
Former USSR	349.8	332.0	197.4	–43.6%	9.3%	8.0%
Middle East	0.5	1.0	0.8	+60.0%	*	0.3%
Africa	72.6	97.5	122.8	+69.1%	5.7%	4.1%
Asia–Pacific	491.8	839.1	924.8	+88.0%	43.3%	43.4%
TOTAL WORLD	1842.2	2292.9	2137.4	16.0%	100.0%	100.0%
OECD	976.6	1090.4	993.4	1.7%	46.5%	50.6%

*Less than 0.05%

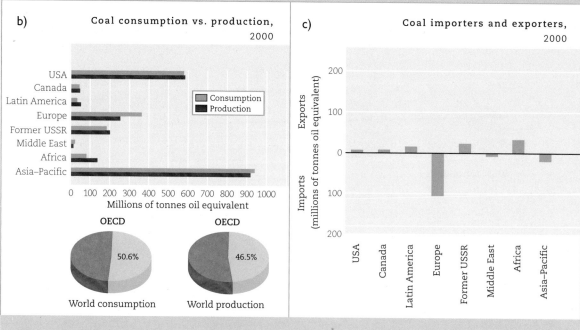

Figure 19–7 *Patterns in world coal production and consumption, 1981–2000 (millions of tonnes oil equivalent).* Source: British Petroleum.

from the United States, but only for use in coal-burning electrical generating plants and for use as fuel in steel plants.

In many countries outside Canada and the United States, coal is widely used (Figure 19–7) as a source of energy for domestic heating and electrical generation, and as fuel for industry. Experts predict a growth in the use of coal because it is often less expensive to mine and transport compared to other sources, and there are still huge reserves in many areas of the world.

Questions

1. Which areas of the world are the most significant producers and consumers of coal? How is this pattern different from that of oil and natural gas?

2. Two regions experienced declines in coal production between 1981 and 2000. These declines occurred for quite different reasons. Identify these regions and suggest why these declines occurred.

3. Compare the growth in coal production in OECD and Asia–Pacific countries. What difference do you see? Why? What environmental significance does this trend have?

NUCLEAR POWER

Fifty years ago, nuclear power seemed to hold a great promise for the future—a seemingly limitless source of clean, cheap energy. For many reasons, that promise proved to be short-lived. For one, the cost of building nuclear power plants turned out to be substantially higher than predicted. Also, it was learned that the intense level of radioactivity inside the reactors affected the structural integrity of the plants' elaborate plumbing. This meant that the life expectancy of the plants, before they needed very costly refits, was much less than anticipated. Both of these unexpected results drove up the cost of the electricity produced.

There also were serious environmental concerns. No method of long-term disposal of nuclear waste products has been put into use. This is a critical shortcoming, as the waste will remain hazardous for thousands of years. It is now being stored in temporary facilities all over the world, but a more permanent solution must be put in place.

The ultimate threat from nuclear power is a **meltdown**, a situation that occurs when the heat generated by a reactor exceeds the capacity of the cooling system. A meltdown causes the reactor's contents to escape into the environment. This worst-case situation occurred in 1986 in the city of Chernobyl in what is now Ukraine, but was then part of the Soviet Union. A massive escape of radiation resulted in numerous deaths. More worrying still, such radiation exposure has been found to cause cancers years after the event. Some experts have predicted that many hundreds, or even thousands, of additional cancer deaths may eventually occur as a result of the Chernobyl meltdown.

The remains of Chernobyl were encased in a concrete "mausoleum" (Figure 19–8), but this will not end the problem permanently. The concrete shell is already starting to crack, and the radiation levels inside will be lethal for thousands of years. A new mausoleum, predicted to cost about $1.5 billion, is needed to protect people from the radiation in the ruins of the power plant.

The highly politicized nature of the debate over the safety of nuclear power can be illustrated by the controversy over the number of deaths that occurred at Chernobyl. The wildly varying estimates of the death toll illustrate the need for observers to consider bias when examining a source document. A study supported by the nuclear industry concluded that 31 people died, including two people who died of heart attacks rather than radiation. Anti-nuclear groups have suggested that the death toll was actually as high as 148 000. The Ukrainian government's estimate of the death toll is 8000.

In spite of the problems with nuclear power, it remains an important source of electricity in many developed countries (Figure 19–9).

Figure 19–8 *Some of those who worked to enclose the remains of the Chernobyl reactor in concrete have since died of radiation exposure. The current enclosure was built quickly and has proven inadequate. It will have to be replaced at great cost.*

	Nuclear Energy Consumption (millions of tonnes oil equivalent)			Change in Use, 1980–2000	Share of Total Use, 2000
	1980	1990	2000		
USA	68.2	156.7	204.7	+200.1%	30.6%
Canada	9.2	18.8	18.7	+103.3%	2.8%
Latin America	0.6	3.3	4.8	+700.0%	0.7%
Europe	61.4	206.6	251.6	+309.8%	37.6%
Former USSR	19.1	54.6	56.3	+194.8%	8.4%
Middle East	—	—	—	n/a	—
Africa	—	2.3	3.5	n/a	0.5%
Asia–Pacific	24.9	74.4	129.0	+418.1%	19.4%
TOTAL WORLD	**183.4**	**516.7**	**668.6**	**+264.6%**	**100.0%**
OECD	158.2	438.9	575.6	+263.8%	86.1%

Figure 19–9 *Patterns in world consumption of nuclear energy, 1980–2000 (millions of tonnes oil equivalent).*
Source: British Petroleum.

Questions

1. Compare the growth of nuclear power between 1980 and 1990 to growth between 1990 and 2000. How has Chernobyl influenced public opinion?

2. In what regions or countries is most nuclear power produced? Why?

3. What parts of Canada rely on nuclear power for a significant portion of their electricity? Why is nuclear power not important elsewhere in Canada?

HYDRO-ELECTRIC POWER

Hydro-electric power can be a wonderful resource—if you are lucky enough to have it in your country and if it can be developed without causing undue social conflict (see the example of the Three Gorges project in Chapter 1). Hydro-electric production has relatively few negative features. It produces little pollution and has virtually zero fuel costs. Some hydro-electric plants, like those at Niagara Falls, Ontario, have been in operation for decades with few problems. Unfortunately, few locations have the right combination of abundant rainfall and elevation change that allow the development of major hydro-electric sites. (Chapter 17 discussed the pros and cons of building large power dams.)

Figure 19–10 shows world consumption of hydro-electricity over a 20-year period.

Questions

1. What parts of the world have significant amounts of hydro-electric power? Why is this not surprising?

2. From your knowledge of world climate and physical features, what regions of the world likely have a significant potential for large-scale hydro-electric development? Why have these sites not been developed previously?

3. Why is the question of reserves of no significance with respect to hydro-electric power?

4. Suggest explanations for reductions in hydro-electric consumption in some world regions.

	Hydro-electricity Consumption (millions of tonnes oil equivalent)			Change in Use, 1980–2000	Share of Total Use, 2000
	1980	1990	2000		
USA	24.3	25.2	23.4	–3.7%	10.1%
Canada	19.1	25.5	30.8	+61.3%	13.4%
Latin America	18.7	33.4	49.9	+166.8%	21.7%
Europe	40.6	42.8	53.4	+31.5%	23.0%
Former USSR	15.8	20.2	19.6	+24.1%	8.6%
Middle East	0.9	0.8	0.7	–22.2%	0.3%
Africa	4.0	5.0	6.5	+62.5%	2.9%
Asia–Pacific	24.8	36.3	46.1	+85.9%	20.0%
TOTAL WORLD	148.2	189.2	230.4	+55.5%	100.0%
OECD	92.1	104.2	118.0	+28.1%	51.2%

Figure 19–10   *Patterns in world hydro-electricity consumption, 1980–2000.* Source: British Petroleum.

OUTLOOK FOR CONVENTIONAL SOURCES OF ENERGY

Oil, natural gas, and coal—our three most important energy sources—are non-renewable. Experts try to determine how many years it will be until we run out of these resources. Even uranium, which is crucial to the production of nuclear power, is a non-renewable resource, but it currently exists in vast quantities. In contrast, the production of hydro-electric power relies upon the use of water, a renewable resource.

Two terms are used to describe the remaining amount of a finite resource. The first is **reserves**, a term that refers to the amount of a resource that can be extracted using current technology. Perhaps a better way to refer to the remaining amount of a finite resource is to use the second term, a measure called the **R/P ratio**. The R/P ratio for a non-renewable resource is calculated by dividing the size of the recoverable reserves (R) by the amount that is produced and used up (P) during the current year. The R/P ratio is measured in years. A simple way of describing this measure is to say that it shows how many years it will be before the region being discussed runs out of that commodity.

This view is somewhat simplistic because several factors can dramatically alter the R/P ratio, either upward or downward. For example, if people use more energy—say, by buying larger, less fuel-efficient vehicles—the R/P ratio for oil will get lower as the rate of use goes up. On the other hand, successful exploration efforts will increase the size of the reserves and increase the R/P ratio. The fact that oil engineers are constantly developing improved recovery technologies that allow oil companies to recover deposits that previously could not be recovered at an economic cost also increases the R/P ratio.

Figures 19–11a and 19–11b show world reserves of oil, natural gas, and coal as of 2000.

	Oil (thousand million tonnes)		Natural Gas (trillion cubic metres)		Coal (million tonnes)	
	2000	R/P Ratio	2000	R/P Ratio	2000	R/P Ratio
USA	3.7	10.4	4.74	8.7	246 643	253.0
Canada	0.8	8.5	1.73	10.3	8 623	125.0
Latin America	17.6	33.8	7.79	71.8	22 785	405.0
Europe	2.5	7.7	5.22	17.5	122 032	165.0
Former USSR	9.0	22.7	56.70	79.6	230 178	>500.0
Middle East	92.5	83.2	52.52	>100.0	*	*
Africa	10.0	26.8	11.16	86.2	61 605*	266.0*
Asia–Pacific	6.0	15.6	10.33	38.9	292 345	159.0
TOTAL WORLD	142.1	39.9	150.19	61.0	984 211	227.0
OECD	11.2	11.5	13.43	12.6	447 100	223.0
OPEC	110.7	74.3	n/a	n/a	n/a	n/a

* Data for Middle East and Africa are combined

Figure 19–11a *World reserves of oil, natural gas, and coal by region, 2000.* Source: British Petroleum.

Questions

1. Which countries and regions have limited reserves of oil? Justify your answer with specific statistics.

2. Why might Canada's oil reserve situation not be as desperate as it might appear?

3. How might world oil markets be affected by the size of reserves in OECD and OPEC countries?

4. Compare the R/P ratios for natural gas to those for oil for different countries and regions. What do you see?

5. Which areas of the world have the greatest natural gas reserves? How easy is it for each of these areas to serve major world demands?

6. Compare the R/P ratios for coal to those for oil and natural gas. What does this comparison suggest about the future importance of coal?

7. How extensive are the coal reserves in OECD countries when compared to the reserves of oil and natural gas?

8. Why does the United States have a particular interest in developing new ways to use coal?

9. What environmental concerns are associated with the use of coal in the future?

10. Describe the relationship that exists between the size of a country's (or region's) reserves and
   a) the rate of use
   b) the amount of exploration
   c) the recovery technology used.

Is There an Energy Crisis?

Some people have suggested that the world faces an energy crisis in the near future. While such pronouncements make good headlines, it is vital that they be examined very carefully. In total, it seems that there may be sufficient conventional energy to meet our needs for the next century or more. Serious problems remain, however. Coal, the energy source that is most readily available, cannot easily replace oil and natural gas in many applications. At the same time, oil—whose products, such as gasoline, are so central to our economy and way of life—has the lowest R/P ratios. Another critical factor in your personal determination of whether there is an energy crisis is the environmental impact of our energy use.

Is there an energy crisis? It depends entirely on how you define the term.

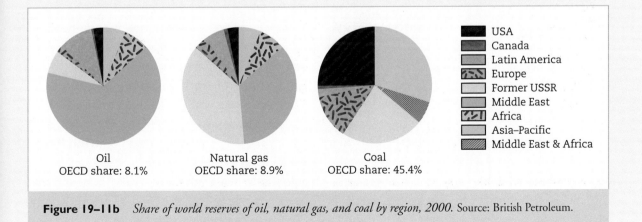

■	USA
▨	Canada
▨	Latin America
▨	Europe
▨	Former USSR
▨	Middle East
▨	Africa
▨	Asia–Pacific
▨	Middle East & Africa

Oil
OECD share: 8.1%

Natural gas
OECD share: 8.9%

Coal
OECD share: 45.4%

Figure 19–11b *Share of world reserves of oil, natural gas, and coal by region, 2000.* Source: British Petroleum.

Alternative Approaches to Energy

Many people challenge the assumptions on which we base our current use of energy. They contend that the ways in which we produce and use energy cause environmental and economic problems that make a sustainable future for life on Earth impossible. Perhaps the most important recommendation to emerge from this point of view is that we must change our basic attitudes towards energy use.

Is There a Better Way?

Today, most people in developed countries think of energy only as a commodity—something to be purchased or sold. Our willingness to use energy wastefully is directly related to its cost and to the way in which we have been influenced by various forms of lifestyle advertising. This can be seen in the creation and growth of energy-intensive recreational activities, such as using snowmobiles and personal watercraft. People may change their behaviour in response to rising energy prices. For example, when gasoline prices rise, people start looking for more fuel-efficient cars. Environmentalists tell us that we can change our lifestyle choices in ways that will significantly reduce the impacts of energy production and use on the Earth.

Key to this new approach to energy is an expansion in the use of **alternative energy**. Several alternative energy sources are being researched and developed. These include wind and solar power for heating and electricity production, tidal power, geothermal energy, and biomass conversion. To describe these as new energy sources would be incorrect. Centuries ago, the Dutch used windmills to pump water from the land that they were trying to reclaim.

Our energy future may include a startling change. For more than a century, oil products have been at the centre of our energy use. In the decades to come, this may shift to a more flexible combination of energy sources. In this section of the chapter you will have a chance to learn about the growing importance of wind power and about the possibility of a hydrogen-electricity–based economy.

Wind Power

For more than 1000 years, various forms of windmills have been used in China, Tibet, India, and the Middle East. Small wind-powered pumps were a common feature of North American farms for more than a century. A company in Chicago produced 800 000 of these pumps starting in the 1890s. The use of wind power declined in the last century as cheap electricity and fossil-fuel–powered alternatives were developed.

Interest and research in wind power continued during the 20th century, but wind power could not compete economically with fossil-fuel energy sources. Wind power has been used only where other sources of power were not available, for example, on farms that did not have electricity. More recently, though, there have been attempts to make wind energy more of a mainstream source of electricity. While the total amount of electricity produced with wind power is only a tiny fraction of that produced by conventional means, the number of installations is increasing each year. By the end of the 1990s, the amount of electricity being generated by wind was about 10 000 MW (megawatts) per year, a fraction of the world total, but was increasing by as much as 20 per cent each year. Most large mills are located on **wind farms**, which mass together windmills in areas with suitable winds. The windmills vary in design and size; most have three-bladed props, although designs can feature anywhere from one to 15 blades.

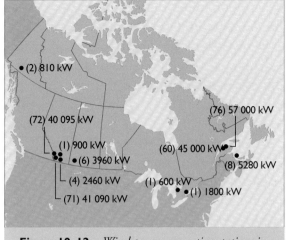

Figure 19–12 *Wind-power generating stations in Canada, 2001, showing number of turbines at each site and total generating capacity in kilowatts (kW)* Source: Can WEA.

In addition to large-scale, fixed generating plants, there are as many as 50 000 small battery-charging windmills produced each year. These are used for applications as diverse as sailboats in the Caribbean and by nomadic cattle breeders in Mongolia. In Canada, wind-power electrical generation is most common in Alberta and Quebec (Figure 19–12).

Use of Wind Power Today

Wind power is attractive for several reasons. It is non-polluting and does not produce greenhouse gases, as it does not use fossil fuels. For countries that import fossil fuels, wind power would create savings for the balance of payments. Windmills can be easily installed and dismantled when their useful life is over. The land on which windmills are located can be used for other purposes, such as farming. Wind power is particularly attractive for developing countries, and for places that have limited energy needs. With improvements in wind-power generation technology, it is expected that this source of power will be fully competitive with fossil-fuel and nuclear generation plants.

There are some disadvantages to wind power. Windmills can be located only in areas that have moderately strong, reliable winds. (Wind power increases with the cube of the wind speed, so if the wind velocity doubles, the amount of energy produced increases eightfold.) They can be noisy. Some are over 90 m in height, and some people consider them to be unsightly. They can be damaged by excessively strong winds, and can interfere with electromagnetic communications, such as radio broadcasts.

Hydricity: A Revolutionary Energy Future

The way in which we produce, transport, and use energy has caused enormous damage to the natural environment. The resulting problems threaten our health and well-being, and have given rise to many of the most important environmental issues of our day. These include global warming, smog, and acid rain. In addition, we are faced with questions about the reliability and cost of the future supply of our most vital energy source, oil. Some experts are suggesting that the time has come to consider a fundamental change in how we use energy. The last such energy revolution began more than a century ago when oil and natural gas came to replace coal as the dominant energy source. The next energy revolution will take many years to accomplish, but plans for it are already under way.

Did you KNOW?

While the number of birds harmed by windmills is small, operators of wind farms in California were horrified to discover that the low-pitched noise of windmills attracted endangered California condors. You can learn more about the condor in Chapter 16.

This energy revolution does not involve the discovery of a new energy source. Rather, it focusses on the development of a new way to use the energy we already have (along with new energy sources that we may develop). It is called the **hydricity** (*hydr*ogen electr*icity*) **revolution**.

Hydricity focusses on the role played by two closely related energy currencies, hydrogen and electricity. An **energy currency** exists when one source (or use) of energy can be replaced with another. We do not yet think in terms of energy currencies today. We use gasoline to operate our cars, electricity to power our lights, natural gas

to heat our homes, and coal to make steel. We have only a limited ability to transfer energy from one part of the "energy budget" to another. For example, we can use natural gas to power our cars, but only by modifying our engines in a way that means that we cannot use gasoline. Other changes are not even feasible—for example, the idea of running our cars on coal.

In our current energy system, largely independent systems of production, transport, and consumption exist for each major energy source (Figure 19–13a). A common energy currency requires that all forms of energy be converted

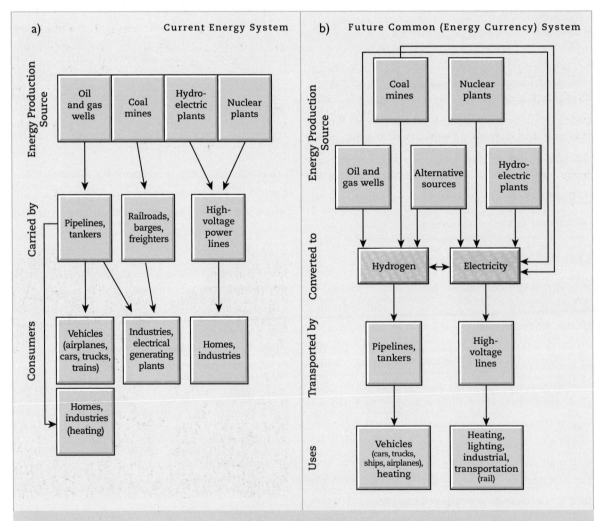

Figure 19–13 *The hydricity revolution will fundamentally change the way in which the world will produce, transport, and use energy. A change of this magnitude will take many years to accomplish.*

into one form of energy. Since conversion between most types of energy is either difficult or impossible, the energy form selected as the common currency will be the one that allows conversion with the least amount of difficulty. In the case of hydricity, all forms of energy will be converted to either hydrogen or electricity (Figure 19–13b). Energy from resources as diverse as falling water, uranium, oil, and the Sun are already being converted to electricity. This electricity is used for a wide range of purposes, but it has one problem: electricity is very difficult to store for later use. Hydrogen, however, is more versatile. Not only can it be used in a variety of applications, but it can also be liquefied and stored.

How Hydricity Would Work

With hydricity in place, electricity would continue to be used for the same purposes for which it is used today. Its use could be expanded, however, to transportation systems operating along fixed routes. For example, North American railways and intracity transit systems could reduce their use of diesel fuel and become significantly more electrified, like those of Western Europe and Japan.

Hydrogen would be used as an energy source in those instances in which energy must be stored. These would include forms of transportation, such as cars, trucks, ships, and airplanes, that do not travel along fixed routes. A jetliner using hydrogen as fuel would be able to fly farther than a conventional aircraft because hydrogen is much lighter than jet fuel. Energy in the form of hydrogen has an advantage in that it can be stored and transported over long distances.

Fundamental to hydricity is the fact that it is relatively easy to convert energy from hydrogen to electricity and back again. The simplest way to produce hydrogen is by electrolysis of water using electricity that has been produced in an electrical generation plant. The plant, in turn, uses fossil fuels, hydropower, nuclear, or, in the future, perhaps solar power.

$$H_2O + energy \longrightarrow H_2 + O_2$$

Figure 19–14 *The* Hindenburg *crashed and burned after exploding over Lakehurst, New Jersey, on May 6, 1937.*

Electricity can be produced from hydrogen using a device called a fuel cell. The fuel cell is not a new idea; it was invented in 1839. But it was not until the 1990s that its potential to help solve the world's energy problems was appreciated. A fuel cell chemically converts a compound containing hydrogen into electricity. This means the process does not involve burning (Figure 19–15).

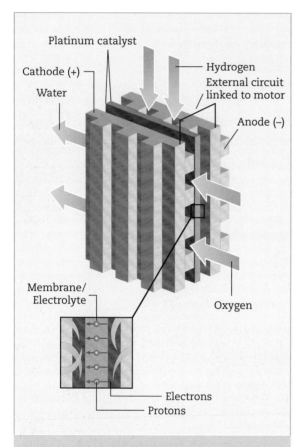

Figure 19–15 *How a fuel cell works: As hydrogen flows into the fuel cell on the anode side, a platinum catalyst separates the hydrogen gas into electrons and protons (hydrogen ions). The hydrogen ions pass through the membrane (centre of the fuel cell) and combine with oxygen and electrons on the cathode side, producing water. The electrons, which cannot pass through the membrane, flow from the anode to the cathode through an external circuit containing a motor, which uses the power generated by the cell.* Source: Los Alamos National Laboratory, *Fuel Cells: Green Power* (p. 4). Copyright © 1998–2001 The Regents of the University of California.

Benefits of the Hydricity System

An energy system that is focussed on hydrogen and electricity offers a number of important economic, political, and environmental benefits.

- *Economic impacts.* The flexibility of hydricity would save people money because energy users would not be tied to one particular type of energy. A simple example will illustrate the danger of an inflexible energy system. In the winter of 2000–2001, Canadians who heated their homes with natural gas were faced with dramatically higher energy costs because of short-term price increases. They had no choice but to pay the increased costs because their furnaces burned only natural gas, and changing furnaces would be costly. Even if they had been using a different heating source, such as fuel oil or electricity, they would have had the same market dependency. But if a hydricity system had existed, a different, more economical fuel source could have been used to provide the hydrogen or electricity used to heat their homes.

- *Political impacts.* Developing a hydrogen–electricity based economy would allow the United States, Japan, and most of the countries of Western Europe to reduce their dependence on imported oil. Vehicles could be powered, indirectly, by abundant fuels like coal and natural gas or by environmentally clean energy sources like wind and solar power. Having viable alternatives to oil would increase the security of developed nations by insulating them from the political uncertainties of the major oil exporters of the Persian Gulf.

- *Environmental impacts.* One of the most important features of a system that uses hydrogen so widely is a great reduction in environmental damage when compared to the current system. When hydrogen is burned—for example, in a vehicle engine—the only by-product is water. This has two huge benefits.

One is that the chemicals responsible for smog production and acid rain (mainly sulphur and nitrogen compounds) are not produced. The other advantage, perhaps more important in the long run, is that the burning of hydrogen does not produce any of the carbon compounds responsible for global warming.

Problems of Implementing a Hydricity System

While there are obvious, and very significant, advantages to a hydrogen–electricity based energy system, it will not be easy to achieve this revolution. The infrastructure of our current energy system (such as pipelines, power dams, and oil refineries) has taken decades to build and has cost trillions of dollars. Replacing it will take a similar length of time and cost a comparable amount.

The only way that a hydricity revolution can happen is by evolutionary change. The first of these changes, the development of a range of practical fuel cells, is well under way. A world leader in this venture is a Vancouver company called Ballard Power Systems. Ballard is focussing on two aspects of hydricity. The first is the creation and testing of fuel cells ranging in size from those that are small enough to be used in a car to those big enough to be used to provide electricity for a small town. The second aspect is finding ways to make the cost of this technology competitive with conventional alternatives. Ballard is working with major auto manufacturers to ensure that fuel-cell–powered cars are on the market by 2005.

It will take many years before an integrated hydrogen supply infrastructure can be built. In the interim, fuel cells can be constructed to use a variety of fuels, such as reformulated gasoline, methanol, ethanol, hydrogen, and compressed natural gas (CNG).

Earlier in *Global Connections*, you learned about the cornucopian view of Earth's future. Some observers believe that the development of a hydrogen–electricity based economy would be nothing more than the next step to a cornucopian future. Others strenuously reject this idea. They feel that the only way we can achieve a sustainable future is by fundamentally changing the way in which we think about and use energy (Figure 19–16).

Figure 19–16 *This Ontario farm uses wind and solar power to meet all its energy needs. The owners have not had to pay a hydro bill since 1992.*

Chapter Questions

Knowledge and Understanding

1. Other than the examples mentioned in the introduction to this chapter, briefly describe three ways in which energy use in the world is a major cause of global problems.

2. Describe the energy situation of each region listed in Figure 19–3. Consider the current production and use of the "big five" energy sources, along with the reserves of fossil fuels.

3. Summarize the important features of a hydricity-based economy.

4. Construct a one-page summary chart to compare the advantages and disadvantages of the "big five" energy sources: oil, natural gas, coal, nuclear power, and hydro-electricity.

5. Consider the pros and cons of wind power. Would this alternative energy source be effective in your region or community? Explain.

Thinking and Inquiry

6. Investigate the history of OPEC. During some parts of its history it has been quite successful in controlling the supply and price of oil on the world market. At other times, its efforts have been less successful. Investigate why this has been so and try to determine if OPEC is likely to have more or less influence in the future.

7. Research what is meant by "clean coal" technology. Why might the development of such technology be of great value in the future?

8. The change to a hydricity-based energy system will be a very complex one. What elements of the current energy system will be a particular obstacle to the change? What elements of the current system could be easily integrated into the new energy revolution?

9. Wood is a commonly used, non-commercial fuel source in many developing countries. Research the environmental implications of this use.

Communication

10. In Canada and many other OECD countries, many large hydro-electric megaprojects have been built over the last century. In these countries, few undeveloped large hydro-electric sites remain. Research and prepare a poster to show one of the following:
    a) the history of one existing major hydro-electric development in Canada or another country. Consider the reasons why the site was chosen, the nature of the construction, the amount of electricity produced, and how the electricity is used. Describe any environmental concerns related to the project.
    b) the potential of, and plans for, development of any undeveloped large-scale hydro-electric site in any country. Be sure to include discussion of environmental concerns related to the development of this site.
    c) the potential for the development of very small hydro-electric power sites that, in the past, may have been ignored as uneconomic.

11. Conduct a round-table discussion focussed on the five conventional energies. One person will represent oil, another natural gas, and so on. Together, rank the potential for each of these energy sources to satisfy future global requirements.

12. Use the regional information for either oil, natural gas, coal, nuclear power, or hydro-electric power to construct a world chloropleth map series, comparing production or consumption in 1980, 1990, and 2000. Prepare a one-page report that discusses important changes over time.

13. Develop a 10-point survey to determine levels of student awareness of various alternative energy sources. Conduct the survey, using a sample of at least 25 students from different grades. Analyse the data to identify patterns and relationships, then prepare a report of your findings.

Application

14. a) Canada has developed a unique nuclear power reactor called the CANDU. Research how the CANDU system differs from other types of reactors.

    b) To what countries has the CANDU been exported? Are there additional sales (or hopes for sales) in progress?

15. Investigate and discuss the viability of a selection of renewable energy sources. Suggested technologies to consider are biomass conversion; high-grade and low-grade geothermal power; and wind, photovoltaic, and solar heating.

16. The subject of nuclear power draws strong reactions from both supporters and opponents. Investigate the arguments on both sides of this issue. After you do your research, decide whether you think that additional nuclear plants should be constructed, and give reasons for your views.

17. Is there an energy crisis? Comment on this question from the following perspectives:

    a) We are running out of energy.

    b) We are running out of some types of energy only.

    c) We are likely to discover additional sources of conventional energy.

    d) The energy crisis is really a cultural construction—we have plenty of energy as long as we are prepared to change our attitudes and behaviour.

18. Research an alternative energy source other than wind. For the source you choose, try to determine the following:

    a) for what purposes it can be used

    b) its advantages and disadvantages

    c) how large a contribution it can make to solving Earth's energy problems

    d) how long it will take to reach its potential.

20

Global Warming—Wealth or Environmental Health?

Expectations

In this chapter, you will:

- understand the inter-
dependence of ecology
and economics

- identify current global
issues related to sus-
tainability and environ-
mental threats

- analyse the role of
the EU in contributing
to solving the problem
of greenhouse gases

- evaluate and commu-
nicate the perspectives
of various stakeholders
in a geographic issue

- evaluate the effective-
ness of international
strategies and agree-
ments

- analyse the distribution
of biomes and deter-
mine the reasons for the
observed patterns

Recent Canadian weather reports suggest that the warmest years on record have occurred since 1990. Indirect evidence of **global warming**, such as Hurricane Mitch's devastation of Nicaragua in 1998 (above), comes from all over the world. Many observers suggest that climate change may be the most serious of all the environmental problems that the world faces.

Climate Change Is Not New

Climates change. Scientists have determined that over the last million years, global temperatures have ranged from about one Celsius degree warmer than they were in 1900 to about four Celsius degrees cooler (Figure 20–1). The time periods during which global temperatures were lowest are called ice ages. During these periods, glaciers advanced to cover large parts of the Earth, including virtually all of Canada.

If we narrow our time focus somewhat (Figure 20–2), we can see that temperatures have changed continuously even in the last 1000 years. While the changes might appear to be insignificant, in the range of plus or minus 0.5 Celsius degrees, historical climatologists maintain that even such small changes can be important. They suggest that

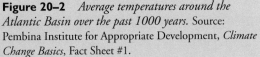

You can learn more about climate change at
<www.pearsoned.ca/globalconnections>.

the warmer period that began 1000 years ago allowed the Vikings to settle southern Greenland and the northern tip of Newfoundland.

Archaeological evidence shows that these settlements lasted only as long as the Mediaeval Warm Period. As the climate started to cool at the beginning of the 14th century, these Nordic settlements had to be abandoned as food production became a problem. Some historians have suggested that the rise and fall of several civilizations, such as ancient Egypt and the Roman Empire, can be tied to climate changes.

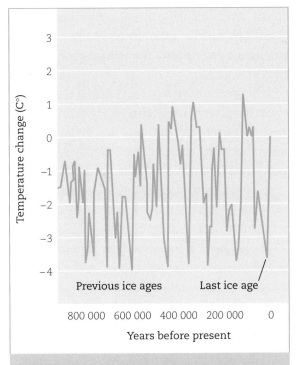

Figure 20–1 *Scientists' estimates of variations in global temperature averages over the last million years.* Source: Pembina Institute for Appropriate Development, *Climate Change Basics*, Fact Sheet #1.

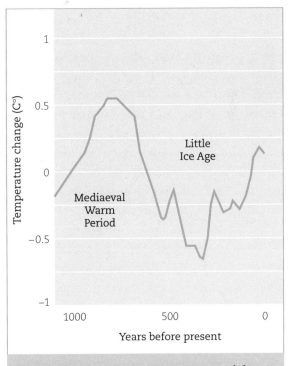

Figure 20–2 *Average temperatures around the Atlantic Basin over the past 1000 years.* Source: Pembina Institute for Appropriate Development, *Climate Change Basics*, Fact Sheet #1.

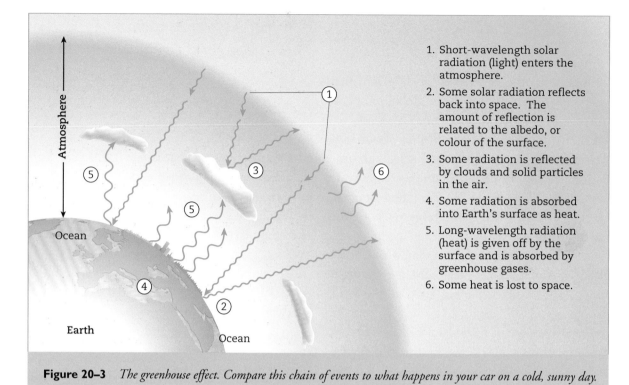

Figure 20–3 *The greenhouse effect. Compare this chain of events to what happens in your car on a cold, sunny day.*

1. Short-wavelength solar radiation (light) enters the atmosphere.
2. Some solar radiation reflects back into space. The amount of reflection is related to the albedo, or colour of the surface.
3. Some radiation is reflected by clouds and solid particles in the air.
4. Some radiation is absorbed into Earth's surface as heat.
5. Long-wavelength radiation (heat) is given off by the surface and is absorbed by greenhouse gases.
6. Some heat is lost to space.

The Greenhouse Effect

Often, newspaper stories discuss the **greenhouse effect** and global warming as if they were the same. This is not so. The greenhouse effect has existed for as long as Earth has had an atmosphere. Without it, there could be no life on Earth. In fact, scientists have calculated that without the greenhouse effect, the average temperature on Earth (which is now about 14°C) would be 33 Celsius degrees cooler (that is, −19°C)—more like the temperature on Mars!

The term greenhouse effect is a metaphor that refers to the fact that Earth with its atmosphere is like an agricultural greenhouse. Instead of glass, however, Earth relies on **greenhouse gases** to hold heat in the atmosphere (Figure 20–3). Most of Earth's atmosphere is composed of nitrogen (78 per cent of the total), oxygen (21 per cent), and argon (0.9 per cent). None of these gases are greenhouse gases. Rather, some of the gases that make up the remaining 0.1 per cent are the greenhouse gases. The most important naturally occurring greenhouse gases are water vapour, carbon dioxide, and methane.

The amount of water vapour in the atmosphere can change relatively quickly from place to place and from time to time. We see evidence of this in humidity changes that occur from one day to the next. The effects of higher concentrations of atmospheric water vapour on global warming are not entirely clear. Water vapour may cause temperatures to rise, but it may also increase cloud cover and lower temperatures by reflecting solar radiation back into space. However, the effects of increased concentrations of methane and, especially, carbon dioxide on global warming are very clear. In fact, studies of air bubbles trapped in ancient glacial ice have identified a strong relationship between levels of greenhouse gases in the air bubbles and the temperature changes that caused the ice ages (Figure 20–4).

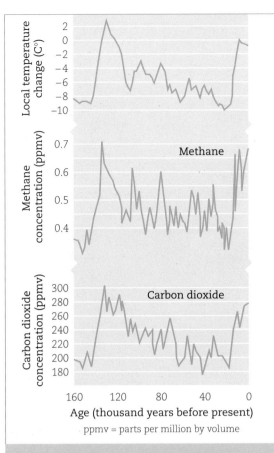

Figure 20–4 *There is a clear relationship between temperature change and the concentration of methane and carbon dioxide in Earth's atmosphere.* Source: Pembina Institute for Appropriate Development, *Climate Change Basics*, Fact Sheet #1.

Anthropogenic Greenhouse Gases

Human activities are increasing the magnitude of the greenhouse effect by producing more of the gases that cause it. If we are to understand what is happening to global temperatures today, we must consider the creation of these **anthropogenic** greenhouse gases. This term refers to the extra greenhouse gases created by people. There are four principal anthropogenic greenhouse gases, the first three of which exist naturally: carbon dioxide, methane, nitrous oxide, and halocarbons. Each of these gases will be discussed in the section that follows.

Carbon Dioxide

Carbon dioxide (CO_2) is the most significant anthropogenic greenhouse gas, but not because of the effectiveness of each CO_2 molecule in holding in heat. Other gases are able to hold more heat on a per molecule basis. Rather, CO_2 is significant because of the vast quantities produced by the activities of human beings.

To understand the role that carbon dioxide plays in global warming, it is critical to understand the **carbon cycle**—how carbon moves through the environment (Figure 20–5, on the next page). For example, a carbon atom in a gasoline molecule might be turned into CO_2 and released into the atmosphere when the gasoline is burned. The carbon dioxide molecule might then be dissolved in ocean water. It could next be taken up by phytoplankton, and so on. Given sufficient time, a particular carbon atom could circulate through all the various parts of the cycle.

Levels of atmospheric carbon are affected by *carbon sources, carbon sinks,* and *fixed carbon.* A **carbon source** is anything that provides additional carbon to the atmosphere, for example, when the vegetation in a swamp decomposes and gives off methane. A **carbon sink** exists when carbon is removed from the atmosphere for a relatively short time, for example, when you plant a tree, which takes up carbon as it grows. In general, carbon will stay in a sink for a period ranging from a few minutes to a few centuries. **Fixed carbon**, on the other hand, has been removed from the atmosphere for a very long period of time. For example, the carbon in limestone or coal has been removed from the atmosphere for perhaps hundreds of millions of years.

The carbon cycle can be disrupted by a variety of human activities. If a forest is cut down or a farmer's field is paved over, the carbon sink that is destroyed contains carbon that will have been out of the atmosphere for from one year to perhaps a few hundred years. A much more

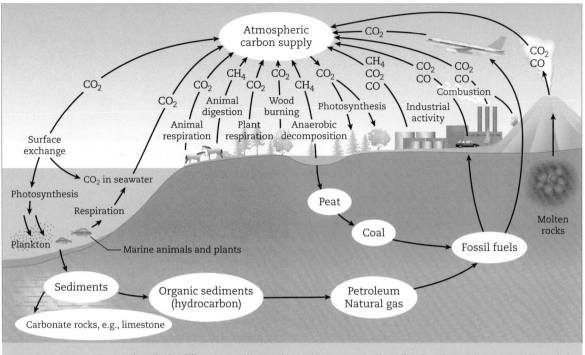

Figure 20–5 *Try to identify the following: carbon sinks, carbon sources, where fixed carbon is being created, and where fixed carbon is released into the atmosphere.*

worrying situation occurs when fixed carbon enters the atmosphere. For example, when gasoline or coal is burned, "new" carbon—carbon that has been locked underground for tens, or even hundreds, of millions of years—is added to the atmosphere. The increased production of anthropogenic carbon dioxide can be directly related to the explosion in the world's population and to the use of fossil fuels since the beginning of the Industrial Revolution.

It is worrisome that a significant reduction in the number of carbon sinks is taking place at a time when more CO_2 is being released into the atmosphere. When forests are cleared for farming, when farmland is paved over for urban centres, and when formerly productive land is degraded as a result of desertification, the Earth loses its ability to absorb carbon dioxide. Scientists estimate that without effective measures to limit carbon dioxide production, the amount of CO_2 in the atmosphere in 2080 will be twice what it was before the Industrial Revolution.

Methane

Methane (CH_4) is produced whenever organic materials break down in the absence of oxygen. (If oxygen is present, carbon dioxide is produced.) Like carbon dioxide, methane is produced naturally, for example, in swamps. Since methane is a carbon-based compound, its cycle can be described, like carbon dioxide's, in terms of sources, sinks, and fixed carbon.

There has been an explosive growth in atmospheric methane levels in the past 200 years. Between 60 per cent and 80 per cent of global methane production now comes from human activities. There are three main sources of anthropogenic methane: decomposing garbage in various kinds of dumps; wastes produced during the extraction and processing of fossil fuels; and gases emitting from the digestive tracts of domestic animals like cows and pigs, and from the decomposition of their solid waste.

Nitrous Oxide

Nitrous oxide (N_2O) comes from both natural and anthropogenic sources. Its main human sources include the burning of fossil fuels in vehicles, the use of nitrogen-based fertilizers, and the production of certain industrial chemicals like nitric acid. Nitrous oxide concentrations have also risen with the growth of population and our industrial economy. While nitrous oxide, on a molecule-by-molecule basis, is a more powerful greenhouse gas than carbon dioxide or methane, its overall impact on global warming is much less significant because it is present in much smaller amounts.

Halocarbons

Halocarbons are a family of highly stable, human-made compounds that are used in refrigerators and air conditioners and for a variety of industrial activities, such as cleaning electronic circuit boards. For many years, the most important halocarbons were chlorofluorocarbons (CFCs). The use of CFCs is being eliminated, as a result of an international agreement, because of their devastating impact on the ozone layer (see Chapter 18). CFCs are being replaced by two other families of halocarbons, hydrochlorofluorocarbons (HCFCs) and hydrofluorocarbons (HFCs). While these compounds are less damaging to the ozone layer, they are still potent greenhouse gases.

Impact of Global Warming

Scientists predict that global warming will have a wide, complex, and at times surprising range of impacts on the Earth.

Higher Average Temperatures

A United Nations–sponsored group of 2500 climate scientists called the Intergovernmental Panel on Climate Change (IPCC) has predicted that average global temperatures will increase by between 1.4 and 5.8 Celsius degrees by the year 2100. This relatively broad range of values reflects the difficulties associated with computerized modelling of the atmosphere, the method used to predict climate change. (Scientists use powerful supercomputers and historical climate change data to check the accuracy of their models.) It is worrying that as research on climate change continues, forecasts of future temperature increases become steadily higher. Temperature increases will not occur evenly in all parts of the world. In general, the farther a location is from the Equator, the greater the amount of increase. The average temperatures of polar areas are expected to increase by as much as 10 Celsius degrees.

Floods

Higher temperatures will melt polar ice caps and mountain glaciers. The meltwater generated will cause sea-level increases that threaten low-lying regions (Figure 20–6). Areas at risk include many of the world's great cities, along with many islands

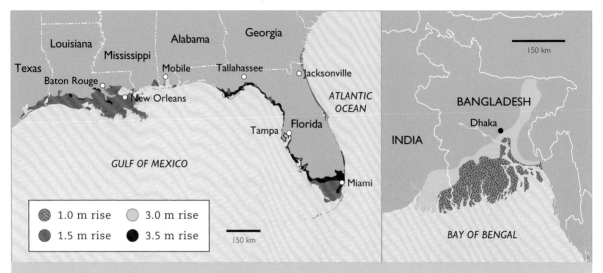

Figure 20–6 *The coasts of both the southeastern United States and Bangladesh are threatened by rising sea levels. Higher sea levels can flood low-lying areas and also increase the risk posed by storm surges caused by hurricanes and other major storms.* Source: Michael D. Lemonick, "Feeling the Heat: Special Report, Global Warming," *Time* magazine, April 9, 2001 (vol. 157, no. 14), p. 23. © 2001 Time Inc. Reprinted by permission.

and highly populated rural lowlands. If all of Earth's glaciers and ice sheets were to melt, global sea levels could increase by as much as nine metres.

Even if the rise were much less than that, hundreds of millions of people would be affected. Countries like the Maldives in the Indian Ocean and the Marshall Islands in the Pacific Ocean could be completely inundated. They have already had to build massive shoreline structures to protect their islands from ocean waves and storms in recent years. Because water expands slightly as it gets warmer, the thermal expansion of ocean water due to global warming will also contribute to higher sea levels.

Did you KNOW?

Long-standing records suggest that sea levels have been rising by about 1.5 mm per year for most of the last century.

Changes in Vegetation

The higher temperatures associated with global warming will increase the rate of evapotranspiration—the release of water vapour from the Earth's surface by evaporation and by transpiration, the biological process whereby plants lose water vapour through pores in their leaves. Unless there is a matching increase in precipitation, most areas will become relatively drier than they were before global warming. This will cause a shift in the location of natural vegetation regions. The impact on the location of the boreal forest in North America is typical of these changes (Figure 20–7). In general, the temperate forest and the grassland will grow northward into the boreal forest, while the boreal forest will expand into the tundra region.

Similar changes will affect agricultural regions. In Canada, many areas will have longer growing seasons than at present. The growing season may become long enough to grow wheat near Yellowknife, while rice cultivation may become common in southern Ontario. At first glance, it might appear that these changes will

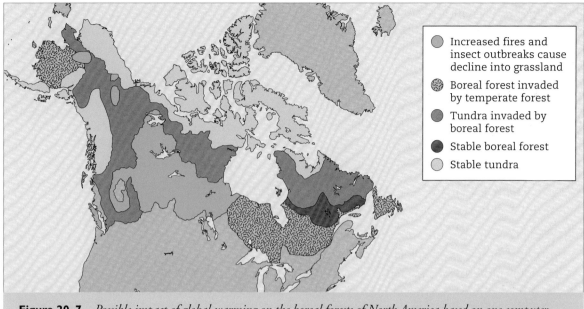

Figure 20–7 *Possible impact of global warming on the boreal forests of North America based on one computer model.* Source: Greenpeace International, *The Carbon Bomb: Climate Change and the Fate of the Northern Boreal Forests* (Amsterdam: Stichting Greenpeace Council, 1994), p. 22.

greatly improve Canada's agricultural capability, but this might not be the case. Most of the current Prairies agricultural region and parts of southern Ontario will be too dry for farming. Areas of northern Canada that might be warm enough for agriculture will not develop suitable soils for several centuries. Irrigation will not be a realistic option in the drier Prairies because the main potential source of water for irrigation (the rivers that flow eastward from the Rocky Mountains) will have greatly reduced flows, since the glaciers that provide their water will be much smaller or entirely melted.

Pests

Global warming will cause an increase in diseases, weeds, and animal pests. For example, as temperatures rise, residents of highland areas in Rwanda and Kenya will be exposed to malaria and yellow fever. Previously they were protected from these diseases, because the mosquitoes that carried them could not survive in the relatively cool mountain

climates. Even now, tropical fish species are moving into the Mediterranean from the Red Sea and starting to threaten indigenous species.

Droughts

Global warming will cause droughts. Water shortages will increase. In some cases, regions with existing shortages, like those in Africa's Sahel and western Canada, will find themselves facing even more critical water problems. Areas that have not experienced shortages will begin to do so. Water levels in the Great Lakes may decline to the point that ships using the St. Lawrence Seaway will not be able to carry full loads. Recreational users of lakes in southern Ontario may find these lakes much smaller and shallower.

Storms

It has been predicted that severe storms will occur more frequently because of global warming. The possibility that there could be more, and more severe, tropical cyclones (hurricanes) is a particular worry in areas that are susceptible to these storms, such as Bangladesh and the coastal southeastern United States. These regions are already suffering from sea-level increases. Higher sea levels will only intensify the impact of storm surges, the most significant cause of death and financial loss during these events.

Lower Temperatures

Remarkably, global warming could even cause a dramatic cooling in some areas. Some marine scientists suggest that the melting of the ice sheets of Greenland and extreme northern Canada will reduce the salinity of northern ocean waters. The lower salinity, in turn, will cause a significant reduction in (or even elimination of) the flow of the warm Gulf Stream into the northern part of the North Atlantic. Without the warmth that the Gulf Stream brings, the climates of Atlantic Canada and, especially, Western Europe will become dramatically cooler. Winter snows will last longer and, if they did not melt in the summer, could even trigger a new ice age. The growth of glaciers will be accelerated by the fact that the increased snow cover will give Earth's surface a higher **albedo**. This term refers to the ability of a surface to reflect light. In this case, the white, snow-covered surface has a high reflectivity that will reflect that more solar energy into space.

Human Migrations

Global warming will cause an enormous growth in the number of **environmental refugees**. People may have to flee their homelands for several environmental reasons. Some may leave because the land they live on has become flooded by rising sea levels. Others may leave because they find themselves living in areas that are dev-

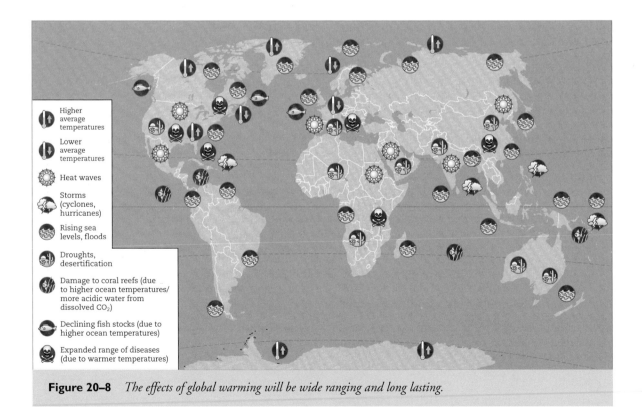

Figure 20–8 *The effects of global warming will be wide ranging and long lasting.*

astated by tropical storms made more severe as a result of climate change. Some may have to find new regions to live in because their homelands suffer a significant reduction in their food production capacity. Some observers suggest that there are already as many as 25 million environmental refugees in the world—in particular in North Africa, where rainfall levels have declined over the years. With global warming, this number is likely to increase dramatically.

Figure 20-8 summarizes the likely effects of global warming worldwide.

Feedback Loops and Global Warming

Of particular concern to those who study global warming is the problem of feedback loops. A feedback loop exists when a result of global warming causes even more global warming. Scientists particularly fear that such loops may push Earth towards a **tipping point**. At a tipping point, global warming and climate change that have started slowly may begin to accelerate uncontrollably. For example, the ability of water to hold dissolved gases is inversely related to temperature. Therefore, as oceans warm they will be unable to hold as much carbon dioxide. The excess CO_2 that is released into the atmosphere will cause more global warming that will, in turn, cause even more carbon dioxide to be released from the oceans (Figure 20–9).

The melting of ice caps reduces Earth's albedo as ice and snow are replaced by rock and soil. The darker surface will absorb more solar radiation and ultimately put more heat back into the atmosphere. This will, in turn, cause more melting of ice and snow. Higher temperatures will cause permafrost to melt in areas of northern Canada, Alaska, and Siberia. The previously frozen muskeg contains vast amounts of organic material that has not decomposed because of the low temperatures. If the muskeg thaws, this material will be able to break down, and vast quantities of methane will be produced—increasing the greenhouse effect and causing even more permafrost to melt.

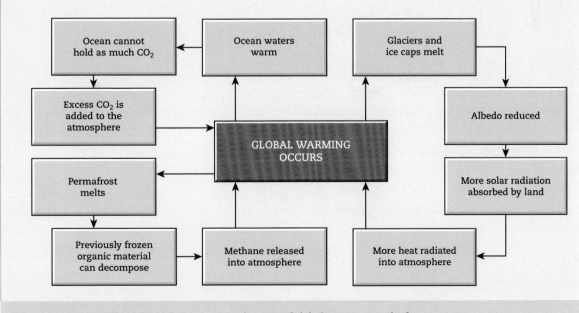

Figure 20–9 *Feedback loops threaten an acceleration of global warming in the future.*

Politics of Global Warming

The issue of climate change can be broken down into two parts: the science of global warming and the politics of global warming. While much more research needs to be done on the science, it is the political aspect of climate change that is more problematic.

Although the first research on climate change was published in the 1970s, it was not until the early 1990s that the issue moved from the scientific world into the political forum. In 1990, the world's leading climate scientists called on governments to find a way to reduce the emissions of greenhouse gases. This call prompted the nations of the world to make climate change a focus of the United Nations Conference on Environment and Development that was held in Rio de Janeiro in 1992.

UN Framework Convention on Climate Change

One of the two most important achievements of the Rio Conference—the other was an agreement to protect biodiversity—was the creation of the United Nations Framework Convention on Climate Change (UNFCC). This agreement is called a "framework convention" because it provided only a basic outline for the international efforts that will be required to prevent climate change. The UNFCC's objective was to "to achieve ... stabilization of greenhouse gas concentrations in the atmosphere at a level that would prevent dangerous anthropogenic inter-

ference with the climate system." The details of how this should be accomplished were to be worked out at later international conferences.

Every country in the world was to take responsibility for the problem. However, the developed countries, recognizing that developing nations had first to ease the poverty of their citizens, were to take the lead in the fight against climate change. First, guidelines were created that would have them reduce their 2000 greenhouse gas emission levels to 1990 levels. Second, they were to provide technological and financial assistance to help the developing world fight climate change.

By the mid-1990s, it was apparent that little progress had been made in slowing climate change. Carbon dioxide emissions continued to increase both in the developed and developing worlds (Figure 20–10), and little assistance to prevent global warming had flowed to the developing countries. Most governments did little more than talk about controlling greenhouse gases.

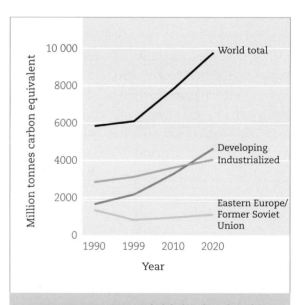

Figure 20–10 *Projected global carbon dioxide emissions, 1990–2020.* Source: Energy Information Administration.

You can learn more about the United Nations Framework Convention on Climate Change and the Intergovernmental Panel on Climate Change at <www.pearsoned.ca.globalconnections>.

Country	Reduction Targets (%)	Country	Reduction Targets (%)	Country	Reduction Targets (%)
Australia	+8	Iceland	+10	Romania	−8
Bulgaria	−8	Japan	−6	Russian Federation	0
Canada	−6	Latvia	−8	Slovakia	−8
Croatia	−5	Liechtenstein	−8	Switzerland	−8
Czech Republic	−8	Monaco	−8	Ukraine	0
Estonia	−8	New Zealand	0	United States	−7
European Union*	−8	Norway	+1		
Hungary	−6	Poland	−6		

*This reduction was to be achieved in the aggregate by the EU. It would not require each of the 15 members to reduce emissions by the same amount.

Figure 20–11 *Kyoto Protocol emission reduction targets for 2012. Iceland, Norway, and Australia could increase their emissions, or trade them.*

Those who were acutely concerned about climate change looked with hope to the next major international conference in Kyoto, Japan, in 1997.

Kyoto Protocol

The purpose of the Kyoto Conference was to set mandatory reduction targets, rather than guidelines, for greenhouse gases produced by the developed countries (Figure 20–11). The outcome of the Conference, the Kyoto Protocol, was not intended to provide a complete solution to the problem of climate change. Scientists had predicted that a complete solution would require emissions reductions of 60 to 70 per cent. Reductions of this magnitude would have economic and political impacts that would be unacceptable. Rather, Kyoto was regarded as merely a first step in the process.

Kyoto's targets actually required countries to cut their emissions below 1990 levels, not just return them to that level. The agreement suggested means by which the reductions could be achieved. These suggestions included passing laws that would encourage organizations and individuals to reduce emissions and expand carbon sinks. The target date for the reductions was to be 2012, although substantial progress was required to be shown by 2005.

Kyoto also established the principle of **emissions trading**. This is a procedure by which a country that exceeds its emissions reduction target, perhaps because of an enhanced commitment to energy efficiency, is able to sell its unused emissions credits on the open market. An important clause of the Kyoto accord was one that created a **clean development mechanism**. The purpose of this clause was to move the developing countries economically in a direction that would minimize the production of greenhouse gases. In addition, the Kyoto agreement included clauses that considered such important details as how reductions were to be calculated and reported, and how technology was to be transferred to developing countries.

To come into effect, the agreement required

that 55 countries approve or ratify it, and that the industrialized countries that ratified the treaty together had to produce at least 55 per cent of the industrial emissions. By 2001, more than 80 countries had ratified the Kyoto agreement, but this number did not include enough industrial countries to bring the treaty into effect. The most important country not to sign was the United States. Shortly after assuming office in 2001, President George W. Bush announced that the United States was withdrawing its support of the Kyoto agreement (Figure 20–12). This was a serious blow to the fight against climate change, since the United States is the largest producer of greenhouse gases in the world. It would be hard to reach the 55 per cent threshold for industrialized countries without US ratification.

The US decision threw the fight for climate-change control into disarray. Another conference was held in Bonn, Germany, in 2001, in an attempt to rescue the Kyoto accord. After vigorous debate, a compromise was reached that would reduce global-warming gas emissions by a total of 5.2 per cent by 2010. The Bonn agreement was approved by more than 180 countries and left the United States isolated from the rest of the world.

Figure 20–12 *The United States has shown great reluctance to be part of the fight against global warming.*

Positions of the International Players on Climate Change

The diplomatic process of negotiating climate-change control has revealed at least five main viewpoints.

United States

The United States is the only major country that has rejected the entire process as flawed. The Americans have three major reasons for opposing the Kyoto Protocol. The first is based on the minority scientific view that, while climate change may be occurring, it may be for natural, rather than anthropogenic, reasons. The US government is not willing to proceed with policies that might have a devastating economic impact without stronger scientific evidence.

The second, perhaps more important, concern is that emissions reduction could not be accomplished without causing profound damage to the economy of the United States. Critics of the US government were quick to point out that President Bush, Vice-President Cheney, and several other members of Cabinet have close ties to the oil industry. Their concern might have been more closely related to the impact that control of greenhouse gas emissions would have on that industry.

The Americans' final concern is that no significant progress had been made on an agreement to limit the growth of greenhouse emissions of developing countries. They pointed out that emissions are growing much more rapidly in percentage terms there than in the developed world, and that attempts to forge an agreement parallel to Kyoto for developing countries had been a failure.

European Union

The EU nations have remained steadfast in their commitment to fight global warming. Both at international conferences and in their actions—for example, by expanding alternative energy use and working towards more efficient use of conventional energy—they have gone the farthest of any of the developed nations in fighting climate change. At Kyoto and at Bonn, they were the leaders in the push to achieve a treaty.

Canada, Russia, Japan, Australia, New Zealand

This group of developed countries occupies the middle ground between the United States and the European Union. They have not gone as far as the Americans in backing away from earlier commitments to fight greenhouse gas emissions. At the same time, as the need to make drastic reforms has approached, they have looked for an easier way out. At Bonn, they were successful in having the value of carbon sinks increased in importance so that targets for reduction of actual greenhouse gas emissions could be lowered. This change was of great benefit to Canada because of its vast areas of forest and agricultural land.

Developing World

Led by China, the world's second largest producer of greenhouse gases, the Group of 77 developing countries rejects any responsibility for a problem that it feels was created by, and

Did you KNOW? The Group of 77 is a loose coalition of countries in the developing world. Originally it had 77 members, but now has many more.

therefore should be solved by, the developed world. The group's attitude was expressed well by the leader of the Chinese delegation at Kyoto: "In the developed world only two people ride in a car, and you want us to give up riding the bus!" At the same time, there is no denying the fact that rapid population increases in developing nations have caused increased greenhouse gas emissions. The clearing (and burning) of rain forests, the use of coal and other fossil fuels, and the expansion of animal herds have added carbon dioxide and methane to the atmosphere.

Alliance of Small Island Nations

Not surprisingly, small island nations, some of which face the potential risk that they may completely disappear under rising ocean levels, take the problem of global warming very seriously indeed. At Kyoto, they pushed for an across-the-board 20 per cent reduction in emissions. Because these countries have little political or economic power in the world, their needs and recommendations received relatively little attention. Citizens of these countries were, understandably, not persuaded by the suggestion that it would be cheaper to relocate all their residents, in the event of flooding, than it would be to solve the problem of global warming.

What Will Happen Next?

In the extended drama that is the climate-change debate today, we have completed only the first few scenes of the first act. While the worst impacts of global warming may not be felt until near the end of the century, scientists suggest that we have only until about 2015 to make substantial changes in our lifestyles. After that, it will be too late to stop the damage. Is there the political will to make these changes? Only time will tell.

Chapter Questions

Knowledge and Understanding

1. Summarize how the greenhouse effect works and how the production of anthropogenic greenhouse gases increases temperatures.

2. a) Define carbon sink, carbon source, and fixed carbon.
   b) Draw a simplified sketch of the carbon cycle, focussing on identifying the sinks, sources, and processes that create and release fixed carbon.

3. It has been said that the history of international efforts to combat global warming has been long on good intentions and short on concrete actions. Demonstrate, using specific details, that this is true. Why is this not surprising?

4. Describe an example of a feedback loop, other than the ones given in this chapter, that contributes to global warming. Use a diagram to explain your description.

Thinking and Inquiry

5. a) What is meant by the term clean development mechanism? How would such a mechanism contribute to reducing climate change?
   b) Describe at least three specific examples of how this could be done.

6. a) Identify at least six cities, on at least three continents, that are located barely above sea level and would be threatened by rising sea levels.
   b) Why is it common for large cities to be located in such areas?

7. This chapter mentioned three reasons why environmental refugees are created. For each of the three reasons, give examples of environmental refugees, naming the countries affected.

8. a) Briefly summarize the impacts that global warming will have on Earth. In your summary, do not forget to include the impacts that are part of feedback loops.
   b) Describe how significant each of these impacts will be on Canada compared to the world in general.
   c) On balance, will Canada be affected by global warming to a greater or lesser extent than most countries?
   d) Will the impacts, on balance, be positive or negative for Canada?

9. Consider the reasons why the US government withdrew from the Kyoto agreement. Were the Americans justified in their action? Why or why not?

Communication

10. Do you agree with the position taken by Canada (and some other countries) that a country should be able to count the size of its carbon sinks against its requirement to cut greenhouse gas emissions? Why or why not?

11. Give specific lifestyle and technological changes that we could make, as a society, that would reduce the production of each anthropogenic greenhouse gas.

12. Chapter 19 quoted the phrase, "If you are not part of the solution, you are part of the problem." Organize a round-table discussion group representing the five main viewpoints on global climate change. Try to reach a consensus on short-term and long-term ways to reduce greenhouse gases.

Application

13. Some scientists feel that there is significant risk of a new ice age in the future. Investigate the reasons why these researchers hold this belief.

14. Research the present stance of the Canadian government and other industrialized countries on the Kyoto agreement. What is your position on this issue?

Unit 5: Conflict and Cooperation

21 Introduction to Geopolitics

Key Terms

geopolitics
nation state
sovereignty
ideology
democracy
direct democracy
referendum
authoritarian nation
  state
nationalism
communism
Cold War
imperialism
containment
sphere of influence

Expectations

In this chapter, you will:

- explain why places and regions are important to the identities of peoples
- identify methods of grouping countries and evaluate the implications
- analyse the changing distribution of political systems worldwide
- analyse the evolving geopolitical roles of selected world regions
- describe biases behind different perspectives on geographical issues
- use maps to analyse change over time
- use geographic terms correctly in written and oral communication

Many of the issues debated today at the United Nations (above) and by governments around the world have geographical components that must be considered before any political decisions are made. Governmental policies on foreign aid, immigration, trade, foreign affairs, and environmental protection, to name only a few, involve geography as well as politics.

What Is Geopolitics? *Who Cares?*

Generally, politics is the administration and management of state affairs. More specifically, it is the exercise of power in the decision-making process of government. A multitude of geographical factors come into play when governments make decisions on such issues as determining their borders, developing political spheres of influence, resolving international conflict, forming military alliances, striking trade agreements, developing and protecting natural resources, or controlling access to sea and air routes. Population size, site and situation, topography, climate, economy, resource base, and unique environmental characteristics will influence many political decisions.

Sometimes geography directly influences a political decision. For instance, the Canadian government decided to develop a non-military satellite communications system because it was the most economical way to provide telephone, radio, and TV links across Canada's vast area. At other times, a political decision will directly affect geography. For example, both Canada and the United States have passed legislation that does not adequately restrict the release of airborne pollutants that acidify lakes in both countries. The interplay of geography and politics, on either a national or international level, is known as **geopolitics**.

This chapter introduces some basic concepts that will help you analyse geopolitical issues.

The Nation State

The **nation state** is comparatively new in recorded history. The concept originated in Europe during the Renaissance (early 1300s to 1600) and subsequently evolved as historical events, such as the French and American revolutions in the 18th century, changed people's views of how they wished to be governed. Prior to the Renaissance, the concept of an independent nation of people ruled by a national government that controlled events within clearly marked geographical boundaries did not exist. Political power usually resided in the hands of a single ruler (or dynasty), who exercised control over various and changing groups of people living within loosely defined borders. The empires of Alexander the Great, Genghis Khan, and Julius Caesar's Rome, and the Katsina Kingdom of northern Nigeria, are examples.

Political Sovereignty

The nation state is more than just a political entity. It is a sizable group of people who have adopted a unique common identity as fellow citizens, and who live together under one government within a certain geographical area. Nation states are set apart from others by their history, language, customs, religion, and unique sense of community. Some nation states, such as Canada, comprise people of different ethnicity from many parts of the world who do not share traditions, religion, or language. In some countries, diversity is viewed as a strength, while in others it leads to conflict.

> **Did you KNOW?**
>
> Vatican City, nominally ruled by the Pope, is the smallest (44 ha) independent state in the world.

A nation state has political autonomy, that is, it is able to create policies and enforce laws within its borders without interference from other states. In other words, the nation state possesses **sovereignty**. Sovereignty is a legal concept that, according to international law, recognizes that the authority of a state is not subject to legal control by any other state (Figure 21–1).

The sovereignty of one nation state is delineated from that of another by a border. Borders mark the limit of a nation's laws and security, and at the same time link a specific geographical area with national identity. When the armed forces of one country cross over the border into another without being invited to do so, they threaten that country's national sovereignty. A threat to national sovereignty often results in an armed clash.

In the mid-1990s, the United Nations (whose 190 members are sovereign nations) was reluctant to become involved in the internal conflicts in the former Yugoslavia and Rwanda, even though it knew that genocide was occurring in both countries. It was reluctant despite the 1991 statement of Javier Perez de Cuellar, the UN Secretary-General at the time, that governments could no longer regard national sovereignty as a protective barrier behind which human rights could be "massively … violated." The concept of national sovereignty as a deterrent to interference was thus a factor in the failure to protect those suffering from human rights abuses within their own countries.

In Chapter 3, you learned how globalization is encouraging the development of the "global village." Agreements such as NAFTA and ASEAN are creating trading blocs in which national borders do not limit the movement of goods. Moreover, most members of the European Union now use a single currency, the Euro, and have done away with border checkpoints. These are forces that are weakening national sovereignty. The loss of sovereignty can reduce the ability of nations to make regulations, and to retain their national character.

Figure 21–1 *In 1969, the US supertanker* Manhattan *attempted to prove that the Northwest Passage could be used to transport oil from Alaska to the east coast of the United States. Because the US considers this passage to be international waters, and not part of Canadian territorial waters (under* Canadian sovereignty), *it did not ask permission of the Canadian government for this voyage. In response, Canada sent an icebreaker to "accompany" the* Manhattan *and to assert Canadian sovereignty over the waters surrounding the Arctic archipelago.*

Political Borders

Political borders are sometimes based on easily recognizable natural features such as mountain ranges, rivers, lakes, deserts, and swamps. Natural features acted as some of the earliest boundaries between countries. For example, four of the Great Lakes, and the divide of the Coast Range Mountains of northern British Columbia, act as boundaries between Canada and the United States. Sometimes borders are purely arbitrary, or artificial, such as lines of latitude and longitude, and cannot be seen on the land. Artificial borders were frequently imposed by European powers in Africa during colonial times, and gave rise to conflict that continues to this day because they divided and united different cultural groups without considering geographic and social factors. Nigeria, for example, comprises a number of tribal and linguistic groups, and has experienced civil war and several tribal-based coups.

Did you KNOW? Point Roberts, a peninsula that juts into the Georgia Strait south of Vancouver, is US territory because it falls south of the 49th parallel. Americans, however, can reach it by car only by driving through Canada. A similar situation exists on the east coast, where Canadians must travel through the US to catch a ferry to Campobello Island, located in Canadian waters.

The majority of nation states were created between 1900 and 1999 (Figure 21–2). Many of these nation states resulted from the decolonization of Africa, Asia, the Caribbean, and the Middle East after World War II. In the 1990s, a number of new nation states were created out of the breakup of the former Soviet Union.

Formation of Nation States

Period	Asia & Oceania	The Americas	Central, Eastern, & Southern Europe	Central & Southern Africa	Middle East & North Africa	Northern & Western Europe	Total
Pre–1000	0	0	0	0	0	3	3
1000–1599	2	0	1	1	1	7	12
1600–1799	3	1	0	0	0	3	7
1800–1899	2	20	2	1	0	4	29
1900–1950	12	1	6	1	6	5	31
1951–1975	11	7	0	40	10	2	70
1976–1999	13	6	15	5	1	0	40
Total (192)	43	35	24	48	18	24	

Figure 21–2 *Historical and regional pattern of nation-state formation. Nation states take a variety of different forms, ranging from democratic to authoritarian.* Source: J. Denis Derbyshire and Ian Derbyshire, *Encyclopedia of World Political Systems.* Armonk, NY: M.E. Sharpe, Inc., 2000, Volume 1, p. 7, Table 2.

What Is an Ideology?

An **ideology** is a set of ideas and beliefs that a nation uses as the basis for its way of life, its political and economic systems, and its social goals. A political system may be based upon one ideology or a combination (Figures 21–3 and 21–4).

A country's political system cannot always be determined by examining its name. For instance, one would never guess that the Democratic Republic of Congo has never had an election—an absolute requirement for a democracy. One would also not expect that the People's Republic of Korea has been ruled since its creation by a father and son who are treated more like monarchs than leaders of a supposedly egalitarian communist state.

Although the nation states of today's world each have a unique ideology based on their history and experience, they can nevertheless be identified as belonging to one of two basic ideologies: democracy and authoritarianism.

Democratic States

In a representative **democracy**, ideally the nation's citizens exercise political power by electing officials who govern in accordance with their wishes. Essential features of democracy include:

- a decision-making system that is based on the rule of the majority of citizens
- protection for the rights of minorities
- accountability of the government to the electorate, namely those citizens who vote
- guarantees for the freedoms of expression, assembly, religion, and the press
- an independent judiciary that is not subject to the political policies of the government in power
- the rule of law that applies to all citizens.

Democracy is practised in different ways. The Greeks in ancient times practised **direct democracy**. Under this system, citizens (who did not include women or slaves) met periodi-

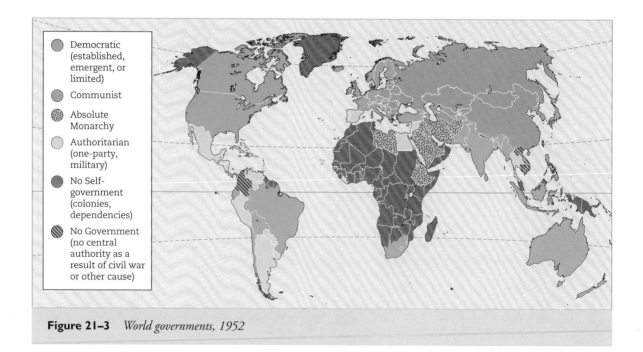

Democratic
(established, emergent, or limited)

Communist

Absolute Monarchy

Authoritarian
(one-party, military)

No Self-government (colonies, dependencies)

No Government (no central authority as a result of civil war or other cause)

Figure 21–3 *World governments, 1952*

cally to make political decisions, and gave a simple yes or no vote to a question. Today, a form of direct democracy, known as a **referendum**, is used to resolve some issues in some nation states, among them the United States and Canada. A proposition or question is posed to citizens who then vote yes or no, and the majority rules.

Quebec held referenda in 1980 and 1995 to determine the province's future relationship with Canada; in 1995, a slim majority (50.6 per cent) voted "no" to full sovereignty. A federal referendum was held on the 1992 Charlottetown Accord that proposed recognition of Quebec as a distinct society, Aboriginal self-government, and a new division of powers between Ottawa and the provinces. (The accord was rejected.) Some political parties believe that Canadians should use referenda more frequently to decide important national issues.

In 1999, there were approximately 74 nation states with well-established political systems based on democratic principles. There were an additional 71 nation states that were either emergent or limited democracies. Emergent democracies, although on the road to democratic stability, may sometimes experience non-democratic events in their government. For example, the governments of Cameroon and Zimbabwe have rigged elections and intimidated members of opposition parties. Limited forms of democracy exist where armed forces are in a position to assert control if the democratically elected government moves in a direction that the military leaders do not like. This has been the case in Angola, Thailand, and several countries in Latin America.

Authoritarianism

Authoritarian nation states limit the participation of their citizens in politics, and often stifle dissent from those who speak out in an effort to change the political system. Political, military, and religious power often rests in the hands of one individual or a small group that often heads the only political party allowed in the country. Many states, but particularly authoritarian states, rely on stirring up **nationalism** in order to obtain the loyalty and support of their citizens.

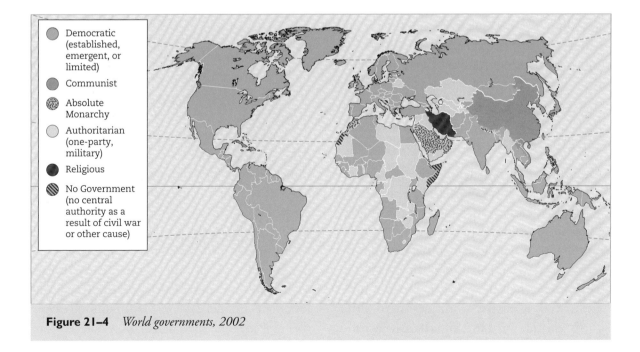

Legend:
- Democratic (established, emergent, or limited)
- Communist
- Absolute Monarchy
- Authoritarian (one-party, military)
- Religious
- No Government (no central authority as a result of civil war or other cause)

Figure 21–4 *World governments, 2002*

Figure 21–5 *A poster of President Saddam Hussein, authoritarian leader of Iraq since 1979, appears on a wall in the Shorja market of downtown Baghdad. The national leader sometimes becomes the symbol of the country's nationalism.*

A number of freedoms that we take for granted are usually missing in totalitarian states. These may include equality before the law, the freedoms of speech and association, and the freedom to create opposition parties. An authoritarian government may be an absolute monarchy, a one-party nation state, or a military-run state.

Absolute Monarchy

An absolute monarchy has no elected officials. Authority rests entirely with the monarch—king, queen, sultan, sheikh, or emir. There is no constitutional form of government, popular assembly, or independent judiciary, nor any political parties to challenge the monarch. Upon the death of the ruler, power to rule the nation state is passed from parent to child. Saudi Arabia, Jordan, Swaziland, Brunei,

Oman, and The United Arab Emirates are absolute monarchies.

One-Party Nation State

In the one-party nation state, authority rests with one political party; other parties are not allowed to exist. A charismatic leader is usually head of the political party, and runs the country in accordance with personal goals without interference from anyone else. Although some nation states have more than one political party, they may in reality be one-party states because restrictions on the opposition parties prevent them from gaining political power. Muammar al-Kadhafi of Libya, Saddam Hussein of Iraq (Figure 21–5), Robert Mugabi of Zimbabwe, Fidel Castro of Cuba, and President Colonel Taya of Mauritania are examples of leaders of one-party nation states.

Military Authoritarianism

In the military-run state, power to govern rests in the hands of one or more military leaders, who often have seized power from an elected government. Since 1960, 51 states in Latin America and central and southern Africa have experienced at least one military *coup d'état* (illegal seizure of power). In some cases, such as Algeria, Chile, Indonesia, Mozambique, Thailand, and Iraq, the military plays an influential role in running the country even though it doesn't form the government.

Religious Nation State

In a religious nation state, political power is held by spiritual leaders who follow one creed, and whose religious beliefs form the political framework of the nation state. Iran is an example of a religious nation state. The spiritual leaders in Iran provide guidance to the political parties, whose policies are formulated according to Islamic religious law (Shari'ah). Shari'ah is regarded as the expression of divine will, and is concerned not only with people's ethical standards of behaviour, but also with what they are bound to do in law. In this latter sense especially, Iran is very different from Western democracies, as well as other Islamic nation states whose people formulate the laws through their elected representatives.

Afghanistan between 1996 and 2001—when it was under the rule of the Taliban—is an example of a nation state in which extreme religious beliefs dominated the political process. Television and non-religious music were illegal; it was against the law for women to work, attend school, or appear outside the home without being completely covered. Men were required by law to wear beards. Many Muslims considered this a mistaken interpretation of Shari'ah, and in most countries where Islam is the state religion, Shari'ah has been interpreted in a way that permits a modern lifestyle.

Communist States

Communist ideology is based on the writings of 19th-century German social scientists Karl Marx and Friedrich Engels, who believed that the ruling class would be overthrown by the working class. The result of this revolution would be a classless society in which all land, capital, and means of production would be collectively owned by citizens. Many nation states call their governments "communist," but true communism as described by Marx and Engels has never been achieved.

All communist regimes share some basic characterics. **Communism** encompasses the political, economic, and social systems of all nation states that adopt it. A communist nation state is a one-party state, and only party members may run for election. In fact, voters simply reject or approve the standing party candidate. In theory, private enterprise does not exist, and a few top party leaders make all major economic decisions. They also formulate the country's laws. The government owns and operates the transportation, agricultural, television, radio, publishing, and film industries, among others. The party holds power through the use of propaganda, state-controlled education, and secret police. Public criticism of government is not permitted, and the rights of the state take precedence over those of the individual.

After World War II, communism spread to many countries throughout the world. Wherever the Soviets helped free countries from Nazi control, they set up communist governments. Germany was divided into two countries, with East Germany under the control of the Soviet Union. Czechoslovakia, Poland, Romania, Hungary, and Bulgaria had communist ideology imposed on them and became Soviet satellites. Communist nation states later developed in China, North Korea, North Vietnam, Albania, Yugoslavia, and Cuba. In each case, strong leaders ran the country as dictators.

Geopolitics and Conflict

Between the mid-1940s and the end of the 1980s, international politics were shaped to a large extent by the intense rivalry, distrust, and suspicion between two groups of countries and their differing political ideologies. These were the democratic, capitalistic United States and its allies, and the communist Soviet Union (USSR) and its allies. The United States and the Soviet Union were known as superpowers. Countries that were not formally committed to either group, or power bloc, were known as neutrals. If they were part of what was known at the time as the Third World, they were called non-aligned nations.

The Cold War

The term **Cold War** was used to describe the fact that relations between the two power blocs had deteriorated to the point of war, but without the actual occurrence of fighting. This situation was essentially the result of the basic incompatibility of the democratic and communist ideologies, combined with the international politics of power. The democratic countries charged the communist countries with spreading communism by fomenting revolution in unstable regions. The communist countries accused their rivals of **imperialism**—trade with, and exploitation of, developing countries through political and military pressure without assuming direct political control. To some degree, both charges were true, as each power endeavoured to enlarge its influence throughout the world (Figure 21–6).

After World War II, **containment** became the foreign policy of the democratic states. The object of this policy was to stop the expansionism of the Soviet Union (and communism) by containing it within its current geographical extent. The Marshall Plan, discussed in Chapter 13, and the formation of the NATO military alliance were used to stop Soviet expansion in Western Europe.

Figure 21–6 *During the Cold War, May Day celebrations in Moscow's Red Square were seen by the West as an attempt to demonstrate the superiority of the communist ideology.*

The Southeast Asia Treaty Organization (SEATO) of 1954, a defence pact, was created to protect Cambodia, Laos, and South Vietnam from communist expansion. US involvement in the Korean and Vietnamese wars was part of an effort to achieve the same purpose. US support for the *mujaheddin* (freedom fighters) in Afghanistan against the Soviet invasion between 1979 and 1989 was again an attempt to contain the USSR's expansionist policies.

The two superpowers brought the world to the brink of war in 1962. According to the Monroe Doctrine, stated by President James Monroe of the United States in 1823, any attempt by a European nation to control any nation in the Western Hemisphere would be viewed as a hostile act against the United States. This established a US **sphere of influence** in the Americas. (After World War II, the Soviet Union established its own sphere of influence in Eastern Europe.) In 1962, the Soviet Union encroached upon the US sphere of influence by placing nuclear missiles in Cuba. Fortunately, a standoff between the two sides was defused.

Rather than risk nuclear war again by facing each other directly, the superpowers began to compete in other ways. They supplied foreign aid, including technological assistance and military support, to non-aligned countries around the world. Where civil war occurred during the 1970s and 1980s (for example, in Angola, Mozambique, and in the Somali–Ethiopian War), each superpower provided money, weapons, military advisers, and sometimes "proxy" troops from other countries to opposing sides. For example, as many as 19 000 Cuban troops were deployed to support a pro-Marxist faction in Angola. In effect, each superpower was trying to enlarge its sphere of influence without an actual confrontation.

One of the most visible competitions between the Cold War combatants was the space race of the 1960s. At the time, successful space exploits were viewed as demonstrations of the superiority of one political ideology over another. In fact, Cold War geopolitics was the most significant factor behind the race to the moon. Since the Soviet Union had been the first to launch a satellite and to send a human into space, the United States was determined to put the first person on the moon. It spent huge amounts of money developing its space program, and when it succeeded in its goal in 1969, the geopolitical victory was monumental.

After the Cold War

The Cold War gave way to détente when both democratic and communist nations realized that nuclear war would probably end in disaster for both sides (see Chapter 24). With the breakup of the Soviet Union in 1990, the Cold War became a thing of the past. The former Soviet states adopted various forms of government, abandoning the command economy in a move to capitalism. Communist China realized that a certain amount of private enterprise would boost its economy, and that an increase in personal freedoms did not threaten the power of its Communist Party. It allowed private ownership of many businesses, including large, previously state-owned enterprises, such as the state oil company. Relations between communist and non-communist countries improved as the desire for increased trade grew and took precedence over political rivalry.

However, geopolitical conflicts did not end with the Cold War. In 1990, the Gulf War erupted when Iraq invaded Kuwait (see Chapter 22). Major civil wars raged in Africa throughout the 1990s and into the 21st century; those in Sierra Leone and the Democratic Republic of Congo involved many of their neighbours. India and Pakistan continued to dispute ownership of Kashmir, and there are fears that nuclear weapons might be used in this conflict. Reports of international disputes over trade policies, environmental degradation, migration, human rights, and Aboriginal self-determination have filled the news, and no doubt will continue to do so.

Chapter Questions

Knowledge and Understanding

1. What does the term geopolitics mean? Use an example to explain how it differs from politics.

2. What does the term political sovereignty mean?

3. How does the modern nation state differ from earlier empires or kingdoms?

4. Explain the role that geography played in the relationships between the United States and the Soviet Union during the Cold War.

5. Why is the UN reluctant to get involved in internal conflicts? Why is this reluctance problematic?

Thinking and Inquiry

6. a) Examine the two maps in Figures 21–3 and 21–4. Describe the changes that have occurred in the type of governments for the following regions:
   - i) South America
   - ii) Africa
   - iii) Eastern Europe and former Soviet Union
   - iv) Southeast Asia

   b) What general global trend do you think is occurring? What reasons may account for this trend?

7. Examine a political map of either Canada or the United States. Identify at least six different ways in which political boundaries have been established, and name the boundary.

8. Examine an area of the world where there is a dispute over the border. Determine:
   a) how and when the borders were created
   b) what geopolitical problems have arisen because of these borders
   c) the arguments put forward by each side to support its position in the dispute
   d) the current status of the dispute.

9. "Some nation states comprise people from different parts of the world who do not share traditions, religion, or language."
   a) Name a state that views this kind of diversity as a strength. Describe how diversity is seen as a strength.
   b) Name a state where diversity has led to conflict. Describe the form that conflict has taken.

Communication

10. Many organizations opposed to globalization feel that agreements such as NAFTA and rulings of the World Trade Organization threaten national sovereignty. Is national sovereignty lost as a result of globalization? In a group, prepare a presentation that fully supports your point of view.

11. Research a country that has an authoritarian government. Construct a chart that conveys the following information:
    a) the person or group who leads the country
    b) how they came to power
    c) how they retain power
    d) major domestic and international policies
    e) relations with other countries
    f) the nature of any opposition parties or groups.

Application

12. Quebeckers who support separatism feel that Quebec meets the criteria for being a nation state and should therefore separate from Canada. Do you think that Quebec meets the criteria for a nation state? Explain your answer.

13. Sovereign nations control what happens within their boundaries without interference from other countries. In what situations is it acceptable for a country (or group of countries) to interfere in another's sovereignty? Explain your point of view.

14. In 1992, Boutros Boutros-Ghali, the Secretary-General of the United Nations, proposed the formation of "peace enforcement units" that could act much more quickly than current peacekeeping missions. Member states would provide money that the Secretary-General could access to start a new operation. Troops would be on stand-by in countries whose governments have committed themselves to such operations, and equipment would be kept at the ready at various locations around the world.
a) What are your thoughts on Boutros-Ghali's proposals?

b) How do you think most countries would react? Explain.

15. a) Research and write a report that traces the evolution of the European Union from French politician Jean Monet's original proposal to its current structure.
b) To what extent can the European Union be called the "United States of Europe"?
c) Use past trends to predict the European Union's probable growth in the future.
d) Could the European Union become a model for other parts of the world? Why or why not?

22

Conflicts

Expectations

In this chapter, you will:

■ identify similarities and differences in the aspirations of selected regional or cultural groups

■ understand the need to respect the cultural and religious traditions of others

■ predict the geographic consequences of separation or independence for a region or cultural group

■ understand how scarcities in the distribution of resources contribute to conflict

■ analyse geopolitical relationships among countries sharing the Nile River

■ research and report on the human and ecological cost of military spending

■ understand the possibility of alternative solutions to a geographic issue

On any given day, chances are that you will see a front-page newspaper article describing armed conflict somewhere in the world. Whether conflict arises between groups within one country or between states, there is usually more than one reason for it. This is because the social, political, economic, religious, and cultural aspects of people's lives are inseparably interwoven.

The Geopolitics of Armed Conflict

Some conflicts are resolved through discussion and compromise. Frequently, however, discussion gives way to violence involving two or more armed factions seeking to gain control over governmental power, territory, or natural resources. Far too frequently, armed conflict occurs in states that can least afford it (Figure 22–1). During 2000, there were 40 armed conflicts in 35 countries (Figure 22–2, on the next page). Africa and Asia accounted for more than 75 per cent of the armed conflicts during 2000. Africa and the Middle East were considered to be the most war-torn regions because 36 per cent of the states in each region were experiencing warfare compared with 19 per cent in Asia.

Theorists have identified many causes of war. Some conflicts arise because people have dissimilar cultural outlooks, different religions, or opposing views on government. Sometimes war breaks out when one country tries to reunite its

Did you KNOW? Terrorism is not a type of conflict, but a weapon that can be used in virtually any dispute. See Chapter 23 for more information on the motives and methods of terrorism.

scattered citizens by taking control of another country. Conflict often occurs when an ethnic group tries to form a homeland. It nearly always arises when one country tries to take over natural resources that legally belong to another.

Most disputes result from the interplay of many factors. For simplicity's sake, this chapter will consider four significant underlying factors in armed conflict: culture, religion, territory, and natural resources.

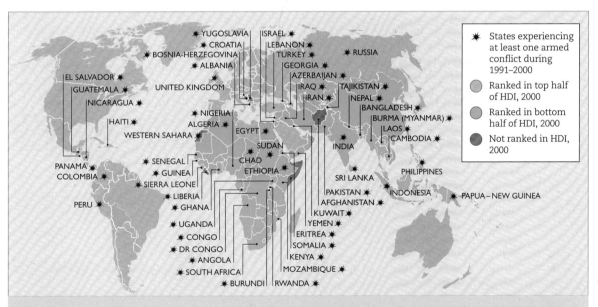

Figure 22–1 *Fourteen per cent of the states ranked in the top half of the UN Human Development Index 2000 (which ranks nations according to life expectancy, literacy, and per capita GDP) experienced armed conflicts during the period 1991–2000. Forty-five per cent of the states in the bottom half of the listing were at war during the same period.* Source: *Human Development Report 2000*; *Armed Conflicts Report* (Project Ploughshares).

Worldwide Armed Conflicts, 2000

	Number of Countries in Region	Number of Conflicts in Region	Number of Countries Hosting Conflicts	% of Countries Hosting Conflicts	% of World Conflicts
Africa	50	17	18	36%	42.5%
Asia	42	14	8	19%	35.0%
Middle East	14	5	5	36%	12.5%
Europe	42	2	2	5%	5.0%
The Americas	44	2	2	4%	5.0%
WORLD TOTAL	**192**	**40**	**35**	**18%**	**100.0%**

Figure 22–2 *A country is deemed to be involved in an armed conflict when political disagreement results in military violence in which at least 1000 people have been killed during the fighting, and which continues with a minimum of 25 deaths per year.* Source: Project Ploughshares.

Cultural Conflicts

North America, Latin America, the Middle East, Asia, and Australasia all have countries in which **indigenous** (native) **peoples** are in conflict with the national government. Indigenous groups generally seek to preserve their language and way of life. They may also demand compensation for land lost during colonization, the implementation of unfulfilled treaty agreements, and greater political autonomy. One such conflict is under way in Mexico.

Conflict in Chiapas

The Mexican state of Chiapas (Figure 22–3) is rich in natural resources. It has large oil reserves, cattle ranching, hydro-electric power, and a variety of agricultural products. In spite of these abundant resources, the indigenous people have benefited very little from the wealth produced in the state. They live in poverty and are subject to repression, both from the government and from large landowners, some of whom have private armies.

The indigenous Mayan communities want the removal of a centuries-old feudal system that has denied them their own land. They wish to protect and encourage their culture by using their own language in schools and in broadcasting. They also want more representation in the federal government and greater autonomy in governing their own affairs. As well, they are opposed to a section of the North American Free Trade Agreement (NAFTA) that removed a key

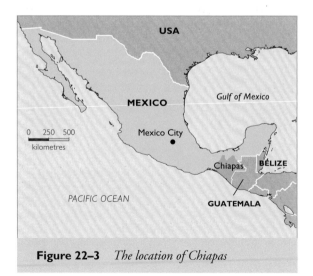

Figure 22–3 *The location of Chiapas*

element of the Mexican constitution protecting communal land holdings from privatization.

To combat these conditions, the indigenous people of Chiapas formed a small rebel group called the Zapatista Army of National Liberation. On January 1, 1994, the Zapatistas staged an armed uprising for 12 days in which 150 people were killed. An unofficial ceasefire put a stop to hostilities.

In 1996, the Zapatistas met with the Mexican government to ask for changes in government policies towards the Mayan communities. Although the meeting led to a set of peace accords, the government did not implement them. Since then, there have been repeated clashes between the Zapatistas and pro-government forces.

When the Zapatistas realized that they could not stand up to the combined power of the Mexican army, federal police, and paramilitaries, they took their case to the Internet to gain world support. Their fight has been called the world's first post-modern revolution. Mass communications technology has spread the Zapatista message, provided a forum for discussion and analysis of neo-liberalism, and acted as a vehicle for grassroots social movements to share their experiences. The Mexican government responded with a Web site of its own to counter criticism from the Zapatistas. In 1996, a Zapatista call for a series of continental and intercontinental "encounters" resulted in a meeting of over 3000 grassroots activists from 42 countries. All over the world, Web sites developed supporting the Chiapas rebellion and similar social causes.

In December 2000, the newly elected President of Mexico, Vicente Fox, renewed talks with the Zapatistas. He ordered federal troops to withdraw from trouble spots in Chiapas, freed rebel prisoners, and sent the 1996 Indian Rights Bill to Congress. This bill sought local autonomy for the indigenous peoples by proposing the adoption of their traditional government, a legal system based on village assemblies, and control over their native languages.

To learn more about the conflict in Chiapas, visit <www.pearsoned.ca/globalconnections>.

The Mexican Congress passed a watered-down version of the bill that gave state legislatures final authority on deciding which customs should become law. It also amended a part of the agreement that would have given the Mayans communal rights to land and natural resources. (The final version gave them preference, but not sole rights.) Conservatives in the government are rumoured to have made these changes because they feared the bill would hurt the interests of large landowners in the region. The Zapatistas rejected the new agreement. President Fox pledged that he would pursue efforts to get the bill approved.

The Zapatistas are one of many examples of indigenous peoples seeking protection of their heritage, greater autonomy, and recognition of the value of their way of life. They have been more successful than many groups in garnering international attention and support because they shifted their emphasis from arms to words, using modern telecommunications.

Religious Conflicts

Religion is one of the most powerful forces in the world. It provides individuals with spiritual guidance, and in many countries forms the basis for secular law. It unites people through common beliefs and experiences. It can also divide those within a nation, create mistrust between nations, and serve as the basis for war.

Dispute over Kashmir

In 1947, when the British government granted independence to India, it partitioned the Indian subcontinent into two nation states: the predominantly Muslim country of Pakistan and the predominantly Hindu country of India. Over

10 million people migrated to take up residence in the country in which their religion was dominant. More than a million people were killed as Muslims and Hindus, fearful and distrustful of each other, scrambled for safety.

Caught between India and Pakistan was the princely state of Kashmir (Figure 22–4). Despite some uncertainty on the part of his mostly Muslim population, Kashmir's Hindu maharaja led his state into union with India. Pakistan then took up arms to wrest Muslim Kashmir away from India. When the United Nations intervened in January 1949, it called for a **plebiscite** that would allow Kashmiris to choose which country they wanted to join. It also established a ceasefire line dividing the territory. More than 50 years later, a plebiscite has still not been held, and the line has become the de facto border between Indian Kashmir and Pakistani Kashmir.

Fierce gun battles across the border continue between Indian government forces and Pakistani troops, despite agreements signed by both sides to end the dispute by peaceful means. India accuses Pakistan of supporting Islamic insurgents in acts of terrorism on its side of the border; Pakistan maintains that it provides only moral and political backing to freedom fighters who want political autonomy for their Muslim cousins in Indian Kashmir.

Pakistan has insisted that the problem could be resolved if the plebiscite that the UN originally recommended were held. India disagrees because, although the Indian state of Jammu and Kashmir (with its Hindu majority), including Ladakh (with its Buddhist majority), would likely vote to stay in India, the large Muslim population of Azad Kashmir would swing the vote in favour of union with Pakistan. The original UN recommendation for a plebiscite does not offer a third option that might appeal to many Kashmiris—independence from both countries.

The chances seem remote of resolving the competing claims of **self-determination** and

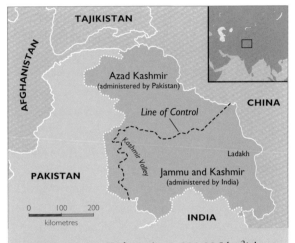

Figure 22–4 *Kashmir (area, 222 236 km^2) has been the subject of a dispute between India and Pakistan since 1947.* Source: *The Economist.*

sovereignty. Would either side accept the line of control as a permanent border? Would Pakistan allow a plebiscite by region rather than by the state as a whole, so that the Hindu and Buddhist areas could remain in India? Even if this were a possibility, what would happen to the Muslim-dominated Kashmir Valley in the mainly Hindu region of Jammu? Finally, would India and Pakistan allow a plebiscite that offered a third option, namely, independence for Kashmir? Future events will answer these questions. The fear is that tensions will escalate into a full-scale war—a prospect that has become all the more chilling as both sides have had nuclear weapons since 1998.

Territorial Conflicts

Among the various reasons why groups of people fight one another, one of the most common is control of territory. Wars may be fought over territory that contains natural resources or offers a strategic location. Conflict often arises when two or more groups wish to occupy the same territory. The Israeli–Palestinian conflict demonstrates some of the issues associated with territorial conflict.

The Israeli–Palestinian Conflict

For more than 80 years, a conflict has raged in the Middle East as Jews and Palestinian Arabs have each sought to build a nation state on one small, disputed piece of land.

Until the end of World War I, the whole of Palestine, an area that extended east and west of the Jordan River, was part of the Ottoman (Turkish) Empire. After the war, the area of Palestine west of the Jordan River was governed by Britain on behalf of the League of Nations. In the 1920s and 1930s, Britain began to admit a limited number of Jewish immigrants fleeing persecution in Nazi Germany and Eastern Europe. Palestinian Arabs opposed the idea of a Jewish homeland in Palestine.

When several hundred thousand Jewish survivors of the Holocaust sought to enter Palestine after World War II, Britain referred the question of the creation of a Jewish state to the United Nations. In 1947, the UN recommended the partition of Palestine into separate Arab and Jewish areas, with Jerusalem an international city. The Arabs rejected the decision, and fighting immediately broke out. When the Jews declared the independent state of Israel on May 14, 1948, the fighting escalated to war between the new nation and its neighbours Egypt, Syria, Lebanon, and Iraq.

The UN arranged a **ceasefire** in 1949, by which time Israel held more territory than it did in 1947. The area to the west of the Jordan River (known as the West Bank) and half of Jerusalem were under Jordanian rule, while a small strip of land on the Mediterranean Sea known as Gaza was ruled by Egypt. The Palestinian Arabs were left with no land of their own in the former Palestine. Hundreds of thousands were displaced and forced into the West Bank and Gaza, while thousands more became refugees in other countries in the Middle East (Figure 22–5).

In 1967, President Nasser of Egypt ordered the UN peacekeeping troops to leave Gaza and

Figure 22–5 *Israel's changing boundaries*

the Sinai Peninsula. Believing it was about to be attacked, Israel struck first. Within six days, Israeli forces had taken the Sinai Peninsula from Egypt, East Jerusalem and the West Bank from Jordan, and the Golan Heights from Syria in what became known as the Six-Day War. Israel now occupied land that was home to over a million Arabs. Israel's leaders stated that it would not withdraw from the occupied territories until all the neighbouring states recognized Israel's right to exist.

After the Six-Day War, the Palestinian Liberation Organization (PLO), a federation of Palestinian groups founded in 1964 to establish an Arab homeland in Palestine, launched a series of **guerrilla** attacks against Israel. Israel answered with raids against PLO camps in neighbouring Arab countries, setting off a long-lasting cycle of hostility.

At the same time, some important steps have been taken in the quest to find a peaceful solution to the problems of the area. In 1973, war broke out once more between Israel and its neighbours. But in 1977, President Anwar Sadat of Egypt travelled to Israel to present a plan for a lasting peace settlement. The following year, Sadat and Prime Minister Menachem Begin of Israel met with US President Jimmy Carter at Camp David. The result was the Camp David Accord, in which Israel returned the Sinai Peninsula to Egypt in return for Egypt's recognition of Israel's right to exist. Sadat and Begin were awarded the 1978 Nobel Prize for Peace. In 1979, the peace treaty was signed, but in 1981, President Sadat was assassinated by Egyptian extremists who opposed the treaty with Israel.

The peace process stalled over difficult issues, including the recognition of Israel, the status of Jerusalem, dismantling of Israeli settlements in occupied territory, security measures and territorial borders. In 1987, after 20 years of frustration from rising unemployment and life under Israeli control, the Palestinians in the occupied territories launched an *intifada* (Arabic for "uprising"). Public demonstrations, riots, rock-throwing, boycotts of Israeli products, and attacks against Israeli settlements drew a military response from Israel. The *intifada* continued for two years. In the meantime, the PLO had formally recognized Israel's right to exist. In 1991, an international peace conference was held in Madrid, and negotiations began between Israel, the Palestinians, Jordan, Syria, and Lebanon. In turn, these led to secret Palestinian-Israeli negotiations in Oslo, Norway. The result was an agreement in 1993 that included mutual recognition, limited self-rule in the West Bank and Gaza, and provisions for a permanent treaty resolving the status of Gaza and the West Bank. (An Israeli-Jordanian peace treaty was subsequently signed in 1994). Israeli Prime Minister Yitzhak Rabin and PLO Chairman Yasser Arafat sealed the agreement with a historic handshake at the White House.

Arafat established limited Palestinian self-rule in Gaza (and parts of the West Bank) in 1994. The Palestinian Authority took control over education, culture, tourism, health, and taxation. In response to this turn of events, Prime Minister Rabin was assassinated in 1995 by a right-wing Israeli extremist who was opposed to making territorial concessions to the PLO. Nevertheless, the peace process continued, with the US acting as a broker. By 2000, a deal had been proposed whereby Israel agreed to return most of the occupied territories to the Palestinians. Yet the challenges were complex, negotiations broke down, and by 2000 a new *intifada* had begun.

The Issue of Water

The water of the Jordan River and its tributaries is shared by Jordan, Israel, Syria, and the occupied West Bank. Water is scarce in this desert region, and is becoming more so because of rapidly growing populations, increased industrialization and agricultural activity, and excessive use of groundwater supplies. Israel, the region's largest consumer of water, is using groundwater at an unsustainable rate even though it has developed drip irrigation and other water conservation techniques. The quality of the water in the coastal aquifer is deteriorating because of pollution, and over-pumping

Figure 22–6 *Settlement on the shores of the Sea of Galilee, Israel's greatest source of water.*

has allowed seawater to seep in from the Mediterranean Sea.

Water has been a disputed resource. In 1964, Syria tried to prevent the waters of the Jordan reaching Israel, resulting in several border disputes. After 1967, the Arabs were prevented from sinking wells over the mountain aquifer that supplies water to the West Bank. In later years, because of advanced technology, Israeli wells were drilled deeper, often causing the Arab wells to become dry. Partly as a result, irrigated Arab farmland declined, and the economic effects contributed to the *intifadas* of 1987 and 2000.

One of the demands Israel attaches to returning the Golan Heights to Syria is a guarantee of the supply of water that flows from the Heights into Israel's greatest source of surface water, the Sea of Galilee (Lake Kinneret) (Figure 22–6). Clearly, reaching an agreement on the sharing of water is a high priority.

It is interesting to note that in the 1980s, when political contact between Israel and Jordan was non-existent, officials from both countries met secretly at a picnic table beside the Yarmuk River to discuss the allocation of the river's water.

This "picnic-table diplomacy" suggests that water will remain an important issue in any future negotiations in the area.

Conflicts over Natural Resources

Disputes over natural resources are often at the heart of wars and civil strife. The combination of global industrial development and population growth increases pressure on natural resources, particularly finite resources. These resources are not evenly distributed over the Earth, and there are often conflicting claims over their ownership and exploitation. In this section we will examine the conflict over oil during the Gulf War and a possible cause for future wars—water.

The Gulf War (1990–1991)

Iraq and Kuwait are Arab countries in the Middle East located at the head of the Persian Gulf (Figure 22–7). The Middle East has approximately three-fifths of the world's known oil reserves, and export of this oil around the world

To learn more about the Gulf War, go to
<www.pearsoned.ca/globalconnections>.

has greatly enriched the economies of Iraq, Kuwait, and Saudi Arabia.

By 1990, Kuwait was exporting two million barrels of oil a day and amassing spectacular wealth from its foreign investments of oil revenues. Iraq, on the other hand, had suffered reduced oil exports, crippling debt in the range of $30 billion, and a depressed economy as a result of a devastating eight-year war with Iran. It had spent 10 years' worth of oil revenues in building up a huge army and an arsenal of sophisticated weapons, ostensibly to defend itself against Iran. In August 1990, Iraq's president, Saddam Hussein, ordered the invasion and occupation of Kuwait with the apparent aim of acquiring that nation's large oil reserves.

Hussein justified his invasion by stating that Kuwait was an artificial state carved from Iraq's natural coastline by the British and French during colonial times. Kuwait's strategic position blocked Iraqi access to the Gulf coast. Furthermore, Kuwait would not negotiate over two islands in the Persian Gulf where Iraq would be able to build deep-water ports. Hussein accused Kuwait and other Persian Gulf countries of conspiring with the United States to hold down the cost of oil by increasing oil production. He also accused Kuwait of encroaching on Iraqi territory and illegally pumping crude oil from the Ar-Rumaylah oilfields that straddled their border. He was angry that Kuwait, along with Saudi Arabia and other Gulf emirates, would forgive only a portion of the $30 billion that he had borrowed during the Iran–Iraq war, and that Kuwait and Saudi Arabia would not give Iraq an additional $30 billion in new grants.

Within days of the invasion, the United States, the UN, the European Community (now the European Union), most members of the Arab

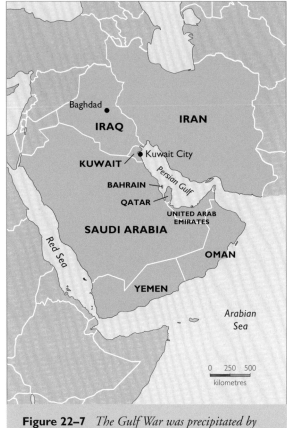

Figure 22–7 *The Gulf War was precipitated by Iraq's invasion of Kuwait.*

League, and even the Soviet Union had agreed to impose an embargo on Iraq. (The Soviet Union was seeking economic assistance from the West that it believed would not be forthcoming if it supported Iraq.) Both the United States and Saudi Arabia believed that Saudi oilfields located on the western coast of the Persian Gulf were vulnerable to Iraqi aggression.

The United Nations gave Saddam Hussein until January 15, 1991, to pull out of Kuwait. Hussein ignored the UN **ultimatum**, and on January 16, 1991, a massive air strike was launched against Iraqi forces. This was followed by an Allied ground offensive a few weeks later. By February 28, Iraqi resistance had collapsed, and a ceasefire was declared. Between 8000 and 10 000 Iraqi soldiers and about 300 Allied soldiers were killed in the conflict.

Water Conflicts

Canada has plenty of fresh water, but this is not the case in many other parts of the world, particularly where water resources are shared among several countries. By 2050, 3.5 billion people will be affected by water shortages, thus creating conditions for conflicts over water.

Forty per cent of the world's people depend on river systems that are shared by two or more countries. Moreover, many of the world's aquifers cross international borders. Conflict has already arisen between the United States and Mexico over water in the Colorado River, between India and Bangladesh over the Ganges River, and among some of the European countries that take water from the Danube River.

Some countries that do not share water resources will not have enough fresh water to meet their needs as their populations increase. China, for example, with 21 per cent of the world's population, has access to only 7 per cent of the world's fresh water.

If global warming brings increasing droughts to countries with shared water resources, to what lengths will they go to obtain the water they need to survive? Arid countries in North Africa and the Middle East have an especially high potential for conflict over this valuable resource.

The Nile Basin

The Nile River and its tributaries supply nine countries with water. Egypt, with its large and rapidly growing population, is the last of the nine countries through which the Nile flows before it enters the Mediterranean Sea (Figure 22–8). Since Egypt has a limited amount of groundwater, it reuses agricultural drainage and recycles treated municipal wastewater. Nevertheless, it still depends almost entirely upon the Nile for its water supply.

In 1959, an agreement between Egypt and Sudan allocated 55.5 billion cubic metres (bcm)

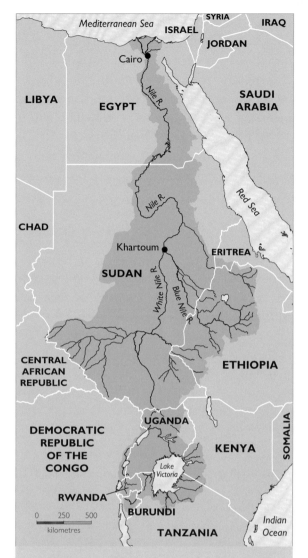

Figure 22–8 *The headwaters of the Nile River originate in countries to the south of Egypt. Eighty-six per cent of the water comes from the Blue Nile, which flows from Ethiopia through Sudan. The White Nile, originating in Lake Victoria, supplies the remainder.*

of Nile water per year to Egypt. By 1990, Egypt needed over 63 bcm. The difference was made up from underground sources in aquifers under the Sahara Desert and from recycled supplies. By 2000, the country needed over 69 bcm. It was obvious that efforts to supply water could not keep pace with the demand.

Egypt had already diverted so much water out of the Nile that very little remained to flow into the Mediterranean. When a plan to build a canal to carry more water into the Nile collapsed owing to war in Sudan, Egyptian hopes for an increased water supply were dashed. Then, in 1990, Egypt blocked a loan from the African Development Bank to Ethiopia, which wanted to use the money to build a dam on the Blue Nile. Conflict is almost inevitable if Ethiopia decides to develop the headwaters for its own irrigation and hydroelectric needs, thereby reducing the flow of water downstream in Egypt. And yet, Egypt is currently developing new projects to irrigate parts of the desert for new settlements, farms, and industries. Where will it obtain the additional water needed to make the "desert bloom"?

The Cost of Conflicts

"Every gun that is made, every warship launched, every rocket fired represents, in the final analysis, a theft from those who hunger and are not fed, who are cold and not clothed."
—President and former General Dwight D. Eisenhower

Military Expenditures

Many governments spend a significant proportion of their budget on defence items such as arms purchases, training and support of military personnel, and research and development for battle equipment. If both industrialized and developing countries spent just a fraction of this money on health care, education, and environmental and economic development programs, then living standards of citizens, especially the disadvantaged ones, could improve significantly (Figure 22–9). The guns-or-butter analogy illustrates this reality. Because the "economic pie" is only so big, countries have to decide where they

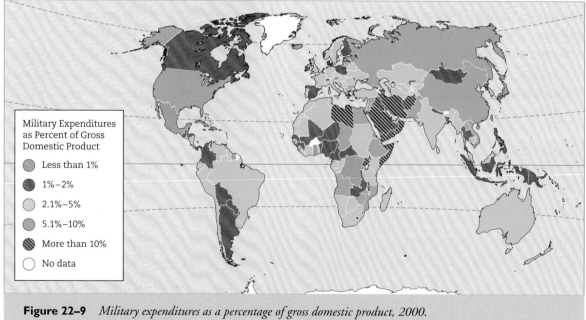

Figure 22–9 *Military expenditures as a percentage of gross domestic product, 2000.*
Source: The McGraw-Hill Companies.

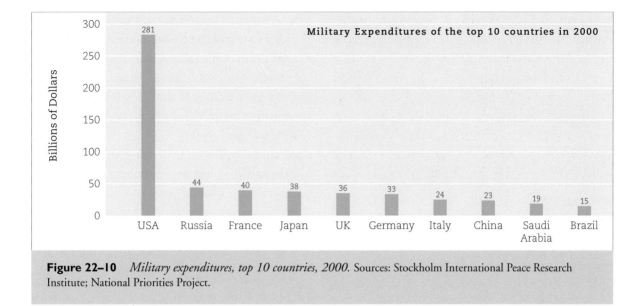

Figure 22–10 *Military expenditures, top 10 countries, 2000.* Sources: Stockholm International Peace Research Institute; National Priorities Project.

will spend their money: on military concerns (guns) or social programs (butter).

Worldwide military expenditure declined from $1.2 trillion to $810 billion in the period from 1985 to 1999 as a result of the end of the Cold War in 1990 (Figure 22–10). This saving in military spending has been called the **peace dividend**. Subsequent world events, however, have prevented the peace dividend from being used for social concerns. Governments have used the money to reduce their budget deficits and the effects of economic recession. Some have used it to fund security measures to defend themselves from terrorist attacks.

In developing countries, expenditures have risen considerably. If we examine the countries that spend the greatest percentage of their GDP on military expenditures, an interesting pattern emerges. Military expenditures are the greatest in countries that can least afford them. Economic loss is compounded because the large percentage of the workforce engaged in military activities reduces the person-hours that could normally be devoted to building the civilian economy.

The world's leader in military spending is the United States, with expenditures over $281 billion in 2000. The Pentagon has requested over $324 billion from Congress for 2002 because of the terrorist attacks of September 2001 (see Chapter 23). Following the US lead, other countries are likely to follow by increasing their military spending.

Trade in arms is a multibillion dollar industry. In 1999, for example, about US$51.6 billion in arms was traded (Figure 22–11). Arms imports in developing countries accounted for 43 per cent of this total value, and this trade is growing. With the end of the Cold War, weapons dealers were anxious to find new markets for their products. Besides the economic gains, dealer countries have political reasons for selling arms. Supplying weapons to one country and not another can shift or maintain the balance of power to the advantage of the selling country. Some countries may sell arms to support a "friendly" government that may face political opposition within its borders or from its neighbours. Such is the case with the United States and Saudi Arabia. The US protects its oil interests in Saudi Arabia by selling arms to the present regime, which may use them to suppress dissenting elements within the country.

Location	Arms Imports (US$ millions)	Arms Exports (US$ millions)
Total	$51 710	$51 710
Developed countries	$29 470	$49 735
Developing countries	$22 240	$1 975
Canada	$1 000	$550
United States	$1 600	$33 000

Figure 22–11 *Developing countries, which can least afford them, are a major destination for arms.*
Source: US Department of State.

Impact on the Environment

The destructive impacts of armed conflict on public buildings, transportation routes, and private property are all too obvious. What is less apparent is the damage that occurs to the environment during modern-day warfare. This includes:

- degradation of the ozone layer from the effects of burning aircraft fuel
- destruction of habitats, plants, and animals owing to shell explosions, movement of tanks and personnel carriers, construction of fortifications and airstrips, and placement of landmines

Did you KNOW? Loud noises from low-flying training flights over areas of northern Canada have adversely affected wildlife in the hunting grounds of the local Innu population.

- severe strains on the water and land resources of regions receiving war refugees
- contamination of the world's oceans by unexploded bombs (some of them nuclear) and weapons dumped at sea
- sabotage of natural resources (water, oil, forests, farmland)
- contamination of soil and groundwater by underground nuclear testing and disposal of military toxic waste such as herbicides, spent tanker oil, and machine lubricants
- toxic substances released into the environment through the bombing of industrial complexes.

One of recent history's most devastating environmental catastrophes occurred during the Gulf War. The movement of tanks and other vehicles, exploding shells, and the creation of huge minefields in western Kuwait severely damaged the landscape, soil, and fragile desert habitats of plants and animals. The deliberate destruction by Iraq of most of Kuwait's oil wells, refineries, and storage depots spewed 60 million barrels of oil onto the land. The effects of contamination on the soil and groundwater remain undetermined. Three hundred "oil lakes" covered 49 square kilometres, and an oil mist carried by wind contaminated over 700 square kilometres, altering temperatures and rainfall.

Smoke from burning oil wells covered vast areas of the Gulf region (Figure 22–12). Tonnes of pollutants from burning oil caused black snow to fall as far away as Kashmir. Oil discharged into the Persian Gulf contaminated 460 km of Saudi Arabia's northern coast, and killed over 30 000 seabirds. Even the saltwater spray used to douse oil fires added another dimension to the environmental damage.

It is significant that the United Nations Security Council resolved that Iraq is liable for all direct damage to Kuwait's natural habitats. Making countries pay might deter future combatants from committing environmental crimes.

Figure 22–12 *Kuwaiti refugees head towards Kuwait City from the Iraqi border during the Gulf War, 1991. On the horizon are burning oil wells.*

What Will Happen Next?

The human, environmental, and economic costs of armed conflicts are enormous. They consume huge amounts of money that could be spent in solving the world's most pressing problems. The Nuclear Age Peace Foundation lists some of the problems that could be addressed if only 30 per cent of the world's annual military expenditure were redirected to peaceful pursuits (Figure 22–13).

During your lifetime, will Earth continue to be embroiled in armed conflict, or will you and other young people around the world make a more peaceful Earth with a sustainable future?

- Eliminate starvation and malnutrition ($19 billion)
- Provide shelter ($21 billion)
- Remove landmines ($4 billion)
- Build democracy ($3 billion)
- Eliminate nuclear weapons ($7 billion)
- Relieve refugee crisis ($5 billion)
- Eliminate illiteracy ($5 billion)
- Provide clean, safe water ($10 billion)
- Provide health care and AIDS control ($21 billion)
- Stop deforestation ($7 billion)
- Prevent global warming ($8 billion)
- Stabilize population ($10.5 billion)
- Prevent acid rain ($8 billion)
- Develop renewable energy sources ($17 billion)
- Stop ozone depletion ($5 billion)
- Prevent soil erosion ($24 billion)

Figure 22–13 *For approximately $174.5 billion, which is approximately 22 per cent of annual world military expenditures, all of the above could be accomplished.*
Source: Adapted from Information from NuclearFiles, a project of the Nuclear Age Peace Foundation.

To learn more about environmental damage caused by war, go to
<www.pearsoned.ca/globalconnections>.

Chapter Questions

Knowledge and Understanding

1. a) Why did the Zapatistas revolt against the Mexican government?
   b) What is the current status of this dispute?
   c) What is the message that other groups fighting against a much more powerful adversary can learn from this dispute?

2. a) Draw a timeline to show the major events of the Israeli–Palestinian conflict.
   b) What has happened in this dispute since the time this book was published?

3. a) Why did Iraq invade Kuwait in 1990?
   b) Why might disputes over natural resources become more prevalent in future?

Thinking and Inquiry

4. Sometimes resources become the tool by which a war can be financed. Examine how a resource, such as diamonds, can be used in this manner.

5. Select a river system (such as the Indus, Colorado, or Tigris–Euphrates).
   a) Draw a map of the river system, showing the conflicting political jurisdictions.
   b) Describe the use that is made of the river's water.
   c) What disputes or conflicts have arisen?
   d) What is the current status of the disputes or conflicts?

6. Investigate the separatist disputes that exist (or have existed) in the following areas. For each, indicate the nature of the dispute and the current status.
   a) Basque region of Spain
   b) East Timor, Indonesia
   c) southern Philippines
   d) Sri Lanka

7. What controls, if any, do you think should be placed on weapons manufacturing and distribution? Explain your reasoning.

8. "In 1995, the vice-president of the World Bank stated that wars in the next century [the 21st] would be fought over water." What are your views on this statement? Use examples to support your views.

9. a) What is meant by the phrase "guns or butter"?
   b) Describe how the conflict between "guns" and "butter" has affected Canada's budgeting and foreign policy since the early 1990s.

Communication

10. You are a newspaper reporter who is investigating a dispute between an indigenous group and the government of a country, province, or state. (For example, in Canada there are disputes in Burnt Church, New Brunswick, and Davis Inlet, Labrador. Globally, there are disputes in many countries, such as the United States, Brazil, Australia, and Nigeria.) Write a short report about the dispute of your choice in which you examine the key issues, how they are being addressed, and the current status.

11. a) The Zapatista revolt has been called the "first post-modern revolution" because of the significant role played by the Internet in helping the Zapatistas fight a much more powerful adversary. Investigate the Web sites at <www.pearsoned.ca/globalconnections> to see how the Zapatista used the Internet.
    b) Investigate other conflicts to see how the Internet is being used in them.

Application

12. A number of political groups, such as the Tamil Tigers, Palestinian Liberation Organization, and Irish Republican Army, raise money from expatriates around the world. Some countries have banned fundraising by such groups because of their terrorist activities. How should Canada deal with fundraising by such groups?

13. India and Pakistan have come very close to another war over Kashmir, with the potential for a nuclear conflict. Your group is a UN delegation sent to the region to negotiate a resolution to this dispute. Use information in the text and from other sources to write a 500-word report outlining the measures you recommend to resolve the conflict.

14. Landmines are used in many conflicts around the world. Research the issues surrounding their use under the following headings:
    a) why and how landmines are used
    b) countries in which landmines are used (How many are in each?)
    c) impact of landmines on
       i) people
       ii) the economy
       iii) the environment
    d) global efforts to remove landmines
    e) countries that have not signed the treaty banning landmines (What are their reasons for not signing?)
    f) ways of persuading countries that have not signed the treaty to stop producing and using landmines

15. Examine Figures 22–1 and 22–9.
    a) Which of the countries that spend 5.1 per cent or more of their GDP on military expenditures have not experienced armed conflict between 1991–2000? Why might they spend so much of their GDP on the military?
    b) Which of the countries that spend 5.1 per cent or more of their GDP on military expenditures experienced armed conflict between 1991–2000? Why might they continue to spend so much of their GDP on the military?
    c) Why do you think so many countries that have experienced armed conflict between 1991–2000 are ranked in the bottom half of the HDI?
    d) In which regions are military expenditures particularly high? What does this reflect?

16. Identify one of the conflicts shown in Figure 22–1 and determine:
    a) key issues in the conflict (include both historical and more recent causes); positions taken by the opposing forces; current status of the conflict; whether other countries are involved, and if so, why and in what capacity; what impact the war is having on the people and their economy.
    b) Write a report on your findings, including what the world community is doing to resolve the dispute. Are these efforts helping to resolve the conflict? What suggestions would you offer?

17. The Nuclear Age Peace Foundation asks the question: "What if we had a concept of security that was not conceived of by the military … [but] in terms of food, a clean environment, health care, education, and other simple ways to improve the human condition?" Do you think this concept is viable? If so, explain how it could be implemented. If not, explain your views.

18. Using information from this chapter and other sources, write a 500-word essay discussing this statement: "Those who make peaceful revolution impossible will make violent revolution inevitable." —US President John F. Kennedy

23

The Globalization of Terrorism

Key Terms

terrorism
state (institutional) terrorism
state-sponsored terrorism
weapons of mass destruction
chemical terrorism
bioterrorism
nuclear terrorism
counterterrorism
civil liberties

Expectations

In this chapter, you will:

■ identify ways in which countries and regions are becoming increasingly interdependent

■ identify current global sustainability issues and environmental threats

■ identify how individuals have made a significant contribution to addressing global issues

■ analyse the changing geopolitical role of the United States in confronting terrorism

■ distinguish between fact and opinion in information sources

■ analyse how the media influence public opinion on geographic issues

Image above: A man grieves over photos of people missing after the collapse of the World Trade Center.

On September 11, 2001, hijackers crashed two airplanes into the 110-storey towers of the World Trade Center in New York City. A third plane hit the Pentagon in Washington, DC; a fourth crashed in a field in Pennsylvania. At least 2500 people died, and the economic damage was estimated at more than $150 billion. The attacks, which were directed at symbols of US power and the Western economy, were linked to an extremist Islamic group called al-Qaeda.

What Is Terrorism?

The events of September 11, 2001, put **terrorism** on the front pages of newspapers around the world. But while terrorism is news, there is nothing new about terrorism. It has existed for centuries.

How would you define terrorism? Surprisingly, there is no generally accepted definition of the term; not even the various departments and agencies of the US government can agree on one.

Examining one definition will illustrate the difficulty. In 1937, the League of Nations declared terrorism to be "all criminal acts directed against a State and intended ... to create a state of terror in the minds of particular persons ... or the general public." This may seem like a reasonable definition, but by modern standards, it is inadequate in several respects. For example, terrorism today often targets not just governments, but also individuals, companies, religious groups, and those who oppose governments. The definition also ignores the fact that the threat of violence can be almost as effective as an actual attack. Lastly, how can we define "criminal"? An action that might be considered criminal by some may be viewed as a legitimate protest by others.

Three other definitions follow:

- Activities "directed toward or in support of the threat or use of acts of serious violence against persons or property for the purpose of achieving a political objective within Canada or a foreign state."—Canadian Security Intelligence Service (CSIS)
- "... Premeditated, politically motivated violence perpetrated against non-combatant targets by subnational groups or clandestine agents, usually intended to influence an audience." ["Non-combatant" means civilians and unarmed military personnel.]—US State Department
- "The calculated use of violence or threat of violence to attain goals that are political, religious, or ideological ... through intimidation, coercion, or instilling fear."—US Army

The last definition has several advantages. First, it is the most comprehensive, and addresses the shortcomings of the League of Nations' definition. It also broadens the motivations for terrorism, and does not limit who can be accused of it. Furthermore, it acknowledges that national governments can be guilty of terrorism.

Some authorities would agree with the US State Department's definition that terrorism is designed to "play" to a larger audience than only those immediately affected. Others would recognize that terrorist acts like those of September 2001 are not random, but are carefully orchestrated and symbolic in nature.

Geography of Terrorism

There are important geographic dimensions to terrorism. Global patterns exist because certain nations harbour terrorists, or even sponsor terrorist acts against their own people or other countries. The distribution of these countries, and the locations of major terrorist incidents, can be mapped. Another geographic aspect relates to the types of threats posed. For example, biological, chemical, and nuclear terrorism threaten natural systems, such as air and water, upon which all life depends. The causes of terrorism often have geographic origins, too. Geopolitics, globalization, economic disparity, and variations in religion and culture are all central to the study of terrorism.

Objectives of Terrorism

Terrorist acts can be carried out for a variety of reasons. Depending on the circumstances, one or more of the following objectives may apply.

- A terrorist group may be trying to attain a specific goal, such as gaining the release of a jailed colleague, broadcasting a revolutionary message, or publicizing its existence.
- Terrorists try to cause widespread fear and anxiety, hoping to break down the normal social order of the targeted population and thus improve their chances to overthrow the government or change the social order.
- Terrorist leaders may want to provoke the target government to overreact and introduce excessively harsh counterterrorism measures. By doing this, they hope to cause a majority of the population to oppose the government.
- Governments may use terrorist methods to force obedience from the general population. This type of terrorism is called **state** (or **institutional**) **terrorism**.

Figure 23–1 *Members of the group Mothers of Plaza de Mayo comfort each other as they participate in the 19th annual Resistance March in the main square of Buenos Aires, Argentina. The march is held every year to demand an accounting for the 30 000 people who disappeared during the armed forces' "dirty war" against alleged subversives in the 1970s.*

State Terrorism

The particular terrorist acts that governments use vary from country to country. In some cases, political opponents are murdered. Elsewhere, torture is used to intimidate opponents and to obtain information. In some countries, those who threaten the government just disappear (Figure 23–1). The uncertainty of their fate merely adds to the terror.

The use of state terrorism has declined considerably since the 1980s because many countries in Latin America, Africa, Eastern Europe, and Asia now have governments that are more inclined to respect human rights. Iraq has been accused of terrorist activities against its ethnic minorities, as has Israel with regard to its Palestinian population, although supporters of Iraq and Israel deny such allegations. In Burma

(Myanmar), the military government has used repressive measures against those who oppose it, including the elected leader, Aung San Suu Kyi (see Chapter 24).

In another form of institutional terrorism, a country that does not actually commit terrorist acts may instead provide a safe haven for terrorist groups. This is **state-sponsored terrorism**. An example is the role played by Afghanistan in hosting the leadership of al-Qaeda, the terrorist group responsible for the 2001 attacks on the United States. Other countries that have a record of harbouring terrorists include Iran, Syria, Libya, and North Korea. The United States has been accused of supporting regimes that are guilty of terrorism or of sponsoring terrorism, for example, by providing financial and military aid to countries such as Argentina and Chile when they were guilty of state terrorism.

Motivations for Terrorism

Human motivation is often complex, and a wide variety of reasons might draw someone to join a terrorist group. However, three types of motivation are often suggested:

- *Rational motivation.* This type of terrorist may have considered other methods for reaching a particular goal, but has abandoned them because they either involved too great a risk or were not effective. He or she balances the risks and effectiveness of a terrorist act against its costs and benefits, including whether the act is likely to create the desired level of fear without causing a backlash among the population. Backlash might cause citizens to demand the destruction of the terrorist movement.

- *Psychological motivation.* These people feel a sense of purpose in their lives that did not exist before they became terrorists. They are "true believers" in their cause, and do not consider the possibility that they might be wrong in either their goals or their methods. They consider their opponents to be evil, and this belief makes it easy to direct violence against them. Because terrorists who are psychologically motivated have absolute beliefs, disagreements within the group are not accepted. The result is that terrorist groups built on this type of motivation frequently splinter into factions.

- *Cultural motivation.* People may join terrorist groups out of fear that their most important cultural or religious values are under threat. To some, terrorism in the defence of one's culture or faith becomes not only acceptable, but a duty. It is important to note that while some members of a cultural or religious group may adopt terrorist tactics, it is generally the case that many others who share the culture or faith do not support such activities.

Freedom Fighter or Terrorist?

There is an old expression that says a lot about the nature of terrorism: *One person's terrorist is another person's freedom fighter.* A violent act can be seen by one person as a terrorist act, while to another it is a necessary step to achieve liberty or to protect one's religion or culture.

In 1988, the United States government produced the *Vice President's Report on Terrorism.* Included in this report was an extensive list of groups that the government considered to be terrorist. One of these organizations was the African National Congress (ANC), which had fought for years against the Apartheid (racial separation) policies of the government of South Africa. The report also indicated that the jailed leader of the ANC, Nelson Mandela, was a terrorist. Only five years later, Mandela won the Nobel Peace Prize for being the man responsible for the peaceful transition of South Africa from the racist Apartheid regime to the democratic government that exists today. In 2001, in recognition for his contributions to world peace, he became only the second foreigner to be given honorary Canadian citizenship (Figure 23–2).

Key to the transition of South Africa to majority rule was Mandela's decision to establish a "Truth and Reconciliation Commission." The Commission was to deal with the crimes, many of which could be considered terrorist in nature, committed by both the government and its opponents in the years leading up to the end of Apartheid. Mandela feared that a series of trials would split the new country apart and destroy its ability to function. The idea of the Commission was a generous one. People on both sides who were guilty of terrorist crimes only had to appear at the Commission and confess their crimes to be granted a pardon. While some people who had suffered from terrorist actions remained bitter that the guilty had remained unpunished, the system of pardons contributed to the peaceful transition.

Mandela was not the first person formerly labelled a terrorist to win the Nobel Peace Prize. In 1978, Israeli President Menachem Begin won the award in recognition for his efforts to establish peace between his country and Egypt. Begin first came to public notice in the 1940s as the leader of an anti-British terrorist group called the Irgun. The Irgun was best known for its bombing of the King David Hotel in Jerusalem, an attack that resulted in the deaths of 91 people. Similarly, Yasser Arafat, founder of the Palestinian Liberation Organization, has been called a terrorist leader, but he shared the Nobel Peace Prize in 1994 with Shimon Peres and Yitzhak Rabin of Israel for their efforts to create peace in the Middle East.

In the early 1950s, Jomo Kenyatta was the leader of a group in Kenya called the Mau-Mau. To create fear and destabilize the British colonial government, the Mau-Mau attacked the isolated farms of European settlers. More than 30 of these settlers were murdered in a fashion that was clearly designed to create terror. During this time, Kenyatta was described in British newspapers as a "terrorist leader." A decade later, when he was negotiating Kenya's independence from the British, the newspapers called him a "nationalist leader." Years later, as the highly respected president of

Figure 23–2 *Former South African President Nelson Mandela, accompanied by Prime Minister Jean Chrétien, shakes hands with school children after receiving honorary Canadian citizenship in a ceremony in Hull, Quebec.*

Kenya, he was frequently called on to help solve problems in other parts of Africa. During this time, the same newspapers that had called him a "terrorist" now described him as the "father of his country" and the "elder statesman of Africa."

In all these cases, terrorism is a relative concept. Perception and changing geopolitical realities affect how the violent actions of groups and individuals are interpreted.

Recent History of Terrorism

While various forms of terrorism have existed for centuries, the word "terrorism" has been used only since the second half of the 19th century. Modern terrorism began in 1968 when an Israeli airliner was hijacked by Palestinian terrorists. Modern terrorism is distinctive in two ways: playing to

the media has come to be a vital part of the planning; and, in comparison to earlier terrorist activities, little care is taken to avoid death and injury among ordinary people. For example, in the past, it was not unusual for a terrorist group to warn authorities about the placement of a bomb. Today, warnings are seldom given, and bombs are often placed to cause the maximum number of deaths.

During the 1970s, there were about 3000 acts of terrorism in the world. This number increased to about 4000 during the 1980s. Some of the more significant terrorist attacks since the beginning of the 1980s are shown in Figure 23–3.

Role of the Media

Publicity is a fundamental part of terrorism. Modern terrorists have come to understand that terrorism is really a shocking form of theatre.

You can learn more about terrorism at <www.pearsoned.ca/globalconnections>.

They have also learned how the media can be used to achieve their goals. This was clearly illustrated by a terrorist attack that occurred at the Munich Olympics in 1972 during which 11 Israeli athletes were killed. The attention of the world's media had been focussed on the Olympics in Munich, and the invasion of the Olympic Village gave the press a huge story to cover. Long after the event, the intelligence chief of the Palestinian Liberation Organization, the group

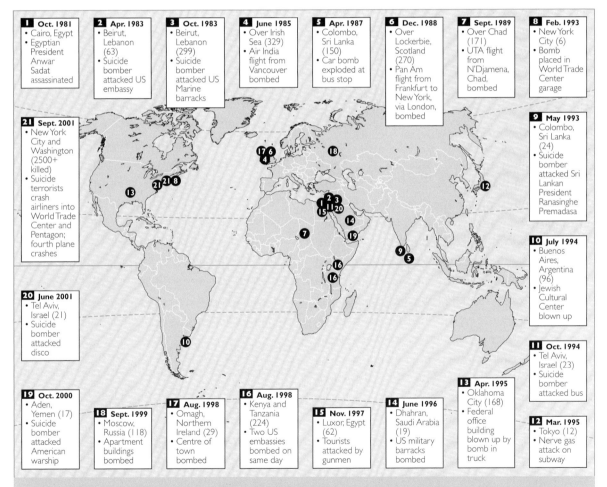

1 Oct. 1981
• Cairo, Egypt
• Egyptian President Anwar Sadat assassinated

2 Apr. 1983
• Beirut, Lebanon (63)
• Suicide bomber attacked US embassy

3 Oct. 1983
• Beirut, Lebanon (299)
• Suicide bomber attacked US Marine barracks

4 June 1985
• Over Irish Sea (329)
• Air India flight from Vancouver bombed

5 Apr. 1987
• Colombo, Sri Lanka (150)
• Car bomb exploded at bus stop

6 Dec. 1988
• Over Lockerbie, Scotland (270)
• Pan Am flight from Frankfurt to New York, via London, bombed

7 Sept. 1989
• Over Chad (171)
• UTA flight from N'Djamena, Chad, bombed

8 Feb. 1993
• New York City (6)
• Bomb placed in World Trade Center garage

9 May 1993
• Colombo, Sri Lanka (24)
• Suicide bomber attacked Sri Lankan President Ranasinghe Premadasa

21 Sept. 2001
• New York City and Washington (2500+ killed)
• Suicide terrorists crash airliners into World Trade Center and Pentagon; fourth plane crashes

20 June 2001
• Tel Aviv, Israel (21)
• Suicide bomber attacked disco

19 Oct. 2000
• Aden, Yemen (17)
• Suicide bomber attacked American warship

18 Sept. 1999
• Moscow, Russia (118)
• Apartment buildings bombed

17 Aug. 1998
• Omagh, Northern Ireland (29)
• Centre of town bombed

16 Aug. 1998
• Kenya and Tanzania (224)
• Two US embassies bombed on same day

15 Nov. 1997
• Luxor, Egypt (62)
• Tourists attacked by gunmen

14 June 1996
• Dhahran, Saudi Arabia (19)
• US military barracks bombed

13 Apr. 1995
• Oklahoma City (168)
• Federal office building blown up by bomb in truck

12 Mar. 1995
• Tokyo (12)
• Nerve gas attack on subway

11 Oct. 1994
• Tel Aviv, Israel (23)
• Suicide bomber attacked bus

10 July 1994
• Buenos Aires, Argentina (96)
• Jewish Cultural Center blown up

Figure 23–3 *Significant terrorist events have occurred all over the world. These are just a few of the thousands of such attacks. For example, there were 37 fatal attacks in Sri Lanka alone between 1986 and 1997. Note: The number of people who were killed is in brackets.* Sources: *New Internationalist*, November 2001, p. 18; Sinhaya.

responsible, gave three goals for the attack. In order of importance, these were to strengthen the sense of identity of the Palestinian people, to demonstrate to the world's press the resolve of the Palestinian people to establish a homeland (see Chapter 22), and to obtain the release of comrades who were in Israeli prisons. At the time of the attack, the only goal stated was the third.

Changing Nature of Terrorist Threats

In the past, most terrorism has involved conventional weapons such as guns and bombs. While these threats still exist, there is now the fear of more novel, and more dangerous, weapons. The use of fuel-laden airliners against New York and Washington was described as a "high-concept, low-tech" approach to terrorism. There are concerns about the use of so-called **weapons of mass destruction**—in particular, biological, chemical, and nuclear weapons.

Biological and Chemical Threats

The threat posed by **chemical terrorism** became a reality in 1995 in Tokyo. An extreme religious cult, Aum Shinrikyo, released a nerve gas, sarin, into the subway. The method of delivery used was simple. While holding their breath, cult members dropped small plastic bags containing sarin onto a train platform, broke the bags by stepping on them, and then ran away before the gas could spread. Twelve people died and more than 1000 were injured. The Aum Shinrikyo attack proved that a small group could acquire and successfully use a chemical agent.

In the weeks after the September 11, 2001, attacks on the United States, letters containing anthrax spores were sent through the mail to media outlets and government offices in the United States and other countries. It seemed that the age of **bioterrorism** had begun. The anthrax attack engendered widespread concern, and Canada, as well as many other countries, took steps to build up supplies of antidotes to biological weapons.

Of particular concern is the use of smallpox virus as a weapon in bioterrorism. For centuries, smallpox was one of the greatest scourges of humanity, but after many years of a cooperative world program of vaccination, the disease was eliminated. But because of the potential usefulness of smallpox as an agent of war, the Soviet Union developed an extensive research and development program. Since the breakup of the Soviet Union, questions remain about the whereabouts of these viruses. If some of this material has slipped into terrorist hands, it poses a serious threat, as smallpox is a highly contagious disease with a mortality rate of about 50 per cent. People in North America and Western Europe have not been vaccinated against smallpox since the early 1970s because the disease had been eliminated in these areas many years earlier. Because vaccinations done before this time may have lost their effectiveness, there have been proposals to vaccinate everyone in North America against smallpox. But there are risks to this precaution. About one person per million could die from an adverse reaction to the vaccine. This would mean that about 300 people could die to provide protection from a risk that may not even exist.

Nuclear Threats

Perhaps the ultimate terrorist threat is **nuclear terrorism**. The death and destruction that would be caused by an act of nuclear terrorism could greatly exceed that of any previous attacks. The mere threat of a nuclear attack, even if such an attack is highly unlikely, accomplishes the terrorist's goal of creating fear and uncertainty. Four main forms of nuclear threat exist.

- A terrorist group could buy an atomic bomb. There is evidence that both Aum Shinrikyo and al-Qaeda attempted to purchase a nuclear device in the former Soviet Union in the early 1990s. The proliferation of nuclear weapons in more nations, and in less stable nations, since the late 1980s increases the risk of an atomic bomb falling into terrorist hands. For example, in the mid-1990s a senior Russian security official claimed that, after the breakup of the Soviet Union, 84 nuclear "briefcase" bombs could not be accounted for. These bombs were small enough that they could be carried for short distances in a backpack and yet could kill as many as 100 000 people. This threat may have declined since these bombs have an operational life span of only five to ten years.

- A terrorist group might attempt to build its own nuclear weapon. While this undertaking would require enormous financial and scientific resources, experts say that it is not impossible. There is evidence that al-Qaeda tried to buy enough weapons-grade uranium or plutonium on the black market to make an atomic bomb, after failing to buy one. In 2001, two scientists who had worked on the construction of Pakistan's atomic weapons were arrested and charged with giving nuclear secrets to the Taliban.

- Terrorists who do not have the technical ability to make a proper atomic bomb could build a hybrid bomb in which high explosives are used to spread dangerous radioactive materials over highly populated areas. While the damage from an attack of this type would be much less than from a standard nuclear weapon, the likelihood of a group's acquiring such a weapon is greater. Not only would it be technically less difficult to build, but high-grade nuclear materials are not needed.

- Nuclear terrorism could involve blowing up a nuclear power plant to release the massive amount of radioactive materials inside. This might prove a more difficult task than it

would seem. In one test, a jet fighter flown at subsonic speeds into a section of a reactor building wall caused only minor damage on impact. The damage did not destroy the wall's integrity.

Containing Terrorism

People must feel safe as they go about their lives: working, travelling, and raising their children. Containing the threat of terrorism involves the process of **counterterrorism**. Counterterrorism can exist at a number of levels. Efforts can be made to interfere with the planning and organization of terrorism. Such efforts include maintaining a network of spies to uncover terrorist plots. This strategy is not easily achieved, since it requires agents who are willing and able to work undercover, perhaps for years, in dangerous conditions. Fighting terrorism in this way can also produce concerns about the invasion of privacy and interference with freedoms of speech and association.

In some cases, especially when terrorism is an internal or domestic problem, arrests may be possible. Sometimes, a settlement may be negotiated between the perpetrators and the government. In extreme cases, the possibility of assassinating terrorists might be considered. Again, the question is, how willing are we to compromise the principles by which we live to gain a feeling of enhanced security? Certainly, assassination is illegal in most countries.

After the 2001 attacks, the United States, supported by the countries of the West, decided to launch a military attack against Afghanistan in an attempt to eliminate both the leadership of al-Qaeda and the Taliban government that had sponsored the terrorists. After the success of this campaign, the question became, what next? Were other countries that harboured and supported terrorists to be attacked? Early in 2002, President George W. Bush identified an "axis of evil" that ed of North Korea, Iran, and Iraq as potential targets in the "war against terrorism." More problematic was the question of how to deal with terrorists and their supporters in other countries that the United States would not consider attacking, such as Saudi Arabia, Sri Lanka, and Ireland. It is likely that even Canada and the United States harbour terrorists, despite efforts to identify and arrest such individuals.

Major terrorist acts require significant funding. Some terrorist activities have been supported by expatriates who fund groups in their home country. For example, there is evidence that money has been raised in Canada for terrorist groups in countries such as Ireland, Sri Lanka, and Afghanistan. Careful monitoring of international banking systems can limit the flow of funds. Globalization both aids and hinders this measure. Financial globalization means that immense sums of money move around the globe each day; support to terrorist organizations can be hidden in this traffic. At the same time, however, technological globalization makes it easier for authorities to track these transactions.

Another approach in containing terrorism is to provide better protection for likely targets of attack. Increasing airport security is an obvious example; others are ensuring adequate protection of nuclear power plants, city water systems, and major sports facilities. Two problems emerge with this approach. One is the question of whether it is possible to protect all potential targets. The other is whether society is prepared to accept the cost of this protection, along with the resulting disruption of normal activities.

A significant concern is that the fight against terrorism is being fought by resorting to tactics that themselves suggest terrorism. For example, after the attacks on the United States in 2001, police arrested a number of people who were suspected of having links with al-Qaeda terrorists. In spite of offers of money, immunity from charges, and the creation of a new identity, these suspects refused to cooperate with police. Because of the ferocity of the September 11 attacks and the fear that future attacks were being planned, some US commentators even called for a relaxation of the rules that outlaw the use of torture in questioning suspects.

Similar concerns were expressed about anti-terrorist laws that have been introduced in many countries in response to various threats. Typically, these laws suspend some of the **civil liberties** that we take for granted; for example, strict limits on how long a person can be held by police without charges being laid, or when wire taps can be used. For some, the loss of civil liberties is acceptable in return for a higher level of security. For others, the protection of hard-won civil liberties is paramount. An additional concern is that innocent members of particular ethnic or religious groups might be deprived of their rights for no reason other than that they may have a background or appearance similar to members of a terrorist group.

Eliminating the Conditions in Which Terrorism Grows

Many feel that the best way to eliminate the problem of terrorism is to remove the conditions that cause it to develop in the first place. For example, if people feel that they have a legitimate way to address their grievances, few will resort to terror. This claim is easy to make but could prove difficult to achieve. The problems that cause terrorism are among the most varied, serious, and intractable in the world. Many of the economic, social, geopolitical, and even environmental issues that are investigated in this book contribute, to a greater or lesser extent, to the growth of terrorism. Our success in eliminating terrorism may be directly related to our success in eliminating these core causes of the problem.

Chapter Questions

Knowledge and Understanding

1. All terrorist acts are crimes, but not all crimes are terrorist acts. What is the difference?

2. What is meant by "terrorism as theatre"?

3. Describe the difficulties faced by governments who are trying to fight terrorism.

4. Using specific examples, describe some of the circumstances that might motivate terrorists.

Thinking and Inquiry

5. Terrorism experts suggest that changing communications technology has fundamentally altered the nature of terrorism twice since the late 1960s. What is the nature of these two technological changes? How has terrorism changed as a result? Why are these changes undesirable?

6. Using specific examples, explain the difference between a freedom fighter and a terrorist. Why is it sometimes difficult to make this distinction?

7. Research one of the terrorist acts described in Figure 23–3.
   a) Who carried out the attack?
   b) What happened? (Include the impact on the general population.)
   c) What were the motivations of the group that carried out the attack?
   d) Were the terrorists successful in achieving their ends?
   e) Compare your results to those of classmates. What conclusions can you draw?

Communication

8. Prepare for a debate on one of these topics.
   a) *Resolved—That the concept that one person's terrorist is another person's freedom fighter is morally acceptable.*

   b) *Resolved—That governments should use all the means at their disposal to deal with terrorism, even if this involves the restriction of constitutionally protected civil rights.*

Application

9. a) Using the characteristics of terrorism provided in the chapter, write a definition of terrorism.
   b) Apply your definition of terrorism to the 2001 attacks on the United States and to another terrorist act (or campaign). How does each of these events illustrate the elements of your definition?
   c) Look at the definition of terrorism created by another student. Could an unscrupulous government use this definition of terrorism to justify restrictions on legitimate dissent? If yes, how could this be done?

10. Investigate the following aspects of terrorist activities for one of the cases listed.
    - motivation and purpose
    - membership—who joins; size of group
    - location (country, region; urban or rural)
    - what types of criminal acts the terrorists perform and for what purpose
    - response of the state (or, in the case of state terrorism, the response of groups opposed to the government)
    - impact of the group (successes, failures, impact on general population)
    a) Colombia: narcoterrorism
    b) Peru: Shining Path
    c) Canada: October Crisis of 1970
    d) United States: ecoterrorism
    e) Spain: ETA Basque separatists
    f) another terrorist group of your choice

Working Together to Reduce Conflict

Expectations

In this chapter, you will:

■ identify methods of grouping countries and evaluate the implications of these categories

■ explain ways in which agreements may affect the environment

■ describe an international economic alliance in Africa or Asia

■ identify individuals who have made contributions to addressing global issues

■ research and report on the human and ecological cost of global military spending

■ evaluate the effectiveness of an international strategy or agreement to address global issues

■ understand technologies used in analysing and synthesizing data

The photo above shows the United Nations Security Council voting to send troops to help restore peace in one of the world's troubled regions. **Peacekeeping** has been one of the UN's most successful efforts. In 1988, UN peacekeepers were awarded the Nobel Peace Prize in recognition of their contributions worldwide.

An Exercise in Cooperation

Why is it that…

- in a world where many go hungry, others are fixated on losing weight?
- in some countries, scientists spend their days inventing new kinds of detergent to make clothes whiter, while in others, there is not enough scientific know-how to improve farming techniques?
- in wealthier parts of the world, billions of dollars are spent on cosmetics, while in developing countries, millions die from easily preventable diseases?
- in some countries, skyscrapers are brightly lit all night long, while in others, tens of millions of people live in shacks with no electricity?

Clearly, some people are able to meet every need and still have money left over for luxuries, while others cannot even meet their most basic needs. Why does this happen? Do the wealthier peoples of the world understand the difficulties faced by those who live in what is sometimes called "the majority world"? Do they care?

In this activity, you and your classmates will be the leaders of nine countries in a fictional mini-world. Your teacher will assign various countries to you. Each nation's characteristics and location are shown in Figure 24–1 on the next page.

You will notice that the population of each country is listed in the first column on the left. It can be compared directly to the amounts of the vital commodities listed for that country. For example, Country 1, with a population of 35 units, has more than enough energy to meet its needs (40 units), but is short of meeting its food needs (26 units). Country 2, with a population of 2 units, has more than enough of everything that it needs.

What you must do in the time given to you is ensure that your country has enough units of each commodity (food, social development, technology, energy, and other resources) to match (or exceed) its population. To do this you must negotiate with the leaders of the other countries. For example, if you have a surplus of technology, but a shortage of food, you may be able to make a trade with a country in the opposite situation.

If you have any questions about the rules governing these transactions, check with your teacher. Record all transactions on the chalkboard in a form similar to that shown in Figure 24–2. You can begin the exercise by deciding upon a name for your imaginary country.

Questions

1. a) Were all nine countries able to meet all their needs?
   b) If not, which ones were unsuccessful?
   c) Why were they not successful?
   d) How could this situation have been avoided?

2. Is it possible for all of the countries to reach the desired goal? Provide proof for your answer.

3. a) In what ways do the results of this exercise mirror the situation in the world today?
   b) How does this exercise differ from the real world? What do the results of this exercise suggest about the difficulty of solving international problems?

4. While the countries in this exercise are fictional, they have many similarities to real countries (or, in some cases, regions). Identify which real countries or regions may be represented by these fictional countries.

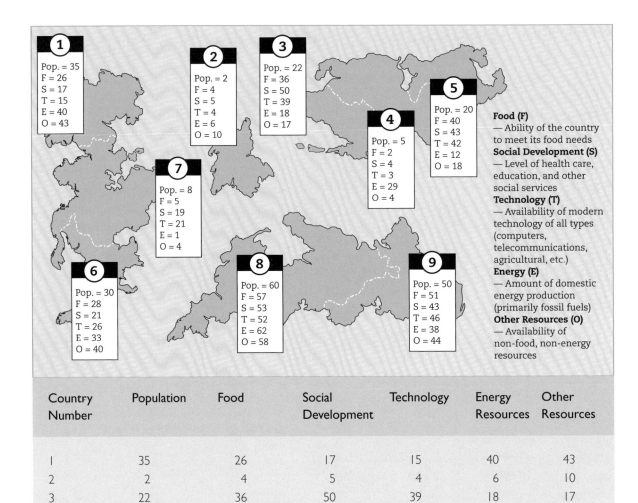

Country Number	Population	Food	Social Development	Technology	Energy Resources	Other Resources
1	35	26	17	15	40	43
2	2	4	5	4	6	10
3	22	36	50	39	18	17
4	5	2	4	3	29	4
5	20	40	43	42	12	18
6	30	28	21	26	33	40
7	8	5	19	21	1	4
8	60	57	53	52	62	58
9	50	51	43	46	38	44

Figure 24–1

Units Transferred	Of Item	From Country No.	To Country No.	In Exchange for Units	Of Item	Comments
2	Energy	1	7	3	Technology	Trade

Figure 24–2   *Use a chart like this on the chalkboard to keep track of the success of all "international" negotiations.*

Solving Problems in the Real World

The preceding activity illustrates how hard it can be for people to cooperate, even when there is little reason for them not to do so. In the real world, cooperation becomes even more complicated as nations and peoples compete for economic success and strategic advantage. In the remainder of this chapter, you will have an opportunity to consider how a variety of organizations and individuals have tried, and continue to try, to solve problems of international conflict.

United Nations

The goals and activities of the United Nations do not always receive universal approval. International cooperation, a requirement basic to the resolution by the UN of any conflict, will sometimes require countries to give up some aspect of their national sovereignty. Some countries will jealously protect their independence and national power, and will not cooperate with the UN if they consider their sovereignty threatened. Others are prepared to follow the UN's recommendations, and will surrender some of their sovereignty when they believe that cooperation offers the best hope for solving a particular issue. Although some countries feel that the UN can sometimes further their national interests, at other times they feel that it threatens them.

The UN was created in 1945 as World War II was ending. Its stated purpose was to maintain international peace and security. One of its tools is the imposition of **sanctions** on nations that are guilty of threatening peace. Three types of sanctions have been used by the United Nations:

- Least severe are verbal sanctions. When the UN imposes verbal sanctions, it is voicing the international community's opposition to an action taken by an offending country and demanding that the action stop.

- More severe are economic sanctions. All trade with the offending country is cut off, and any aid that it might otherwise receive is terminated.
- Most severe are military sanctions. Member countries provide appropriate troops to stop the transgressor and help restore peace.

How Successful Has the UN Been?

The United Nations has been most successful in its non-political role. Its many agencies, such as the Food and Agricultural Organization (FAO), International Labour Organization (ILO), and United Nations Educational, Scientific, and Cultural Organization (UNESCO), play vital roles in their particular fields of expertise.

While many dozens of local wars have been fought since 1945, a third world war has been avoided. Although we cannot say for sure that this was a result of the UN's existence, the achievement is a significant one. The possibility of nuclear annihilation was very real in the decades after 1945.

The most powerful political body in the UN is the **Security Council** because it is the body that can impose sanctions. The Council includes five permanent and 10 temporary members. The real power lies with the five permanent members: China, France, Russia (the former Soviet Union), the United Kingdom, and the United States.

Each of the permanent members has the ability to **veto** any resolution being considered by the Security Council. All five members must therefore agree before any resolution that imposes sanctions can be passed. Since unanimous agreement is difficult to achieve, the Security Council rarely takes strong action when peace and security are threatened. This was especially true in the years of the Cold War (1945–1989). During that period, the Soviet Union frequently used its veto to prevent action from being taken against itself and its allies. Over the last few decades, the United States has used the veto to protect its interests. For example, it has prevented passage of motions critical of Israel.

Peacekeeping

Peacekeeping occurs when the United Nations (and occasionally some other international agency) provides a force of soldiers, and sometimes police, to maintain order in a country or region that has experienced significant conflict. A prerequisite for peacekeeping is a ceasefire or treaty between the warring parties. The peacekeeping force exists only to encourage compliance with such an agreement. Canada is the only nation in the world that has been active in every UN peacekeeping operation (Figure 24–3).

On a few occasions, the UN has played a role in active **peacemaking**, imposing peace on warring factions by using troops under UN control.

Peacemaking has not occurred very often because it requires powerful military forces and can be very dangerous. Examples of successful efforts include the Korean War (1950–1953) and the Gulf War (1990–1991) after the invasion of Kuwait by Iraq. Less successful, by far, was a much smaller peacemaking effort in Somalia in 1993. Besides proving ineffective as an attempt to bring order to the country, the Somalia campaign was a public relations disaster for the United States. When news broadcasts across the world showed the bodies of 18 dead American soldiers being dragged through the streets of the capital city, Mogadishu, this well-publicized failure of UN peacemaking reinforced long-standing US reluctance to be involved in UN campaigns.

NATO

The **North Atlantic Treaty Organization (NATO)** has been a powerful and influential body since its founding in 1949. NATO was created as a US-led defence and security agency to counteract the threat to Western Europe posed by

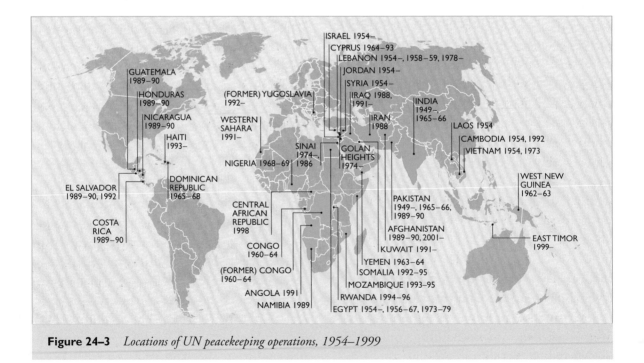

Figure 24–3 *Locations of UN peacekeeping operations, 1954–1999*

Figure 24–4 *The end of the Cold War has resulted in a realignment of military security in Eastern Europe.*

the Soviet Union and its allies. Under the NATO agreement, a threat to any member was regarded as a threat to all. Originally, NATO consisted of the United States, Canada, and 10 European states (Figure 24–4). Later, Greece and Turkey (1952), West Germany (1955), and Spain (1982) joined the alliance. In 1955, the Soviet Union and its allies created a similar military alliance, the **Warsaw Pact**, to counteract NATO.

From 1949 to 1989, the world's geopolitics came to be dominated by the Cold War (see Chapter 21). Both sides in the Cold War had overwhelming nuclear and non-nuclear military strength that deterred them from taking overt action against each other. In the case of nuclear weapons, this was described as mutually assured destruction, or the MAD principle. Neither side was prepared to use its nuclear arsenal because it knew that the enemy had sufficient power to devastate the attacker. Many observers suggest that the main reason the Warsaw Pact and the communist regime in the Soviet Union collapsed in 1989 was the sheer cost of fighting the Cold War against the much wealthier economies of the United States and its NATO allies.

With the breakup of the Soviet Union and the dissolution of the Warsaw Pact, NATO had to find a new purpose. In the early 1990s, it reinvented itself because in the "new world order" in which the United States was the only superpower, the peace and security of its members were no longer threatened by the Soviet Union and its allies. East Germany, a former Warsaw Pact nation, had become a part of NATO when it reunited with West Germany in 1990. Then in 1999, three more former Warsaw Pact nations—Poland, Hungary, and the Czech Republic—became members.

Did you KNOW? According to US experts, the Soviet Union had so many stockpiled warheads that it could have targeted three against Toronto alone: one at Pearson International Airport, a second at downtown Toronto, and a third at the Pickering nuclear plant.

The 19 members of NATO then established a special working relationship, known as the NATO+1 initiative, with Russia. They went on to create the **Partnership for Peace (PfP)**, which comprises NATO and additional countries such as former Warsaw Pact members Albania and Bulgaria, former Soviet republics Ukraine and Kazakhstan, and the traditionally neutral Western European countries of Sweden, Switzerland, and Ireland (Figure 24–5). The PfP provides a forum for discussion on a wide range of topics such as regional security, the prosecution of war criminals, international law, and the limitation of the spread of small arms. It conducts joint military exercises and provides training in peacekeeping and the removal of landmines. The hope is that communication among these nations, often former enemies, will inspire confidence and trust, and will reduce the chance of conflict in the future.

NATO has taken an active role as both peacemaker and peacekeeper in Europe. This was demonstrated by its actions in 1995 in Bosnia-Herzegovina, part of the former Yugoslavia. In the early 1990s, after the breakup of Yugoslavia, warring ethnic and religious factions threatened to plunge the Balkans into chaos. After the signing of the 1995 Dayton Accord to halt fighting in the region, NATO air forces, including Canada's, used controversial air strikes to bring the fighting to an end. Later, NATO countries provided 60 000 troops for a one-year implementation force to ensure peace. This was followed by the imposition of a smaller stabilization force that was still in the region in 2002. These forces had many functions, including defusing of conflicts, removal of landmines, collection of arms, prevention of crime, repair of roads and bridges, and cooperation with NGOs that were providing humanitarian assistance.

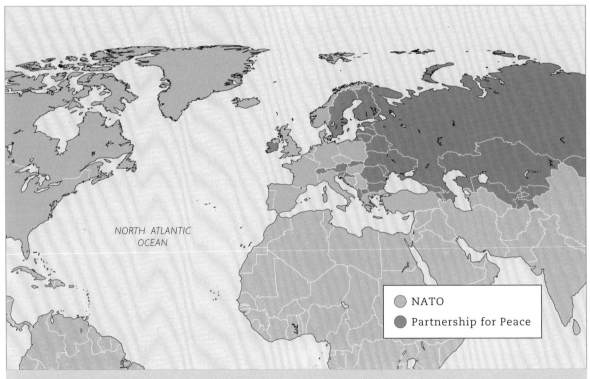

NORTH ATLANTIC OCEAN

○ NATO
● Partnership for Peace

Figure 24–5 *Together, NATO and the Partnership for Peace include many of the most economically and militarily powerful nations in the world.*

The Special Role of the United States

After its victory in the Cold War, the United States found itself in a position that is perhaps unique in history. It is the most powerful nation in the world in virtually every way: militarily, economically, and culturally. This position of power gives the United States a special place in the world, together with special responsibilities—whether Americans want them or not.

What will the US do with its power and influence? The historical record over the last century is not always promising. After World War I, a powerful "America First" lobby fought to keep the United States isolated from the rest of the world. In this, they were successful. The US did not join the League of Nations, the first world body set up to attempt to prevent war. Its absence seriously compromised the League's ability to prevent World War II.

Although the United States was a key founding member of the United Nations after the war, it soon became a somewhat reluctant participant in many aspects of the organization's work. For example, US troops have rarely participated in peacekeeping efforts, and for many years, the US government did not pay its share of the UN's operating expenses. It chose to fall behind in these payments as a way of showing lack of confidence in the way the UN worked. By not paying their dues, the Americans hoped to influence the organization's operations. In 2000, they finally agreed to pay their dues, but only if the amount they had to pay was reduced, and only if the UN agreed to the potentially dangerous principle that any member who disagreed with UN decisions had the right to withhold dues.

Frequently, the United States has chosen not to participate in international efforts to improve conditions in the world. This places it in a small minority of nations that have not agreed to a variety of international agreements, such as:

- the Kyoto Protocol to fight climate change (see Chapter 20)
- a treaty, sponsored by Canada, that forbids the use of anti-personnel landmines
- the Comprehensive Test Ban Treaty to stop all forms of testing of nuclear weapons
- a convention to outlaw the use of biological weapons
- attempts to create an international criminal court.

In simple terms, the US government, like all national governments, acts to further what it sees as the interests of the United States. For example, the US was willing to fight the Gulf War in 1991 to protect the source of much of its imported oil, but it (and other countries) did not intervene to stop the genocide that occurred in Rwanda in 1994, since Rwanda had no strategic value for the United States.

Since December 25, 1991, when the flag of the Soviet Union was lowered for the last time, the United States has been able to pursue a **unilateralist foreign policy**. That is, its government could act, at each stage, in whatever direction that suited it without worrying much about the concerns or interests of other nations. For example, the US decision not to support the Kyoto Protocol was based on the fear that meeting Kyoto targets would harm the US economy, and threaten a lifestyle that is based on the use of massive quantities of fossil fuels.

In 2001, when the US government decided that it was in the country's national interest to build a missile defence system, it rejected the Anti-Ballistic Missile Treaty that had existed with the former Soviet Union since 1972. (Details of this treaty are described in the section that follows.) Similarly, in 2002, when President George W. Bush announced that the war against terrorism would be expanded to include North

Korea, Iran, and Iraq, he knew that any such actions would not be supported by such countries as the European Union and Canada, even though they are usually American allies.

To some observers, the terrorist attacks of September 11, 2001, forced the United States to abandon its unilateralist approach. The US's need to respond to terrorism originating halfway around the world forced it to enlist the support of many nations, including some that had been former enemies. The success of the coordinated, international response to terrorism showed the United States that there are advantages to working with other nations to solve a common problem. At the same time, the US might well find this multilateral approach to be limiting, since all decisions that are made must be acceptable to its allies.

In the past, great empires, such as those of Rome and Britain, were able to act unilaterally. Today, in a globalized world, the actions of all nations are open to public scrutiny. Many people believe that the United States has a responsibility to act, not just in its own national interest, but in the best interests of all the peoples of the world. Only time will tell whether this will happen.

To learn more about the challenges facing US foreign policy after the attacks of September 11, 2001, read the essay at <www.pearsoned.ca/globalconnections>.

Role of Treaty-Making

One of the most important ways in which conflicts are resolved is through treaties among nations. Some treaties involve only two countries, and may deal with issues of local or regional significance. Others involve every country in the world and deal with fundamental issues ranging from environmental problems, such as global warming and endangered species, to cultural exchanges.

The process of treaty-making involves three stages.

- The first is negotiation, which may last for years.
- The second stage—the signing of the treaty—often happens soon after negotiations are concluded.
- The last phase is ratification (formal approval) by individual governments, which may take many years. A treaty does not come into effect until an agreed number of nations have ratified it.

The Nuclear Threat

Perhaps most important of all treaties are those aimed at preventing nuclear conflict. The complex history of nuclear treaties illustrates how difficult and time-consuming it can be for nations to agree to and implement international treaties. There are two distinct types of nuclear weapons treaties. The first type is the bilateral treaties signed by the United States and the former Soviet Union to prevent a nuclear holocaust. The second type is the international treaties undertaken to minimize the spread of nuclear weapons worldwide.

Bilateral Agreements

- *Anti-Ballistic Missile (ABM) Treaty.* This treaty, signed in 1972, forbade the parties from implementing any defensive devices that could be used to shoot down the other country's strategic missiles. Lack of defence was considered essential if the deterrent of mutually assured destruction was to work. Yet, the actions of subsequent US administrations revealed an ambivalence to the ABM Treaty. On two occasions—during the 1980s and early 1990s, under Presidents Ronald Reagan and George H. Bush—the US worked on the so-called Star Wars scheme, a space-based missile defence system, claiming that this research did not break the treaty. During President William Clinton's eight years in office (1993–2000), Star Wars was scaled back. In 2001, President George W. Bush announced that the United States was withdrawing from the ABM Treaty and would work towards building a strategic defence system. In contrast, the Russians keenly supported the ABM Treaty because they feared that they could not compete with the United States in building a weapons system capable of shooting down ballistic missiles.

- *Strategic Arms Limitations Talks (SALT).* These negotiations (SALT I, 1969–1972; SALT II, 1972–1979) were initiated to stop the growth of the nuclear arsenals of the two countries.
- *Strategic Arms Reduction Treaty (START).* This was intended as a process for reducing the size of the US and Russian nuclear arsenals (Figure 24–6). Since START I (1981–1991) was signed only five months before the breakup of the Soviet Union, it was soon necessary to make this a treaty between the United States

and the successors of the Soviet Union that inherited strategic nuclear weapons: Belarus, Kazakhstan, Russia, and Ukraine. The provisions of START II (1992–1993; ratified in 1996 by the US and in 2000 by Russia) included total elimination of these weapons from Belarus, Kazakhstan, and Ukraine, and a reduction of 30 to 40 per cent in Russia and the United States by 2001. In 2002, START III was still in the early negotiation stages. Because of the September 11, 2001, terrorist attacks, and because the US administration strongly supports a powerful military, these negotiations will probably proceed slowly. Furthermore, the United States created a problem when it introduced the notion that weapons removed by START could be mothballed rather than destroyed.

International Treaties

- *Limited Test Ban Treaty (LTBT).* Signed in 1963, this treaty outlawed tests of nuclear weapons in the atmosphere and the oceans. Underground tests were allowed only if the products of the explosion were not released into the atmosphere.
- *Nuclear Non-Proliferation Treaty (NPT).* The NPT came into effect when the US government ratified it in 1970. It requires the five acknowledged nuclear powers (the United

	START I	START II (Phase 1)	START II (Phase 2)	START III
Total strategic warheads	6000	3800–4250	3000–3500	1500–2500
MIRVed ICBM warheads	Didn't exist	1200	0	0
Heavy ICBM warheads	1540	650	0	0

Figure 24–6 *The START process focussed on reducing the total number of warheads and on eliminating the most dangerous delivery systems, MIRVed ICBMs (intercontinental ballistic missiles), to the limits shown above. A MIRVed warhead is carried by one missile but contains several nuclear devices that can be independently targeted.* Source: Adapted from Federation of American Scientists.

States, Russia, the United Kingdom, France, and China) not to share their nuclear weapons or nuclear weapons technology with other countries. Other signatories to the treaty agree not to acquire or produce nuclear weapons. They also agree to ensure that nuclear materials are not diverted from peaceful activities, such as nuclear power plants, to weapons programs. The NPT is the most widely accepted arms control treaty in history. As of 2000, 187 nations were parties to it. At that time, the only countries that had not signed were Cuba, Israel, India, and Pakistan. Of these, only Cuba has made no significant efforts to develop nuclear weapons. It is widely thought that Israel has developed nuclear weapons in a secret program, while both India and Pakistan have openly produced and tested nuclear weapons.

- *Comprehensive Test Ban Treaty (CTBT)*. The CTBT prohibits nuclear explosions of any sort. It is aimed at countries (such as North Korea and Iraq) that are thought to be developing nuclear weapons capability, and at existing nuclear powers (such as the United States and China) that might want to test new generations of nuclear devices. The 44 countries that have nuclear weapons—or, like Canada, significant peaceful nuclear capabilities—are listed in Annex 2 to the treaty. All Annex 2 countries must sign and ratify the treaty before it comes into effect. By 2001, 41 of these nations had signed the treaty; 30 had ratified it. India, Pakistan, and North Korea had not signed. Among those that had signed, but not ratified, were the United States and China. These significant gaps indicate that considerable work remains to be done before this important treaty comes into effect.

- *START IV.* The ultimate phase of the START process moves strategic arms limitation beyond the realm of the two great nuclear powers. It will not be pursued until after START III is negotiated and ratified. Since START III is proceeding very slowly, the outlook for START IV is hazy at best.

The Role of Individuals

The cause of world peace is served by the actions of countless organizations and individuals. Millions of people all over the world agree that we can do a better job of promoting peace and reducing economic and social disparity. They lobby their governments to support policies that will reduce global conflict and improve the lot of all people. They also give their time and their money to support the efforts of a myriad of NGOs.

The Nobel Peace Prize

The **Nobel Peace Prize** is awarded annually to an individual, group of people, or organization that has made a significant contribution to world peace. It was first awarded in 1901. Four stories of some Nobel laureates will illustrate the achievements that are recognized by the awarding committee.

The tradition of recognizing outstanding contributions to peace was established in the first year of the award. One of the co-winners of the 1901 award was Jean-Henri Dunant (1828–1910). Until he was 34 years of age, Dunant was a businessman. Then he witnessed the bloody battle of Solferino, in northern Italy, in 1862. He was horrified by the battle and by the chaos that followed as untrained, unprepared people tried to respond to help the wounded and bury the dead. This experience changed his life.

Dunant's first response was to write a small book called *A Memory of Solferino*. In it, he proposed that the countries of the world sponsor agencies to care for those who are wounded in war. Within two years, 12 nations had signed a treaty that recognized the neutrality of these relief workers, who adopted a red cross as a symbol of their work. From this humble beginning developed today's multifaceted national and international Red Cross societies (and Red Crescent societies, in Islamic countries). Dunant's Nobel award is typical in that it recognized someone for a lasting contribution to world peace.

As of 2001, only one Canadian had received a Nobel Peace Prize: Lester Pearson received this honour in 1957 (Figure 24–7). Like many other Nobel laureates, he was acting as a politician representing his nation when he made his contribution to world peace. Before entering politics, Pearson had been an academic and a senior diplomat. This experience helped him gain a

Figure 24–7   *Lester Pearson received the Nobel Peace Prize while serving as Canada's Foreign Secretary. He would become prime minister in 1963.*

Cabinet posting in 1948 as Foreign Secretary (a position equivalent to the current Minister of Foreign Affairs and International Trade). In this role he was an important contributor to international relations for a decade.

Pearson's most significant contribution to world peace occurred during the Suez crisis in 1956. The emergency began when the government of Egypt decided to nationalize (take over) the Suez Canal and control access to it. This action prompted Britain, France, and Israel to invade Egypt to try to retake control of the canal. Pearson proposed the creation of a United Nations emergency force that would allow the invaders to withdraw from Egypt without losing face. The action would also ensure that the canal would remain open to ships of all countries. Not only did Pearson's action defuse an explosive situation; it also established the principle of peacekeeping that was to become a key part of the UN's work in reducing conflict in the world.

Did you KNOW?

Nobel prizes are awarded in several scientific disciplines, in economics, and for contributions to peace. The Nobel prizes are named for Alfred Nobel, the Swedish discoverer of dynamite, who originated the idea. He left a substantial part of his estate to fund the creation of the Nobel committee in his home country.

Figure 24–8 *Aung San Suu Kyi has become a vital symbol of opposition to a repressive government.*

Some Nobel laureates receive the award not for what they have accomplished, but for their struggle to promote democracy and human rights by peaceful means against overwhelming odds. One such laureate is Aung San Suu Kyi (Figure 24–8), who won the prize in 1991. In 1988, as leader of a democratic opposition party in Burma (Myanmar), she led a non-violent protest against a ruling party that often used brutal methods to enforce its policies. Suu Kyi also led a campaign to bring together traditionally hostile regional and ethnic groups in the country. In 1990, her party decisively won a national election, but was not allowed by the military to assume power.

Suu Kyi was released from house arrest in May 2002. In spite of her house arrest, she continued her struggle against the government. More significantly, she has become an international icon for all those who fight against powerful opponents who have little respect for human rights and human dignity.

Alfred Nobel originally intended that his Peace Prize be awarded to an individual.

However, it has sometimes been awarded to an NGO. The 1999 award was given to Médecins Sans Frontières (MSF, known in English as Doctors Without Borders). MSF was founded in France in 1971 by a group of physicians and journalists. Their intention was simple—to provide medical aid to those in crisis. Often they do this in conditions of great danger, and even when other NGOs are leaving a region because of the risk. At a more profound level, MSF helps people regain the dignity and human rights that conflict has taken from them. This requires more than the simple provision of medical aid. The agency views its mandate as including a responsibility to challenge governments and non-governmental military forces that deny people their dignity and rights. This belief contrasts with the approach of most NGOs, which strive to maintain their neutrality.

Is World Peace Possible?

When the Cold War ended in the early 1990s, many people hoped and expected that the world would become a safer place in which to live. Unfortunately, this has not proved to be the case, for many reasons:

- the spread of nuclear weapons and other weapons of mass destruction
- the unrivalled military, economic, and cultural power of the United States
- a world in which "the rich get richer and the poor get poorer"
- the worldwide spread of communications technology that allows the poor to learn of the economic disparity that exists between themselves and others
- cultural globalization, which some see as a threat to their culture and religion
- the growth of terrorism, as some people see no other way to contest powerful enemies
- growing populations that increase stress on the environment.

Chapter Questions

Knowledge and Understanding

1. Examine the United Nations under the following headings:
   a) purpose
   b) types of sanctions and their purpose
   c) role of the Security Council
   d) peacekeeping role
   e) role played by the UN's specialized agencies.

2. What are the stages in the treaty-making process? Indicate the likelihood that exists at each stage for the goals of a treaty to be lost.

3. Compare the role of NATO during and after the Cold War.

4. a) Describe America's unilateralist foreign policy, using three different examples.
   b) Explain why there is hope that this foreign policy could change in the future.

5. a) Explain how the various international nuclear weapons treaties mentioned in this chapter have contributed to a safer world.
   b) What remains to be done to reduce the risk posed by nuclear weapons?
   c) What should be done to address the risk posed by other weapons of mass destruction, such as chemical and biological weapons?

6. The four Nobel Peace Prize laureates described in this chapter won their awards for different reasons. Identify these reasons, and give one additional winner in each category, with a brief description of the winner's achievement. How has each winner contributed to the goal of world peace? (You may wish to visit <www.pearsoned.ca/globalconnections> for additional information.)

Thinking and Inquiry

7. In 1994, genocide in Rwanda resulted in the deaths of some 800 000 people. Investigate the failure of the United Nations to prevent this genocide. In what way can this failure be related to
   a) the strategic interests of the United States and other Western nations?
   b) the events that occurred in Somalia a few years earlier?

8. a) Work in a group of three or four students to investigate the success of the United Nations. Each student should investigate a branch of the UN's organization (for example, the Security Council) or the operation of one of its specialized agencies.
   b) What specific reforms might make the UN more effective? Explain your reasoning.

9. a) Why was NATO created?
   b) How did NATO "reinvent itself" after the breakup of the Soviet Union?
   c) How has NATO become an active peacemaker and peacekeeper in Europe?
   d) How might NATO continue to grow and change in the future?

Communication

10. Using data provided by your teacher, create a map to show the pattern of acceptance for the Comprehensive Test Ban Treaty. Your teacher will tell you whether you will do this with ArcView GIS software or on a paper base map of the world. Your teacher will also give you questions to answer based on the map you create.

11. Prepare to debate the question, *"Resolved— That the unchallenged military power of the United States offers the best chance for world peace."*

12. Investigate an NGO of your choice and prepare a report that includes the following information:
    - the organization's purpose
    - its history
    - how it tries to accomplish its purpose
    - an analysis of the organization's usefulness.

13. Research and report on the human and ecological cost of global military spending. Present your findings in the form of a five-minute speech, PowerPoint presentation, or illustrated brochure.

Application

14. Research the role played in solving world problems by one of these organizations:
    - European Union
    - Organization of American States
    - African Union
    - International Monetary Fund/World Bank
    - another organization that works to reduce conflict and solve problems in the world.

15. Go to <www.pearsoned.ca/globalconnections> to read an essay called, "The Imbalance of Terror" by Thérèse Delpech. Do you agree with this author's thesis? Explain why or why not in an essay of 300 to 500 words.

16. What do you think Canada's role should be in resolving world conflicts?

Unit 6: Quality of Life

Diseases in the Developing World

Expectations

In this chapter, you will:

- identify ways in which countries and regions are becoming increasingly interdependent

- identify the social, economic, cultural, and political components of a geographic issue

- compare statistical indicators of quality of life for different world regions

- evaluate the performance of transnationals regarding human rights

- understand how the work on diseases by the UN and other organizations relates to your own life

- describe biases that may inform different viewpoints on geographical issues

- use written, oral, and visual skills to present the results of a geographic enquiry

Image above:
Bujumbura Health Clinic, Bujumbura, Burundi

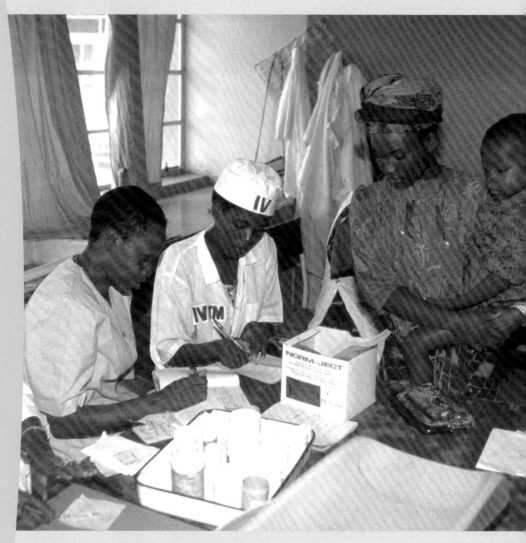

Diseases can be divided into two groups: **infectious diseases** such as AIDS, tuberculosis, and malaria, which are dominant in developing nations; and **lifestyle diseases**, such as heart conditions, obesity, and diabetes, which are dominant in the developed world. This chapter will focus on the former, particularly the AIDS epidemic that is devastating Africa and threatening other regions of the developing world.

AIDS—The Great Epidemic

Look around your geography class. Imagine that 10 of your classmates carry the human immuno-deficiency virus (HIV) or have already developed acquired immune deficiency syndrome (AIDS). If your class has 28 students, this number would represent 36 per cent—the same percentage as the adult population of Botswana, a nation in southern Africa, that is infected with **HIV/AIDS**. In comparison, the percentage of adult Canadians with this disease in 2000 was only 0.13 per cent, or about one person in 770. The crisis in South Africa is so severe that one study suggests as many as half of all boys under the age of 15 are likely to die of AIDS-related causes.

In Africa, and to a lesser extent in other parts of the developing world, HIV/AIDS has become a **pandemic**, a disease that affects a significant portion of the population at any given time (Figure 25–1). The most famous pandemic of all was the Black Death (the bubonic plague), which affected Europe in the 14th century. AIDS is likely to kill more people than the Black Death.

While HIV/AIDS remains incurable, most people in Canada who carry the virus can expect to live for many years with a reasonable quality of life, thanks to a range of new and costly pharmaceuticals called **anti-retroviral drugs**. But in Botswana and other developing countries, where the per capita annual GDP is less than $500 and the drugs cost as much as $15 000 per year, treatment for HIV/AIDS is problematic. As these drugs control HIV/AIDS rather than cure it, the costs continue each year for as long as a person lives. The impact on developing countries has been devastating: South Africa's life expectancy is predicted to drop from 60 to 35 years between 2000 and 2010, and Botswana's may decline to as little as 29 years, by far the lowest in the world.

World AIDS Infections

	New infections of HIV/AIDS (thousands)	Deaths due to HIV/AIDS (thousands)	Prevalence of HIV/AIDS (% of total adults)
Sub-Saharan Africa	3400	2300	8.4
South and Southeast Asia	800	400	0.6
Eastern Europe and Central Asia	250	23	0.5
Latin America	130	80	0.5
East Asia and Pacific	270	35	0.1
North Africa and Middle East	80	30	0.2
Caribbean	60	30	2.2
North America	45	20	0.6
Western Europe	30	7	0.3
Australia and New Zealand	0.5	<0.2	0.1
Total	5065.5	2925	1.2

Figure 25–1 *World AIDS infections, deaths, and prevalence, 2001.* Source: UNAIDS.

A Brief History of HIV/AIDS

HIV/AIDS is a very new disease. It first appeared in the early 1980s in Uganda. It spread widely in the world, but caught the attention of North Americans only when it became common here. At first, it came to be identified with three groups of people: homosexual men, intravenous drug users, and Haitians. Among drug users, HIV is transmitted by the sharing of hypodermic needles. For others, HIV/AIDS is spread primarily by sexual activity. But because of the early identification with these three groups, many people mistakenly concluded that the disease affected only a few specific populations, and that others were immune. This misconception not only stigmatized people who carried the virus, but also placed millions of others at risk.

A similar situation accelerated the spread of HIV/AIDS in Africa and elsewhere in the developing world. In most of these countries, it was considered impolite to talk about a disease that is spread primarily through sexual activity. Public silence bred an ignorance that provided fertile ground for the spread of the virus.

With most serious diseases, the ill are likely to receive the sympathy and support of their community. But the ignorance and fear surrounding HIV/AIDS caused those infected with the virus to be rejected, much as lepers once were. In an extreme case, an AIDS activist in South Africa named Gugu Dlamini was stoned to death by her neighbours when they discovered that she was HIV positive. An expert from the Centers for Disease Control and Prevention in Atlanta, Georgia, described the situation of people in Africa living with HIV/AIDS in four words: silence, stigma, discrimination, and denial.

By 2001, it was estimated that 54 million people had been infected with HIV/AIDS and that 18 million people had died. AIDS activists suggest that it is easier to appreciate the scale of this tragedy if we consider that the death toll in Africa alone is equivalent to two large, fatal airliner crashes (450 people) per hour, every hour. Worldwide, 16 000 more people are being added to the total each day.

More than 70 per cent of all people who have HIV/AIDS live in central and southern Africa (Figure 25–2). The rest of the developing world ranks next, with the developed world having the smallest number of infected people.

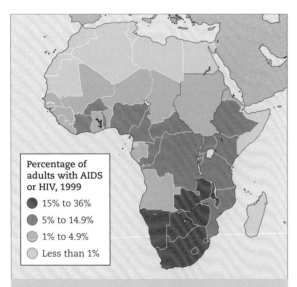

Percentage of adults with AIDS or HIV, 1999

- 15% to 36%
- 5% to 14.9%
- 1% to 4.9%
- Less than 1%

Figure 25–2 *The prevalence of AIDS in southern and central Africa is far greater than that elsewhere in the world. Africa's lowest infection rates are in the Muslim-dominated north. For the sake of comparison, in 1999 about 0.1 per cent of Canadian adults had HIV/AIDS.* Source: *UNAIDS.*

The Impact of HIV/AIDS in Africa

HIV/AIDS is having, and will continue to have, a profound impact on the world's poorest continent.

- Life expectancies are declining, not just by months or years, but by decades. The AIDS pandemic is bringing an end to the population explosion in southern and central Africa, but in a way that no one could have predicted or wanted.

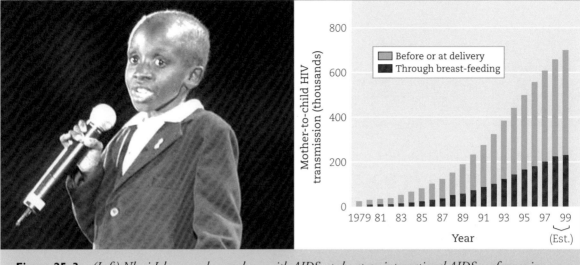

Figure 25–3 *(Left) Nkosi Johnson, who was born with AIDS, spoke at an international AIDS conference in Durban, South Africa, in 2000. He died of AIDS-related brain damage and viral infections the following year at the age of 12. (Right) The graph shows the growth of mother-to-child HIV/AIDS infections in the world.* Sources: UNAIDS; *Science.*

- Many children are being born with HIV/AIDS because their mothers are infected (Figure 25–3). By 2000, about 70 000 children per year were being born with AIDS in South Africa alone.

- By the end of 1999, 12.5 million children were orphaned as their parents died of AIDS. Most African countries have no formal infrastructure to look after these children. Informal, family-based supports are often overwhelmed by the scale of the problem.

- The pandemic is putting critical pressure on African health care systems that were inadequate to begin with. Most hospital beds are filled with those in the final stages of the disease, not because they are being treated, but because there is nowhere else for them to go. For example, in 2001, up to 80 per cent of adult patients and 33 per cent of children in the main hospital in Gaborone, Botswana, were in the terminal stages of AIDS.

- The economies and social structures of many countries are being devastated as large numbers of skilled workers in mines, schools, and the health care system are dying. By 2010,

the GDP of sub-Saharan Africa may be cut by as much as 17 per cent because of AIDS. Unlike most diseases, AIDS usually kills adults in their prime. This fact is dramatically altering the population structures of African countries such as Botswana (Figure 25–4).

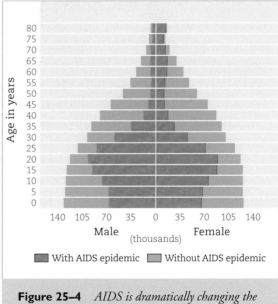

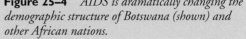

Figure 25–4 *AIDS is dramatically changing the demographic structure of Botswana (shown) and other African nations.*

Solving Africa's Problem

HIV/AIDS in Africa is a complex problem that cannot be solved by any one action. It will require a wide range of initiatives, both within the continent and in the developed world.

Steps to Be Taken in Africa

In 2001, Stephen Lewis, the Canadian ambassador to the United Nations, was appointed the UN's special envoy on AIDS in Africa. Lewis's job is to work with the governments of African nations affected by AIDS to implement measures, such as those that follow, that are most likely to succeed in each country.

- *End the "silence, stigma, discrimination, and denial" associated with the disease.* Africans must do a better job of discussing and dealing with the ways in which people become infected. As late as 1997, Fela Kuti, a popular musician and brother of the health minister of Nigeria, was telling people that AIDS did not exist. His death that year from AIDS-related illnesses demonstrated the danger of such denial.
- *Treat HIV-positive pregnant women with medications to prevent transmission of the disease.* Some experts feel that, while attempts to treat all people with AIDS are probably unrealistic, it is possible to prevent women from passing the disease on to their unborn children.
- *Empower African women in a culture that often permits them to be exploited sexually.* Women, including workers in the sex industry, must feel they can say no to unprotected sex.

Steps to Be Taken in the Developed World

- *Accelerate research on a vaccine for AIDS.* Pharmaceutical manufacturers have so far concentrated on producing medicines for treating the disease rather than on creating a preventive vaccine, because treatment is more profitable in the short term.
- *Provide medication at prices that are affordable to developing nations.* As a first step, drugs that reduce the chance of mother-to-child transmission in the womb should be made widely available. The most commonly used of these is AZT. If a mother receives AZT before delivery and the baby receives it for a week after birth, the chances that the infant will be HIV positive are cut in half.
- *Fund the fight against AIDS.* The UN Secretary-General estimates the cost of fighting AIDS worldwide at between $10 billion and $15 billion per year. The inadequacy of current efforts can be seen in the fact that in 2000, when the United States promised to double its AIDS assistance, this meant an expenditure of only $370 million per year. Canada has decided to direct most of its African aid of $288 million per year towards fighting AIDS. However, the scope of existing and promised AIDS spending was, in 2001, far below what is needed.

In a group of three or four, briefly discuss the situations that follow. Both are based on real-life cases. Then, continue reading the text to see what actually took place.

Situation 1: You are the president of an African nation that is being devastated by AIDS. Your nation needs vast quantities of pharmaceuticals that, when purchased from major drug companies, are far more costly than your country can afford. You have located a company operating in another developing country that will provide you with copies of the brand-name pharmaceuticals at a fraction of the normal cost. Accepting them means you will have to ignore international patent laws that are designed to protect intellectual property (anything produced as a result of creativity). What would you do?

Situation 2: You are the president of a transnational pharmaceutical company that produces an effective, but costly, anti-AIDS drug. Your company invested hundreds of millions of dollars to develop and test this medicine. You now hear that an African government intends to ignore your patent protection by buying a cheap, but in your view illegal, copy of your drug. You are sympathetic to the needs of Africans who have AIDS, but you are responsible to your shareholders and are afraid that if you create cheap copies of your drug to sell to the developing country, they will find their way back to the developed world. What would you do?

Providing Drugs to Developing Countries

In the first case in the activity above, if you answered that you would go ahead and buy the drug copies, then you are taking the route followed by the government of South Africa in the late 1990s. It decided to purchase drugs from an Indian company that would provide Africans with anti-retroviral drugs through the non-governmental organization, Doctors Without Borders, for $350 per patient per year. Its legal justification for doing this was a clause in the World Trade Organization agreement that allows a country to ignore patent laws in the case of a national emergency. The major pharmaceutical companies point out that their much higher prices reflect the fact that they spend huge amounts on research ($27 billion in North America alone in 2001) to develop new drugs.

In the second case, if you said you would take legal action to protect your intellectual property, then you are taking the route followed by an international association of 39 pharmaceutical companies. The drug companies felt that their role is to develop effective new medications and to make a fair profit in return—not to overcome the economic disparities in the world that make it impossible for some people to buy their products. They contend that this responsibility belongs to the United Nations, aid groups, and the governments of the developed world.

The pharmaceutical companies were also concerned that cheap drugs in Africa could be diverted into the black market and end up being sold in the developed world. Under considerable inter-

Figure 25–5 *South Africa's Minister of Health, Manto Tshabalala-Msimang, celebrates after a coalition of the world's top pharmaceutical companies withdrew legal action to protect AIDS drug patents on April 19, 2001.*

Drugs for Neglected Diseases

The controversy over affordable anti-AIDS medications is just one indication that the globalized pharmaceutical industry does a poor job in meeting the health needs of the developing world. Another is that the industry virtually ignores many of the world's deadliest infectious diseases. It does so because there is greater profit in developing drugs that address the lifestyle diseases common in developed countries, such as obesity, high blood pressure, and depression. As a result of the focus on profit, little attention has been paid to the so-called **neglected diseases**—infectious diseases that are not common in developed countries. For example, between 1975 and 1997 there were 1223 new drugs patented. Of these, only 13 were aimed at infectious diseases, such as tuberculosis and malaria, which are of greater concern in the developing world.

Access to Essential Medicines

The problem of access to essential medicines by people with neglected diseases can be seen in the case of sleeping sickness. Sleeping sickness is spread by the bite of the tsetse fly. It causes people to suffer from a form of sleep disturbance in which they sleep all day. In its terminal stages it causes insanity, coma, and death. Sleeping sickness causes about 350 000 deaths a year in Africa (Figure 25–6).

By chance, a drug called eflornithine, which had been developed as a cancer treatment, was found to be effective against sleeping sickness. In fact, it was called the "resurrection drug" because it would make the sleeping wake. Unfortunately, it proved to be relatively ineffective as a cancer drug, and so its manufacturer, Aventis, decided to stop making it. Doctors treating sleeping sickness soon found themselves in a difficult situa-

national pressure, they agreed to offer their medication for $1000 per patient. Later, they agreed to supply pharmaceuticals at below-cost prices and to refrain from defending their patent rights in the courts (Figure 25–5). In spite of this decision, the flow of anti-AIDS drugs into Africa has been very slow.

The ultimate solution to the problem may be **tier pricing**. This is a system in which different prices would be charged for the same medication in different parts of the world. Historically, the drug companies have opposed tier pricing because it would reduce their cash flow. Supporters of this system suggest that pharmaceutical manufacturers could be protected in two ways. Strict controls could be put in place on the re-export of drugs from one country to another. Also, manufacturers could be given patent protection for an extended period of time to increase the return they receive for the costs of their research.

tion: they had to ration use of existing doses of the drug. Aventis finally decided to resume production of eflornithine, but only because it was also found useful for removing facial hair on women.

As with anti-AIDS medications, eflornithine was made available only because pharmaceutical companies were serving First World needs. Public health experts in developing countries complain that this is not good enough. They point out that only 0.2 per cent of pharmaceutical research dollars are spent on diseases such as tuberculosis, sleeping sickness, and malaria, which together are responsible for 20 per cent of all deaths in the world.

You can learn more about the battle to provide access to essential medicines at <www.pearsoned.ca/globalconnections>.

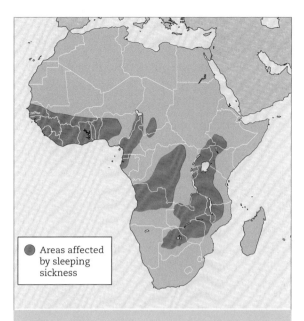

Figure 25–6 *While sleeping sickness is unrelated to HIV/AIDS, it affects many of the same countries in Africa.*

Pandemics Past and Future

It was called the "Spanish flu," even though it almost certainly did not originate in Spain. As World War I ended, millions of soldiers from all over the world were crowded onto the battlefields of France and Belgium in extremely unsanitary conditions. Soon, the troops were sent home. Along with their souvenirs and horrific war memories, they also took home the deadly virus responsible for the most serious pandemic that the world had faced in five centuries. Within only six months, 25 million people all over the world were dead.

We have all read about the fearsome death toll of the Great War, but the influenza pandemic killed twice as many people in one-eighth the time. In Canada, one in six people got sick and 60 000 died. (With today's population, an equivalent death toll would be over 200 000.) The death toll would have been even higher if it were not for the extraordinary steps that were taken to prevent people from passing the infection on to others. Schools were closed and public meetings were outlawed (Figure 25–7). The outbreak was so severe that the 1919 Stanley Cup playoffs were never finished; they were called off part-way through.

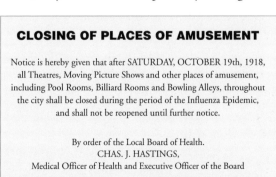

CLOSING OF PLACES OF AMUSEMENT

Notice is hereby given that after SATURDAY, OCTOBER 19th, 1918, all Theatres, Moving Picture Shows and other places of amusement, including Pool Rooms, Billiard Rooms and Bowling Alleys, throughout the city shall be closed during the period of the Influenza Epidemic, and shall not be reopened until further notice.

By order of the Local Board of Health.
CHAS. J. HASTINGS,
Medical Officer of Health and Executive Officer of the Board

Figure 25–7 *At the height of the flu epidemic, this advertisement appeared in the October 8, 1918, edition of the Toronto Globe.*

The Next Pandemic

Medical historians have determined that there have been 32 major pandemics in the past 400 years. What will be the next great disease outbreak, and when will it happen? No one knows, but there are some general predictions.

- Significant influenza outbreaks occur, on average, every 11 years. Since the 1918 outbreak, more minor pandemics occurred in 1933, 1946, 1957, 1968, and 1977. Health Canada predicts that the next major influenza outbreak will come by 2010 and will kill between 9000 and 51 000 Canadians.

- Outbreaks of extraordinarily dangerous disease strains appear from time to time, particularly in Africa. Best known of these is Ebola, a horrifying disease that causes victims to bleed from every orifice as their internal organs liquefy. So far, Ebola has appeared only in remote areas of the Democratic Republic of Congo, Sudan, and Uganda, where population densities are relatively low and people are less mobile. If Ebola, or a similar deadly disease, were to move into a denser, more mobile population in the developed world, its spread could become much more rapid, with catastrophic death tolls.

To read more about the work of "virus hunters" and the 1918 flu epidemic, go to <www.pearsoned.ca/globalconnections>.

Did you KNOW? Research on the 1918 pandemic used DNA taken from the tissues of flu victims whose bodies were preserved because they had been buried in permafrost. A Canadian medical geographer led an expedition to Spitsbergen, an island in the Arctic Ocean north of Norway, where the remains of the victims were recovered.

Human–Animal Interactions

Scientists worry about diseases that cross species, such as those that pass from animals to humans and vice versa. These little-understood interactions have been seen with several diseases.

- For many years, influenza has been known to spread through birds. In fact, in 1997 when a child died of influenza in Hong Kong, officials took the drastic step of killing all the chickens in the city (more than one million) to reduce the risk of further animal-to-human transmission. Was this action justified? There is no way to be sure, but this was one influenza outbreak that did not spread to the rest of the world.

- More recently, evidence has emerged that the 1918 influenza pandemic may have been transmitted to humans from pigs, and that the virus may have been passed, in turn, back to pigs in Iowa by infected returning soldiers. This incident was likely responsible for the introduction of swine fever into North America. Swine fever remains a damaging animal disease on this continent.

- In recent years, the United Kingdom has faced two devastating disease outbreaks, one involving animals and people, the other only animals. The first was mad cow disease (bovine spongiform encephalopathy, or BSE). This incurable disease, which destroys an animal's nervous system, can be transmitted to humans through consumption of contaminated meat. When it appears in humans, it is called Creutzfeldt-Jakob disease. The second outbreak was foot-and-mouth disease. While this illness rarely affects people, it has enormous economic impacts. Trade in animals is forbidden, and many thousands of animals must be destroyed to prevent the disease from spreading (Figure 25–8). The only response to an outbreak of either disease is to severely limit animal movements and to destroy any animals that might be infected.

Figure 25–8 *Workers from the Ministry of Agriculture, Fisheries, and Food survey piles of sheep and cattle corpses in preparation for burning, in Ellonby, England, 2001. Hundreds of thousands of animals were gathered and destroyed to help prevent the spread of the foot-and-mouth epidemic.*

Impact of Mobility

Just as the unprecedented human movement at the end of World War I contributed to the 1918 influenza outbreak, future pandemics are likely to be made worse because of today's greatly increased mobility of people, animals, and products. The fact that more people travel, and travel to more places, increases the risk of an exotic disease being imported into areas where there may be no natural resistance and no medical system prepared to deal with it. The vastly increased trade in agricultural products and live animals also significantly increases the likelihood that a disease in one place will spread to other countries, or even other continents.

What Will Happen Next?

The decades to come are likely to bring a sequence of news stories about outbreaks of known and unknown diseases. In some cases, these will end up as false alarms, while in others the death toll (and economic damage) will be high. The great fear is that the next pandemic, whenever and wherever it may occur, could be the "big one," a disease that will kill tens of millions of people worldwide. It might be a massive outbreak of influenza (or some other known infection), or an entirely new disease, such as AIDS was in the 1980s.

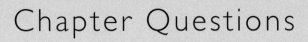

Chapter Questions

Knowledge and Understanding

1. Describe at least two differences that exist between the diseases that affect the developing world and those that are most common in the developed world.

2. What is a pandemic? Give at least three examples.

3. a) Explain how "silence, stigma, discrimination, and denial" contributed to the spread of HIV/AIDS in Africa.
   b) Can a similar argument be made about the spread of this virus in Canada?
   c) How can these four attitudes be overcome?

4. a) What are neglected diseases?
   b) Why is a profit-based drug creation system unlikely to provide pharmaceuticals for these diseases?
   c) Give examples of prescription medications that are widely advertised by pharmaceutical companies. Why are these so heavily promoted? Would these medications be of much use in developing countries?

5. a) Explain the reasons why the world is vulnerable to the risk of devastating pandemics in the future.
   b) What might be done to minimize these risks? Consider both the actions that could be taken by individuals and those that should be taken by national governments or international agencies.

Thinking and Inquiry

6. Summarize how Africa's current social structures, economies, and development prospects are being damaged by HIV/AIDS.

7. In many countries of southern Africa it is common for men to become migrant workers, leaving home for months at a time to work in mines or at other jobs in distant cities and towns. How has the common use of migrant labour contributed to the spread of HIV/AIDS? How might this impact be reduced?

8. a) What are anti-retroviral drugs?
   b) Why would pharmaceutical companies focus their attention on vaccines and treatments for HIV/AIDS in North America and Europe rather than on vaccines for infectious diseases in developing countries?
   c) Explain how this situation has a negative impact on the globalization of business.

9. a) What is tier pricing? How would it improve the quality of health care in poorer countries?
   b) What problems would have to be overcome for tier pricing to become a reality?

Communication

10. Put yourself in the role of health minister of a developing country that has yet to experience a major AIDS outbreak. Outline the policies you would implement to minimize the risk of a major epidemic in your country.

11. Summarize, in a visual fashion of your choice, the various initiatives that are needed to fight AIDS in Africa.

12. Your class is to simulate hearings that might be held at the United Nations. A non-profit agency is to be created that would organize research into vaccines and other pharmaceuticals needed to fight infectious diseases in the developing world. The purpose of the hearings is to establish guidelines within which the agency will be created.

    The roles that must be filled in these hearings are:
    a) the commissioners who will hear the presentations and create the guidelines
    b) the governments of developing countries that are suffering infectious diseases
    c) the governments of developed countries that ultimately would have to fund this endeavour

d) international groups such as the World Bank that would directly finance any initiatives

e) major transnational pharmaceutical manufacturers

f) smaller pharmaceutical manufacturers that make copies of the drugs made by the pharmaceutical companies after patent protection runs out

g) non-governmental organizations that provide health care in Africa and elsewhere in the developing world

All of the groups from (b) to (g) in this list are to present their suggestions for how the agency should operate and what role should be taken by the various players. Your teacher will give you specific instructions about how to stage the hearings in your classroom.

Application

13. a) Investigate the origins of HIV/AIDS.
b) What can we learn from the world's experience of HIV/AIDS that might be useful in dealing with new diseases in the future?

14. Many countries, including Uganda and Canada, have developed methods for curbing the spread of HIV/AIDS. Discuss with classmates why some countries have apparently not benefited from this experience in preventing the spread of the virus.

15. Prepare a report on one of the infectious diseases that affects the developing world. Your teacher will give you a list of diseases. For the disease you choose, include the following information:
a) cause of the disease
b) impact on a person's health
c) map of the distribution of the disease
d) number of cases in the world
e) what is being done to provide cures and/or protection against the disease
f) impact the disease has (or might have) on Canada and other developed nations

16. Consider the following questions from your personal perspective as an individual Canadian.
a) What should Canada and other developed countries do to stop the AIDS pandemic in the developing world?
b) What sacrifices are you prepared to make to help? (For example, would you accept an additional tax levy focussed on this problem?)

26

The Universal Declaration of Human Rights

Key Terms

human rights
Universal Declaration
  of Human Rights
cultural exceptionalism
World Conference on
  Women
Convention on the
  Rights of the Child
caste
bonded labour
forced labour

Expectations

In this chapter, you will:

■ understand the roles and status of men and women in different parts of the world

■ evaluate the effectiveness of an international strategy or agreement designed to address global issues

■ understand the need to consider social differences when analysing global problems and issues

■ evaluate and effectively use information from primary and secondary sources

■ produce an action plan to conduct an independent inquiry related to a geographic issue

Image above: Election posters of President Chandrika Kumaratunga, Colombo, Sri Lanka, 1999

The "greater good" for human society means different things to different people. To some, it is the growth of wealth. To others, it is the advancement of science or the creation of a great work of art. But to many, it means that a growing proportion of the world's population lives in freedom, peace, and dignity—in other words, that there is a growth in respect for **human rights**.

What Are Human Rights Issues?

Read the following scenarios. Each describes a situation that might be regarded as a violation of human rights. For each, identify the specific human right that may have been abused.

- In downtown Toronto, a man who was living under a bridge is found dead on a cold winter night.
- Along the border with Afghanistan, fleeing refugees are denied entry into Pakistan.
- In North America, young black men driving expensive cars are more likely than other motorists to be stopped and questioned by police.
- In Quebec City, police use so much tear gas to break up anti-globalization protests that they must place emergency orders for more.

- In Saudi Arabia, a convicted thief is punished by having his hand amputated in a public ceremony.
- In India, a young woman is expected to marry a much older man selected by her parents.
- In China, thousands of illegal copies of a CD featuring a famous Canadian singer are produced.

You are probably able to identify at least some of the rights being violated in these cases. (If you are having difficulty, check the United Nations Universal Declaration of Human Rights on the next two pages.) Like most people, you likely have a working knowledge of what human rights are. But can you give a clear and comprehensive definition of the term? Try to do this in your notebook.

Next, make a list of the key rights that you feel all citizens of the world should have.

What Are Universal Human Rights?

The concept of human rights is a complex one. The political and legal rights that Canadians are familiar with evolved over centuries as democracy developed in Western nations. The idea that social and economic factors may also be human rights issues is relatively modern. Spurred by the events of World War II and the desire for world peace, the newly formed United Nations decided in 1946 that there should be a code of human rights for the entire world, calling this a "blueprint for the future of humanity."

A Canadian diplomat was asked to write the code. John Peters Humphrey was the director of the Human Rights Division of the United Nations. He completed a 400-page working paper on human rights in 1947, and the **Universal Declaration of Human Rights**

(Figure 26–1) was approved by the United Nations in December 1948. This document—the most detailed analysis of human rights ever produced—embodied the traditions of Western culture.

While the Universal Declaration of Human Rights does not have the force of international law, most countries have signed it. However, not all of these countries have put the principles of human rights into practice. The United Nations has little power to force a country to follow the conditions of the Declaration. While the UN can impose economic and even military sanctions on a member who does not respect the human rights of its citizens, such action is almost never taken. Rather, the UN relies on persuasion and public opinion to achieve compliance.

... THE GENERAL ASSEMBLY proclaims THIS UNIVERSAL DECLARATION OF HUMAN RIGHTS as a common standard of achievement for all peoples and all nations, to the end that every individual and every organ of society, keeping this Declaration constantly in mind, shall strive by teaching and education to promote respect for these rights and freedoms and by progressive measures, national and international, to secure their universal and effective recognition and observance, both among the peoples of Member States themselves and among the peoples of territories under their jurisdiction.

Article 1.
All human beings are born free and equal in dignity and rights. They are endowed with reason and conscience and should act towards one another in a spirit of brotherhood.

Article 2.
Everyone is entitled to all the rights and freedoms set forth in this Declaration, without distinction of any kind, such as race, colour, sex, language, religion, political or other opinion, national or social origin, property, birth or other status. Furthermore, no distinction shall be made on the basis of the political, jurisdictional or international status of the country or territory to which a person belongs, whether it be independent, trust, non-self-governing or under any other limitation of sovereignty.

Article 3.
Everyone has the right to life, liberty and security of person.

Article 4.
No one shall be held in slavery or servitude; slavery and the slave trade shall be prohibited in all their forms.

Article 5.
No one shall be subjected to torture or to cruel, inhuman or degrading treatment or punishment.

Article 6.
Everyone has the right to recognition everywhere as a person before the law.

Article 7.
All are equal before the law and are entitled without any discrimination to equal protection of the law. All are entitled to equal protection against any discrimination in violation of this Declaration and against any incitement to such discrimination.

Article 8.
Everyone has the right to an effective remedy by the competent national tribunals for acts violating the fundamental rights granted him by the constitution or by law.

Article 9.
No one shall be subjected to arbitrary arrest, detention or exile.

Article 10.
Everyone is entitled in full equality to a fair and public hearing by an independent and impartial tribunal, in the determination of his rights and obligations and of any criminal charge against him.

Article 11.
(1) Everyone charged with a penal offence has the right to be presumed innocent until proved guilty according to law in a public trial at which he has had all the guarantees necessary for his defence.

(2) No one shall be held guilty of any penal offence on account of any act or omission which did not constitute a penal offence, under national or international law, at the time when it was committed. Nor shall a heavier penalty be imposed than the one that was applicable at the time the penal offence was committed.

Article 12.
No one shall be subjected to arbitrary interference with his privacy, family, home or correspondence, nor to attacks upon his honour and reputation. Everyone has the right to the protection of the law against such interference or attacks.

Article 13.
(1) Everyone has the right to freedom of movement and residence within the borders of each state.

(2) Everyone has the right to leave any country, including his own, and to return to his country.

Article 14.
(1) Everyone has the right to seek and to enjoy in other countries asylum from persecution.

(2) This right may not be invoked in the case of prosecutions genuinely arising from non-political crimes or from acts contrary to the purposes and principles of the United Nations.

Article 15.
(1) Everyone has the right to a nationality.

(2) No one shall be arbitrarily deprived of his nationality nor denied the right to change his nationality.

Article 16.
(1) Men and women of full age, without any limitation due to race, nationality or religion, have the right to marry and to found a family. They are entitled to equal rights as to marriage, during marriage and at its dissolution.

(2) Marriage shall be entered into only with the free and full consent of the intending spouses.

(3) The family is the natural and fundamental group unit of society and is entitled to protection by society and the State.

Article 17.
(1) Everyone has the right to own property alone as well as in association with others.

(2) No one shall be arbitrarily deprived of his property.

Figure 26–1 *The Universal Declaration of Human Rights of the United Nations*

Article 18.

Everyone has the right to freedom of thought, conscience and religion; this right includes freedom to change his religion or belief, and freedom, either alone or in community with others and in public or private, to manifest his religion or belief in teaching, practice, worship and observance.

Article 19.

Everyone has the right to freedom of opinion and expression; this right includes freedom to hold opinions without interference and to seek, receive and impart information and ideas through any media and regardless of frontiers.

Article 20.

(1) Everyone has the right to freedom of peaceful assembly and association.

(2) No one may be compelled to belong to an association.

Article 21.

(1) Everyone has the right to take part in the government of his country, directly or through freely chosen representatives.

(2) Everyone has the right to equal access to public service in his country.

(3) The will of the people shall be the basis of the authority of government; this shall be expressed in periodic and genuine elections which shall be by universal and equal suffrage and shall be held by secret vote or by equivalent free voting procedures.

Article 22.

Everyone, as a member of society, has the right to social security and is entitled to realization, through national effort and international co-operation and in accordance with the organization and resources of each State, of the economic, social and cultural rights indispensable for his dignity and the free development of his personality.

Article 23.

(1) Everyone has the right to work, to free choice of employment, to just and favourable conditions of work and to protection against unemployment.

(2) Everyone, without any discrimination, has the right to equal pay for equal work.

(3) Everyone who works has the right to just and favourable remuneration ensuring for himself and his family an existence worthy of human dignity, and supplemented, if necessary, by other means of social protection.

(4) Everyone has the right to form and to join trade unions for the protection of his interests.

Article 24.

Everyone has the right to rest and leisure, including reasonable limitation of working hours and periodic holidays with pay.

Article 25.

(1) Everyone has the right to a standard of living adequate for the health and well-being of himself and of his family, including food, clothing, housing and medical care and necessary social services, and the right to security in the event of unemployment, sickness, disability, widowhood, old age or other lack of livelihood in circumstances beyond his control.

(2) Motherhood and childhood are entitled to special care and assistance. All children, whether born in or out of wedlock, shall enjoy the same social protection.

Article 26.

(1) Everyone has the right to education. Education shall be free, at least in the elementary and fundamental stages. Elementary education shall be compulsory. Technical and professional education shall be made generally available and higher education shall be equally accessible to all on the basis of merit.

(2) Education shall be directed to the full development of the human personality and to the strengthening of respect for human rights and fundamental freedoms. It shall promote understanding, tolerance and friendship among all nations, racial or religious groups, and shall further the activities of the United Nations for the maintenance of peace.

(3) Parents have a prior right to choose the kind of education that shall be given to their children.

Article 27.

(1) Everyone has the right freely to participate in the cultural life of the community, to enjoy the arts and to share in scientific advancement and its benefits.

(2) Everyone has the right to the protection of the moral and material interests resulting from any scientific, literary or artistic production of which he is the author.

Article 28.

Everyone is entitled to a social and international order in which the rights and freedoms set forth in this Declaration can be fully realized.

Article 29.

(1) Everyone has duties to the community in which alone the free and full development of his personality is possible.

(2) In the exercise of his rights and freedoms, everyone shall be subject only to such limitations as are determined by law solely for the purpose of securing due recognition and respect for the rights and freedoms of others and of meeting the just requirements of morality, public order and the general welfare in a democratic society.

(3) These rights and freedoms may in no case be exercised contrary to the purposes and principles of the United Nations.

Article 30.

Nothing in this Declaration may be interpreted as implying for any State, group or person any right to engage in any activity or to perform any act aimed at the destruction of any of the rights and freedoms set forth herein.

Figure 26–1 (cont'd) *The Universal Declaration of Human Rights of the United Nations*

By the time of the UN World Conference on Human Rights in Vienna in 1993, another difficulty had become apparent in the application of human rights. There was a growing feeling that **cultural exceptionalism** might make a universal agreement on human rights impossible. Many countries have their own political, social, economic, and cultural traditions that differ from those of the West. For example, some nations have suggested that their religious beliefs justify their not accepting provisions of the Declaration dealing with the equality of women. They reject the idea of a universal standard for human rights. Some of the articles of the Declaration have not been implemented in Western countries. Look again at the examples of human rights issues listed at the beginning of this chapter, and think of some reasons why these situations might occur.

Many challenges remain in achieving universal human rights. In the remainder of this chapter you will have the opportunity to learn about just a few of the human rights issues that exist today. As well, we will look in more detail at why the protection of human rights is often so complex and difficult.

Women and Power

Women have long recognized that a fundamental aspect of gender equity is access to political and decision-making power. When women lack this power, institutions that discriminate against women continue to exist, and societies are deprived of women's experiences, perspectives, and approaches.

In 1995, at the United Nations' Fourth **World Conference on Women** in Beijing, the governments of 189 countries promised to provide women with "equal access to" and "full participation in" political decision making and the power structures of government. They also pledged to ensure "measures to increase substantially the number of women ... in all governmental and public administration positions."

Why did so many countries have to make such promises? Women are under-represented in governments all over the world, even though they had gained the right to vote and to stand for elections in 95 per cent of 189 countries by the beginning of this century. The obstacles to political participation that women face are similar worldwide, though they tend to be greater in the developing world.

Some of these obstacles are socio-economic. Cultural values may restrict women's opportunities for education and work outside the home. Primary responsibility for child rearing and household tasks may leave little time for non-domestic obligations. Lack of financial resources can also prevent women from participating in the political process. Furthermore, women who do not enjoy equality are less likely to voice their concerns or to request a share in decision making.

Political obstacles also restrict women from seeking public office in both developed and developing countries. The type of electoral system may increase or limit political opportunities for women. For example, in "winner-take-all" systems (such as Canada's), the winning political party forms the government. Women are better represented in proportional representative systems where the seats are allocated in proportion to the votes that each party receives. Countries with high percentages of women in government tend to have proportional representation systems.

Some governments have a selection and nomination process within political parties that traditionally excludes women. The lack of financial support from political parties to women members may prevent them from conducting an effective election campaign. Financing a campaign is more difficult when women lack access to political networks that raise money from private organizations and individuals. Women starting their political careers have a better chance of being elected in local politics. But frequently, there are no grassroots political networks to recruit and support women candidates.

A number of suggestions have been made to increase the number of women in government. In 1995, the Sixth UN Human Development Report recommended that at least 30 per cent of government representatives, regarded as a "critical mass," should be women. It states that without this percentage, the representation of women is merely tokenism, insufficient to provide a continuous pool of qualified women to ensure that institutional barriers are eliminated.

Because campaign financing is often a major barrier to women candidates, it has been suggested that laws be implemented to limit the amount of money spent on political campaigns, and that public funding be used for this political purpose.

Austria, Botswana, Denmark, Finland, Germany, the Netherlands, Norway, Sweden, Venezuela, and Israel have established quotas for women in their governing bodies (Figure 26–2). Other countries, including Argentina and Tanzania, have implemented quotas that reserve a minimum number of seats in legislatures for women. In the Nordic countries, quotas of 40 to 60 per cent for each gender are applied to all public boards and committees.

In spite of international recognition of the difficulties faced by women and the progress they have made, many challenges remain to be resolved before they can claim a meaningful role in decision making and the political process.

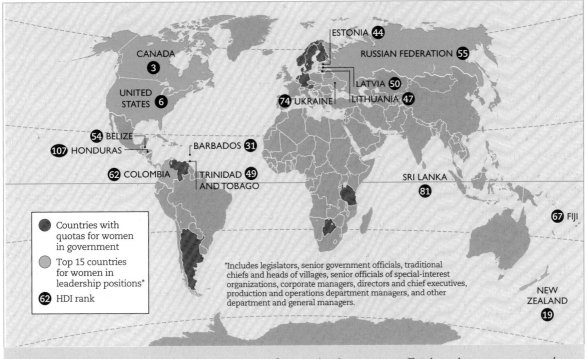

Figure 26–2 *Top 15 countries based on percentage of women legislators, senior officials, and managers compared to their HDI rank.* Source: United Nations Development Programme.

Women in Government: Closing Ranks

1. Examine Figure 26–3, which lists the top and bottom 15 countries of the world according to the Human Development Index. Next to each country is the percentage of government seats held by women in 2001.
a) For each of the top 15 countries, write down the names of the countries in the bottom 15 that have a higher percentage of women in government.
b) Explain any surprises you have found.
c) Suggest possible reasons why some countries in Figure 26-3B have a higher percentage of women in government than some countries in Figure 26-3A.

d) Does a high HDI ranking indicate that there will be a high percentage of women in a government's legislature?

2. a) Which of the top 15 countries in Figure 26–2 are in the top 15 HDI rankings in Figure 26–3?
b) What does this tell you about the access of women to decision-making positions in the countries with the highest HDI rankings?
c) Is the HDI ranking a good indicator of the advancement of women into decision-making positions? Explain why or why not.

A: HDI Ranking, Top 15 Countries

HDI Rank	Country	Seats in Legislature Held by Women (%)
1	Norway	36.4
2	Australia	25.4
3	Canada	23.6
4	Sweden	42.7
5	Belgium	24.9
6	United States	13.8
7	Iceland	34.9
8	Netherlands	32.9
9	Japan	10.8
10	Finland	36.5
11	Switzerland	22.4
12	Luxembourg	16.7
13	France	9.1
14	United Kingdom	17.0
15	Denmark	37.4

B: HDI Ranking, Bottom 15 Countries

HDI Rank	Country	Seats in Legislature Held by Women (%)
148	Eritrea	14.7
149	Gambia	2.0
150	Guinea	8.8
151	Malawi	9.3
152	Rwanda	25.7
153	Mali	12.2
154	Central African Republic	7.3
155	Chad	2.4
156	Guinea-Bissau	7.8
157	Mozambique	30.0
158	Ethiopia	7.8
159	Burkina Faso	11.0
160	Burundi	14.4
161	Niger	1.2
162	Sierra Leone	8.8

Figure 26–3 *Top and bottom 15 countries of the Human Development Index: Percentage of government seats held by women, 2001.* Source: United Nations Development Programme.

Human Rights and War

Soldiers are not the only victims of war. Civilians in war zones, especially women and children, also suffer death and injury. They face severe difficulties when food production and distribution are disrupted, when law and order breaks down, and when basic needs for potable water, medical care, shelter, and clothing cannot be met. Women and children are often the innocent victims of landmines and bombing "mistakes." Even war-time sanctions imposed by external nations tend to affect women and children most severely because any available medical and food supplies are directed to military and governmental officials. Women and children also become victims of serious human rights abuses that occur as a result of war.

In 2001, the United Nations estimated that 300 000 children, mostly boys under 18 and some as young as eight, were fighting in 34 conflicts around the world in countries such as Angola, Colombia, Mozambique, Ethiopia, Guatemala, Sri Lanka, Sudan, Lebanon, Sierra Leone, and El Salvador. The use of child soldiers is escalating as governments, opposition movements, and guerrilla factions recruit or kidnap children from streets, schools, and orphanages. Child soldiers are valued because they are expendable and obedient, and do not ask to be paid. They are easily indoctrinated, sometimes through the use of drugs, sometimes through exposure to brutalizing acts of violence. They are given a range of military duties, but are especially effective as messengers and spies because they are small and inconspicuous. Moreover, the proliferation of light, relatively inexpensive, and easy-to-operate weapons has made child soldiering more feasible.

Some armed groups work through the school system to indoctrinate children who then volunteer to become soldiers. Some children volunteer simply in an effort to survive the chaos of war, particularly if they have been orphaned or separated from their families. Others are willing to fight because they have grown up knowing no alternative to warfare.

The international community has taken action to curb the use of child soldiers. The UN Child Soldiers Protocol of January 2000 stipulates that no child under the age of 18 can be recruited or required to engage in conflicts of any kind. Whether this treaty will reduce the number of child soldiers remains to be seen.

During times of conflict, the breakdown of law and order in war zones takes a terrible toll on women and girls. In societies where they have less status, women often suffer higher incidences of neglect and violence during times of war. Rape is considered a weapon because it humiliates and demoralizes both civilian and military populations. It is especially widespread in conflicts where ethnic cleansing is a primary objective, because causing women to bear the enemy's children destroys family relationships and weakens cultural stability. Women who become pregnant through rape are often ostracized by their society or considered unmarriageable. Many abandon their babies at birth.

The Geneva Convention of 1949, which codifies the laws regarding armed conflict, neglected to specify sexual violence against women as a war crime. It was not until the 1993 UN World Conference on Human Rights in Vienna that sexual atrocities against women were condemned as human rights violations. In 1995, the Fourth World Conference on Women in Beijing recognized that as a result of armed conflict, women suffer not only sexual violence, but also many social, economic, and traumatic consequences.

You can learn more about the campaign to eliminate the use of child soldiers, and the UN response to sexual violence during armed conflict, at <www.pearsoned.ca/globalconnections>.

Human Rights and Children

Children are among the most vulnerable of the world's citizens. As a result, they suffer some of the most abusive conditions. Because they cannot speak for themselves, they must rely on others to speak for them.

Child Labour

The exact number of children worldwide who work is unknown. The International Labour Organization recently estimated that more than 80 million (some under the age of 14) work in hazardous conditions such as fireworks manufacturing, stone quarrying, or the sex trade. Children are considered desirable workers for a variety of reasons, depending on the industry. For example, their sharp eyes are ideal for weaving carpets or doing fine needlework. More generally, children can be paid less than adults, and seldom are able to stand up for their rights (Figure 26–4).

Figure 26–4 *Kra Nhana, age 13, pulls a 44-gallon drum of water in Phnom Penh, Cambodia. He makes this trip eight to 10 times a day, travelling from Phnom Penh to a village one and a half kilometres away, where he sells the water to villagers for double the price it cost him to buy.*

Some authorities suggest that child labour is a necessary evil in the face of widespread poverty in the world, and that child labour will continue until the problems of poverty are overcome. Because many parents cannot afford to support their families, their children must work to supplement the family income. Many governments in developing nations feel that child labour is needed to sustain and increase economic growth. This does not necessarily mean that they support dangerous or exploitative forms of child labour. They point out that child labour was a common feature of industrialization in Western Europe and North America.

Experts suggest that several factors must be considered in determining the seriousness of child labour.

- The age of the child. There is a big difference between a four-year-old and a 16-year-old in the labour force.
- The work conditions to which the child is exposed. Compare the situation of a child working in a dangerous fireworks factory to that of a child weaving in the family home.
- Whether the work hinders the child's ability to get an education.

The fight against child labour occurs at many levels. The most obvious is the legal one. Child labour is illegal under the provisions of the United Nations and under laws that exist in most countries. The problem is that governments do not always have the will or resources to enforce these laws.

Child labour can also be fought in the world's marketplaces. Some of the products made by child workers, clothing for example, are sold in developed countries. NGOs have been established to make consumers aware of the role of child labour in producing these items, but it is difficult for consumers to monitor the use of child labour thousands of kilometres away. Boycotts are only marginally successful, since only a small percentage of the products may be exported to developed countries. Campaigns against child labour can also fail to help children much. A successful campaign in one business may simply force children into another, possibly more dangerous, line of work.

Another way of assisting children is being tried in many countries that practise child labour. Projects have been created that recognize the economic necessity of child labour and yet provide children with a practical education that will serve them well in adulthood. One example is a project for homeless street children in Brazil. Children are taken off the street and given a chance to live, work, and learn in a "children's village." They receive lessons in woodworking and other crafts, along with basic academic training. The furniture and other products that the children make are sold to help pay for the program.

Child Poverty

Some children in Canada face situations that are abusive under the terms of the Universal Declaration. In 2000, a UN report, *Child Poverty in Rich Nations*, estimated that 47 million children live in poverty in the 23 wealthiest nations in the world. Canada did not do very well in this report, which calculated the rate of child poverty in Canada at15.5 per cent. This means that more than one million Canadian children lived below the poverty line. This is not a new problem. The House of Commons voted unanimously in 1989 to eliminate child poverty in Canada by 2000. But by 2000, the number of children living in poverty was 28 per cent higher than in 1989. The use of food banks almost doubled during these years, and about 40 per cent of the food provided went to children.

There was also a dramatic increase in the number of homeless families with children.

Why did this happen? Canada experienced a period of slow economic growth during the 1990s. Government deficits increased, and governments responded by reducing spending and cutting taxes. While these actions proved positive for many people, they were devastating for the economically vulnerable, including poor families. There was less money for affordable housing, subsidized day care, and education.

Protecting the Rights of the Child

Few people would dispute that the rights of children are worthy of the highest possible protection. While the provisions of the Universal Declaration of Human Rights generally cover the rights of children, the international community agreed that more specific protection was needed. The result was the **Convention on the Rights of the Child**, adopted by the United Nations in 1989. By 2001, this agreement had been ratified by every country in the world except Somalia and the United States. The purpose of the Convention is to ensure the following rights:

- right to life
- right to be free from discrimination
- right to be protected in armed conflicts
- right to be protected from torture or cruel, inhumane, or degrading treatment or punishment

- right to be free from arbitrary deprivation of liberty
- right to special treatment within the justice system
- right to education, health care, and an adequate standard of living
- right to be free from economic exploitation and other abuse.

Since the adoption of the Convention, considerable progress has been made. Many countries have ensured that their own child protection laws meet the Convention's requirements. In some countries, senior government officials have been appointed as children's advocates. However, much remains to be done before all children worldwide can feel safe.

You can learn more about attempts to protect the rights of children at <www.pearsoned.ca/globalconnections>.

Slavery in the 21st Century

Slavery in one form or another still exists in the world today. Traditional slavery can be found in the societies of Mauritania, Niger, and Sudan, the first two of which have a **caste** system. Castes are hereditary social classes. Members of a higher caste can own people in the lowest or slave caste. Slaves who manage to attain their freedom may still have to pay tribute to their former owners. This is the least significant form of slavery in the world today.

In Sudan, the situation is somewhat different. Northern and southern Sudan are ethnically and religiously distinct from each other. Militia groups from the north abduct women and children from the south and sell them to families in the north. An NGO called Christian Solidarity began a campaign to free these slaves by purchasing them from their abductors. The going price was about $75 each. Over a five-year period in the late 1990s, Christian Solidarity reported that they were able to free about 40 000 people. Critics of the group, including UNICEF (United Nations Children's Fund), argued that the purchase of slaves served only to encourage slavers to abduct even more people.

Bonded labour is the most common form of slavery. In 1999, the UN estimated that there were about 20 million bonded labourers worldwide, about half of whom were in India. In this form of slavery, people who borrow money from an individual or company cannot repay the loan because of high interest rates. Instead, they must continue to work for that individual or company. Bonded labourers are frequently farm workers, domestic workers, carpet weavers, or sex-trade workers.

Trafficking in people can also lead to a form of bonded labour. People who want to migrate to another country borrow the money for their trip from smugglers who agree to transport them to their country of choice (see Chapter 8, Population Migration). They are told that they can earn enough in the new country to pay for their passage. When they arrive, they find themselves in a form of bonded labour, because they can never earn enough money to pay off their debt. The US government estimates that between 700 000 and 2 000 000 women and children (along with an unknown number of men) are smuggled across international borders each year (Figure 26–5).

Forced labour is usually imposed by a government or paramilitary group. In this form of slavery, the threat of violence or other intimidation coerces people into working against their will. One example of this is the Laogai system in China. Political prisoners, such as members of the Falun Dafa religious group, are sent to Laogai camps until they are no longer considered a threat to the state. While there, they work on farms and in factories. More than 200 products from these camps are sold on the international market. Observers suggest that as many as 1000 Laogai camps, holding as many as eight million people, existed in China in 2001.

You can learn more about modern slavery at <www.pearsoned.ca/globalconnections>.

Figure 26–5 *In 1999, 190 illegal migrants crowded aboard this "mystery ship" for passage from China to the west coast of Vancouver Island.*

The Issue of Cultural Exceptionalism

Why is the fight for human rights so difficult? One reason is the increase in feelings of cultural exceptionalism—the idea that the traditions of a country are more important than a universal concept of human rights. In 2000, during the Taliban rule in Afghanistan, a woman could be stoned to death for adultery. By the standards of the Declaration, this is a clear violation of human rights. But by the prevailing morality and laws of Afghanistan at that time, it was an acceptable punishment. The outrage of the international community was clear and vocal, but was considered irrelevant by the Taliban.

Consider the question of capital punishment. In almost the entire developed world, capital punishment is regarded as inappropriate and unacceptable. The exception to this is the United States. In many American states and federally, capital punishment is mandated for first-degree murder and for a few other crimes. When criticized for their use of capital punishment, Americans often reply that this is the business of citizens of the United States. This was exactly the argument used by the Taliban to explain their actions. Both situations are examples of cultural exceptionalism. The United States and the Taliban both believe that their use of capital punishment does not constitute a human rights abuse because each society considers it an acceptable penalty for certain crimes.

Canada also may be charged with cultural exceptionalism for its treatment of Aboriginal peoples. A disproportionate number of Aboriginal people suffer serious social ills, such as poverty and disease. The Canadian government, and many Canadian citizens, have responded to international criticism in a manner similar to that of the Taliban and the United States—that how we treat our citizens is our business. Similar situations can be found in virtually every country in the world.

The essential question of human rights in the world today is how to reconcile the sovereignty of individual nations and cultures with a cultural globalization that favours a universal view of human rights.

Chapter Questions

Knowledge and Understanding

1. How would respect for human rights help prevent war?

2. At the beginning of this chapter, you had the opportunity to list what you consider to be vital human rights. Compare your list with the rights described in the articles of the Universal Declaration. Identify which article corresponds to each of the rights in your list. Which articles did you miss? Why might you have missed them?

3. The Universal Declaration of Human Rights has been described as a "blueprint for the future of humanity." Do you agree or disagree? Explain.

4. Describe the socio-economic and political obstacles that confront women who seek elected office.

5. a) What is meant by "critical mass" in the political process?
   b) Why is it important for a critical mass to be achieved if women are to gain political equity?

6. What are the less obvious forms of destruction that occur as a result of war, and how do they affect people's lives?

7. In what ways do forced labour and bonded labour deny people their human rights?

9. a) Some of the rights described in the Universal Declaration are denied to a relatively small number of people in the world. Identify at least two such rights, and the people who are denied them.
   b) Other rights are not available to large numbers of people in many countries. Identify at least two of these.
   c) Some of these rights are not available to all Canadians. Identify at least two of these, and explain why this happens.

10. What are the similarities and differences between child soldiers and youth gangs?

11. Use the Universal Declaration to identify three examples of human rights abuses (other than poverty) against children in Canada. For each, identify the article, and briefly explain the nature of the abuse.

12. It is fair to assume that the United States supports the idea that the rights of children deserve protection. Keeping this in mind, investigate why the United States has not ratified the Convention on the Rights of the Child. Why has Somalia not ratified it?

13. Examine the map in Figure 26–2. Describe world, continental, and regional patterns of those countries in which the importance of women in government is recognized. Suggest reasons for the patterns that you observe.

Thinking and Inquiry

8. Since the Universal Declaration of Human Rights came into effect in 1948, many political movements have developed based on the demand for recognition of the rights enumerated in the Declaration. One example is Child Labour Day. Identify at least two other movements, and explain how they are linked to the articles of the Declaration.

Communication

14. Prepare to debate the statement below. Your teacher will tell you which side of the debate to prepare for. *Resolved—That it is a mistake for aid groups to buy slaves in Sudan.*

15. Prepare a short report explaining the pros and cons of establishing a quota system to ensure that women have access to a certain number of seats in Canadian government.

16. Write a letter to the editor in which you outline recommendations that have been made for increasing the number of women in government. Add some more of your own suggestions.

17. Develop a plan of action and gather information to prepare a report about the extent of child labour in an Asian country such as India, Pakistan, Bangladesh, or Cambodia.

Application

18. Assume that you have decided to take up the mantle of John Peters Humphrey. How would you amend the Universal Declaration of Human Rights to meet the needs of the 21st century? Explain your reasoning.

19. The Fraser Institute is an organization that supports a neo-liberal economic agenda. What relationship might there be between this political slant and the fact that a report they published had an estimate of child poverty that was significantly lower than that of either the United Nations or Statistics Canada?

20. Government is not the only place where the representation of women in decision-making positions needs to be increased. A report in 1999 of the Fortune 500 companies indicated that only 11.9 per cent of corporate officers were women and that women held only 5.1 per cent of the highest positions.
    a) What barriers are there for the advancement of women in corporations?
    b) What is being done to remove these barriers to advancement?

21. Does cultural exceptionalism exist in Canada regarding Aboriginal peoples? Investigate the federal government's treatment of Aboriginal peoples and compare your findings with the Universal Declaration of Human Rights. Cite specific articles from the Declaration to support your views.

27

Empowerment in a Globalized World

Expectations

In this chapter, you will:

- explain how point of view and paradigm influence perception

- understand the roles and status of women and men in different world regions

- evaluate the signifi-cance of non-violent movements to protect environments

- identify individuals who have addressed global issues

- explain how local participation can build sustainable communities

- evaluate the role of NGOs and local com-munity initiatives in sus-tainable development

- identify practical applications in the com-munity of conclusions reached by inquiry

This coffee picker sells her produce to a transnational company that buys it at the lowest possible price. How does this low price affect her? How can citizens convince a distant government to care about environmental damage in their local area? What can people do when they cannot get the credit they need to build a business? This chapter explores some answers to these questions.

Powerlessness versus Empowerment

The problem with globalization is that it is so *global*. In other words, the world is so large and its population so great that individuals often feel insignificant and unable to control important aspects of their lives. Today, this is especially true when strangers make decisions that affect people halfway around the world. These decisions are frequently made without regard to the impact they will have on people or the environment. As a result, many individuals feel they are powerless to manage their own lives.

People react to feelings of powerlessness in a variety of ways. Some do nothing, believing that the global forces they face are just too powerful to overcome. Others may take to the streets to protest the movement towards globalization at meetings of the World Trade Organization or the G8. Still others respond by finding ways to empower themselves to solve the environmental, economic, political, or social problems they face.

Empowerment is the act of taking authority or control over some aspect of your life.

In this chapter, you will have a chance to learn about just a few of the many **community initiatives** that have been developed all over the world to allow individuals, working together, to find solutions to their problems.

India's "Tree Huggers"— The Chipko Movement

Much of India is mountainous and hilly terrain that is covered by lush forests (Figure 27–1). As in Canada, these forests are an important source of commercial products. More significantly, they provide food for people and animals, as well as fuel for cooking and heating. In addition, particularly in the hilly areas of northern India, forests provide protection from soil erosion.

Figure 27–1 *Many of India's hilly regions are suitable for commercial forestry. (Right) An Indian logger displays a large log from a hardwood tree. Logging of hardwood trees is widespread, especially in the country's northeast.*

India has a population that now stands at over one billion. Consequently, the country's forests have been under great pressure for decades. The demand for lumber and the destruction associated with cutting timber have caused deforestation. Deforestation has accelerated soil erosion, caused flooding and landslides, and damaged the water supply. It has also lowered the quality of life for those living in forested areas by reducing available food and fuel.

As early as 1904, residents of rural villages fought India's British-led government to protect their forests. They wanted to limit both settlement by outsiders and development by companies that cut down the forests for profit while returning nothing to the local area. Their protests were an early example of **civil disobedience**, the intentional and non-violent breaking of a law that one considers unjust. Civil disobedience includes taking responsibility for one's illegal actions, because willingness to accept punishment demonstrates the strength of one's beliefs.

India's forest protests continued sporadically after 1904, but the number and intensity increased after 1973. These protests followed the civil disobedience model that Mohandas Gandhi had used so successfully in India's fight for independence from the British. The rural villagers fought to protect their forests by physically placing themselves between the trees and the loggers, often by hugging the trees. Since the Hindi word for "to hug" or "to stick to" is *chipko*, the protests became known as the **Chipko Movement**. (The term "tree hugger" is now often used derisively to refer to any type of environmentalist.)

Chipko was primarily a movement of rural women who wanted to protect the forests that were vital sources of food and fuel for their families. Women's active role in this movement was based on several historical factors.

- During the 1940s, a group of women, some of whom were disciples of Gandhi, became active **agents of social change** in the logging debate. They identified the problems associated with logging in the foothills of the Himalayas and helped to organize the Chipko protest.
- Because women did most of the forest harvesting for food and fuel, they were keenly aware of the close relationship between the health of the forests and the social and economic well-being of their families.
- The Chipko Movement of the 1970s was not the first female-led protest in northern India. In 1965, thousands of women fought a successful battle against the opening of government liquor shops.
- As a result of increasing poverty in the highlands of northern India, many men migrated to the great cities in the south to find work, leaving behind a woman-dominated society.

The goal of the Chipko protests was to make the distant Indian government aware of the fact that the forests were being seriously damaged, and that they were important for more than just commercial forestry. The struggle was one based on fundamentally different ideas about the relationship between nature and human beings and about private versus public ownership of resources. (Chapter 3 examined the conflicts that arise from such differing points of view.) The Indian government, and the businesses that were cutting down the forests, believed in the industrial, Western concept that progress is more

Did you KNOW?

The British East India Company dominated India from the 1770s until 1858, when the British government put India under its direct control. Mohandas Gandhi became world-famous in the 20th century for leading the movement for independence from Britain, using the techniques of civil disobedience, or passive resistance as he called it. India became independent in 1947.

important than nature, and that nature exists to serve human needs. The local people held the more traditional, non-industrial belief that humans exist as part of nature and should do nothing to destroy its balance. They also believed that resources should be available to all, not controlled by just landowners or governments.

The Chipko women faced many obstacles. Their role in society was limited by cultural norms. They lacked access to adequate means of communication, such as the telephone. Since many of their followers were unable to read, the movement had to grow by word of mouth. Early in Chipko's history, its leaders decided to make long treks to educate people about the issues and to publicize their protest. These journeys were time-consuming and arduous, especially for those who had many family responsibilities. In one case, a group trekked 5000 km.

The Chipko Movement's first great victory came in 1980, when Prime Minister Indira Gandhi agreed to a 15-year ban on logging in several vital forest areas. In addition, Chipko pushed the government to adopt a comprehensive forest conservation policy. The Chipko Movement continues its fight today to protect the forests that are vital to the small farmers of northern India. Its representatives do this by continuing to push for sustainable forestry policies. While the Chipko Movement has had numerous successes, the struggle is far from over, as India continues to suffer significant deforestation each year.

Microcredit

Microcredit is the provision of small sums of money to people to help them develop a better livelihood and break out of the cycle of poverty. It was pioneered by Muhammad Yunus, a Bangladeshi academic who had returned to his homeland in 1972 after completing a doctoral degree in economics in the United States.

You can learn more about the role that women played in the Chipko Movement at <www.pearsoned.ca/globalconnections>.

Bangladesh's Grameen Bank

The Grameen Bank is a community initiative that began with a chance meeting between Dr. Yunus and a young woman who made bamboo stools. Yunus was appalled to learn that the stool-maker earned only three cents a day for her work and lived in grinding poverty. The reason for her poverty was distressingly simple: her only source of raw materials was the person who bought the finished stools. Because the same person set the price of both the raw materials and the finished product, he had complete control of the transaction. Furthermore, the man would supply materials only for stools that the woman would sell to him. Had the stool-maker been able to accumulate 30 to 40 cents, she could have bought bamboo from other suppliers and made more stools to sell to a variety of buyers.

Yunus was shocked to realize that for the sake of little more than a quarter, this woman was doomed to a life of abject poverty. He wondered if her situation was common, and if an individual could do anything to help alleviate such poverty. A few days' research in the village where the stool-maker lived identified 42 such people who needed a total of only about $40 to dramatically improve their ability to earn a living. Yunus gave these 42 people the money they needed in the form of loans, which they used to invest in the making of stools, pots, and other products. He told them to pay him back when they could. The villagers were able to improve their standard of living and repaid the loans. With this simple experiment, Yunus identified the potential of microcredit. But this was only the beginning of the story.

Yunus's next move was to approach the banks of Bangladesh. He demonstrated the desperate need of Bangladesh's poorest people for small amounts of credit and described the success of his experiment—but the bankers dismissed him. They said the poor could offer no collateral to guarantee their loans. (Collateral is a key feature of most bank loans. For example, when you get a car loan, the car is the collateral. If you do not make your loan payments, the bank can seize the car to cover its loss.) The bankers also told Yunus that the poor would not be able to pay back their loans. Finally, they believed the loans involved were so tiny that they were not worth the bother to process and administer. The only thing that Yunus could do was borrow money in his own name, and use it to provide loans to the poor.

In spite of warnings from bankers that poor people were a bad credit risk, the rate of repayment from Yunus's borrowers turned out to be remarkably high—far higher than the rate the banks received from their wealthier, more "creditworthy," clientele. Yunus's scheme continued to expand until he was providing microcredit loans in more than 100 villages. But he was still unable to interest the banks in microcredit.

Yunus realized that while his small efforts had been successful beyond all expectation, a more formal organization was necessary if the scheme were to expand. He concluded that if existing banks would not provide credit to the poor, a new kind of bank should be set up. In 1983, the Grameen Bank was established to provide small loans to people. In less than 15 years from its founding, the Grameen Bank had grown to the point that it operated in 36 000 villages and had more than two million borrowers (Figure 27–2). By 1994, microcredit loans in Bangladesh had expanded from Yunus's initial $40 to more than

Figure 27–2 *A volunteer worker meets with a group of women seeking loans to start small businesses in the Manikgonj district of Bangladesh, north of the capital city of Dhaka. Microcredit loans have helped over two million people in Bangladesh since the early 1980s.*

$1.5 billion. More than one-third of the borrowers had been able to rise above the poverty line, and another third were approaching it. More importantly, the Grameen Bank had become the model for similar schemes in almost 60 other countries. The specifics of microcredit are adjusted to meet the needs of each country.

The Grameen Bank of Bangladesh operates under the following principles.

- Loans are made at market rates and must be paid back within one year. A borrower who repays a small loan becomes eligible for a larger loan. Most loans are less than $50.
- More than 90 per cent of the borrowers are women. They are given priority because the economic potential of Bangladeshi women has generally not been appreciated. As well, experience has shown that the money earned by women is much more likely to be spent on their children than money earned by men.
- Borrowers are set up in groups of five. The women in the group provide moral support for one another and critique the business plan of any member who wishes to take out a loan. If one member of the group defaults on a loan, all members are cut off from future loans. This tactic emphasizes each member's responsibility to succeed and not let others down.
- Because the ultimate goal of the Grameen Bank is social development rather than profit, borrowers must agree to certain conditions. For example, they agree to limit the size of their family and to boil their drinking water. It has been found that twice as many "Grameen families" adopt family planning practices compared with Bangladeshi families that have not become involved with microcredit.

You can learn about a variety of lending models at <www.pearsoned.ca/globalconnections>.

Microcredit in Canada

Canada is one of the countries to which Dr. Yunus's idea has spread. While the scale of poverty in Canada is much smaller than that in Bangladesh, there are many Canadians who find themselves in a position similar to that of the young stool-maker: they are involved in what is called a microenterprise. In Canada, a microenterprise is defined as a non-farm business that is not incorporated and has no paid employees. Microentrepreneurs are typically women who earn less than they would if they were employees, or were entrepreneurs with paid employees. Most of their businesses are less than two years old.

About 15 per cent of Canadian microentrepreneurs who need financing are not able to qualify for conventional loans from banks or from the government agencies that support small business. The reasons that they cannot get loans are the same as those faced by the poor in developing countries—they have not established a positive credit history, they do not have a formal business plan, and they do not have collateral against which to borrow money. Beyond these formal barriers to getting a loan, there are informal barriers as well. Microentrepreneurs often lack the experience and confidence to deal with banks or government bureaucracies. Also, they may operate in the informal economy and are afraid to reveal this status to the government. Finally, as in Bangladesh, the banks tend to view such small loans as more trouble than they are worth.

In 2001, there were 34 non-profit loan funds across Canada, serving about 1200 borrowers. These funds barely scratched the surface; it was estimated that some 127 000 microentrepreneurs were unable to obtain credit from regular banks or government agencies. This gap between supply and demand in microcredit exists largely because microcredit agencies lack sufficient financial resources to fill the demand.

According to Dr. Yunus, poverty exists to a great extent because society has created institutions, including banks and governments, that discriminate against a wide variety of people, including the poor. The discrimination is not necessarily deliberate; more often, it reflects a lack of understanding about people's practical situations. The ultimate solution lies in recognizing that institutions have a responsibility to ensure that all people have the same access to respect and human dignity. To achieve this, we must redesign society's institutions. To date, there has been considerable discussion in organizations including the United Nations and the World Bank about what should be done. But few substantive changes have been made.

Free Trade versus Fair Trade

Free trade is a fundamental part of the economic globalization that has been such an important trend since the late 1980s. It allows commodities to be produced and sold as cheaply as possible. As a result, people have greater access to goods, and economic growth is promoted.

When there is free trade, each nation or region will focus on producing commodities for which it has the greatest **comparative advantage**, that is, the advantage of producing goods better and more cheaply than other nations (Figure 27–3). With the elimination of trade barriers under free trade, Canada has experienced economic growth based primarily on its comparative advantage (its rich natural resource base and advanced manufacturing), as has China based on its comparative advantage (its immense, cheap labour force).

Critics contend that there are many people who do not benefit from free trade even if it is efficient and promotes economic growth in general. Agricultural and manufacturing workers in developing countries in particular bear the brunt of the constant competition that free trade entails. For example, if farmers do not keep their production costs low, then purchasers will buy the same product where prices are lower. Farmers therefore accept a very low price for their produce just to stay in the market. If industry does not keep its labour costs low, then it too runs the risk of losing jobs to other countries where labour costs are even lower. Workers in developing countries suffer because they have to accept low wages just to keep their jobs. Fair trade is one way of addressing this problem.

The terms "free trade" and **"fair trade"** sound alike, but they have very different meanings and implications for the poor. Free trade is based on the belief that a free market economy works best for everybody. Fair trade is based on the belief that marginalized and disadvantaged producers

	Country A	Country B
Corn	10% advantage results in a...	10% disadvantage
Soybeans	30% advantage results in a...	30% disadvantage

Figure 27–3 *Country A has a comparative advantage of 10 per cent for corn and 30 per cent for soybean production over Country B. Since Country A has a greater comparative advantage in the production of soybeans, it will focus on producing this crop. Country B has a comparative disadvantage in both crops. However, it will focus on producing corn because its comparative disadvantage is less for corn than for soybeans.*

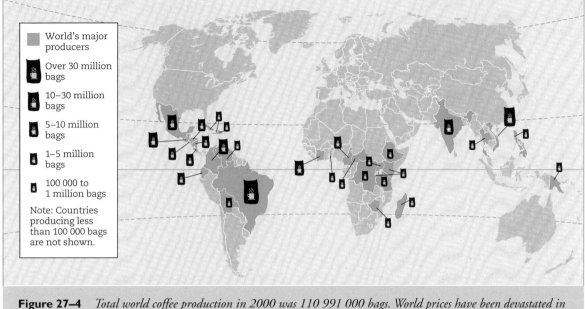

Figure 27–4 *Total world coffee production in 2000 was 110 991 000 bags. World prices have been devastated in recent decades by the enormous growth in production in Brazil and Vietnam. These two countries now produce almost 40 per cent of the world's supply.* Source: International Coffee Organization (ICO).

in developing countries do not benefit from free trade. Fair trade supporters believe that the poor can benefit only if the free market system is regulated to some degree. To illustrate how producers in developing countries can benefit from fair trade, consider the production of coffee.

Fair Trade in Coffee

About 15 billion cups of coffee are drunk in the world each day. Each cup is the culmination of a long supply chain that begins in the tropical upland areas of countries such as Brazil, Vietnam, and Côte d'Ivoire (Figure 27–4).

The greatest part of the price that a consumer pays for coffee does not go to the farmer who grew and dried the coffee "cherries" (so called because of the deep red colour of the ripe beans). For each dollar that a consumer pays for coffee, about 10 cents goes to the grower, another 10 cents to the local buyer (called a "coyote"), and 55 cents to the shipper and roaster, usually a large company such as Nestlé or Kraft General Foods that actually makes the coffee product that the consumer buys. Twenty-five cents goes to the retailer, namely, the grocery store or coffee-house from whom the consumer buys the product.

This economic system provides, at best, a meagre living for the farmers when world coffee prices are high. When coffee prices are low—which is usually the case unless the supply drops for some reason (Figure 27–5)—the farmers suffer even more. In recent years, coffee prices have dropped significantly for two reasons. First, since the late 1980s, there have been few crop failures in Brazil, the world's largest producer, or in any of the other major coffee-growing countries. The second, and more significant, reason is that during the 1990s, Vietnam, formerly a minor grower, became the world's second-largest producer. The increased supply of coffee throughout the world lowered the farmers' sale price, and even though the cost of a cup of coffee remained the same at coffee-houses, the growers got even less for their product. The coffee growers' income will rise to a higher level only if a disaster such as frost or drought reduces the world's supply.

Figure 27–5 *World coffee prices, 1982–2001. Prices are traditionally given in terms of US dollars per pound. The fair trade price is US$1.26 per pound.* Source: International Coffee Organization (ICO).

The world coffee market is dominated by a few large buyers who buy from producers with the lowest prices. In order to make a sale, producers are forced to keep their prices low. They accomplish this by keeping their output high. To grow as much coffee as possible, they use potent herbicides and pesticides that cause serious health risks to planters and their families.

The world price of coffee often drops to less than US$1 per pound, leaving farmers with an income of less than 10 cents for each pound they produce. If the principle of fair trade is applied to coffee production, growers get a fair return for their efforts. Under the fair trade scheme, growers are guaranteed a minimum price of US$1.26 per pound. If the free market price goes higher than the minimum, the growers will get at least five cents more per pound than the free market price. If it goes lower, the growers continue to receive US$1.26. This is accomplished by reducing the number of steps in the supply chain that takes coffee to market. In particular, the coyotes

and the shippers/roasters are eliminated. They are replaced by growers' cooperatives that market the coffee directly to fair trade importers in the developed world.

In developed countries, fair trade focusses on two activities: replacing the commercial shippers/roasters with non-profit equivalents, and finding retailers willing to sell fair market coffee. In most developed countries, non-profit groups have emerged to distribute fair trade coffee. Fair trade products are marked with a distinctive logo, indicating that they were produced and marketed following fair trade principles. In Canada, this is the TransFair certification label (Figure 27–6). Other countries have similar distinctive marks. Fair trade coffee is generally more expensive than free market brands and is most readily available in smaller, specialty food stores or over the Internet. However, it has made little progress in finding its way into supermarkets and large coffee chains. Until customers ask for it, fair trade coffee will be slow to spread to these mainstream sources.

Figure 27–6 *The TransFair certification label, a fair trade logo for products in Canada*

Fair trade is still in its infancy. It has not yet been fully developed in the coffee market, or in similar schemes that exist for some other tropical agricultural products (tea, sugar, bananas) and some traditional handicrafts. All these commodities have one thing in common: they require relatively little processing in order to travel from the worker in a developing country to the purchaser in a developed country. Generally speaking, instituting fair trade for other items, such as brand-name manufactured goods, is more problematic.

Taking the Initiative in Your Community

How does a community initiative, such as those described in this chapter, begin? First, people must be able to identify a problem, or several related problems that threaten their well-being. The problem may be environmental, social, ethical, or political. Second, someone—a Dr. Yunus, for example—must identify a possible way to tackle the problem. This person must have not only an idea, but also the courage to translate that idea into action.

Can one person bring about world peace? Reverse global warming? Eliminate poverty? Probably not—at least, not all at once. But there is evidence that one person can make a difference. A young Canadian, Craig Kielburger (Figure 27–7), was only 12 years old when he began a campaign against child labour in the developing world. He had been horrified to learn of the murder of a 12-year-old child labour activist in Pakistan, and wanted to do something about it. He created an organization called Free the Children that has worked since the mid-1990s to eliminate child labour in the developing world. Kielburger's efforts have done much to bring the plight of these young workers to the world's attention.

If you would like to learn about Free the Children and 50 other outstanding examples of community activism, go to <www.pearsoned.ca/globalconnections>.

Figure 27–7 *Activist Craig Kielburger talks about child labour with Munna, a 10-year-old food vendor at a market in New Delhi, India, in 1996.*

The PIR Approach

How would you organize an initiative to address an issue? You could use the **PIR** (**Planning, Implementation, Review**) approach.

Planning

Effective planning is the best way to ensure that your initiative will be successful. You must be certain that you understand the problem you wish to help solve. Your study of world issues is a good starting point, but you must investigate all aspects of the problem. This might include doing research on the Internet or contacting those directly involved in the situation to get answers to your questions. You might also wish to survey your classmates or members of your community, so that you are aware of the attitudes you will be dealing with in your efforts.

Implementation

Identify the resources that are available to help you in your class and school. Beyond your school, a variety of people and organizations may be able to provide expertise and, in some cases, financial aid. Local, national, and international non-governmental organizations in your field of interest may be able to help. Local service groups, such as the Lions and Kiwanis clubs, and religious organizations may also be useful.

Plan a campaign that is realistic for the time that you have available. Your goal should be achievable so that you can experience some measure of success. A good approach is to establish a series of staged targets. When one is achieved, then you can work towards the next one. You should determine whether your initiative will be active for a fixed period of time or will continue indefinitely. If the latter, build in a way for new people to take over when those who started it leave the school or end their involvement with the project.

Figure 27–8 *Profits from Beverly Mascoll's personal-care products, which are made for black consumers, go back into the community. Entrepreneurs in the ethnic beauty-products industry are among the most committed agents of social change.*

Review

Build a mechanism into your initiative to review, on an ongoing basis, your progress and to make whatever adjustments are needed in the implementation.

Your Local Initiative

What kind of issues can you work on? Any issue that you feel particularly concerned about. For example, Toronto entrepreneur Beverly Mascoll (Figure 27–8) returns some of the profits from her beauty-products business back into the black community. You are most likely to succeed in an initiative that truly matters to you.

See the questions at the end of this chapter for just a few suggestions for starting your local initiative.

Chapter Questions

Knowledge and Understanding

1. a) In what ways did women play a leading role in the Chipko Movement?
   b) Why was it difficult for them to do so?

2. a) Explain, in general, how a microcredit scheme works.
   b) How do the specific requirements of Grameen Bank loans contribute to the success of the scheme?

3. a) Why do commercial banks have little interest in helping the poor to build successful businesses in both developing and developed countries?
   b) Explain how a microcredit system addresses this problem.

4. Briefly describe the comparative advantage that each of the following has in a globalized economy:
   i) United States
   ii) Southeast Asia (including Vietnam, Cambodia, Thailand)
   iii) Japan

5. How has free trade contributed to the economic marginalization of many workers in the developing world?

6. Explain how fair trade for coffee is accomplished in
   a) a coffee-producing country
   b) a coffee-consuming country.

Thinking and Inquiry

7. Describe one situation in Canada or elsewhere (other than those given in this chapter) that illustrates how globalization has resulted in a loss of local empowerment.

8. Explain why the following statement is true: "While microcredit may help many poor people, it may be of most help to the poorest of the poor."

9. Why is it difficult to establish fair trade for manufactured goods?

10. What changes could governments and banks make to become less discriminatory towards the poor?

11. Outline the reasons why advocates of free trade might disagree with the concept of fair trade.

Communication

12. Create a one-page handout to encourage people in your community to buy fair trade products. Begin by researching the availability of fair trade products, like coffee, in your community. Include an explanation of the benefits of fair trade, along with information about where people can purchase fair trade products.

13. Make a presentation on the role of women in Indian, Bangladeshi, and Canadian society in a selected area of education, health care, business, or any other field that interests you. Use visual and statistical information to illustrate the similarities and differences you discover.

14. Use the Internet to investigate the efforts of Habitat for Humanity to construct homes in Canada and abroad. Prepare a presentation, using transparencies or PowerPoint, to explain this group's principles. If there is a chapter in your community or region, perhaps you can arrange for a guest speaker to visit your school.

Application

15. Investigate the different attitudes that exist towards the relationship between people and nature in the Western tradition and in South Asian and/or North American Aboriginal belief systems. What implications do the differences in beliefs have on the way in which resources are used?

16. Research efforts being made to reduce poverty internationally or in Canada by one of the following agencies:
    a) Sleeping Children Around the World
    b) Doctors Without Borders
    c) Mennonite Central Relief Committee
    d) Grameen Bank
    e) Calmeadow
    f) another agency

17. Investigate the supply chain, from grower to your table, of one of the following commodities: sugar, tea, chocolate, spices (such as cinnamon), or bananas. Try to determine prices at each step, and find out how fair trade either could be or has been applied to the commodity.

18. Working in small groups, devise a plan to start your own local initiative, using the PIR approach and the suggestions in Figure 27–9 as a starting point. (Feel free to tackle any other issue that interests you.) Identify appropriate targets for each of the Planning, Implementation, and Review stages.

- Create a chapter of Free the Children at your school to help fight child labour. (Visit www.pearsoned.ca/globalconnections> to find out how.)
- Organize a cleanup of a local ravine or valley.
- Make your schoolmates more aware of the plight of refugees living in camps in war zones.
- Found an environmental club in your school.
- Organize a fund-raising campaign to support the efforts of an international charity like Sleeping Children Around the World or World Vision.
- Plant trees on your school's land, or other vacant land, to provide improved habitats for animals and birds, and to create carbon sinks to fight global warming.
- Publicize and coordinate a campaign in your school to reduce the production of greenhouse gases as a result of travel to and from school.
- Become involved in the work of Amnesty International or another group that fights to protect human rights.
- Collect used clothing for an organization such as Goodwill.
- Become involved with a local food bank.

Figure 27–9 *Some suggestions for community initiatives*

Unit 7: Responsibility and Hope for the Future

Chapter 28: Achieving a Sustainable Future in a Globalized World

Achieving a Sustainable Future in a Globalized World

Expectations

In this chapter, you will:

■ select and compare quality-of-life indicators in different regions

■ evaluate the effectiveness of ways to promote sustainable development

■ assess government policies that promote sustainable resource development in Canada

■ explain the difficulty of making predictions about human use of the Earth

■ compare the biodiversity of selected ecosystems

■ analyze the impacts of urbanization and urban growth

Economic globalization is closely tied to the idea that maximum economic growth is desirable and necessary. Unfortunately, economic growth often leads to reduced sustainability. Today, many people (like the demonstrators, above) are challenging world business and government leaders to find a balance between economic growth and sustainability.

Economic and Social Progress

Sustainability and globalization's drive towards maximum economic growth dominate world issues today. The goals of one, however, conflict with the demands of the other. We must therefore develop lifestyles that enhance living standards at the same time that they protect the environment for use by future generations. Before we can do this, we need to formulate some way to measure our economic success and the progress we are making towards ecological sustainability. Then, when we have the information about the progress we are making, we will have to determine how we should change our behaviour to obtain decent living standards for all in a sustainable manner.

The word *recession* evokes fear in government and business leaders, the media, and the public. During a recession, economic growth declines. Corporations lose sales, governments lose tax revenues, workers lose jobs. But something else happens, as well. The use of fossil fuels declines as factories cut output and people travel less. Other resource use decreases, as the demand falls for metals, forest products, and agricultural goods. Air pollution, global warming, and other environmental degradation lessen. While a recession may be bad for the economy, it is good for the environment.

A recession is defined as a period during which gross domestic product (GDP) declines for two consecutive quarters of one year. Many observers question the GDP's worth as an indicator of economic and social progress. As an example of how GDP can be misleading, critics point to the terrorist attacks on the United States in September 2001. The airplane hijackers had all lived for some time in the United States, spending money on housing, food, transportation, and other expenses. After the attacks, billions of dollars were spent on repairing the damage, increasing border and airline security, and waging a war on terrorism. These expenditures were added to the GDP of the United States and other countries, and so could be seen as contributing to economic progress. Clearly, however, this spending enhanced no one's quality of life.

There are other indicators besides GDP that might assess both economic success and progress towards ecological sustainability.

Measuring Sustainable Development

One of the initiatives taken at the 1992 Earth Summit in Rio de Janeiro, Brazil, was a call for new ways to measure sustainable development. We need to know if the steps we are taking to preserve the environment are sufficient to allow us to continue to take from it what we need. To do this, we have to be able to measure the development that is taking place. In response to this challenge, numerous academics, government agencies, companies, NGOs, and international organizations have suggested a variety of ways to measure sustainability, not only at local community levels but also at world levels.

In 1996, a group of measurement experts and researchers met in Bellagio, Italy, to develop new ways to measure and assess progress towards sustainable development. **The Bellagio Principles** (Figure 28-1) serve as guidelines for assessing progress towards sustainable development, and for choosing, designing, and interpreting sustainable development indicators. They encompass a remarkable range of ideas that are central to the accurate monitoring of progress towards sustainability. Use them to evaluate how effective a particular sustainable development indicator is working.

1. GUIDING VISION AND GOALS

Assessment of progress should:

- be guided by a clear vision of sustainable development and goals that define that vision

2. HOLISTIC PERSPECTIVE

Assessment of progress should:

- consider the well-being of social, ecological, and economic sub-systems, their state as well as the direction and rate of change of that state, of their component parts, and the interaction between parts
- consider both positive and negative consequences of human activity, in a way that reflects the costs and benefits for human and ecological systems, in monetary and non-monetary terms

3. ESSENTIAL ELEMENTS

Assessment of progress should:

- consider equity and disparity within the current population and between present and future generations, dealing with such concerns as resource use, overconsumption and poverty, human rights, and access to services, as appropriate
- consider the ecological conditions on which life depends

4. ADEQUATE SCOPE

Assessment of progress should:

- adopt a time horizon long enough to capture both human and ecosystem time scales, thus responding to needs of future generations as well as those current to short-term decision making
- define the space of study large enough to include not only local but also long-distance impacts on people and ecosystems

5. PRACTICAL FOCUS

Assessment of progress should be based on:

- an explicit set of categories or an organizing framework that links vision and goals to indicators and assessment criteria
- a limited number of key issues for analysis
- standardizing measurement wherever possible to permit comparison

6. OPENNESS

Assessment of progress should:

- make the methods and data that are used accessible to all
- make explicit all judgements, assumptions, and uncertainties in data and interpretations

7. EFFECTIVE COMMUNICATION

Assessment of progress should:

- be designed to address the needs of the audience and set of users
- draw from indicators and other tools that are stimulating and serve to engage decision makers
- aim, from the outset, for simplicity in structure and use of clear and plain language

8. BROAD PARTICIPATION

Assessment of progress should:

- obtain broad representation of key grass-roots, professional, technical, and social groups, including youth, women, and indigenous people—to ensure recognition of diverse and changing values
- ensure the participation of decision makers to secure a firm link to adopted policies and resulting action

9. ONGOING ASSESSMENT

Assessment of progress should:

- develop a capacity for repeated measurement to determine trends
- adjust goals, frameworks, and indicators as new insights are gained
- promote development of collective learning and feedback to decision making

10. INSTITUTIONAL CAPACITY

Continuity of assessing progress towards sustainable development should be assured by:

- clearly assigning responsibility and providing ongoing support in the decision-making process
- supporting development of local assessment capacity

Figure 28–1 *The Bellagio Principles. These principles should be used as guidelines for the practical assessment of progress towards sustainable development.* Source: International Institute for Sustainable Development.

Indicators of Sustainable Development

Indicators of sustainable development fall into two broad categories: specific and comprehensive. **Specific indicators** are single measures, often collected for different statistical purposes, that show progress towards sustainability in one specific area. In contrast, a **comprehensive indicator** shows overall progress towards sustainability.

Specific Indicators

Specific indicators are existing, easily obtained measures. For example, the number of sidewalks determined by a study of the streets of Richmond, BC, was used to measure the improvement of pedestrian safety. This number can also be used as a specific indicator of sustainability. It indicates that less air pollution will be produced because more sidewalks encourage more people to walk rather than drive.

Living Planet Index   In addition to using existing statistics as indicators of sustainable development, we can use a variety of "purpose-built" indicators. One is the Living Planet Index created by the World Wildlife Fund (Figure 28–2). It measures the wealth of species diversity in forests, freshwater ecosystems, and marine ecosystems (Figure 28–3). While this is a useful measure, and one that suggests there is a problem with what you are measuring, it is like most specific indicators—it measures only one aspect of sustainability.

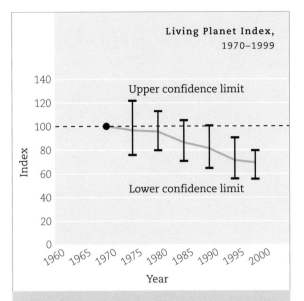

Figure 28–2   *The Living Planet Index is an example of a specific indicator of sustainability. It measures the level of species diversity within a range of statistical probability in a wide variety of terrestrial and aquatic ecosystems around the world.*
Source: World Wildlife Fund.

Comprehensive Indicators

Like the GDP, a comprehensive indicator is easily understood; it is the sort of measurement that often is featured in news headlines and on the six o'clock news. Since the Rio Summit, the following indicators have been proposed, but none have successfully seized the interest of governments or the public, or satisfied a broad range of the Bellagio Principles. It is likely to take several more years before a generally acceptable measure is found.

Ecosystem type	Number of species monitored	Decline in species diversity, 1970–99	Comments
Forests	319	12%	Includes both tropical and temperate
Freshwater	194	50%	Measured on six continents
Oceans	217	35%	Measured in six ocean areas

Figure 28–3   *These are the components used to determine the Living Planet Index. The decline in forest species may seem modest compared to that of aquatic ecosystems, but many more extinctions occurred before 1970.*
Source: World Wildlife Fund.

Your Ecological Footprint

1. Calculate the ecological footprint for each member of your family. To do this, go to <www.pearsoned.ca/globalconnections> and follow the instructions. After you have determined each person's EF, calculate the average value for your family. Why does it make sense to use this average to represent your EF, rather than the amount you calculated as your own EF?

2. How does your family's average EF compare to the North American average of 10.2 ha? If your own EF value is significantly different from the average, explain why this might be.

3. a) There are about 8.63 billion hectares of productive land in the world. How many people with your EF could be supported by the world's productive land? What implications does this figure have for Earth's future, especially if we remember that people in developing countries are working to improve their own standards of living?

   b) Assume that the world's population is 6.2 billion. How many planets with the productive capacity of the Earth would be needed to support all of Earth's people at your standard of living?

4. Calculate the fair Earthshare. This is how large everyone's EF should be if Earth's productive land were shared equally among all people of the world. What options exist if the EF of some people is much higher than the fair Earthshare, while that of others is much lower?

Ecological Footprint You have probably heard about one of the most commonly used comprehensive measures of sustainability, the **ecological footprint (EF)**. The EF uses a physical metaphor, a measure of land area, to suggest the ecological pressure created by the residents of a country. Human activities are related directly to the amount of land needed to support them. For example:

- The food we eat depends on western Canada wheat land, market gardens in Mexico, coffee plantations in Brazil, and so on.
- The clothing we wear is related to cotton fields in China, pastureland for sheep in Australia, and grazing areas in Alberta used to raise cows that produce leather for shoes.
- Our homes, other buildings, and roadways degrade land that could be used for agriculture or other purposes.

The American humourist Mark Twain summed it up when he said, "Buy land; they're not making it anymore." This is especially true for productive land. The world's population continues to increase and the residents of virtually all countries continue to use more and more resources on a per capita basis. The impact of both these factors on the average worldwide EF is clear (Figure 28–4a). The regional pattern of EFs is also much as you might expect (Figure 28–4b). What is most worrying is what will happen to Earth's ecological integrity as the footprint for Asia, in particular, gets larger. In China and India alone, there are more than 2.3 billion people working to improve their living standards, thus increasing their EFs.

Genuine Progress Indicator While the EF is helpful, it is unlikely to replace GDP as a measure

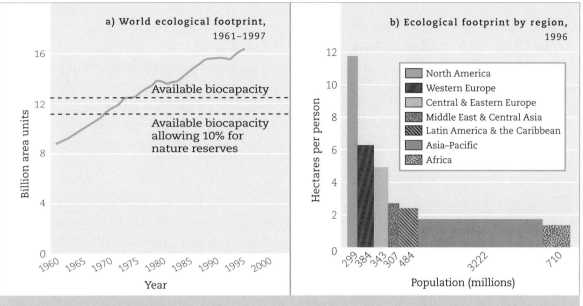

Figure 28–4 *(a) An ever-increasing world ecological footprint is putting unsustainable pressure on Earth's biocapacity (its capacity to supply resources and assimilate wastes). (b) The height of the bars is proportional to the EF, while the width is proportional to the population of the continent. Hence, the area of the bar is proportional to the EF of the continent.* Source: World Wildlife Fund.

of economic and social progress. EF values measure sustainability alone; they say nothing about economic measures that make the GDP such a valuable economic indicator. What is needed is a dollar-based measurement that addresses the shortcomings of the GDP. One dollar-based measure is the **genuine progress indicator (GPI)**. Following is a summary of how the GPI attempts to address the concerns that have been expressed about GDP measures.

- The GDP assumes that if an activity lacks a dollar value, it is not valuable. For example, the cost of fighting crime, such as police forces and prisons, is included in the GDP, while the value of stable family environments to prevent young people from becoming criminals is not.
- The GPI assigns an economic value to such activities as childrearing, looking after elderly parents, and volunteering, since these contribute to a society's quality of life.
- Increases in the uneven distribution of income are recognized in the GPI but ignored in the

GDP. An increase in the Gini index (Chapter 13) is a negative factor in the GPI.

- Resource depletion contributes to the GDP. For example, an oil company receives a tax benefit as it uses up its oil reserves. In the GPI, resource use is treated as a liability.
- Habitat degradation and restoration contribute equally to the GDP. In the GPI, degradation is a liability, while restoration costs are neutral activities.
- When people are forced to work longer hours or at multiple jobs to survive, the GDP considers it a gain, but the GPI sees it as a loss.
- The building of public infrastructure and the manufacture of consumer products are handled differently by each measure. With GDP accounting, it is better to make cars, electronics, and household goods that will be obsolete or unreliable in a few years and so will need to be replaced. With GPI accounting, a desirable product is a high-quality one that will depreciate slowly and provide benefits for many years.

Index of Sustainable Economic Welfare

Another alternative to the GDP has been created in Europe. The **Index of Sustainable Economic Welfare (ISEW)** works like the GPI in that a conventional measure of economic progress is adjusted in two ways: positively by traditional non-economic factors that improve well-being, and negatively by consumption patterns that are ultimately unsustainable. When we compare GPI and ISEW trends to those of GDP, the results are striking (Figure 28–5) and in keeping with what many average citizens have felt.

For a number of years since the 1950s, the patterns for GPI/ISEW have been similar to those for GDP. In recent years, though, this has not been the case. Since the late 1980s, while GDP and other economic measures rocketed ahead, many people had the feeling that they were not better off. They were working harder, yet experiencing a lower quality of life. According to supporters of these new indicators, what had happened was that social and environmental costs of economic growth came to outweigh the benefits.

Not all observers agree that these measures are valid. Some criticize ISEW (and GPI) as being too subjective, since these measures rely on the fact that someone had to assign arbitrary economic values to non-economic items.

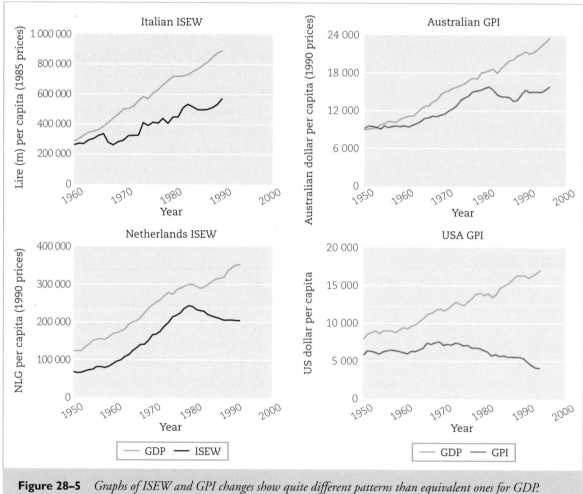

Figure 28–5 *Graphs of ISEW and GPI changes show quite different patterns than equivalent ones for GDP.*
Source: Friends of the Earth.

Achieving a More Sustainable Future

So far, we have looked at how we might measure our progress towards sustainability. The next step is to consider changes that could be made in our lifestyle, government, and economy that would help us to achieve sustainability. The examples that follow have been called a movement towards **smart growth**.

ISO 14000

What does it mean when you see a sign on a commercial building declaring that a company is ISO 9000 or ISO 14000 certified? The International Organization for Standardization (ISO) is an old and very important agency that, for the most part, works behind the scenes. It has created more than 11 000 specialized standards in dozens of industries. For example, its standards allow the nuts produced by a company in Mexico to fit the bolts made by a company in the European Union. As a result of discussions at the Rio Summit on the Environment in 1992, the ISO was asked to develop a series of environmental standards for industry. A technical committee of the ISO, with representatives from 55 countries, published the first set of environmental standards in 1996. There are now more than 350 individual environmental standards. A company or government agency that has been declared as ISO 14000 certified meets the appropriate ISO environmental standards for that industry.

Extended Producer Responsibility

The last time your family bought a new computer or television, you probably had to dispose of a big cardboard box and lots of Styrofoam packaging. The principle of **extended producer**

You can learn more about the Standards Council of Canada's experiences with ISO 14000, and about the EPR, at <www.pearsoned.ca/globalconnections>.

responsibility (EPR) changes this. Just as a company has long been held responsible for any waste or pollution produced by its manufacturing processes, now with EPR, the same manufacturer becomes responsible for the product and its packaging *over the product's entire lifespan*. This responsibility might take several forms. For example, a manufacturer might choose more environmentally sound materials for its packaging, or might take steps to ensure that its product can be easily recycled at the end of its useful life.

Ultimately, it is the individual consumer who bears the cost of these measures. The logic behind EPR is that the person buying a product should pay for its total cost. Till now, much of the economic and environmental cost has been shared by the entire society, including those who cannot, or choose not to, buy many consumer goods.

Extended producer responsibility is in its infancy, but the idea is fast catching on. Apple Computer's Clean Earth Campaign includes free recycling of its laser cartridges in 15 countries. The automaker BMW now clearly identifies all components in its cars to make recycling easier. The city of Ottawa has created a "Take It Back!" program for a range of consumer goods, such as burned-out fluorescent tubes and old car parts. City residents can return these materials to participating businesses that sell them, and these companies will dispose of them appropriately.

Green Taxation

Many years ago, Canadians used reusable shopping bags to bring home their groceries. Later, it became common for stores to give away brown

paper bags for this. More recently, the ubiquitous plastic shopping bag has replaced the paper bag. At each stage there has been an increase in convenience but a decrease in sustainability. Plastic shopping bags have become an environmental problem. Politicians in Italy decided to do something about this. They imposed a tax of about four cents on each bag produced in Italy or imported into the country. The tax, which was about five times as high as the cost of producing a bag, made alternatives cheaper. The use of taxation to encourage environmentally responsible behaviour is called **green taxation**. Green taxation has a second benefit: it allows the burden of taxation to be shifted from income taxes and sales taxes to environmental taxes.

To be effective, green taxes must be publicized and must be high enough to encourage people to change their behaviour. For example, Ontario imposes a Tax for Fuel Conservation (TFC) on new vehicles (Figure 28–6). There are significant penalties, as much as $7000, for those who choose a wasteful vehicle. In fact, Transport Canada ratings indicate that only a small number of cars have highway ratings above 10 L/100 km. Furthermore, no SUVs manufactured today have fuel-efficiency ratings worse than 14.5 L/100 km. The TFC has lost its original purpose and has become primarily a source of income for the government, rather than a measure to encourage more sustainable consumer practices. A final problem with green taxes is that most people hear of their existence only when it comes time to sign the contract to buy a new vehicle.

Highway Fuel Use Ratings (L/100 km)	Tax on New Passenger Vehicles	Tax on New Sport Utility Vehicles
under 6.0	$ 0	$ 0
6.0 to 7.9	$ 75	$ 0
8.0 to 8.9	$ 75	$ 75
9.0 to 9.4	$ 250	$ 200
9.5 to 12.0	$ 1200	$ 400
12.1 to 15.0	$ 2400	$ 800
15.1 to 18.0	$ 4400	$ 1600
over 18.0	$ 7000	$ 3200

Figure 28–6 *How the Ontario Tax for Fuel Conservation is calculated. The fuel economy ratings are based on Transport Canada highway fuel-economy ratings.* Source: Green Ontario/The Conservation Council of Ontario.

Città Lente

In many parts of the developed world, people are questioning the very assumptions that underlie both economic and cultural globalization. In most situations, this involves one or more decisions by an individual—to buy less, to live in a more ecologically responsible way, or to value local culture more. Increasingly, though, people are taking these actions collectively.

A particularly good example of a collective action is the Città Lente, or **Slow Cities**, movement. A group of about 50 Italian towns and small cities has decided not to become part of the globalized world of the 21st century (Figure 28–7). Instead, the people are setting out to protect the qualities that make these communities and the regions around them special. They are doing this, not by one large action, but by many small ones. For example, they do not allow the construction of fast-food restaurants or cell-phone antennas, and they ban the use of car alarms and garish neon signs. Local traditions are protected and encouraged—restaurants serve local foods and wines; laws are being passed that protect farmland so that consumers can buy directly from local farmers.

Most Slow Cities rely on tourism for much of their income. The residents of these communities realize that the main reason people want to visit their region is that it is different; it has not become a homogenized, globalized kind of place. Something similar to the Slow Cities movement has emerged in a number of smaller communities in Canada. Places such as Niagara-on-the-Lake (Ontario), Lunenburg (Nova Scotia), and Grand Bruit (Newfoundland) have built an economy based on the unique nature of their communities.

Figure 28–7 *The hillside town of Positano, on the west coast of southern Italy, is a member of the Slow Cities movement.*

Changing Our Behaviour

Ultimately, the fight to achieve sustainability comes down to the question of whether people, particularly in developed countries, are prepared to change their behaviour. The Brundtland Report on sustainable development suggests what must be done (Figure 28–8):

- The concept of sustainable development implies that there are limits—not absolute limits, but limitations—on our use of environmental resources. These limits are imposed by the present state of technology and social organization, and also by the ability of the biosphere to absorb the effects of human activities.
- Sustainable development requires meeting the basic needs of all and extending to all the opportunity to fulfill aspirations for a better life.
- Meeting essential needs requires not only a new era of economic growth for nations in which the majority are poor, but an assurance that those poor get their fair share of the resources required to sustain growth.
- Sustainable global development requires that those who are more affluent adopt lifestyles within the planet's ecological means, for example, in their use of energy.

Consider what each of these points suggests about how *your* behaviour, and your expectations for the future, may have to change.

Figure 28–8   *Dr. Gro Harlem Brundtland, currently Director-General of the World Health Organization, was chair of the committee that wrote* Our Common Future *(also known as the Brundtland Report) for the UN World Commission on Environment and Development.*

Chapter Questions

Knowledge and Understanding

1. Explain the relationship between economic cycles and environmental degradation.

2. a) Explain, using a specific example not given in this chapter, why GDP is a flawed measure of economic and social progress.
   b) Identify at least three ways in which the Bellagio Principles demonstrate the limitations of the GDP.

3. Briefly comment on the significance of any four of the Bellagio Principles in assessing progress towards sustainable development. Comment on the difficulty of measuring progress.

4. Make a chart to compare, in a general way, the (a) characteristics, (b) strengths, and (c) limitations of specific indicators and comprehensive indicators of progress towards sustainability.

Thinking and Inquiry

5. Examine the sample indicators of sustainable development at <www.pearsoned.ca/globalconnections>.
   a) Choose one of the indicators given and explain why it is a suitable specific indicator of sustainable development.
   b) Choose a different statistical measure that you think could be used to measure sustainable development. Provide evidence, similar to that given in the Web site, to prove that it is an appropriate indicator.

6. Refer to the principles of sustainable development cited by the Brundtland Report in the conclusion of this chapter. Describe how your behaviour, now and in the future, might have to change if sustainability is to be achieved.

Communication

7. Write a short essay outlining the greatest advantages and limitations of working with ecological footprints.

8. Complete a mapping activity on the ecological footprint. Your teacher will tell you whether you will do this on paper or using GIS.

9. Identify a community in your area that could adapt the Slow Cities concept and flourish as a tourist destination. Explain your choice in a letter to the editor of the local newspaper.

Application

10. Work in a group of three or four students to complete this question. You are to create a working, comprehensive indicator of sustainability. To do this, consider what the Bellagio Principles suggest as requirements for an effective indicator. Your indicator must include at least six statistical measures for a minimum of 30 countries from all Five Worlds. Your work should include an explanation of why you chose the measures that you did, and why your indicator is a useful measure of sustainability.

11. a) Describe how each of the following initiatives contributes to the achievement of a more sustainable future:
    i) ISO 14000
    ii) extended producer responsibility
    iii) green taxation
    iv) Città Lente

    b) Discuss the usefulness of each in Canada.

12. Apply the Bellagio Principles to (a) the ecological footprint and (b) the Genuine Progress Indicator. To what degree does each of these indicators satisfy the Bellagio Principles? Where do they seem to fall short?

Glossary

agents of social change People or institutions that promote social change through their actions or policies. For example, the women of the Chipko Movement made the Indian government ban logging in several vital forest areas in order to preserve the way of life of those who depended on the forests for survival.

agricultural revolution The cultivation of plants and domestication of animals that likely started in the Middle East about 10 000 years ago.

aid fatigue Reluctance on the part of donor countries to continue giving foreign aid (development assistance) when it does not seem to improve conditions in the countries receiving it.

albedo The ability of a surface to reflect light. For example, a snow-covered surface has a high albedo because it reflects a great deal of solar energy into space.

alternative energy Sources of energy other than fossil fuels, nuclear energy, and hydro-electric power. Alternatives include wind and solar power, tidal power, geothermal power, ocean thermal energy conversion, and biomass conversion.

amnesty Pardon granted to people who admit to an offence (such as entering a country illegally).

anthropogenic Generated by human activity; e.g., the extra greenhouse gases created by humans (principally carbon dioxide, methane, nitrous oxide, and halocarbons).

anti-retroviral drugs Drugs that treat retroviruses, especially HIV/AIDS.

aquifers Rock and sediments deep underground that hold water and let it pass through.

artesian well A well in which water is forced up to the surface from a closed aquifer without the aid of a pump. When a well is drilled into the aquifer, the pressure of the water flowing downhill (owing to gravity) forces the water in front up to the top of the well.

asylum seekers People who enter a country claiming to be refugees but who do not qualify as such under the strict requirements of the UN protocol (i.e., they must be fleeing persecution).

authoritarian nation state A state that limits the freedoms of its citizens, demands strict obedience to government authority, and often does not allow criticism of its policies.

Auto Pact Signed in 1965 between Canada and the United States, this treaty eliminated trade barriers in the manufacture of automobiles produced by the "Big Three" (GM, Ford, and Chrysler). The Auto Pact is an example of managed free trade in that it required at least one vehicle to be assembled in Canada for each car that was sold there. The Canadian government insisted on this rule because it feared that all auto assembly might end up in the US. The Auto Pact ended in 2000 when the WTO ruled that it gave the Big Three an unfair advantage over other companies selling cars in North America.

bankruptcy A legal process that cancels the debts of people or institutions that are unable to pay them.

basic activity A good or service that brings money into a city or region (e.g., corporate head offices).

Bellagio Principles A set of guidelines established in 1996 to assess the accuracy of measurements of sustainable development.

bias A prejudice or preference for or against a particular point of view.

bilateral Involving two parties (e.g., aid from one country to another).

bioaccumulation The buildup of chemicals such as POPs in the fatty tissues of organisms. These substances become increasingly concentrated as they move upward in the food chain.

biodegradable The ability of organic materials and some industrial pollutants to break down as a result of natural processes in the environment.

biotechnology The application of biological processes to agricultural and industrial purposes.

bioterrorism The use of biological agents, e.g., viruses, in terrorist acts.

birth control Technological means used to prevent conception (e.g., oral contraceptives). The term also applies to the desire of couples to limit the number of children they have for any reason.

birth dearth Low total fertility rate that causes a population to decline.

birth rate Number of births per 1000 people in a country or region in a given year.

bonded labour A form of modern slavery affecting some 20 million people worldwide. For example, people who borrow money and cannot repay the loan because of high interest rates must work for the company or individual until the loan is repaid.

carbon sinks Natural features (such as forests) that remove carbon (in the form of CO_2) from the atmosphere for a period ranging from a few minutes to a few centuries.

carrying capacity The maximum number of people that can be sustained by an environment (e.g., the Earth's resources).

cash crop A crop grown for sale or barter rather than for personal use.

caste Hereditary social class in the Hindu society of India and in the traditional societies of Mauritania, Niger, and Sudan in Africa.

ceasefire A temporary period during which the fighting in a conflict stops.

chain of custody The tracking of logs harvested from certified forests through transportation and processing to the final product. The chain of custody ensures that the end product is made of wood from a certified forest (see *forest certification*).

change by diffusion Change in a country's economic or social structure that is accomplished gradually as people recognize the benefits of change. For example, in Kerala, India, population growth declined as people came to recognize the benefits of smaller families.

chemical deterioration Deterioration of soil as a result of leaching, salinization, acidification, or pollution.

chemical terrorism The use of chemical agents, e.g., poison gas, in terrorist acts.

chlorofluorocarbons (CFCs) Chemicals created for use as fire retardants, propellants in spray cans, and coolants in refrigerators and air conditioners. They are inert at ground level but when exposed to UV radiation in the upper atmosphere, they release chlorine atoms that break down ozone.

chronic persistent hunger Lack of a balanced diet leading to many conditions of malnutrition that weaken people, making them susceptible to infectious diseases.

civil disobedience The refusal to obey certain laws using non-violent means, together with acceptance of responsibility for such illegal acts, as a way to make one's cause known to government and the public.

civil liberties The rights of citizens to certain freedoms established in law, such as freedom of speech, political association, and religion.

civil society A largely unorganized group of NGOs and independent citizens concerned about labour rights, the environment, human rights, and social development. Members have participated in street demonstrations because they believe that people in developing countries do not benefit from free trade and globalization.

clean development mechanism A program created as part of the Kyoto Protocol in 1997. It allows developed countries to invest in projects in developing countries that reduce greenhouse gas emissions, and to receive credit for these reductions. Developed countries then apply this credit against their 2008–2012 emission targets, thereby reducing the cutbacks they would have to make within their own borders. Developing countries benefit because they receive investment that builds new infrastructure and provides jobs and new technology, which, in turn, helps further reduce greenhouse gas emissions.

cogeneration Generation of thermal electricity through use of the heat produced by burning garbage in incinerators.

Cold War A state of hostility without actual warfare that existed between the power blocs led by the US and the USSR from the mid-1940s to the end of the 1980s.

colonialism Acquisition and settlement of a territory or country by another nation.

command economy An economic system in which the supply and pricing of goods and services are determined entirely by government as part of a total plan.

community initiatives Projects begun by individuals within a community working together to find solutions to mutual problems.

comparative advantage Economic advantage that one country has over another because of an ability to produce goods more cheaply as a result of abundant raw materials, cheap labour, better marketing, cheaper transportation costs, or better quality control.

comprehensive indicator A measure that shows overall progress towards sustainability. For example, the ecological footprint relates to the amount of land needed to support various human activities.

concession company A company created by an imperialist country to develop trade in its colonies; e.g., the British created the Hudson's Bay Company in Canada. Concession companies traded in particular products and often acted as the government in remote parts of empires.

containment The policy of Western democracies after World War II to stop the expansion of the Soviet Union beyond its borders through defence agreements (e.g., NATO) and to prevent the spread of communism through the use of aid programs (e.g., the Marshall Plan).

cornucopian thesis The belief that as science and technology advance, new resources will be developed to take the place of depleted ones.

counterterrorism Efforts made by governments and businesses to interfere with the planning, organization, and carrying out of terrorist acts.

counter-urbanization The movement of people from suburban and central city locations to small and medium-sized towns and rural areas to escape from congestion, noise, pollution, crime, and high land values.

critical load The amount of pollution (e.g., acidic deposition) that an ecosystem can tolerate before that pollution harms the environment.

cultural diffusion The spread of knowledge and influence from one place to another.

cultural exceptionalism The rejection of certain rights or values by a country because its political, social, economic, and cultural traditions differ from those embodied in the Universal Declaration of Human Rights.

death rate Number of deaths per 1000 people in a country or region in a given year.

debt relief Some form of debt reduction or elimination, usually granted to developing countries.

decentralization The movement of people from central city areas to suburban locations (also see *suburbanization*).

deep ecology An approach to protecting the environment that uses confrontational, direct action and that does not accept compromise solutions.

demographic transition A theory that states that birth rates and death rates will decline over time as a result of economic and social development. It is the most widely accepted theory explaining population change over time.

demographic trap A situation in which a developing country continues to have a high birth rate instead of experiencing the declining birth rate of the late transition stage. Combined with declining death rates, this situation causes a population increase that threatens the country's economic and social development.

dependency load The percentage of a country's population that is considered dependent because it includes people not of "working age," i.e., those younger than 15 and older than 64 years of age.

desertification The process by which an arid or semi-arid area loses its productivity to the point that it resembles a desert. Desertification results mainly from human activities (e.g., deforestation, overgrazing).

developed/developing worlds A geopolitical model dividing the world into economically and socially developed countries and economically and socially progressing countries. This model recognizes that economic and social development is progressive, and that countries can move towards developed status.

developed/underdeveloped worlds A geopolitical model dividing the world into economically and socially advanced countries and economically and socially underdeveloped countries. It ignores the fact the underdeveloped countries may become advanced economically and socially over time, and often have sophisticated cultures.

drip irrigation an irrigation system that uses pipes with tiny holes that continuously drip small amounts of water directly to plant roots, thereby reducing evaporation. It was developed in Israel to increase crop yields while using less water.

early transition Stage in demographic transition in which a high birth rate and a falling death rate result in a high population growth rate (population explosion).

ecological footprint (EF) A measure of sustainability in which a unit of land area is used to demonstrate the ecological pressure created by residents of a country. The EF is based on the principle that human activities are related to the amount of land needed to support them, e.g., how much land is needed to support a country's transportation infrastructure.

ecological integrity The condition of a natural environment that has not been changed or interfered with by outside forces, such as human development.

ecological migration The movement of people from one place to another because something in their environment upon which they depend disappears or relocates.

economic base Functions and activities on which a city or region depends for its existence.

economic development A community's material wealth and trade; determined by such measures as per capita GDP, ratio of cars to people, and per capita electrical power capacity.

economic disparity An inequality in which some people or countries are much better off economically than other people or countries.

economic globalization The trend towards a worldwide economic system that permits easy movement of goods, production, capital, and resources. Economic globalization occurs as trade restrictions, such as tariffs and quota systems, are removed in favour of free trade.

economic liberalism An economic system that functions without the intervention of government. The concept was developed by Adam Smith in 1776 as an alternative to mercantilism.

emigration rate Number of people leaving an area per 1000 population in a given year.

emissions trading A procedure whereby a country that exceeds its greenhouse gas emissions reduction targets sells its unused emissions credits on the open market.

empowerment The act of taking authority or control over some aspect of one's life.

energy currency A form of energy that can be replaced or be exchanged with another (e.g., hydrogen can replace gasoline to power a vehicle).

environmental refugees People who flee their homelands for environmental reasons, e.g., land may be flooded by rising sea levels (also see *ecological migration*).

environmentalism A philosophy that reflects concern for the environment. Its main tenet is that humans have a responsibility to protect the environment.

erosion The breakdown of a land surface (weathering) and the carrying away of materials (transportation) by wind, rain, gravity, and ice.

eutrophication The depletion of oxygen in water caused by excess growth of vegetation and decomposition. It occurs as a result of the washing into lakes of detergents, sewage, and agricultural fertilizers. As a result, organisms not suited to low oxygen levels die.

extended producer responsibility (EPR) A corporate and public policy in which the manufacturer is deemed responsible for the environmental impact of its product's packaging and the product itself during its entire lifespan.

fact Knowledge that is considered to be true because it can be verified by experience or observation.

fair trade A market system that is to some degree regulated, to ensure that producers benefit from trade; e.g., producers are guaranteed a minimum price when they sell their product. Fair trade is based on the belief that marginalized producers in developing countries do not benefit from free trade.

feedback loop A self-perpetuating situation in which each consequence eventually causes the initial condition to recur.

fiscal squeeze The economic constraint that results when money raised through taxes is insufficient to pay for all the services that a city needs to function efficiently.

Five-World model A geopolitical model that divides the world's countries into five groups according to their similarities in economic and social development. Some consider it a more accurate model of categorizing countries than more simplified models.

fixed carbon Carbon that has been removed from the atmosphere for a very long time; e.g., carbon in limestone or coal has been removed from the atmosphere for millions of years.

forced labour A form of slavery, usually imposed by a government or paramilitary group, in which the threat of violence is used to force people into working against their will.

forest certification A system devised by the Forest Stewardship Council (FSC) to identify forest products derived from forests that are being managed according to a set of standards. Products meeting these standards carry the FSC logo. Consumers who do not wish to contribute to deforestation can look for lumber products bearing the FSC logo.

Forest Stewardship Council (FSC) A worldwide organization formed in Toronto in 1993 to fight deforestation by improving forest conservation and by encouraging the wise use of forests.

fossil water Water that entered sedimentary rock thousands or millions of years ago and was subsequently sealed off from other water by overlying rock layers.

free market economy An economic system in which the prices of all goods and services are determined by supply and demand.

Free Trade Agreement (FTA) An agreement signed by Canada and the United States in 1988 to remove all tariffs and other restrictions to trade by 1999.

free trade agreements Agreements that promote commerce among countries by removing barriers to investment, the movement of technology, and trade, such as quotas and tariffs (e.g., the European Union, NAFTA, ASEAN).

Gaia hypothesis The theory of James Lovelock that views Earth as a self-regulating, living entity made up of organisms that modify the environment for their survival.

genetically modified organisms (GMOs) Organisms whose genetic structure has been changed to give them characteristics that are seen as desirable. For example, a plant might be made tolerant of herbicides or resistant to insects. GMOs have both beneficial and undesirable aspects.

genuine progress indicator (GPI) A measurement that addresses the shortcomings of the GDP by assigning a dollar value to all activities that positively contribute to society's quality of life, by treating all activities that detract from quality of life as liabilities.

geopolitics The interplay of political, economic, and geographical factors (such as location and physical environment) at a national or international level. This interplay affects governmental decision making and relationships among countries.

germ theory of disease The theory that some diseases are caused by organisms too small to be seen (except under a microscope).

Gini index A measurement of how evenly wealth is distributed among classes in a society. The diagonal line indicates an even distribution; the gap between the diagonal line and the actual curve measures the inequality. The lower the Gini index, the more evenly spread the income.

global warming The increase in average temperatures and related weather effects all over the world as a result of increased emissions of greenhouse gases in the atmosphere.

globalization The trend towards greater interconnectedness of the world's financial, economic, technological, political, cultural, sociological, ecological, and geographical systems. Some argue that globalization improves living standards throughout the world, while others say that its effects are more harmful than beneficial.

grasshopper effect A global phenomenon in which Persistent Organic Pollutants (POPs) move from warmer to colder regions. The pollutants evaporate, travel through the atmosphere on air currents, and then condense in a new location. They tend to concentrate in cold regions because there is less evaporation in colder areas.

Green Revolution The development, in the second half of the 20th century, of high-yielding crops of wheat and rice that led to increased yields. It had both positive and negative ecological and economic impacts.

green taxation Taxation that encourages environmentally responsible behaviour in individual consumers and businesses.

greenhouse effect The warming of the atmosphere as some of its gases absorb heat given off by Earth's surface. This is a natural phenomenon that maintains Earth's temperature at a level that supports life (e.g., about 14°C).

greenhouse gases Atmospheric gases that create the greenhouse effect by absorbing and holding heat in the Earth's atmosphere. They include naturally occurring gases such as water vapour, carbon dioxide, and methane, and human-made gases such as chlorofluorocarbons (CFCs).

guerrilla Unofficial, irregular combatant using "hit-and-run" tactics against regular or government troops.

Habitat Conservation Plan/Sustained Yield Plan (HCP/SYP) A plan developed in California that provides protection for endangered species while recognizing the right of landowners to earn a living from their land (HCP); it also requires that forest harvesting take place over a 100-year period (SYP). Together, these two strategies will protect land, rivers, and wildlife from undue damage.

hard currencies Currencies (such as the US dollar, British pound, and Japanese yen) that are sufficiently sound to be generally accepted internationally at face value. Payments associated with international trade or loans are made using hard currencies.

Highly Indebted Poor Countries (HIPCs) An initiative by the World Bank and International Monetary Fund to reduce the debt of the 41 poorest nations in the world.

Human Development Index A measure of quality of life developed by the UN using three criteria: life expectancy at birth, adult literacy rate, and per capita GDP.

human rights The basic rights to which all people are entitled, such as freedom, peace, and dignity.

hunters and gatherers People who hunt game and gather fruits and vegetables for food.

hydricity revolution An energy system in which all forms of energy would be converted to either hydrogen or electricity.

ideology A set of ideas and beliefs that form the basis of a nation's political and economic systems and its social goals.

illegal migration The movement of people into a country without following its immigration laws and procedures.

immigration rate Number of people (immigrants) arriving at a destination for every 1000 people living at that location in a given year.

imperialism The control (political and/or economic) of one or more countries by a dominant nation.

Index of Sustainable Economic Welfare (ISEW) An alternative measure to the GDP that adjusts economic progress in two ways: positively for factors that improve societal well-being, and negatively for consumption patterns that are non-sustainable.

indigenous people People who originate from and have remained in a specific region. Canada's Aboriginal peoples are indigenous to North America.

Industrial Revolution The use of non-muscular sources of power that began in late 18th-century Britain and spread to other parts of the world. It was a technological revolution (involving new machinery and new processes) that was accompanied by social and political changes.

infant mortality rate Number of infants under one year of age who die for every 1000 live births in the country in a year.

infectious diseases Illnesses caused by microorganisms, such as bacteria, viruses, or protozoa, that may be transmitted from one person to another. Infectious diseases, such as AIDS and tuberculosis, are very prevalent in developing nations.

infrastructure Facilities (e.g., transportation, power, and communication networks; sanitation systems) and institutions (e.g., education, business, banking, health) that allow a society to function.

internally displaced persons (IDPs) People who are forced to move from their home area for reasons similar to those that motivate refugees. However, IDPs remain within the borders of their country.

International Joint Commission (IJC) A body set up by Canada and the United States in 1909 to deal with issues associated with the Great Lakes.

intifada Uprising by Palestinians in protest of constraints on life under Israeli control. It includes public demonstrations, riots, rock-throwing, boycotts of Israeli products, and attacks against Israeli citizens.

involuntary migration Movement of people against their will. It is often associated with persecution or fear of persecution.

issue An important subject open to discussion and debate.

Jubilee+ Campaign An international campaign, spearheaded by the world's major faith communities, to forgive the debts of the world's 50 poorest countries.

Keynesian economics Economic system conceived by John Maynard Keynes advocating government spending to create jobs in poor economic times. A government-sponsored policy of high employment is viewed as the means to relieve economic depression.

land degradation Deterioration of the productive capacity of soil for either present or future use.

land reform The breakup of large estates and redistribution of land into small holdings for the poorest rural residents in a country.

land tenure Manner in which land is held, e.g., owner-occupied farms, plantations owned by individuals or large companies that use paid labour, and land owned and worked by collectives. In developing countries, it is common for a wealthy elite to own land and pay others to work it, or to act as landlords to those who live on the land and who pay their rent in the form of produce (known as share-cropping).

late transition Stage in demographic transition in which a declining birth rate and a relatively low death rate lead to a slowed population growth rate.

life expectancy Average lifespan that a newborn can expect to live if current mortality trends were to continue.

life experience Participation in events and contact with ideas that affect how one perceives things. Life experience is a result of such factors as age, education, religion, and ethnic background.

lifestyle diseases Diseases that are the result of the way in which people live. For example, heart conditions, obesity, and diabetes are very prevalent in developed countries.

limits-to-growth thesis Theory based on computer models developed by the Club of Rome that predicted pessimistic outcomes for Earth's environment if the growth trends of the 1970s continued.

local integration An immigration policy in which refugees remain living in the first country (usually bordering on their home country) to which they have fled and become part of the host community.

logarithmic graphing A method of graphing data that extend over three or more orders of magnitude, e.g., 10s, 100s, and 1000s.

malnutrition A condition in which health is damaged by a diet that includes too much or too little of one or more essential nutrients over an extended period of time.

Malthusian Pertaining to the 1798 hypothesis of Thomas Malthus that population grows geometrically while food production increases arithmetically. The result is that population will eventually outstrip food supply and thus fall prey to famine, disease, and warfare. Any person or idea that supports Malthus's pessimistic viewpoint is described as neo-Malthusian.

managed free trade Free trade that has some restrictive clauses (also see *Auto Pact*).

meltdown An event in a nuclear reactor in which the fuel overheats, melts the reactor core, and allows radioactive material to escape into the environment.

mercantile system A system of trade in which the mother country viewed its colonies as a source of raw materials as well as a captive market for its manufactured goods.

microcredit Loans to help people develop small businesses in order to break out of the cycle of poverty.

mixed economy An economic system that combines elements of both free enterprise and government intervention.

monkey-wrenching Tactics that are sometimes illegal, used by NGOs to interfere with logging. These range from removing survey stakes to tree-spiking.

multilateral Involving more than two parties (e.g., aid from the World Bank or International Monetary Fund, institutions that are funded by many governments).

multinational companies Companies that operate in several countries. This term has been largely replaced by the term *transnational companies* because many are not clearly identified with any particular nation.

nation state An independent nation of people who have adopted a unique common identity and who live together under one government within a defined geographical area. The nation state possesses sovereignty, i.e., the ability to create policies and enforce laws within its borders without interference from other nations.

nationalism The feeling of pride that results from being a citizen of a particular country; a belief in the value of one's own country's sovereignty.

natural increase rate Rate at which a population increases (or decreases) in a given year expressed as a percentage of the total population. This percentage can be calculated by subtracting the death rate from the birth rate and dividing by 10.

neo-liberalism A set of economic policies that reduce the role of government because government control and regulation are seen to impede or distort economic growth. Governmental deregulation of industries, privatization of state-owned enterprises, and removal of restrictive trade practices are examples of neo-liberal policies.

net migration rate Total effect of immigration and emigration on an area's population. The rate can be an increase or a decrease.

non-basic activity A good or service provided only for residents of a city or region.

non-renewable Finite or limited; unable to be restored or regenerated in nature, e.g., petroleum and natural gas.

North American Free Trade Agreement (NAFTA) A treaty signed in 1994 by Canada, the United States, and Mexico that phased out trade restrictions among the three countries.

North–South model Still in use, this geopolitical model was first used in a 1980 publication, the Brandt Report (*North–South: A Program for Survival*). It divides countries into two groups, North and South, and places developed countries farther north than developing countries. A more accurate geographical grouping is temperate–tropical.

nuclear terrorism The use of radioactive materials in terrorist acts.

objective Not distorted by personal feelings or bias.

odious debt Debt created by unscrupulous leaders to meet their own needs rather than the interests of the state. For example, a despotic ruler who borrows money for personal gain or to repress the population creates an odious debt that the state does not have to repay when the ruler leaves power.

old-growth forest Forest that has never been logged with the result that its ecology is unchanged.

opinion Judgement or belief that is not necessarily based on certainty or proof.

organic farming A natural method of farming in which no herbicides, pesticides, antibiotics, or genetically modified products are used.

Organization for Economic Co-operation and Development (OECD) Formed in 1961 by the United States, Canada, and 20 countries in Western Europe, the OECD now has 30 members. It provides member governments with a forum in which to discuss and develop social and economic policy with the goal of maximizing economic growth and assisting non-member states to develop more rapidly.

overpopulation An excess of people that prevents a country from meeting the needs of its citizens, whether social, economic, or resource-based.

overurbanization Condition that results when a city's population grows faster than the number of jobs or housing units available.

pandemic Continent- or worldwide outbreak of an infectious disease.

peace dividend The amount of money saved as a result of the cut in military spending when the Cold War came to an end. It was hoped that the peace dividend would be used to develop worldwide social programs.

peacekeeping The use of an international military force, under the auspices of the UN, to keep a truce already agreed to by the combatants.

peacemaking Use of an international military force, under the auspices of the UN, to impose a ceasefire or truce on combatants.

persistent organic pollutants (POPs) Highly toxic substances used in pesticides and industrial chemicals such as PCBs. They are also found in dioxins, the by-products of industrial processes. Insoluble in water, they are very stable, and last for years in the environment before breaking down.

perspective Point of view or way of looking at things. A perspective is the product of influences such as family, schooling, religion, country, friends, and the media.

phantom carrying capacity Earth's ability to support an immense population at a high standard of living only because it is using up its non-renewable resources to the detriment of future generations.

physical deterioration Degradation of land caused by compaction, waterlogging, or subsidence that leads to reduced land productivity.

plantations Large farming operations, often developed by colonial powers, to grow tropical and subtropical crops such as bananas, coffee, cocoa, cotton, rubber, sugar, spices, and tea. Plantation owners often pushed the local population off the land and then hired the dispossessed farmers back to work for low wages.

plebiscite A vote on a specific issue by all those entitled to vote. A plebiscite is usually held to decide a major political issue.

population control Limitation of population growth through such measures as sterilization, contraception, and abortion, or, in the case of China, limiting couples to one child.

population growth rate Rate at which a population increases or decreases in a given year through natural increase and net migration, expressed as a percentage of the total population.

population implosion Rapid population decline in developed countries as a result of low fertility rates.

population pyramid Special type of graph that shows the distribution of a population by age and sex. Each bar graph indicates an absolute value (number of people) or a percentage of people of each sex in a specific age group.

post-transition Stage in demographic transition in which a low birth rate and a low death rate lead to very low population growth. When the birth rate equals the death rate, zero population growth occurs. If the birth rate is below the death rate, the population will decline.

pre-transition Stage in demographic transition in which a high birth rate and a high death rate equal little or no population increase. The number of people in each age group is less than the previous one. No country in the world today is in the pre-transition stage.

progressive government A government that is an agent of social and economic change. For example, it might use taxation as a way to redistribute wealth from richer to poorer citizens.

pronatalist strategies Ideas that encourage people to have more children, e.g., tax benefits and monthly grants (such as the Baby Bonus in Canada after World War II).

R/P ratio A calculation that gives the number of years remaining before a non-renewable resource runs out. It is computed by dividing the size of the recoverable reserves (R) by the amount that is extracted in a given year (P), assuming that production will continue at the same rate.

range The distance that people travel to purchase a good or a service. High-order goods or services (e.g., cars, medical care) have greater ranges than low-order goods or services (e.g., newspapers, dry cleaning).

reconcentration Movement of people from small towns and rural areas back to cities.

reduced-impact logging (RIL) Logging conducted in a way that ensures a forest's long-term economic and ecological sustainability. It includes conducting accurate inventories to determine how much timber can be cut, planning the location of roads to minimize erosion, and cutting trees without damaging nearby trees. Because less wood is wasted, RIL is about 12 per cent cheaper per hectare than conventional methods.

referendum A direct form of democracy in which citizens are asked to vote on a single political issue.

refugees People who leave their country under threat of persecution because of their race, religion, nationality, or social or political group. Environmental scarcities and declining socio-economic conditions also cause people to become refugees.

renewable Not diminished when used; replenishable in nature. For example, tidal or wind energy, forests, and fish are renewable resources.

replacement migration Rate of migration that maintains the general or working-age population at a given level.

replacement rate The fertility rate required for a population to replace itself. Usually, a fertility rate of at least 2.1 is needed, taking into account infant mortality and women who do not have children.

reserves The proportion of a natural resource that can be exploited under prevailing economic conditions and current technology.

resource Anything that meets people's needs; includes natural resources (water, air), human-made items (labour, technology), or items appreciated for their aesthetic qualities (landscapes, ecosystems).

rule of 70 Simple method to estimate how long it will take a population to double; calculated by dividing 70 by the population growth rate. For example, if the population growth rate of a country is 0.5 per cent, the population would double in (70/0.5) 140 years.

salinization Buildup of salts at or near the surface of the soil, particularly in dry, hot climates.

sanctions Measures placed on a state by other countries in an effort to force it to change its policies or behaviour. Sanctions may involve cutting off trade or aid with the offending country.

secondary recovery A process in which natural gas is injected back into the ground to increase pressure on the oil deposit and thus assist in recovering more oil. Secondary recovery is usually practised in places where natural gas cannot be economically moved to market.

sectoral free trade Free trade in only one specific part of the economy (also see *Auto Pact*).

self-determination The right of countries or groups of people to be independent and to have control of their own affairs.

SLAPP (Strategic Lawsuit Against Public Participation) Lawsuit by a corporation against an individual or NGO. The purpose is to stop a protest by forcing the NGO or individual to focus time and money on its legal defence rather than on fighting the company.

Slow Cities Cities that protect and encourage local traditions and develop an economy based on the communities' unique nature.

smart growth Economic growth that occurs while sustainability is maintained. Smart growth occurs as a result of environmentally wise choices made by governments, businesses, and people with regard to their lifestyle.

social development The level of education, health care, jurisprudence, life expectancy, and rate of infant mortality in a society.

solid waste management Garbage disposal, involving primary, secondary, or tertiary treatment of waste.

source reduction Reducing garbage at its source, e.g., by using less packaging for products.

sovereignty A concept in international law recognizing that the authority of the state is not subject to control by other states.

Spaceship Earth concept The idea that our home, Earth, is a spaceship, and that Earth's resources must be protected because we have nowhere to turn if they run out.

specific indicator A single measure that shows progress towards sustainability, e.g., changes in greenhouse gas emissions over time.

sphere of influence Area in which a nation has a special interest and in which it is politically and economically active. It is understood that one nation may not encroach upon the sphere of influence of another.

squatter settlements Areas of illegally built, makeshift housing, usually on the edge of cities in developing countries. They spring up because the demand for cheap housing outstrips the supply.

state (institutional) terrorism   The use of terrorist methods by a government to force obedience from the general population.

state-sponsored terrorism   Terrorism not actually committed but funded by a nation state, which may also provide safe haven to terrorists.

Structural Adjustment Program (SAP)   A program whereby the world's 41 poorest countries must make severe spending cuts and changes to their economies in order to qualify for debt relief.

structural change   Change in a country's economic and social structure that is legislated by government. For example, China's one-child policy is changing the social structure of the country.

subjective   Resulting from personal feelings, thoughts, experiences, and prejudices.

suburbanization   Movement of people and industry to the outskirts of cities, enabled in great part by the building of expressways that allow people to drive to work in city centres while living on the outskirts (also see *decentralization*).

sustainability   Development that meets the needs of people today without jeopardizing the ability of future generations to meet their needs.

temperate rain forest   Forest with tall trees and thick undergrowth located in temperate climatic locations (between subtropical and subarctic) where rainfall exceeds 1000 mm annually.

terrain deformation   Change in the landscape caused by natural or human forces.

terrorism   The use of violence and intimidation to achieve political or ideological goals.

theory of demographic regulation   A theory developed by D.J. Bogue in the 1960s stating that over an extended period of time, a society limits its population.

third-country resettlement   The relocation of refugees to a third country willing to accept them, when they cannot return to their home country and the country to which they first fled refuses to let them stay.

Three-World model   A geopolitical model, developed in the 1950s during the Cold War, in which the developed capitalist countries make up the First World, the (now formerly) communist countries the Second World, and the remaining countries with poorly developed economies the Third World.

threshold population   The minimum number of customers required by a service to succeed.

tier pricing   The practice of charging different prices for the same product (e.g., HIV/AIDS medication) in different parts of the world. For example, the price of a drug in developing countries is less than the price of the same drug in developed countries.

tipping point   A threshold beyond which a situation cannot return to what it was before. For example, once global warming reaches a certain point, it may be impossible to stop because the changes have passed the tipping point.

total fertility rate   Average number of children borne over the lifetime of a typical woman in a particular country. This figure answers the question, "How many children are women currently having?"

transnational corporations   Corporations that operate in two or more countries (also called *multinational corporations*). Transnationals are probably the major force affecting global shifts in economic activity, since many have profits greater than the GDPs of some countries.

ultimatum   A final, uncompromising demand or set of terms issued by one party in a dispute, the rejection of which may lead to a severance of relations or the use of force.

ultraviolet (UV) radiation   Invisible short-wave radiation from the Sun. The ozone layer absorbs much of this radiation, thereby protecting Earth from dangerously high levels.

unilateralist foreign policy   The approach followed by one country in its dealings with other countries in which it does not consider points of view other than its own. Since the breakup of the USSR in 1991, the United States has pursued a unilateralist foreign policy with little regard for the concerns or interests of other nations because no nation is powerful enough to challenge it.

urban growth   An increase in the number of people living in a city.

urbanization   Percentage of a country's population living in urban places.

veto   A vote to refuse or stop a course of action. For example, any permanent member of the Security Council of the UN has the right to veto a resolution if it disagrees with the Council's proposed course of action.

voluntary repatriation   The return of refugees to their home country of their own free will when they believe that their lives or liberty are no longer in danger.

weapons of mass destruction   Biological, chemical, and nuclear weapons that are capable of killing many people at one time and possibly devastating large areas.

wind farm   A grouping of windmills in an area with winds suitable for a steady supply of energy.

World Bank   A specialized agency that furthers the economic development of member nations, chiefly through guaranteed loans. The Bank obtains most of its funds through borrowing, and the remainder through government subscription. Since voting power is proportional to the amount of money received from each government, the Bank is essentially controlled by the richer countries.

Index

Credits

The publisher has made every reasonable effort to trace the ownership of extracts, data, and visuals to make full acknowledgement of their use. If any errors or omissions have occurred, they will be corrected in future editions, providing written notification has been received by the publisher.

Documents

Chapter 1: Figs. 1–7, 1–8 From *Making Connections: Canada's Geography*, by Bruce W. Clark and John K. Wallace **Chapter 3:** Fig. 3–1 From P.J. Taylor & C. Flint, *Political Geography: World, Economy, Nation, State and Locality* (4th ed.). Harlow, UK: Prentice Hall, 1999, 2000; Fig. 3–4 Reprinted with permission of ITP Thomson Learning, a division of Thomson Learning, Fax 1-800-730-2215; Fig. 3–8 Reprinted by permission of Arnold Publishers **Chapter 4:** Fig. 4–4 From M. Fagen, *Challenge for Change*, fig. 2-2, p. 18. Whitby, ON: McGraw-Hill Ryerson; Fig. 4–8 From *Making Connections: Canada's Geography*, by Bruce W. Clark and John K. Wallace; Figs. 4–9, 4–11 From *Facing the Future: Global Issues in the 21st Century* by Ron Chasmer and Pamela Perry-Globa. Copyright © Oxford University Press Canada 1998. Reprinted by permission of Oxford University Press Canada **Chapter 5:** Fig. 5–19 United Nations Publications, <www.un.org/esa/population/wpp2000.html>; Fig. 5–21 Statistics Canada **Chapter 6:** Fig. 6–4 Data from CensusIndia.net, <www.censusindia.net/variation.html>; Fig. 6–11 United Nations Publications **Chapter 7:** Figs. 7–1, 7–2, 7–3, 7–5 Data from International Institute for Applied Systems Analysis, <www.iiasa. ac.at>; Fig. 7–4 From W. Lutz (ed.), *The Future Population of the World: What Can We Assume Today?* (rev. ed.), p. 370. London, UK: Earthscan, as found at IIASA, <www.iiasa.ac.at/Research/POP/news.html>; Fig. 7–11 1960, 1980 data from <http://woodstock.wesleyan.edu/acsocsci/jmcguire/table/demography.htm>, 2000 data from *CIA World Factbook 2000*, <www.odci.gov/cia/publications/factbook/index.html>, and 2050 data from US Census Bureau International Programs Centre, <www.census.gov/ipc/htm> **Chapter 8:** Fig. 8–1 Statistics Canada; Figs. 8–6, 8–7 United Nations Publications, <www.unhcr.ch/statist/2000provisional/main.htm>; Fig. 8–10 United Nations Publications, <www.un.org/esa/population/publications/migration/execsum.htm> **Chapter 9:** Figs. 9–2, 9–3, 9–4, 9–5, 9–6, 9–8 United Nations Publications, <www.un.org/esa/population/publications/wup199/urbanization.pdf>; Fig. 9–15 United Nations Economic and Social Council, Commission on Sustainable Development, 8th session 24 April to 5 May 2000, Report of the Secretary-General, *Progress made in providing safe water supply and sanitation for all during the 1990s* (E/CN.17/2000/13) **Chapter 10:** Fig. 10–10 James Hughes on the basis of data from Lester R. Brown, et al., *Vital Signs: The Environmental Trends That Are Shaping Our Future* (Worldwatch Institute, 2000), p. 35. (Originally from data prepared by the USDA.); Fig. 10–11 Courtesy of Judy Harrington Research Associates, Soil and Crop Sciences, Colorado State University, <www.colostate.edu/programs/lifesciences/TransgenicCrops> **Chapter 11:** Fig. 11–3 World Bank, *World Development Report 1982* and World Development Indicators database, July 2001, <www.worldbank.org/data/countrydata/countrydata.html> **Chapter 12:** Fig. 12–5 World Trade Organization, <www.wto.org>; Fig. 12–7 (graph) Statistics Canada **Chapter 13:** Fig. 13–1 M. Weisbrot, R. Naiman, & J. Kim, "The Emperor Has No Growth: Declining Economic Growth Rates in the Era of Globalization," Center for Economic and Policy Research, <www.cepr.net/IMF/Emperor_Table_1.htm>; Fig. 13–6 World Bank Group, <www.world-bank.org/data/wdi2000/pdfs/tab2_8.pdf> **Chapter 14:** Fig. 14–1 Worldwatch Institute, Vital Signs 2000, copyright 2000, <www.worldwatch.org>; Fig. 14–3 New Economics Foundation, Jubilee 2000, <www.jubilee2000uk.org/databank/data.htm>; Fig. 14–7 Map by Deborah Crowle, from M. Cranny & G. Moles, *Counterpoints: Exploring Canadian Issues* **Chapter 15:** Figs. 15–3 Global Assessment of Soil Degradation (GLASOD) project (ISRIC/UNEP, 1991); Figs. 15–5, 15–6 Global Assessment of Human-induced Soil Degradation (ISRIC/UNEP, 1991); Fig. 15–7 Courtesy of R. Anderson Environmental Consultants, <www.yorku.ca/faculty/academic/anderson/olddump/html>; Fig. 15–9 From WORLD BOOK ONLINE © 2002 World Book, Inc. By permission of the publisher. www.worldbook.com; Fig. 15–10 Brewers of Ontario, as found at Container Recycling Institute, <www.container-recycling.org; Fig. 15–11 Courtesy of the California Integrated Waste Management Board; Fig. 15–14 Parks Canada; Fig. 15–15 Mistaya.com, as found at <www.canadianrockies.net/maps/bantown.pdf> **Chapter 16:** Fig. 16–1 California Resources Agency (CERES); Fig. 16–3 Denman Island, <http://denmanis.bc.ca>; Fig. 16–5 FSC Trademark © 1996 Forest Stewardship Council A.C. **Chapter 17:** Fig. 17–1 Adapted from "How Does a Sewage Treatment Plant Work?," McMaster University Department of Biology, <www.science.mcmaster.ca/Biology/Harbour/SEWAGE/STP.HTM>; Fig. 17–2 From the report *Tracking Key Environmental Issues*, Chapter Air and Water—Freshwater Quality, URL: <www.ec.gc.ca/TKEI/air_water/watr_qual_e.cfm>; Fig. 17–3 Public Works & Government Services Canada, as found at Environment Canada, <www.on.ec.gc.ca/glimr/raps/areas-concern.html>; Fig. 17–6 Map by Deborah Crowle, from M. Cranny & G. Moles, *Counterpoints: Exploring Canadian Issues*. **Chapter 18:** Fig. 18–3 © Her Majesty the Queen in Right of Canada. All rights reserved. Source: "The Grasshopper Effect on Global Distillation" in Persistent Organic Pollutants, The Green Lane™, *Science and the Environment Bulletin*, http://www.ec.gc.ca/copy_e.html, Environment Canada, 2002. Reproduced with the permission of the Minister of Public Works and Government Service, 2002; Fig. 18–6 Data from Environment Canada, <www.ec.gc.ca/acidrain/acidfact.html>; Fig. 18–10 Encyclopedia of the Atmospheric Environment.aric © 2000: Air Quality, Great London Smog, <www.doc.mmu.ca.uk/aric/eae>; Fig. 18–13 Reproduced with the permission of the Minister of Public Works and Government Services, 2002. **Chapter 19:** Figs. 19–2, 19–3, 19–4, 19–5, 19–6, 19–7, 19–9, 19–10, 19–11 Data from British Petroleum, <www.bp.com>; Fig. 19–12 Data from CanWEA, <www.canwea.ca/production.htm> **Chapter 20:** Fig. 20–1, 20–2, 20–4 From *Climate Change Basics*, Fact Sheet #1, © Pembina Institute for Appropriate Development; Fig. 20–5 From *Earth Matters: Studies in Physical Geography* by Ron Chasmer. Copyright © Oxford University Press Canada 2001. Reprinted by permission of Oxford University Press Canada.; Fig. 20–6 © 2001 Time Inc. Reprinted by permission; Fig. 20–7 Greenpeace Canada, <www.greenpeace.ca>; Fig. 20–10 Energy Information Administration, <www.eia.doe.gov/oiaf/ieo/tbl_1.html> **Chapter 21:** Fig. 21–2 © Helicon Publishing, a division of Research Machines plc.; Fig. 21–3 Matthew White; Fig. 21–4 Matthew White **Chapter 22:** Figs. 22–1, 22–2 Project Ploughshares, <www.ploughshares.ca/content/ACR/ACR00/ACR00.html>; Fig. 22–3 ChiapasLink <www.chiapaslink.ukgateway.net/ch0.html#Editorial>; Fig. 22–4 © 2002 The Economist Newspaper Group, Inc. Reprinted with permission. Further reproduction prohibited. www.economist.com; Fig. 22–7 PBS Online and WGBH/Frontline, <www.pbs.org/wgbh/pages/frontline/gulf/art/maps5b.gif>; Fig. 22–8 Nile Basin Initiative Secretariat, <www.nilebasin.org/images/nilema1.gif>; Fig. 22–9 From *Student Atlas of World Politics*, Fifth Edition, by John L. Allen, copyright © 2002 by The McGraw-Hill Companies, Inc. Reprinted by permission of McGraw-Hill/Dushkin; Fig. 22–10 National Priorities Project, and SIPRI; Fig. 22–11 US Department of State, adapted from "Table II, Value of Arms Transfer Deliveries and Total Trade, 1989–1999, by Region, Organization and Country," <www.state.gov/t/vc/rls/rpt/wmeat/99_00>; Fig. 22–13 Adapted from NuclearFiles, a project of the Nuclear Age Peace Foundation, <www.nuclearfiles.org/ethics/economic/global.html> **Chapter 23:** Fig. 23–3 *The New Internationalist*, November 2001, p. 18; Sinhaya, <www.sinhaya.com/attacks.htm> **Chapter 24:** Fig. 24–3 From C.M. Bain, D. DesRivieres, P. Flaherty, D.M. Goodman, E. Schemenauer, & A.L. Scully, *Making History: The Story of Canada in the Twentieth Century.*; Fig. 24–4 Map by Deborah Crowle, from M. Cranny & G. Moles, *Counterpoints: Exploring Canadian Issues.*; Fig. 24–5 North Atlantic Treaty Organization, <www.nato.int/multi/map.htm>; Fig. 24–6 Adapted from Federation of American Scientists, <www.fas.org/nuke/control/start-comp.htm> **Chapter 25:** Figs. 25–1, 25–2 Reproduced with kind permission from UNAIDS; Figs. 25–3 (graph), 25–4 © 2000 The Economist Newspaper Group Inc. Reprinted with permission. Further reproduction prohibited, <www.economist.com>; Fig. 25–6 *The Globe and Mail*, Sept. 23, 2000, p. A15; U.S. Center for Disease Control; University of Western Ontario; Albert Schweitzer, *Out of My Life and Thoughts* **Chapter 26:** Figs. 26–2, 26–3 UNDP, Human Development Report, 2001 **Chapter 27:** Fig. 27–1 (left) Mapience India Limited, <www.mapsofindia.com/maps/india/forest.htm> **Chapter 28:** Fig. 28–1 Adapted from *Assessing Sustainable Development: Principles in Practice* by Peter Hardi and Terrence Zdan. Published by the International Institute for Sustainable Development, <www.iisd.org>; Figs. 28–2, 28–3, 28–4 World Wide Fund for Nature; Fig. 28–5 Friends of the Earth/New Economics Foundation, 2002; Fig. 28–6 Conservation Council of Ontario from data provided by the Ontario Ministry of Finance

Photographs

AP: Associated Press; C/M: Corbis/Magma; CP: CP Picture Archive; GI/S: Getty Images/Stone; NAC: National Archives of Canada

Chapter 1: p. 1 *Archivo Iconografico*, S.A./C/M, CS007867; p. 2 Detail from M.C. Escher, "Day and Night," M.C. Escher Heirs/Cordon Art—Bearn—Holland; Fig. 1–1 CP/Quebec *Le Soleil*/Vincent Fradet, PLS 1388400; Fig. 1–3 CP/AP/Fredrik Persson, PLS 2390695; Fig. 1–5 CP/AP/Greg Baker, PLS 325856; Fig. 1–6 CP/AP/Chien-min Chung, PLS 1697122 **Chapter 2:** p. 18 Map from Abraham Ortelius's *Theatrum Orbis Terrarum*, 1570, The Granger Collection, New York; Fig. 2–1 Bob Crist/C/M, RI006430; Fig. 2–4, CP/AP/Mikhail Metzel, PLS 1243913; Fig. 2–5, UN Photo Service; Fig. 2–11 Danny Lehman/C/M, DY003603 **Chapter 3:** Fig. 3–2 CP/AP/Rene Volfik, PLS 1381371; Fig. 3–3 CP/AP/Itsu Inouye, PLS 1241854; Fig. 3–7 NASA **Chapter 4:** p. 45 Bob Krist/C/M, R1008025; p. 46 Wolf Kutnahorsky; Fig. 4–3 James Marshall/C/M, JL003158; Fig. 4–6 Hulton-Deutsch/C/M, HU043839 **Chapter 5:** p. 60 Bettmann/C/M, BE039115; Fig. 5–7 Owen Franken/C/M, OF001427; Fig. 5–16 CP/AP/Ben Margot, PLS 2380848; Fig. 5–17 Bettmann/C/M, BE081964 **Chapter 6:** p. 76 Brian A. Vikander/C/M, B3007254; Fig. 6–2 CP/AP/John Moore, PLS 68786; Fig. 6–5 Tom Nebbia/C/M, EB 001203; Fig. 6–9 Philip Reeve/GI/S, 306813-001 **Chapter 7:** p. 92 Robert Holmes/C/M, RH003870; Fig. 7–6 Keren Su/GI/S, AF5929-001; Fig. 7–8 Lori Adamski Peek/GI/S, EA0108-004; Fig. 7–9 Bettmann/C/M, BE071254 **Chapter 8:** p. 106 CP/Clement Allard, PLS 271965; Fig. 8–3 CP/Paul Chiasson, PLS 211683; Fig. 8–4 CP/AP/J.M. Vidal/EFE, PLS 1355106; Fig. 8–5 CP/AP/David Longstreath, PLS 2490402; Fig. 8–8 CP/*Sarnia Observer*/Nora Penhale, PLS 2657574 **Chapter 9:** p. 124 With permission of the Royal Ontario Museum, © ROM, Cat. no. 961.162.1; Fig. 9–7 Michael S. Yamashita/C/M, YM019007; Fig. 9–11 CP/Kevin Frayer, PLS 1329212; Fig. 9–12, C/M, LL001956; Fig. 9–13 CP/*Toronto Star*/Mitchell Smyth, PLS 167171; Fig. 9–14 Robert Frerk/GI/S, EC2064-001; Fig. 9–16 Jeremy Horner/C/M, HR005333; Fig. 9–17 CP/AP/Ricardo Choy Kifox, PLS 239079 **Chapter 10:** p. 145 Kathleen Campbell/GI/S, AB8006-001; p. 146 Chris Rainier/C/M, CR002513; Fig. 10–2 (top left) Jeremy Horner/C/M, HR004647; Fig. 10–2 (top right) Michael S. Yamashita/C/M, YM008261; Fig. 10–2 (bottom right) Frank Blackburn/C/M, EC005836; Fig. 10–2 (bottom left) CP/AP/Kelley McCall, PLS 2236133; Fig. 10–4 David R. Frazier/GI/S, 308941-001; Fig. 10–7 CIMMYT/M. Listman; Fig. 10–8 CIMMYT/M. Listman; 10–12 Reprinted with permission from *The Globe and Mail*; Fig. 10–13 Ontario Ministry of Natural Resources; Fig. 10–14 Jeremy Horner/C/M, HR006342 **Chapter 11:** p. 168 Stewart Cohen/GI/S, EC2044-001; Fig. 11–4 (left) Will Curtis/GI/S, BC1891-001; Fig. 11–4 (right) David H. Wells/C/M, DW002746; Fig. 11–7 NAC/George Hunter, PA-166448; Fig. 11–8 CP/Michael Hale, PLS 15330548; Fig. 11–11 Source unknown; Fig. 11–12 Bettmann/C/M, BE02973 **Chapter 12:** p. 188 Roger Ressmeyer/C/M, RR006564; Fig. 12–7 (photo) CP/*Windsor Star*/Don McArthur, PLS 2663683; Fig. 12–8 (left) Reuters/Larry Downing/C/M, UT0074200; Fig. 12–8 (right) Reuters/JP Moczulski/C/M, UT0072295 **Chapter 13:** p. 200 The Purcell Team/C/M, PT008055; Fig. 13–2 Owen Franken/C/M, OF007898; Fig. 13–3 Reed Kaestner/C/M, AX036899I; Fig. 13–7 CP/AP/David Guttenfelder, PLS 86564; Fig. 13–9 CP/Frank O'Connor, PLS 2096427; Fig. 13–10 CIDA/ACDI; Fig. 13–11 Reprinted with permission from *The Globe and Mail* **Chapter 14:** p. 216 CP/AP/Julie Plasencia, PLS 1631049; Fig. 14–4 World Vision; Fig. 14–6 Reuters/C/M, UT0005205 **Chapter 15:** p. 229 CP/Andrew Vaughan, PLS 89353; p. 230 Salinity Laboratory, USDA-ARS Staff; Fig. 15–2 Crop Science Department, University of Guelph; Fig. 15–4 Bernard & Catherine Desjeux/C/M, DQ001112; Fig. 15–11 Courtesy of the California Integrated Waste Management; Fig. 15–12 Al Harvey, The Slide Farm; Fig. 15–16 CP/*The Calgary Sun*, PLS 1224810 **Chapter 16:** p. 250 CP/AP/Seth Hettena, PLS 645453; Fig. 16–4 James P. Blair/*National Geographic Magazine*, NGM 1987/11 648–9; Fig. 16–5 FSC Trademark ©1996 Forest Stewardship Council A.C.; Fig. 16–6 Courtesy of Tropical Forest Foundation; Fig. 16–7 (left) W. Perry Conway/C/M, IH063772; Fig. 16–7 (right) Richard A. Arnold/Entomological Consulting Services **Chapter 17:** p. 264 WorldSat International; Fig. 17–4 CP/Len Wagg, PLS 1988468; Fig. 17–7 Ontario Ministry of Tourism & Recreation; Fig. 17–8 Robert Cameron/GI/S, 885454-001; Fig. 17–9 WorldSat International; Fig. 17–12 CP/AP/Douglas Engle, PLS 1414579 **Chapter 18:** p. 284 CP/Hamilton Spectator, PLS 1222015; Fig. 18–8 CP/AP/Aris Messinis, PLS 646581; Fig. 18–9 Bettmann/C/M, U1358829; Fig. 18–11 Environment Canada **Chapter 19:** p. 300 Vandystadt/Allsport, PLS 868531; Fig. 19–1 Peter Turnley/C/M, TL014648; Fig. 19–8 CP/AP/Efrem Lukatsky, PLS 1672866; Fig. 19–14 Bettmann/C/M, BE040132; Fig. 19–16 CP/*Ottawa Citizen*/Pat McGrath, PLS 340914 **Chapter 20:** p. 322 AFP/Rodrigo Arangua/C/M, FT0000187; Fig. 20–12 Brian Gable/Cartoonists & Writers Syndicate **Chapter 21:** p. 338 Doug Armand/GI/S, 246916-001; Fig. 21–1 CP/SL Staff, PLS 1700829; Fig. 21–5 CP/AP/Murad Sezer, PLS 813609; Fig. 21–6 Bettmann/C/M, U223984ACME **Chapter 22:** p. 350 David H. Wells/C/M, DW003030; Fig. 22–6 Shai Ginott/C/M, GX001337; Fig. 22–12 CP/AP/David Longstreath, PLS 2137892 **Chapter 23:** p. 366 Reuters NewMedia Inc./C/M, UT0090497; Fig. 23–1 CP/AP/Walter Astrada, PLS 1253935; Fig. 23–2 CP/Fred Chartrand, PLS 2834465 **Chapter 24:** p. 376 CP/AP/David Karp, PLS 121265; Fig. 24–7 CP/AP, PLS 2443532; Fig. 24–8 AFP/C/M, FT 0007442 **Chapter 25:** p. 391 Wally McNamee/C/M, WL002148; p. 392 Howard Davies/C/M, HD001805; Fig. 25–3 (photo) CP/AP/Themba Hadebe, PLS 2408850; Fig. 25–5 AP/World Wide Photos; Fig. 25–8 CP/AP/Alastair Grant, PLS 2248459 **Chapter 26:** p. 404 AFP/John MacDougall/C/M, FT0024342; Fig. 26–4 AFP/Rob Elliott/C/M, FT0005038; Fig. 26–5 CP/Chuck Stoody, PLS 1119033 **Chapter 27:** p. 418 CP/AP/Kent Gilbert, PLS 2631673; Fig. 27–1 (photo) Lindsay Hebberd/C/M, LY002601; Fig. 27–2 CP/AP/Pavel Rahman, PLS 262530; Fig. 27–6 TransFair Canada; Fig. 27–7 CP/Tom Hanson, PLS 176170; Fig. 27–8 CP/*The Globe and Mail*/Peter Tym, PLS 107054 **Chapter 28:** p. 431 Getty Images/EyeWire; ID844961; p. 432 CP/AP/Michel Spingler, PLS 2893613; Fig. 28–7 Morton Beebe/C/M, BB003587; Fig. 28–10 CP/AP/Eric Gay, PLS 2476582

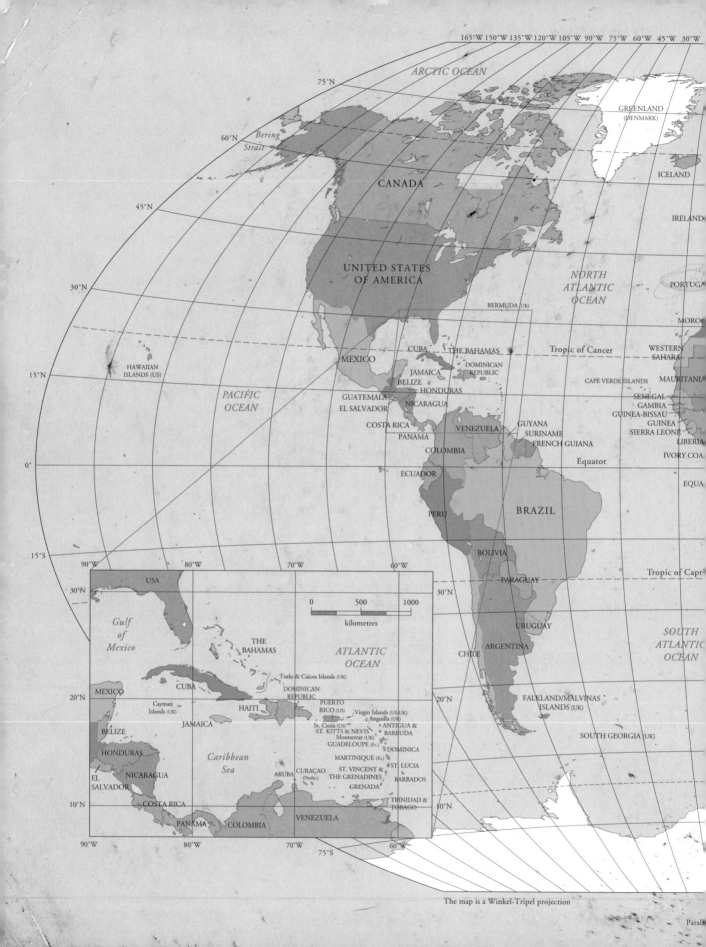

ARCTIC OCEAN

165°W 150°W 135°W 120°W 105°W 90°W 75°W 60°W 45°W 30°W

75°N

GREENLAND
(DENMARK)

60°N   *Bering*
        Strait

ICELAND

CANADA

45°N

IRELAND

30°N

UNITED STATES
OF AMERICA

NORTH
ATLANTIC
OCEAN

PORTUGA

BERMUDA (UK)

MOROC

CUBA   THE BAHAMAS   Tropic of Cancer   WESTERN
MEXICO   DOMINICAN   SAHARA
          JAMAICA   REPUBLIC   CAPE VERDE ISLANDS   MAURITANIA

15°N   HAWAIIAN
        ISLANDS (US)   SENEGAL
                    PACIFIC   BELIZE   HONDURAS   GAMBIA
                    OCEAN   GUATEMALA   GUINEA-BISSAU
                           EL SALVADOR NICARAGUA   GUINEA
                                                                     SIERRA LEONE
                          COSTA RICA   GUYANA   LIBERIA
                                   PANAMA   VENEZUELA SURINAME
                                                      FRENCH GUIANA IVORY COA
0°   COLOMBIA   Equator

ECUADOR   EQUA

                                        BRAZIL
                           PERU
15°S
        90°W   80°W   70°W   60°W   BOLIVIA

                                                        Tropic of Capr
                                        PARAGUAY

                                        URUGUAY   SOUTH
                                                      ATLANTIC
                                   CHILE ARGENTINA   OCEAN

                                   FALKLAND/MALVINAS
                                   ISLANDS (UK)

                                   SOUTH GEORGIA (UK)

30°N   USA

        Gulf
        of   THE
        Mexico   BAHAMAS   ATLANTIC
                                       OCEAN

                    Turks & Caicos Islands (UK)
                    DOMINICAN
        MEXICO   CUBA   REPUBLIC
20°N   Cayman   PUERTO
             Islands (UK)   RICO (US)   Virgin Islands (US/UK)
                    HAITI   Anguilla (UK)
        JAMAICA   St. Croix (US) ANTIGUA &
        BELIZE   ST. KITTS & NEVIS BARBUDA
                           Montserrat (UK)
                    Caribbean GUADELOUPE (Fr.) DOMINICA
        HONDURAS   Sea   MARTINIQUE (Fr.) ST. LUCIA
        EL   ARUBA CURAÇAO ST. VINCENT & BARBADOS
        SALVADOR NICARAGUA   (Neth.) THE GRENADINES
                              GRENADA
                    COSTA RICA   TRINIDAD &
                                            TOBAGO   10°N
        PANAMA   COLOMBIA   VENEZUELA

        90°W   80°W   70°W   60°W
                        75°S

0   500   1000
kilometres

The map is a Winkel-Tripel projection

Paral